INTRODUCTION
THIRD TROPICAL EDIT

G000310698

By the same author

Advanced Biology (with C.J. Clegg)
Introduction to Biology: Fifth Edition
Introduction to Biology: Second West African Edition
Introduction to Human and Social Biology: Second Edition (with Brian Jones)
GCSE Biology

Human Life
Life Study

Slides: six sets, each of 20 colour slides, with notes
Transparencies: 84 b/w unmounted overhead projector transparencies on Human Physiology. 17 on Insects

Foreign editions

Original edition

Holland	*Inleiding tot de Biologie*, Wolters-Noordhoff NV, Groningen
Italy	*Biologia*, Casa Editrice, Scode, Milan

Tropical edition

Singapore	*Introduction to Biology* and *Introduction to Biology* (Chinese edition), Eastern Universities Press, Singapore

© D. G. Mackean 1962 (original edition)
© D. G. Mackean 1969 (Tropical Edition)
© D. G. Mackean 1976 (New Tropical Edition)
© D. G. Mackean 1984 (Third Tropical Edition)

This edition first published in 1984 by
John Murray (Publishers) Ltd,
50 Albemarle Street, London W1X 4BD

Reprinted 1987, 1989, 1991 with revisions, 1992 with revisions,
1994 with revisions, 1995 (twice), 1997, 1998 (twice)

Printed in Great Britain by
Redwood Books, Trowbridge, Wiltshire

British Library Cataloguing in Publication Data
Mackean, D. G.
  Introduction to Biology: Third Tropical Edition
  1. Biology
  I. Title
  574

ISBN 0 7195 4130 1

JOHN MURRAY · LONDON

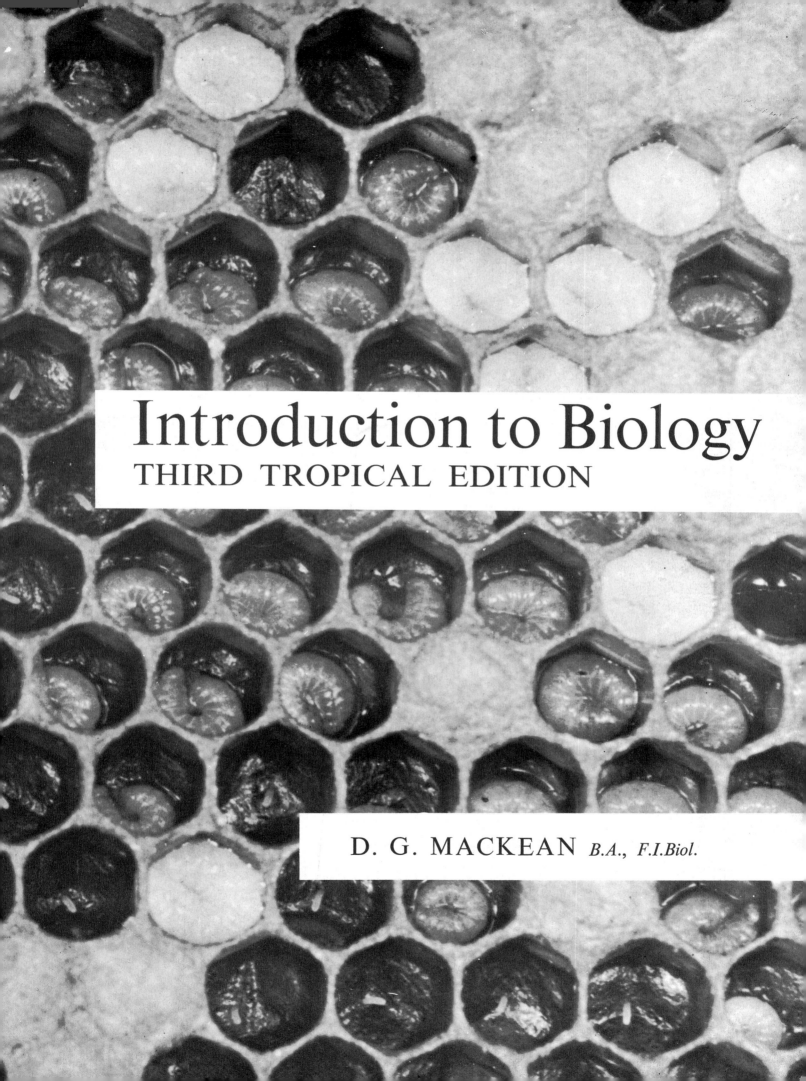

Introduction to Biology
THIRD TROPICAL EDITION

D. G. MACKEAN B.A., F.I.Biol.

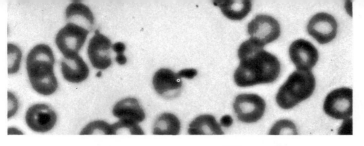

Preface

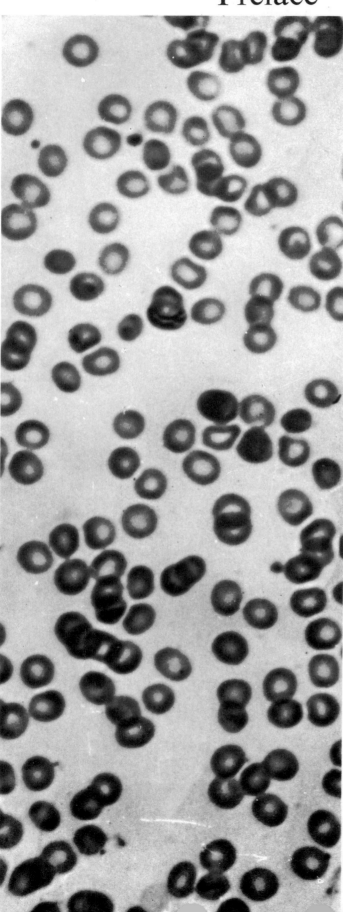

Introduction to Biology is written for students working for the G.C.E. O level or Schools' Certificate examination and the contents represent a body of biological knowledge common to syllabuses of the East African Examinations Council, and the Cambridge and London Overseas examinations.

The book does not reflect a particular attitude or offer a novel approach to the subject but is meant as a reference book with clearly explained and fully illustrated information from which students can readily find the facts they need. It is hoped that the teacher will refer students to the text at appropriate points in his own programme of teaching rather than treat it as a course to be followed chapter by chapter, since the chapters, to a large extent, are independent. However, it is assumed that fundamental information presented in earlier chapters has been assimilated before the later ones are consulted.

The experimental work described in the text is intended mainly for revision or for students who have been unable to carry out the experiments for themselves.

Note to the Third Edition

The Third Edition is the successor to the New Tropical Edition of *Introduction to Biology* and has been adapted to the changes in syllabuses which have taken place since 1976.

New chapters have been added on Ecology, The Microscope, Personal Health and World Health. Additional coverage has been given in existing chapters to topics such as methods of nutrition, transmission of disease, economic importance of fungi, soil fertility, the work of Mendel and Morgan, applied genetics, viruses and first aid.

In addition, a glossary of Scientific Terms has been included, defining physical and chemical terms used, but not specifically explained, in the text. There is also a glossary of Biological Terms giving short, working definitions of over 350 biological words.

DGM

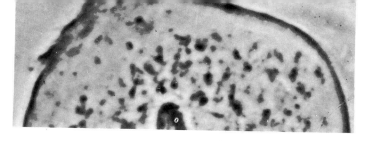

Contents

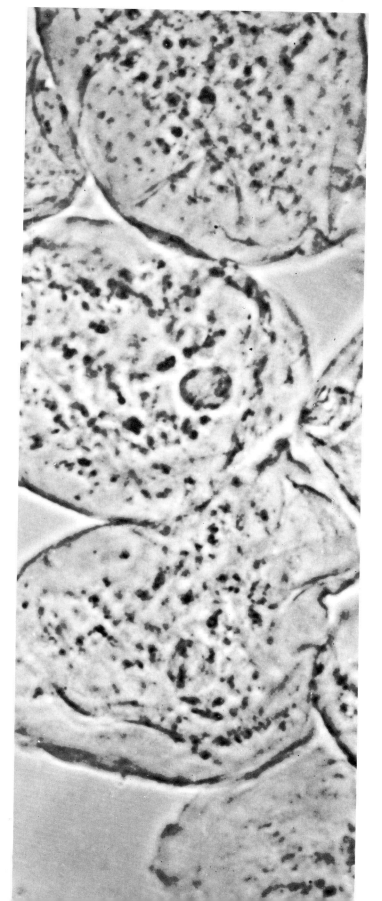

The diagrams are by the author

1 | The Varieties of Living Organisms

THERE are millions of different kinds of living things in the world. There are fish, frogs, birds, mosses, trees, jelly-fish and mushrooms. These are all quite different in appearance but because they are all living, they are alike in some very important ways; they breathe, feed, grow, reproduce and, in many cases, they make movements.

Most of this book deals with the activities which are common to all living things; how they get their food, what use they make of it, how they breathe, reproduce and so on. In this chapter, however, we look at how they are different from each other. This is best done if we try to sort out the enormous variety of living things into groups.

There are many ways in which living things could be grouped; by size, by colour or by the places where they live. The biologist looks for what he regards as important features which are shared by as large a group as possible. In some cases it is easy. Birds all have wings, beaks and feathers; there is rarely much doubt about whether something is a bird or not. In other cases it is not so easy. As a result, people change their ideas from time to time about how living things should be grouped. New groupings are suggested and old ones are abandoned.

The method of grouping organisms is called **classification** and one system of classifying living things is into five main groups:

> Monera
> Protoctista
> Fungi
> Plants
> Animals

Each of these main groups is divided into smaller sections, and these sections are subdivided.

All the animals which lack a vertebral column are sometimes called **invertebrates**. This is a convenient term to use but it does not represent a proper classifactory group.

Classification is discussed more fully on p. 206 but the scheme below shows some (but by no means all) of the main groups of living organisms.

Kingdom MONERA
Bacteria and blue-green 'algae'. Single-celled, microscopic organisms with a cell wall and cytoplasm but without a proper nucleus (p. 70). A few species of bacteria cause diseases but most are harmless or beneficial.

Kingdom PROTOCTISTA
A group of very diverse organisms, but all having a proper nucleus in their cells. Many are single-celled creatures.
   Sub-kingdom **Protozoa**. Single-celled organisms that feed like animals by taking substances in through their cell membranes (p. 174).
   Sub-kingdom **Algae**. Have chloroplasts in their cells and feed by photosynthesis (p. 48). Some algae are unicellular, others, e.g. seaweeds are multicellular and large.

Kingdom FUNGI
Made up of thread-like hyphae rather than cells (p. 75). Familiar as moulds, mildews, mushrooms and toadstools. Some species cause serious crop diseases.

Kingdom PLANTS
All have chloroplasts, cells with cell walls and they make their food by photosynthesis (p. 48).
   Liverworts. Flat, simple, leaf-like plants growing in damp places. Reproduce by spores.
   Mosses. Small green plants with simple stems and leaves. They grow in dense colonies. Reproduce by spores.
   Ferns. More complex plants with proper stems, leaves and roots. Reproduce by spores.
   Coniferous plants. (e.g. pine, cypress, cycad, ginko). Usually trees, often with needle-like leaves. Reproduce by seeds.
   Flowering plants. Herbs, trees and shrubs. Well developed stem, leaves and roots. Reproduce by seeds.
      Monocotyledons. Narrow leaves, parallel veins, one seed-leaf (cotyledon p. 39). Grasses, cereal crop plants, lilies, palm trees.
      Dicotyledons. Broad-leaved plants with net-veined leaves and two cotyledons in their seeds (p. 38). Herbs (e.g. *Salvia*, sunflower), shrubs (e.g. *Hibiscus, Bauhinia*), trees (e.g. *Delonix, Caiba, Cassia*, mango, citrus).

Kingdom ANIMALS
Many are able to move about freely and eat plants or other animals. Their cells have no cell walls.
   Coelenterates. Sea anemones, jelly-fish, corals, They are mostly marine and have tentacles and stinging cells for catching their prey.
   Flatworms. Small, flat, mostly aquatic organisms. Tape-worms and flukes are parasitic flatworms (p. 224).
   Nematodes. Round-worms; unsegmented. Some species cause diseases (p. 227).
   Annelids. Segmented worms e.g. earthworms, lugworm, bristle-worms.
   Molluscs. Snails, slugs, mussels, squid and octopus are examples. Some of these have a shell outside or inside their bodies.
   Arthropods. Segmented creatures with jointed legs and a hard outer skeleton (cuticle).
      Crustacea. Crabs, lobsters, shrimps, water fleas.
      Insects. Distinct head, thorax and abdomen. Three pairs of legs and (typically) two pairs of wings on the thorax. (p. 146). Beetles, butterflies, ants, bees, grasshoppers.
   Arachnids. Spiders, scorpions, ticks. They have four pairs of jointed legs.
   Echinoderms. Starfish, sea urchins; all marine.
   Vertebrates. Animals with a vertebral column and skull.
      Fish. Aquatic vertebrates with fins and scales. Breathe with gills (p. 158). Shark, *Tilapia*, guppy, perch.
      Amphibia. Can live on land or in water. Moist skins without scales (p. 161). Frogs and toads.
      Reptiles. Land-dwelling animals with dry, scaly skins. Lizards, snakes, crocodiles, turtles.
      Birds. Warm-blooded vertebrates with wings and feathers (p. 31). Crow, duck, egret, vulture, sparrow.
      Mammals. Warm-blooded vertebrates with fur-covered bodies. Their young are born fully formed and suckled on milk. Dogs, cats, lions, antelopes, whales, apes, humans.

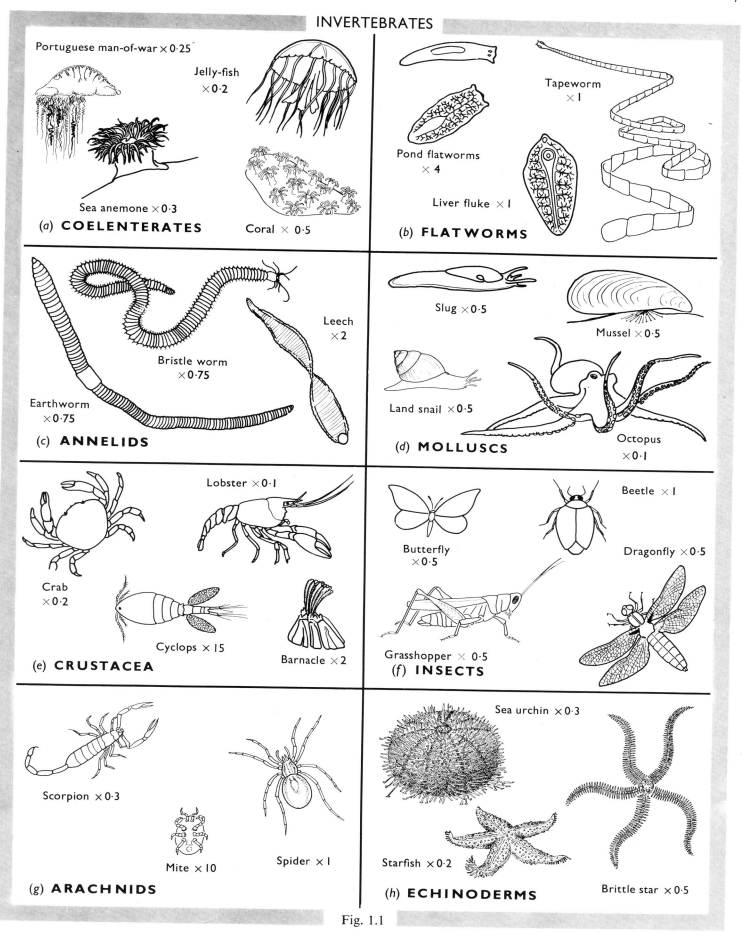

Portuguese man-of-war × 0·25

Jelly-fish × 0·2

Sea anemone × 0·3

Coral × 0·5

(a) **COELENTERATES**

Pond flatworms × 4

Liver fluke × 1

Tapeworm × 1

(b) **FLATWORMS**

Leech × 2

Bristle worm × 0·75

Earthworm × 0·75

(c) **ANNELIDS**

Slug × 0·5

Mussel × 0·5

Land snail × 0·5

Octopus × 0·1

(d) **MOLLUSCS**

Lobster × 0·1

Crab × 0·2

Cyclops × 15

Barnacle × 2

(e) **CRUSTACEA**

Butterfly × 0·5

Beetle × 1

Dragonfly × 0·5

Grasshopper × 0·5

(f) **INSECTS**

Scorpion × 0·3

Mite × 10

Spider × 1

(g) **ARACHNIDS**

Sea urchin × 0·3

Starfish × 0·2

Brittle star × 0·5

(h) **ECHINODERMS**

Fig. 1.1

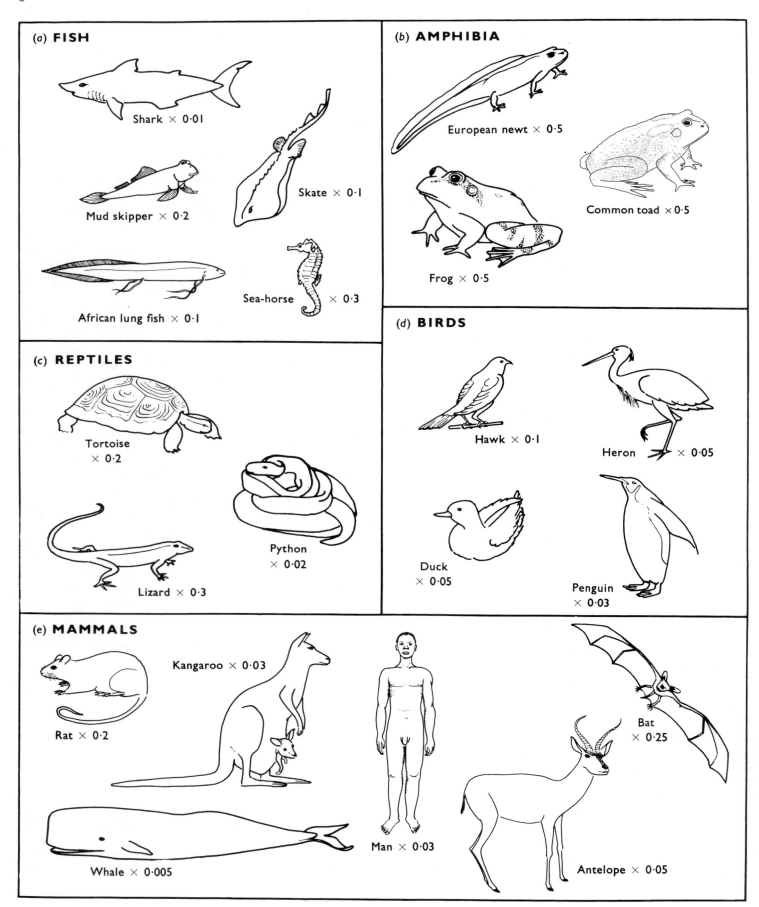

Fig. 1.2   Vertebrates

2 | Characteristics of Living Organisms

BIOLOGY is the study of life (Greek *bios*=life, *logos*=knowledge) which, in practice, means the study of living things.

In most animals, the characteristics by which we know they are alive are self-evident: they move about, they feed, they have young, and they respond to changes in their surroundings.

These features are less obvious in plants and certain small animals; and when dealing with organisms like bacteria and viruses the distinctions between living and non-living can often be drawn only by a trained scientist with the appropriate apparatus and techniques at his disposal. The main differences between living organisms and non-living objects can be summarized as follows:

1. **Respiration.** This is the process by which energy is made available as a result of chemical changes within the organism, the commonest of which is the chemical decomposition of food as a result of its combination with oxygen. This is not a particularly obvious occurrence in plants and animals; but it is fairly easy to demonstrate that living creatures take in air, remove some of the oxygen from it and increase the volume of carbon dioxide in it. More simply expressed it can be said that living organisms take in oxygen and give out carbon dioxide. Sometimes this takes place with obvious breathing movements. Respiration also results in a rise of temperature, which is more easily detectable in animals than in plants.

2. **Feeding.** This is an essential preliminary to respiration, since energy comes ultimately from food. The production of food in the leaves of a tree is less obvious than the feeding of an animal, which moves actively in search of food. Feeding may also result in growth.

3. **Excretion.** Living involves a vast number of chemical processes, including respiration, many of which produce substances that are poisonous when moderately concentrated. The elimination of these from the organism is called excretion.

4. **Growth.** Strictly, growth is simply an increase in size, but it usually implies also that the organism is becoming more complicated and more efficient. An illustration of this is an animal which changes its form from larva to adult, for example, a frog or a butterfly.

5. **Movement.** An animal can generally move its whole body, whereas the movements of the higher plants are usually restricted to certain parts such as the opening and closing of petals, or to the movements of parts as a result of growth.

6. **Reproduction.** No organism has a limitless life, but although individuals must die sooner or later their life is handed on to new individuals by reproduction, resulting in the continued existence of the species.

7. **Irritability** (Sensitivity). Irritability is the ability to respond to a stimulus. Obvious signs of sensitivity are the movements made by animals as a result of noises, on being touched or on seeing an enemy. Fully grown plants do not show such responses under casual observation, but during growth they respond to the direction of light, gravity and moisture.

Differences between animals and plants

Both plants and animals have in common, to a greater or lesser extent, all the features listed above, but there are some fundamental differences between them of which one of the most important is the method of feeding.

1. **Method of feeding.** Animals take in food that is chemically very complicated (i.e. composed of large molecules); it consists either of plant products or of other animals. This food is reduced to simpler material by the process of digestion, and in this form it can be taken up by the body.

Plants, in general, take in very simple substances that are composed of small molecules, namely carbon dioxide from the air, and water and dissolved salts from the soil. In their leaves they combine this carbon dioxide and water into sugar, using sunlight as a source of energy. From the sugar so produced, and the salts taken in from the soil, green plants can make all of the substances needed for their existence. The feeding of animals thus involves a breaking-down process, while that of plants is a building-up, or synthesis.

2. **Chlorophyll.** The green colour found in most plants is important for the absorption of sunlight and is due to chlorophyll, which is not present in any animal. This difference is one indication of the fundamental difference in feeding. (However, many plants such as fungi do not possess chlorophyll.)

3. **Cellulose.** In their structures, notably their cell walls, plants have a large quantity of a substance called cellulose, which is never present in animal structures.

4. **Movement.** Unlike animals, most of the familiar plants do not move about as complete organisms, but certain microscopic plants move as actively as microscopic animals.

5. **Sensitivity.** Although both plants and animals respond to stimuli, the response of an animal usually follows almost immediately after the application of even a very brief stimulus. In plants, on the other hand, a response may take place over a matter of hours or days, and then only if the stimulus persists for a relatively long time.

QUESTIONS

1. A motor car moves, takes in oxygen and gives out carbon dioxide, consumes fuel but nevertheless is not a living creature. In what ways does it not "qualify" as a living organism?
2. A sponge-like organism is found adhering to a rock in a marine pool. How would a microscopic examination help to decide whether it was a plant or an animal?

3 | The Microscope and its Use

THE kind of microscope used in schools is an optical instrument for magnifying specimens so that they can be studied in great detail. Fig. 3.1 shows the construction of a fairly inexpensive microscope. The object is placed on a glass slide which, in turn, is placed on the *stage*. If the object is a small organism or a thin slice of tissue, it will be transparent.

The angle of the *mirror* below the stage is adjusted until light from a window or a bench lamp is directed through the specimen and into the microscope. The light then passes through the lens systems, the *objective* and the *eyepiece*, into the eye of the observer.

The objective lens magnifies the specimen to produce an image from 10–40 times life size. The eyepiece further magnifies this image 5–10 times. The final size of the image seen by the observer will be the product of the two magnifications, e.g. a × 10 objective and a × 5 eyepiece will give an image 50 times larger than life size. By changing the combination of eyepiece and objective, it is possible to obtain magnifications of up to about × 400 with school microscopes. Some microscopes have two or three objectives mounted on a *turret* so that when the turret is rotated, a different objective is brought into position.

To bring the image of the specimen into focus, you have to turn the *coarse* and *fine adjustment* wheels. The safest way to do this is to turn the coarse adjustment to bring the objective close to the specimen but not touching it, while watching carefully from the side. Then, while looking through the eyepiece, rotate the coarse adjustment so that the objective is lifted up *away* from the slide, until you see the image come into focus. By following this procedure, you will avoid forcing the objective through the slide and so damaging the specimen and the lens.

The focusing adjustment on some microscopes moves the stage rather than the tube but the principle of focusing is the same. Start with the specimen close to the objective and turn the adjustment to *increase* the gap between them. If the microscope has a fine adjustment, this can be used to sharpen the image.

By moving the slide about on the stage, you will be able to study different parts of the specimen, but you will have to get used to the fact that the image moves in the opposite direction to the slide, i.e. to move the image to the left, you will have to move the slide to the right.

Small specimens, such as pollen grains can be placed on a slide and studied dry. Other specimens are best placed in a drop of water and covered with a cover slip (*see* Fig. 5.15, p. 22).

To examine plant tissues, it is usual to cut very thin slices (called *sections*) of the plant organ, and mount these in water on a slide as described above.

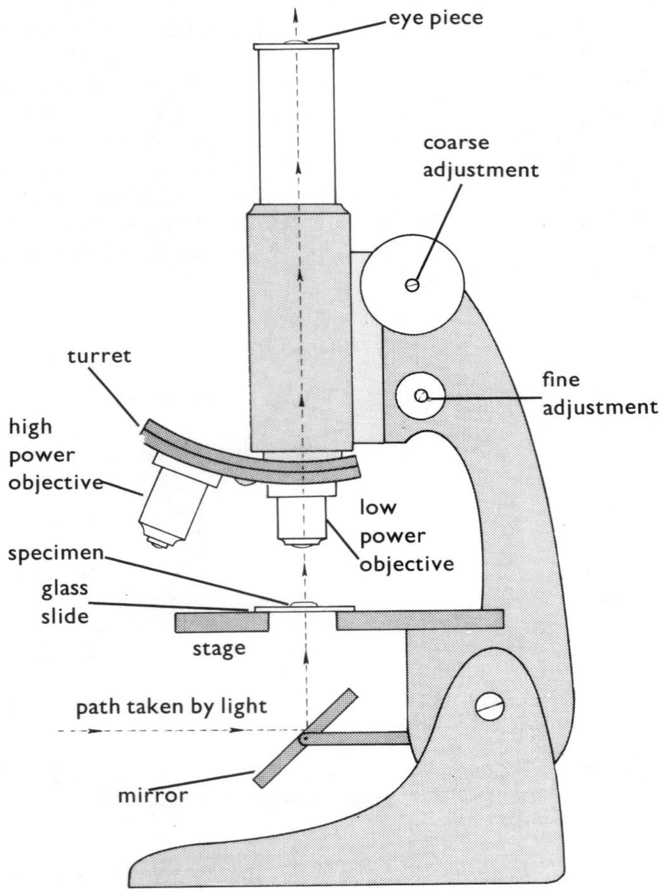

Fig. 3.1 The microscope

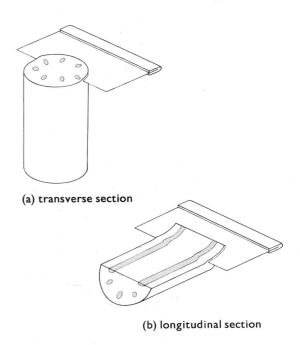

(a) transverse section

(b) longitudinal section

Fig. 3.2 Cutting sections of a plant stem

4 | Cells

Nearly all plants and animals have one characteristic in common: they are made up of cells. If any structures from plants or animals are examined microscopically they will be seen to consist of more or less distinct units—cells—which, although too small to be seen with the naked eye, in their vast numbers make up the structures or organs.

Since the cells of any organ are usually specially developed in their size, shape and chemistry to carry out one particular function (e.g. muscle cells for contracting) there is, strictly speaking, no such thing as a "typical" cell of plants or animals. Nevertheless, certain of the features common to most cells can be illustrated diagrammatically.

Parts of the cell (*see* Figs. 4.1–4.6)

Cell membrane. All cells are bounded by a very thin flexible membrane which retains the cell contents and controls the substances entering and leaving the cells.

Cell wall. In plant cells only, there is a wall outside the cell membrane. It confers shape and, to some extent, rigidity on the cell. While the cell is growing the cell wall is fairly plastic and extensible, but once the cell has reached full size, the wall becomes tough and resists stretching.

Unless impregnated with chemicals, as in the cells of corky tree bark, the cell wall is freely permeable to gases and water, i.e. it allows them to pass through in either direction. The cell wall is made by the cytoplasm and is non-living, being made of a transparent substance called cellulose.

The *middle lamella* is the layer which first forms between cells after a plant cell has divided (Fig. 4.5c) and may remain visible between mature cells in microscopical preparations.

Protoplasm is the material inside the cell which is truly alive. There are two principal kinds of protoplasm; the protoplasm which constitutes the nucleus (*see* below) is called *nucleoplasm*. All other forms of protoplasm are referred to as *cytoplasm*.

Cytoplasm appears to be a transparent jelly-like fluid and may contain particles such as chloroplasts or starch grains. In some cells it is able to flow about. In the cytoplasm the chemical processes essential to life are carried on. The cell membrane is partially permeable, allowing some substances to pass through more readily than others. This selection helps to maintain the best conditions for chemical reactions in the protoplasm.

The **nucleus** consists of nucleoplasm bounded by a nuclear membrane. It is always embedded in the cytoplasm, is frequently ovoid in shape and lighter in colour than the cytoplasm. In diagrams it is often shaded darker because most microscopical preparations are stained with dyes to show it up clearly. It is less easily seen in the unstained cell. The nucleus is thought to be a centre of chemical activity, playing a part in determining the shape, size and function of the cell and controlling most of the physiological processes within it.

Without the nucleus the cell is not capable of its normal functions or of division, although it may continue to live for a time. When cell division occurs, the nucleus initiates and controls the process (Fig. 4.5).

Vacuole. In animal cells there may be small droplets of fluid in the cytoplasm, variable in size and position. In plant cells the vacuole is usually a large, permanent, fluid-filled cavity occupying the greater part of the cell. In plants, this fluid is called cell sap and may contain salts, sugar and pigments dissolved in water. The outward pressure of the vacuole on the cell wall makes the plant cells firm, giving strength and resilience to the tissues.

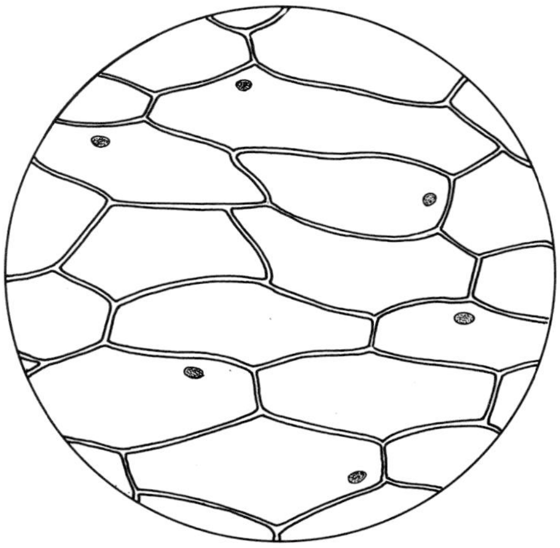

Fig. 4.1 Epidermis from onion scale seen under the microscope

The epidermis is one cell thick, so that under the microscope the transparent cells can be seen. The shape of each cell is partly determined by the pressure of the other cells round it. If a cell were isolated it would be rounded or oval.

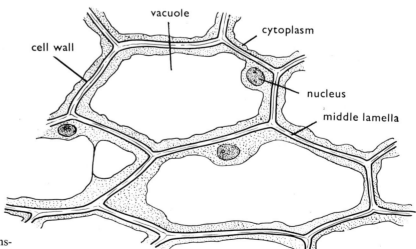

Fig. 4.2 A group of similar cells highly magnified to show cell structures

12

Cell division

Some, but not all, cells are able to divide and produce new cells as shown in Fig. 4.5. Cell division and subsequent cell enlargement taking place in many cells results in the growth of organisms.

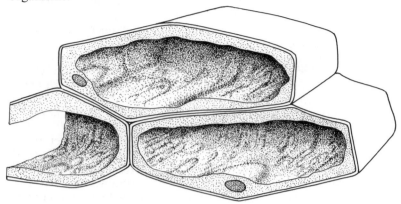

Fig 4.3   Stereogram of plant cells

It is important to remember that, although cells look flat in sections or thin strips of tissue, they are three-dimensional and may seem to have different shapes according to the direction in which the section is cut.

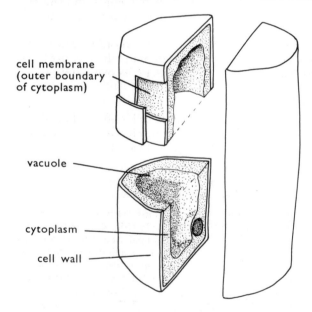

Fig. 4.4(a)   Stereogram of one plant cell

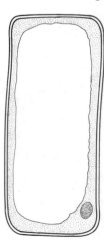

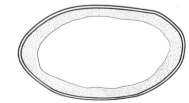

Fig. 4.4(b)   Transverse section

If the cell at (a) is cut across, it will look like (b) under the microscope; if cut longitudinally it will look like (c).

Fig. 4.4(c)   Longitudinal section

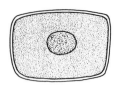

(a) A plant cell about to divide has a large nucleus and no vacuole.

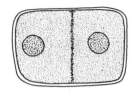

(b) The nucleus divides first.

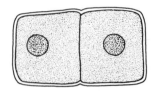

(c) The middle lamella develops and separates the two cells.

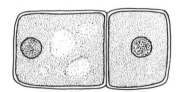

(d) The cytoplasm lays down a primary wall and layers of cellulose on each side of the middle lamella.

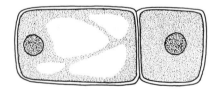

(e) One of the cells develops a vacuole and enlarges. The other cell retains the ability to divide again.

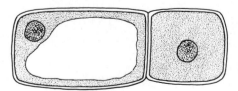

(f) Although each cell has its own primary wall, these often give the appearance of a single, intermediate wall between cells.

Fig. 4.5

Differences between plant and animal cells

1. Although there is a very wide range of variation, the cells of plant tissues are usually easier to demonstrate under the microscope than are the cells of animal tissues. This is partly because the plant cells are larger and their cell walls give them a distinctive outline.

2. Plants have cell walls made of cellulose. Animal cells have no cell walls and do not possess any cellulose.

3. Mature plant cells have only a thin lining of cytoplasm, with a large central vacuole. Animal cells consist almost entirely of cytoplasm (Fig. 4.7 and Plate 1). If any vacuoles are present they are usually temporary and small, concerned with excretion or secretion.

4. Animal cells never contain chloroplasts (p. 19) whereas these are present in a great many plant cells.

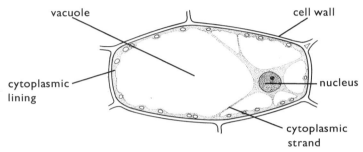

Fig. 4.6   A plant cell

Sometimes the nucleus appears in the centre of the cell, but it is still surrounded by cytoplasm connected by strands to that lining the wall.

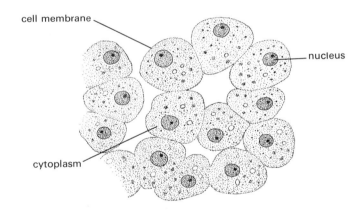

Fig. 4.7   A group of animal cells

Plate 1.   CELLS FROM THE LINING OF THE CHEEK (×1000)   (Brian Bracegirdle)

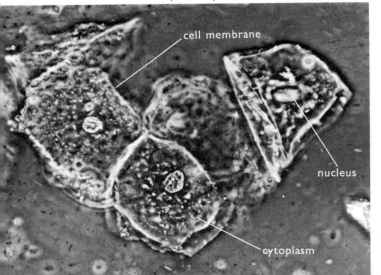

Relation of cells to the organism as a whole

Although each cell can carry on the vital chemistry of living, it is not capable of existence on its own. A muscle cell could not obtain its own food or oxygen. Other specialized cells, present in a tissue or organ, collect food or carry oxygen. Unless individual cells are grouped together in large numbers and made to work together by the co-ordinating mechanisms of the body, they cannot exist for long.

Tissue. A tissue such as bone, nerve or muscle in animals, and epidermis, phloem or pith in plants, is made up of many hundreds of cells of one or a few types, each type having a more or less identical structure and function so that the tissue can also be said to have a specific function, e.g. nerves conduct impulses, phloem carries food.

Organs consist of several tissues grouped together making a functional unit: for example, a muscle is an organ containing long muscle cells held together with connective tissue and permeated with blood vessels and nerve fibres. The arrival of a nerve impulse causes the muscle fibres to contract, using the food and oxygen brought by the blood vessels to provide the necessary energy.

In a plant, the roots, stems and leaves are the organs.

System usually refers to a series of organs whose functions are co-ordinated to produce effective action in the organism: for example, the heart and blood vessels constitute the circulatory system; the brain, spinal cord and nerves make up the nervous system.

An organism results from the efficient co-ordination of the organs and systems to produce an individual capable of separate existence and able to perpetuate its own kind.

Specialization

In its structure and physiology, each cell is often adapted to a particular function in the organ of which it is a part. The notes and drawings (Fig. 4.8 a–e) on page 14 illustrate this.

PRACTICAL WORK

Plant cells. The epidermis can be stripped fairly easily from the inside of an onion scale or other bulb scale (Fig. 4.1) or the lower surface of certain fleshy leaves. Since the epidermis here is one cell thick, the cells can be seen in transparency if a small piece of the tissue is placed flat on a slide, covered with a drop of water, and examined under the low power of the microscope. A little iodine solution may stain the nuclei light brown, and any starch grains present will turn dark blue. Cells and chloroplasts can be seen in a moss leaf if it is mounted flat on a slide with a drop of water.

Animal cells. To avoid any possibility of cross-infection, it is perhaps best not to use human tissues, such as cheek epithelium.

A safer alternative is to study prepared slides of such tissues (Plate 1).

QUESTIONS

1. What features are (a) possessed by both plant and animal cells, (b) possessed by plant cells only?

2. With what materials must cells be supplied if they are to survive?

3. In what ways would you say that the white blood cell (Fig. 4.8b) is less specialized than the nerve cell (Fig. 4.8e)?

4. In many microscopical preparations of animal tissues, it is difficult to make out the cell boundaries and yet the disposition and numbers of cells can usually be determined. Which cell structure makes this possible?

SPECIALIZED CELLS

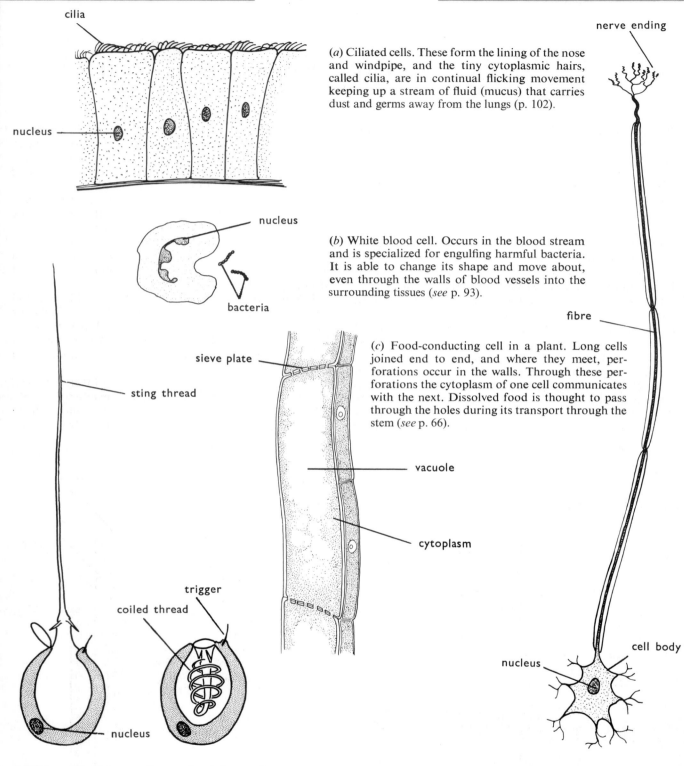

cilia

nucleus

(a) Ciliated cells. These form the lining of the nose and windpipe, and the tiny cytoplasmic hairs, called cilia, are in continual flicking movement keeping up a stream of fluid (mucus) that carries dust and germs away from the lungs (p. 102).

nerve ending

nucleus

bacteria

(b) White blood cell. Occurs in the blood stream and is specialized for engulfing harmful bacteria. It is able to change its shape and move about, even through the walls of blood vessels into the surrounding tissues (see p. 93).

fibre

sieve plate

sting thread

(c) Food-conducting cell in a plant. Long cells joined end to end, and where they meet, perforations occur in the walls. Through these perforations the cytoplasm of one cell communicates with the next. Dissolved food is thought to pass through the holes during its transport through the stem (see p. 66).

vacuole

cytoplasm

trigger

coiled thread

nucleus

cell body

nucleus

(d) Sting cell. There are thousands of these cells on the tentacles of the sea-anemone, jelly-fish and hydra. When a small creature swims past and touches the trigger, the coiled thread shoots out, pierces the skin, and injects a paralysing poison.

(e) Nerve cell. Specialized for conducting impulses of an electrical nature along the fibre. A nerve consists of hundreds of fibres bound together. The fibres may be very long, e.g. from the foot to the spinal column (see p. 138).

Fig. 4.8

5 | Structure of the Flowering Plant

THE flowering plant consists of a portion above ground, the shoot, and a portion below ground, the root, although this does not imply that any part of a plant below ground must be a root.

The shoot is usually made up of a stem, bearing leaves, buds and flowers.

Stem

General characteristics (Fig. 5.1). A stem has leaves at regular intervals and a terminal bud at the growing point. The region of the stem from which the leaf springs is called the *node*, and the length of stem between the nodes, the *internode*.

Commonly, the stem is erect, but it may be horizontal as in runners; underground as in rhizomes; very short and never showing above ground as in bulbs and corms; long, thin and weak as in climbing plants; or stout and thick as in trees. Young stems are usually green and contain chlorophyll.

The cells in young stems are living and obtain a supply of oxygen from the air through openings, stomata or lenticels (described below), in their epidermis. Older stems are supported by woody and fibrous tissues which are added layer by layer, so increasing their thickness. Young stems depend for

their rigidity on the turgidity of their cells, the cylindrical distribution of their conducting tissues and the opposing stresses of the pith and epidermis. Running through the stem are tubes which conduct water from the soil up to the leaves and food from the leaves to various parts of the plant.

Functions of the stem. It (*a*) supports the structures of the shoot; (*b*) spaces out the leaves so that they receive adequate air and sunlight; (*c*) allows conduction of water from soil to leaves, and food from leaves to other parts of the plant; (*d*) holds flowers above ground, thus assisting pollination by insects or wind. (*e*) If the stem is green, photosynthesis (Chapter 10) may occur in it.

Detailed structure (Figs. 5.2, 5.3 *a* and *b*, Plates 2 and 3). A fairly typical stem, such as that of a sunflower, is in the form of a cylinder. The outer layer of cells forms a skin, the *epidermis*, the inner cells make up the *cortex* and *pith*. Between the cortex and pith lie a number of *vascular bundles* containing specialized cells which carry food and water.

EPIDERMIS. The single layer of closely fitting cells is effective in holding the inner cells in shape, preventing loss of water, affording protection from damage and preventing the entry of fungi, bacteria and dust. This layer is relatively impermeable to

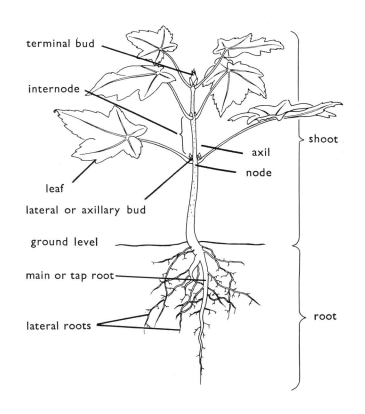

Fig. 5.1   Structure of a typical flowering plant

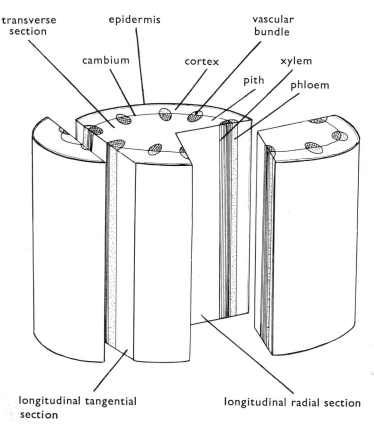

Fig. 5.2   Stereogram of plant stem

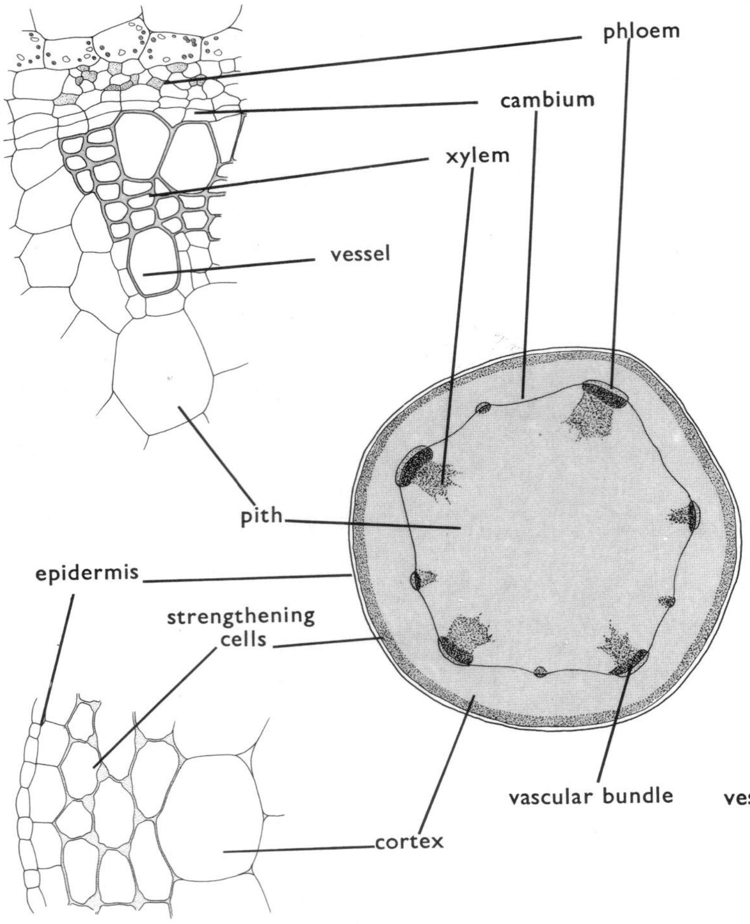

phloem

cambium

xylem

vessel

pith

epidermis

strengthening cells

cortex

vascular bundle

Fig. 5.3(a)   Section through stem of *Impatiens*

Plate 3.   LONGITUDINAL SECTION
THROUGH SUNFLOWER STEM (×300)
showing vessels thickened internally with bands of
woody material

(Brian Bracegirdle)

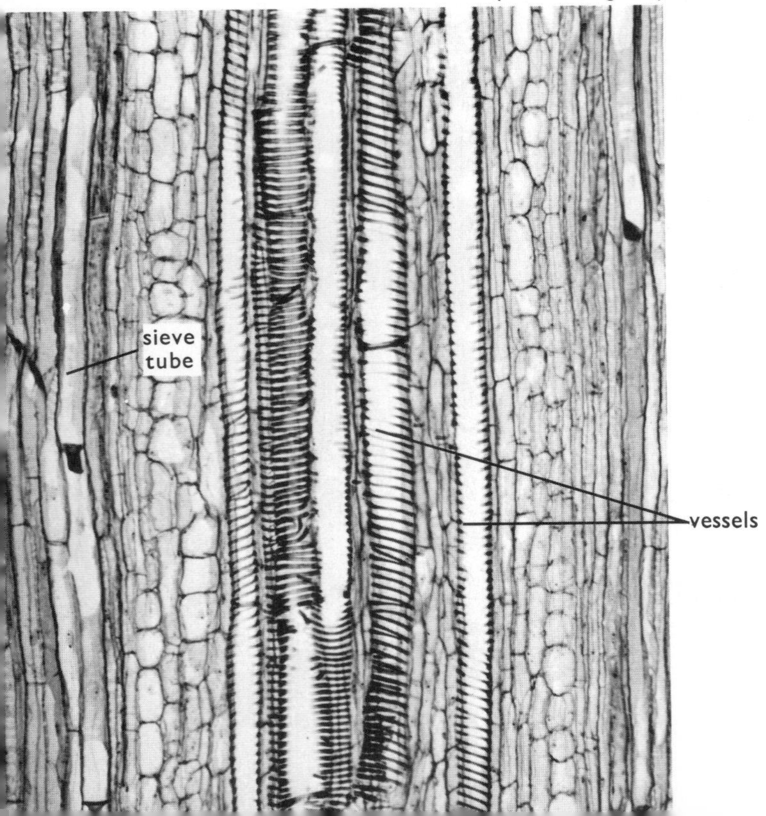

sieve tube

vessels

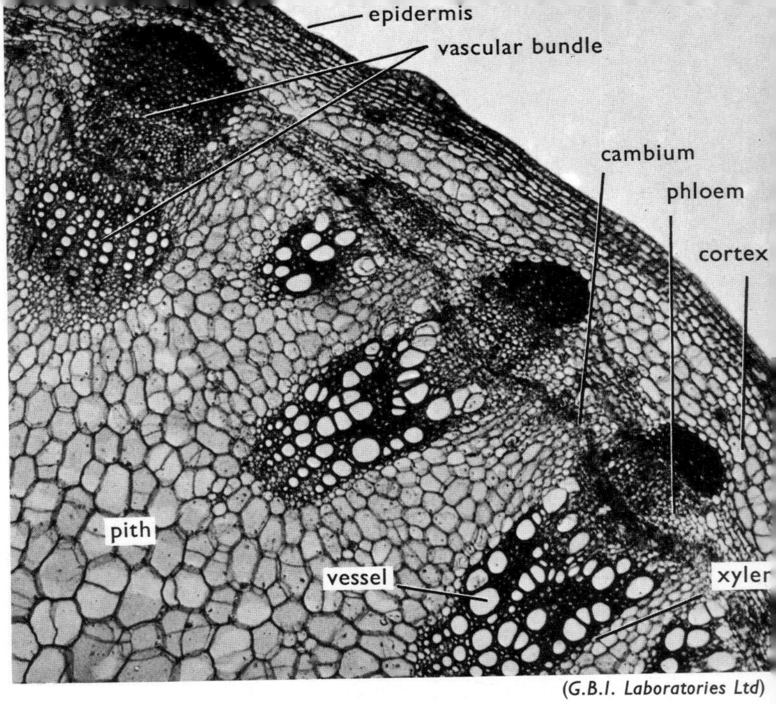

epidermis

vascular bundle

cambium

phloem

cortex

pith

vessel

xyler

(G.B.I. Laboratories Ltd)

Plate 2.   TRANSVERSE SECTION THROUGH
SUNFLOWER STEM (×70)

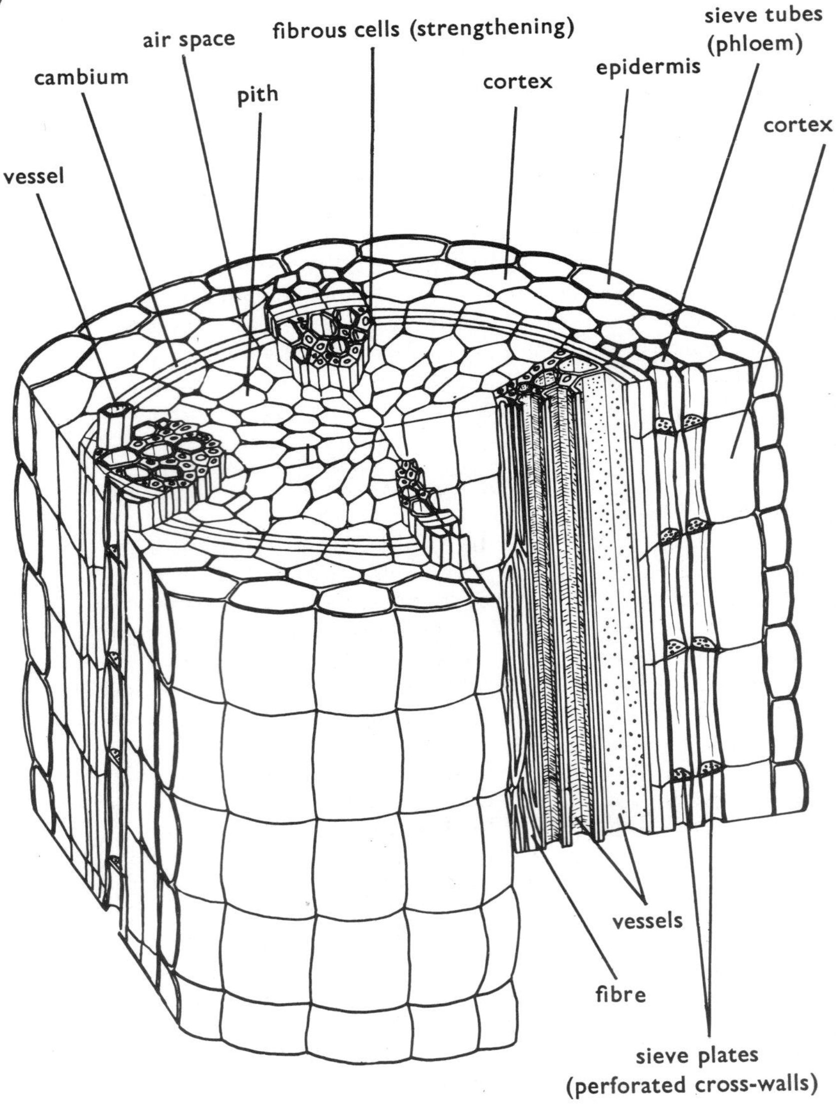

cambium

air space

pith

fibrous cells (strengthening)

cortex

epidermis

sieve tubes
(phloem)

cortex

vessel

vessels

fibre

sieve plates
(perforated cross-walls)

Fig. 5.3(b)   Stereogram of plant stem sectioned, showing
cells (cell contents not shown)

liquids and gases, and oxygen can enter, and carbon dioxide escape, only through stomata (described below) in young stems, and lenticels in older stems. The *lenticels* are small gaps in the bark, usually circular or oval and slightly raised on the bark surface. In them, the cells of the bark fit loosely, leaving air gaps which communicate with the air spaces in the cortex (Fig. 5.4). The epidermis is usually in a state of strain, in which it tends to shrink along its length. This shrinking effect contributes to the rigidity of the stem.

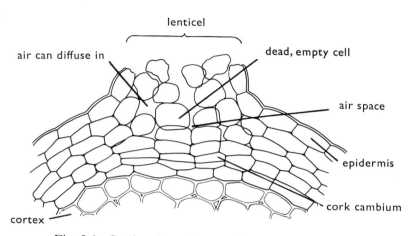

Fig. 5.4   Section through stem showing lenticel

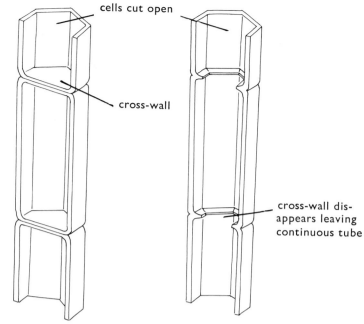

Fig. 5.5   Diagram to show how vertical columns of cells give rise to vessels

CORTEX AND PITH. These are tissues consisting of fairly large, thin-walled cells with air spaces between them. This air-space system is continuous throughout the living tissues and allows air to circulate from the stomata or lenticels to all living regions of the stem. The cortex and pith contribute to the rigidity of the stem by pressing out against the epidermis and by tending to increase in length against the shrinking tendency of the epidermis. These tissues also space out the vascular bundles and have a general value as packing. Many stems, however, are hollow with only a narrow band of pith within the cortex.

VASCULAR BUNDLES, sometimes called veins, are made up of vessels and sieve tubes, with fibrous and packing tissue between and around them.

Vessels consist of long tubes a metre or so in length. They are formed from columns of cells whose walls have become impregnated with a substance called *lignin* which makes them very hard (woody). The horizontal cross-walls of these cells have broken down before the cells are lignified and the cells finally form a long continuous tube (Fig. 5.5). In these vessels water is carried from the roots, through the stem and to the veins in the leaves (Fig. 5.6).

Sieve tubes are formed from columns of living cells the horizontal walls of which are perforated (Fig. 4.8c). These perforations allow dissolved substances to flow from one cell to the next, so carrying food made in the leaves to other parts of the plant, e.g. to the ripening fruits, growing points or underground storage organs, according to the species of plant and the time of year.

Vessels and sieve tubes are surrounded by cells that space them out and support them. The tissue, consisting of vessels and the long fibre-like cells among them, is called *xylem*. The sieve tubes and their packing cells are called *phloem*.

CAMBIUM. Between the xylem and the phloem is a layer of narrow, thin-walled cells called cambium.

Once cells have been formed from the growing point and have grown to their full extent, they are no longer capable of dividing

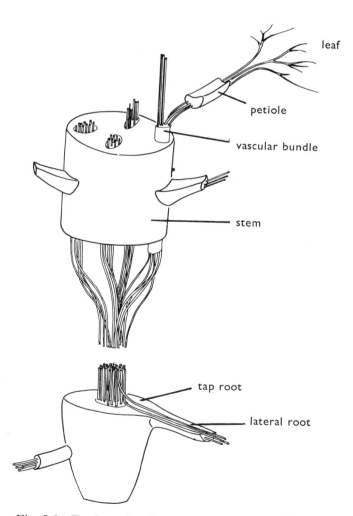

Fig. 5.6   To show distribution of veins from lateral root to leaf

to make new cells. They may have become changed in structure and specialized to a particular function, as has, for example, a sieve tube. The cells in the cambium, however, do not lose their ability to divide and are able to multiply and make new cells.

Although at first the cambium is restricted to the vascular bundles, it later forms a continuous cylinder within the stem between the cortex and pith. Its cells divide in such a way as to make new xylem cells called *secondary xylem*, on the inside and new phloem cells called *secondary phloem* on the outside. In woody plants like trees, this continues throughout their life-time, and as the cambium continues to divide and add new cells the stem increases in thickness, a process called *secondary thickening*. In such woody stems the epidermis is often replaced by a dead, corky layer, bark, which itself is made by a separate layer of cork cambium just beneath the epidermis. The phloem becomes a thin layer of living cells between the bark and the woody core of xylem (Fig. 5.7).

Strength of stems. Vertical stems are likely to experience side-ways forces when the wind blows against them. The turgor (*see* Chapter 12) of the cells, the opposing forces of the epidermis tending to shrink, and the pith tending to extend, all contribute to the stem's resilience. The vascular bundles usually contain the toughest structures in the stem, the lignified vessels and, often, long stringy fibrous cells running alongside them. When the vascular bundles are arranged in a cylinder near the outside of the stem they add to its strength, a cylindrical structure being much more resistant to bending than a solid structure of the same weight.

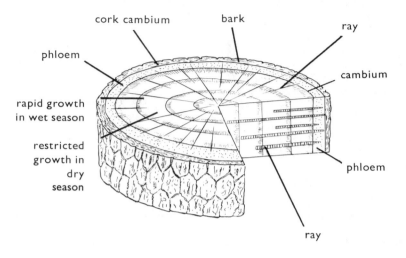

Fig. 5.7   Diagrammatic section through a woody stem

In this diagram the growth rings shown in the secondary xylem are characteristic of those trees whose growth is seasonal, but in many tropical trees, growth is continuous and growth rings are not observable.

Leaf

General structure (Fig. 5.8 *a* and *b*). A leaf is a flat, green *lamina* or blade made from a soft tissue of thin-walled cells, supported by a stronger network of veins. Leaves are sometimes joined to the stem by a stalk, *petiole*, which continues into its *midrib* (or the main vein). Sometimes there is no leaf stalk.

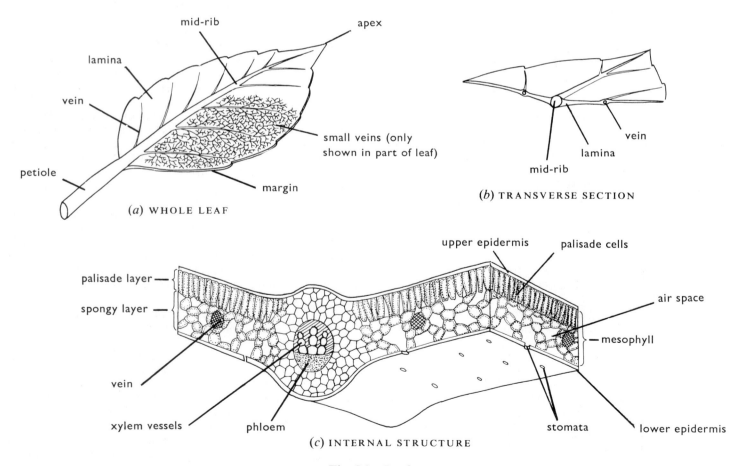

Fig. 5.8   Leaf structure

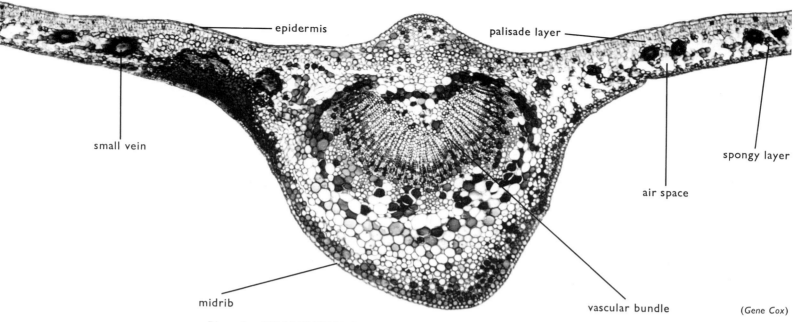

epidermis

palisade layer

small vein

spongy layer

air space

midrib

vascular bundle

(Gene Cox)

Plate 4. TRANSVERSE SECTION THROUGH A LEAF (×30)

Functions. The important function of leaves is to make food, in the form of carbohydrates, by *photosynthesis*. The water necessary for this process is conveyed through the vessels which run in the vascular bundles branching from the stem, and through the petiole and midrib, dividing repeatedly to form a network of tiny veins throughout the lamina. In addition, for photosynthesis, the leaf needs a supply of carbon dioxide from the air. This diffuses in through the pores, stomata (*see* below), in one or both of its surfaces. For respiration, all living cells need a supply of oxygen, which also enters through the stomata.

The broad, flat shape of the leaf presents a large surface area to the air, facilitating rapid absorption of oxygen and carbon dioxide and allowing the maximum sunlight to fall on its ex-posed surface. Most leaves are thin in section and, in consequence, the distance through which the gases have to diffuse, from the atmosphere to the cells inside, is small, and gaseous exchange can be fairly rapid. The permeability to gases and the large surface area of the leaf are also characteristics which encourage rapid evaporation of water vapour.

Detailed structure (Figs. 5.8c, 5.9 and 5.10, Plate 4). The EPIDERMIS is a single layer of cells fitting closely together with no air spaces between them except at the stomata. The epidermis may secrete a continuous waxy layer, *cuticle*, which reduces evaporation. The epidermis helps to maintain the shape of the leaf, protects the inner cells from bacteria, fungi and mechanical damage, and reduces evaporation. The epidermal cells, except the guard cells (*see* below) of the stomata, do not usually contain chloroplasts and are transparent. In consequence, sunlight can pass through to the cells below, which do contain chloroplasts.

PALISADE LAYER. In the one or more rows of tall cylindrical cells, with narrow air spaces between them, which comprise the palisade layer, most of the photosynthesis (carbohydrate formation) occurs. There are many chloroplasts in the cytoplasm lining the walls. Lying immediately below the epidermis, the palisade cells receive and absorb most of the sunlight. The chloroplasts arranged along the side walls are not far from the supplies of carbon dioxide in the air spaces, and they can move up or down the cell according to the intensity of the sunlight. The elongated cells result in very little sunlight being absorbed by horizontal cross-walls before it reaches the chloroplasts.

CHLOROPLASTS are small, often discoid (discus-like) bodies made of protein. They contain *chlorophyll*, the green pigment which gives green plants their characteristic colour, and which can absorb energy from sunlight and use it in the chemical build-up of sugars and starch. This chemical activity is thought to occur in the chloroplast when it is receiving light.

SPONGY LAYER. The cells in this region do not fit closely together, and large air spaces are left between them. The air spaces communicate with each other and, through the stomata,

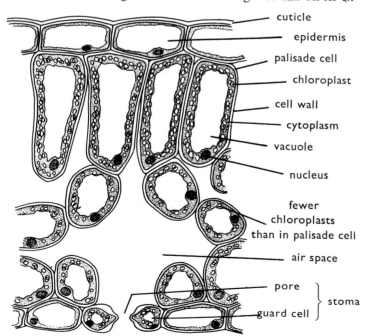

cuticle

epidermis

palisade cell

chloroplast

cell wall

cytoplasm

vacuole

nucleus

fewer chloroplasts than in palisade cell

air space

pore

guard cell

stoma

Fig. 5.9   Section through leaf to show cell structure

with the atmosphere, thus allowing air to circulate in them and reach most of the internal cells of the leaf. The cells of the spongy layer can photosynthesize, but they receive less sunlight than do the palisade cells, and contain fewer chloroplasts. The palisade and spongy layers are known collectively as *mesophyll*.

STOMATA (Fig. 5.11, Plate 5). Usually more abundant on the lower side of the leaf, stomata are openings in the epidermis. They are formed between two *guard cells* which, according to their internal pressure, or *turgor*, can increase or reduce the size of the stoma or close it completely. The conditions which affect the opening or closure of the stomata are thought to be connected principally with light intensity and, in some cases, with the loss of water. The mechanism by which they open is a chain of events leading to an increase in the concentration of sugars in the cell sap in the vacuoles of the guard cells. When this happens, the water potential (p. 61) of the cell sap decreases and the guard cells withdraw water from their neighbours. This increases the turgor pressure in the guard cell, which tends to swell. The wall of the cell is particularly thick along its inner border so that it does not readily stretch. The stretching of the outer walls, however, causes the guard cells to curve away from each other and so increases the gap between them.

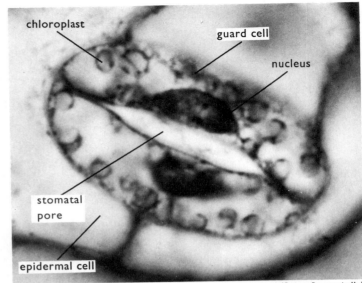

(Brian Bracegirdle)

Plate 5.   A STOMA OF A LEAF (×800)

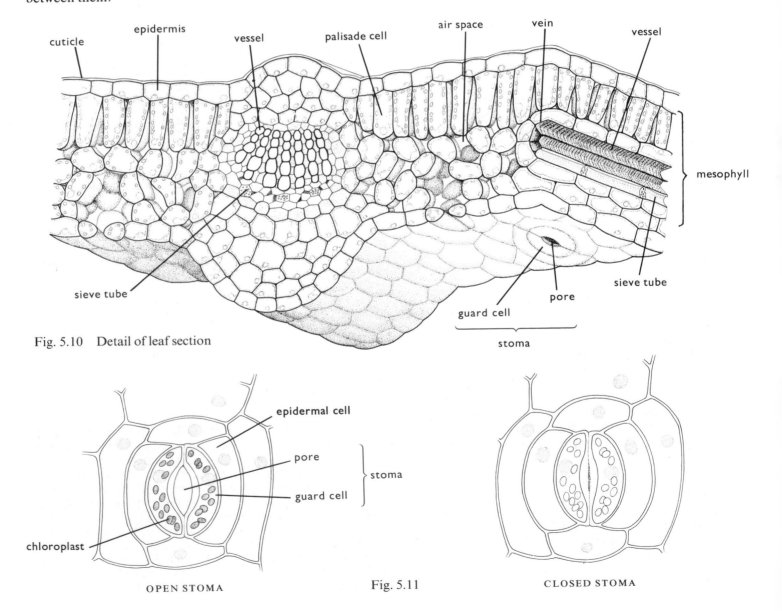

Fig. 5.10   Detail of leaf section

OPEN STOMA   Fig. 5.11   CLOSED STOMA

MIDRIB AND VEINS support the leaf, conducting water into it and food away from it. They contain vascular bundles surrounded by other fibrous and strengthening cells. Each cell of the leaf is not supplied with its own vein, but the network of veins is very fine, and water has to pass from a vein through only a few cells to reach, say, a palisade cell.

Roots

Root systems. TAP ROOT (Fig. 5.12*a*). When a seed germinates, a single root grows vertically down into the soil. Later, lateral roots grow from this at an acute angle outwards and downwards, and from these laterals other branches may arise. Where a main root is recognizable the arrangement is called a tap-root system.

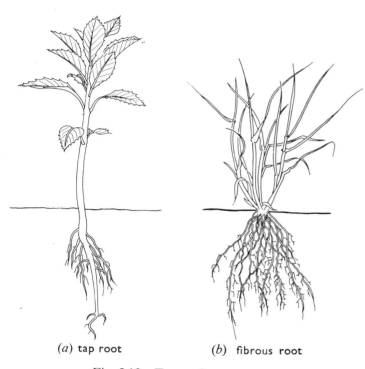

(*a*) tap root   (*b*) fibrous root

Fig. 5.12   Types of root system

FIBROUS ROOT (Fig. 5.12*b*). When a seed of the grass and cereal group germinates, several roots grow out at the same time and laterals grow from them. There is no distinguishable main root, and it is called a fibrous system.

ADVENTITIOUS ROOT. Where roots grow, not from a main root, but directly from the stem as they do in bulbs, corms or rhizomes, they are called adventitious roots, but such a system may also be described as a fibrous rooting system.

General structure of roots. Usually white, roots cannot develop chlorophyll. They never bear leaves or axillary buds.

Function. Roots anchor the plant firmly in the soil and prevent its being blown over by the wind. They absorb water and mineral salts from the soil and pass them into the stem. Frequently they can act as food stores.

Detailed structure (Fig. 5.13). EPIDERMIS. This is a layer of cells without a cuticle. The younger regions, particularly those with root hairs, permit the uptake of water and solutes.

CORTEX. The cortex consists of large, thin-walled cells with air spaces between them. The cortical cells store food material and the innermost layer of cells may regulate the inward passage of water and dissolved substances.

VASCULAR TISSUE. This is in the centre of the root, and initially the phloem strands lie between the radial arms of the central xylem. The branches that form the lateral roots grow from this region and force their way through the cortex, bursting through the outer layer to reach the soil. The centrally placed vascular tissue well-adapts the root to the strain that it is likely to experience along its length while holding the plant firmly in the soil when the shoot is being blown sideways by the wind. This makes an interesting comparison with the cylindrical distribution of vascular tissue in the stem and the lateral strain to which it might be subjected in the same conditions.

GROWING POINT (Fig. 5.14). At the root tip (Plate 6) is a region where the cells are dividing rapidly. Behind the root tip, the new cells produced by the dividing region absorb water and develop vacuoles, the intake of water causing the cells to elongate, the cell walls still being relatively plastic. This area behind the root tip is thus the region of extension and, since the upper part of the root is firmly anchored, it pushes the root tip down, or sideways, between the soil particles. The root tip is protected from damage by the *root cap*, layers of cells which are continually produced by the dividing region and replaced from the inside as fast as the outer ones are worn away by the abrasion of the soil particles.

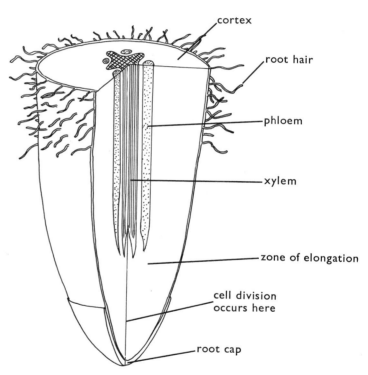

cortex

root hair

phloem

xylem

zone of elongation

cell division occurs here

root cap

Fig. 5.13   Stereogram of root (vertically shortened)

ROOT HAIRS (Fig. 5.14) provide the main absorbing region of the root. They are tiny, finger-like outgrowths from the cells of the epidermis before it dies. They appear just above the zone of elongation, and there are none at the root tip or in the older regions of the root. The root hairs grow out from the cells and between the soil particles, their shape therefore being determined, to some extent, by the position of the particles between which they grow. Their cell walls stick to the soil particles, which cannot easily be washed off. This helps to keep the soil firm round the roots and reduces erosion by wind and rain. The total absorbing area of the millions of root hairs in a root system is very great (*see* also Fig. 12.8).

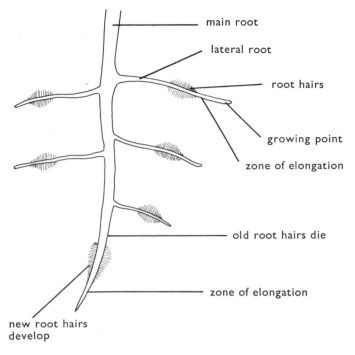

Fig. 5.14   Regions of a root system

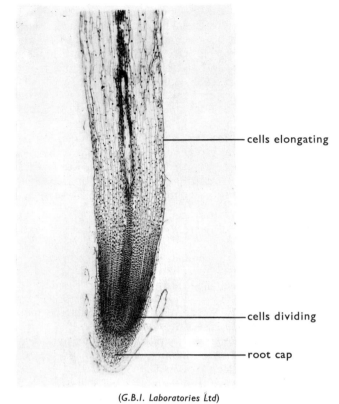

(G.B.I. Laboratories Ltd)

Plate 6.   LONGITUDINAL SECTION OF
THE ROOT TIP OF AN ONION (× 20)

PRACTICAL WORK

1. ***Cells and vessels.*** Some flower stalks or leaf petioles are cut up into pieces about 2 cm long and left for a few days in a macerating fluid of 10 per cent chromic and nitric acids. This will break down the intercellular material so that the cells can be teased apart with mounted needles. The macerating acids should be washed off or repeatedly diluted before the material is handled. A little of such material, torn into pieces which are as small as possible, is put on a slide with a little water and covered with a cover slip (Fig. 5.15). It should be possible to see individual cells and vessels under the lower power of the microscope.

2. ***Stomata.*** Stomata can be seen if a piece of the lower epidermis of a leaf such as *Rheo discolor* or a lily is stripped off and placed on a slide under the microscope. The stomata can be made to close by putting a little strong salt or sugar solution on the tissue. This will withdraw water by osmosis and cause the guard cells to lose their turgor.

QUESTIONS

1. What are the main functions of (*a*) stems, (*b*) roots, (*c*) leaves?
2. What are the differences in (*a*) structure, (*b*) function, between vessels and sieve tubes?
3. How do roots, stems and leaves obtain supplies of oxygen for respiration?
4. What are the advantages of having a network of veins in a leaf (e.g. Fig. 5.8*a*)?
5. By what means does a rooting system achieve a large absorbing surface?
6. How is lateral stress resisted by (*a*) a young stem, (*b*) an old stem?
7. In what ways does the broad, thin structure of dicotyledonous leaves adapt them to their functions?

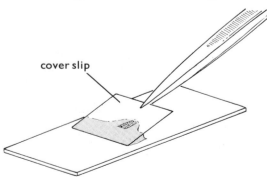

Fig. 5.15   Lower the cover slip carefully on to the water
drop to avoid trapping air bubbles

6 | Storage Organs and Vegetative Reproduction

Annual plants survive the dry season as seeds only, for after germination, flowering and seed formation, the rest of the plant dies off. *Impatiens* and maize are examples of these. In certain cases the whole germination–reproduction cycle lasts only a few weeks, but may be repeated many times in one season, e.g. *Ageratum conyzoides*. Plants such as these are called *ephemerals*.

Perennial plants. *Woody perennial* plants are trees and shrubs in which the trunk and branches persist and grow from year to year. Those which shed all their leaves in the dry season are called *deciduous*, e.g. *Delonix* (flame of the forest) and *Ceiba* (silk cotton), while evergreen trees such as the mango and coconut shed their leaves throughout the year.

Herbaceous perennials are plants which do not die after producing flowers and seeds but persist from season to season, though with reduced growth during dry periods. In some cases the vegetation above ground may die off entirely in the drought, as in certain of the grasses of the dry savannah. In perennial plants such as the canna lily, some leaves and flowers may remain in regions where the dry season is less prolonged and interrupted by storms, or in gardens where plants are watered. In either case, the structures such as bulbs, tubers or rhizomes, which persist below ground usually contain a store of food which is used for the rapid production of a new flowering shoot.

Vegetative propagation

In the rainy season, the terminal and lateral buds of herbaceous perennials sprout and produce new shoots. The shoots formed from some of the lateral buds often develop their own adventitious roots and by the end of the season have become independent of the parent plant and other lateral shoots. Thus, new plants are produced from buds without pollination or fertilization being necessary. This is called *asexual* or *vegetative* reproduction and is illustrated by the accounts of the life cycles described below.

Buds can be made to produce whole new plants by artificial means, e.g. cuttings and grafts. These are described more fully on p. 27.

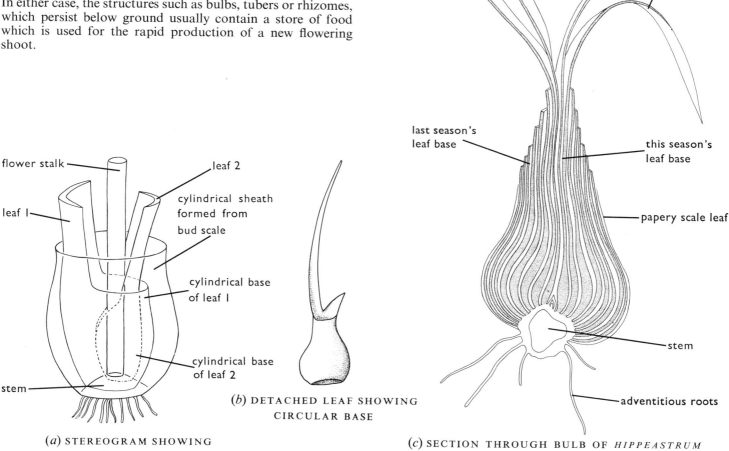

(a) STEREOGRAM SHOWING STRUCTURE

(b) DETACHED LEAF SHOWING CIRCULAR BASE

(c) SECTION THROUGH BULB OF *HIPPEASTRUM*

Fig. 6.1 Bulb structure

23

Bulbs

Bulbs are condensed shoots with fleshy leaves. The stem is very short and never grows above ground. The internodes are short; the leaves are very close together and they overlap. The outer leaves are scaly and dry and protect the inner ones which are thick and fleshy with stored food. In *Hippeastrum equestre* and the crinum lily, the bulb is formed by the bases of the leaves which completely encircle the stem (Figs. 6.1 and 6.2), and it is to these cylindrical leaf bases that the food is sent

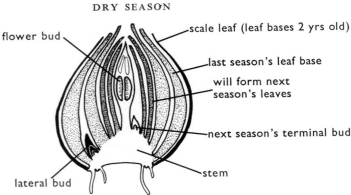

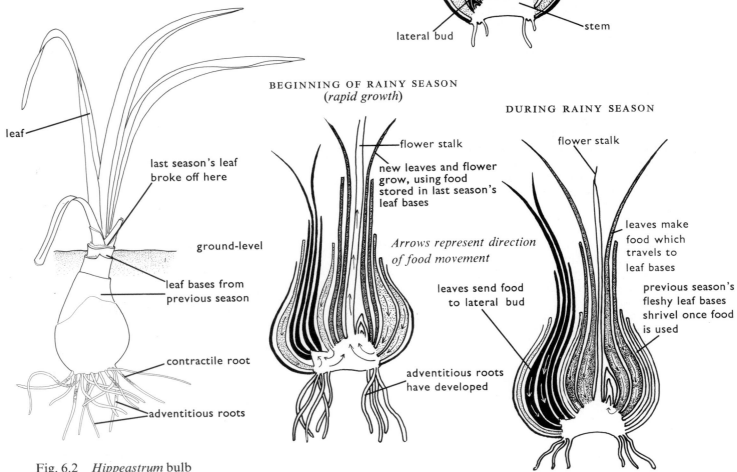

Fig. 6.2　*Hippeastrum* bulb

by the rest of the leaf above ground. In the onion bulb, all the storage leaves are cylindrical and are not part of the leaves appearing above ground; the latter are produced separately by a terminal bud. In the leaf axils of both types of bulb are lateral buds which can develop into new bulbs and shoots.

Life cycle (Fig. 6.3). In the rainy season, adventitious roots grow out of the stem, and a terminal or lateral bud, according to the species, begins to grow above the ground, making use of the stored food in the fleshy leaves which consequently shrivel. During the wet months some of the food made in the leaves of the lily is sent to the leaf bases, which swell and form a new bulb inside the old one. In the onion type of bulb, the food is not sent to the leaf bases but to the lateral buds between the circular scales, so that as the buds enlarge, two or more new bulbs are formed inside the old one. In either type of bulb, the shrivelled storage leaves of the old bulb become the dry, scaly leaves which surround the newly formed daughter bulbs. When the daughter bulbs of the onion or the lateral buds of the

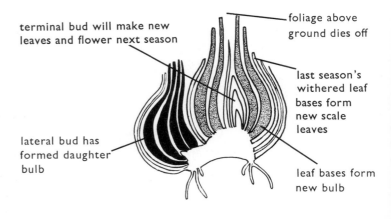

Fig. 6.3　Seasonal cycle in a *Hippeastrum* type of bulb

Hippeastrum sprout in the following year, there appear two plants where the original single parent grew. This cycle of events may be repeated several times during the wet season or while the plants are being watered. Several species, e.g. zephyr lily (*Zephyranthes*) are sensitive to water and flower after rain following a period of drought.

Rhizomes and stolons (Figs. 6.4 and 6.5)

In plants with rhizomes or stolons, the stem remains below ground but continues to grow horizontally. The old part of the stem does not die away as in bulbs, but lasts for several years. In the canna lily, the terminal buds turn up and produce leaves and flowers above ground. The old leaf bases form circular scales round the rhizome, which is swollen with food reserves. A stolon forms in a similar way but does not become swollen with food.

Life cycle (Fig. 6.5). The life cycle of a rhizome is similar to that of a bulb. Food from the leaves passes back to the rhizome, and a lateral bud uses it, grows horizontally underground, and so continues the rhizome. Other lateral buds produce new rhizomes which branch from the parent stem. The terminal buds of these branches curve upwards and produce new leafy shoots and flowers. Adventitious roots grow from the nodes of the underground stem.

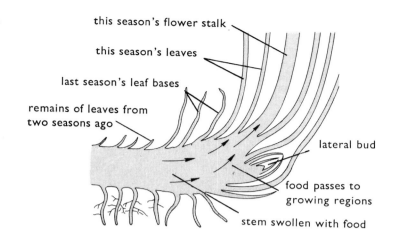

BEGINNING OF RAINY SEASON

MIDDLE OF RAINY SEASON

Fig. 6.5   Diagram showing rhizome growth

Note: In Figs. 6.1–6.5 the term season denotes the period of active growth and not necessarily a particular time of year. There may be several periods of active growth during one wet season.

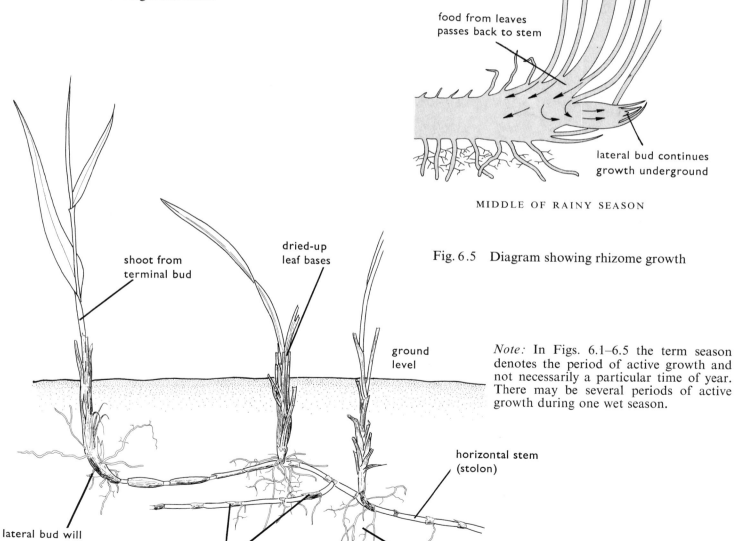

Fig. 6.4   Stolon of *Imperata* grass

VEGETATIVE AND SEXUAL REPRODUCTION COMPARED

VEGETATIVE REPRODUCTION	REPRODUCTION BY SEED
1 Offspring can obtain food reserve from parent.	*1* Food reserves limited to cotyledons or endosperm.
2 New plants produced in conditions already favourable to parents.	*2* Many seeds arrive in situations unfavourable to germination and subsequent development.
3 Colonization of new areas slow and localized.	*3* Dispersal methods distribute seeds over wide areas, some of which may be favourable and so lead to new colonies springing up.
4 As a rule, produces no new varieties. In agriculture this may be an advantage where the characteristics of a food or flower crop need to be preserved.	*4* New varieties can arise as a result of seed production. Some of these new varieties may be more successful than the parent stock.

Stem tubers (Fig. 6.6)

In the European potato *Solanum tuberosum*, lateral buds at the base of the stem produce shoots which grow laterally at first and then down into the ground. These are comparable to rhizomes, as they are underground stems with tiny scale leaves and lateral buds. They do not, however, as do rhizomes, swell evenly along their length with stored food. The yam (*Dioscorea*) is another example of a stem tuber.

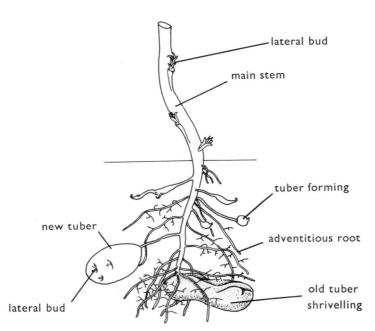

Fig. 6.6(*a*)   Stem tubers growing on a potato plant

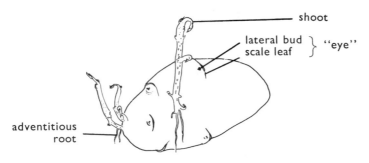

Fig. 6.6(*b*)   Potato tuber sprouting

Annual cycle. Food made in the leaves passes to the ends of these rhizomes, which swell and form the tubers we call potatoes. Since the potato tuber is a stem, it has leaves and axillary buds; these are the familiar "eyes". Each one of these can produce a new shoot in the following year, using the food stored in the tuber (Fig. 6.6*b*). The older tubers shrivel and rot away at the end of the season.

Advantages of food storage

Food in the storage organs enables very rapid growth in favourable conditions, e.g. the rainy season, and acts as a reserve in periods of drought, often allowing limited growth to continue. Early growth enables the plant to flower and produce seeds before competition with other plants for water, mineral salts and light reaches its maximum.

In agriculture, man has exploited many of these types of plant and bred them for bigger and more nutritious storage organs for his own consumption, e.g. yam (*Dioscorea*), cassava (*Manihot*), sweet potato (*Ipomea*).

Advantages of vegetative reproduction

Since food stores are available throughout the year and the parent plant with its root system can absorb water from a wide area, two of the hazards which beset seed germination are reduced. Whereas buds are produced in an environment where the parent is able to flourish, many seeds dispersed from plants never reach a suitable situation for effective germination. Vegetative reproduction does not usually result in the rapid and widespread distribution of offspring achieved by seed dispersal, but tends to produce a dense clump of plants with little room for competitors between them. Such groups of plants are very persistent and, because of their underground food stores and buds, can still grow after their foliage has been destroyed by insects, fire, or man's cultivation. Those of them in the "weed" category are difficult to eradicate by physical methods, since even a small piece of rhizome bearing a bud can give rise to a new colony.

Farmers and gardeners make use of vegetative propagation when they divide up the rhizomes, tubers or rootstocks at the end of the growing or flowering season. Each section will grow in the following year to make a separate plant. Grafting, layering and taking cuttings are artificial methods of vegetative propagation. Vegetative reproduction by cuttings or grafting is often the only way of propagating a crop plant, e.g. cultivated bananas, which are seedless, or of preserving the useful characteristics of the plant which reverts to a wild form if grown from seed.

Artificial propagation

(*a*) **Cuttings.** It is possible to produce new individuals from certain plants by putting the cut end of a shoot into water or moist earth. Adventitious roots grow from the base of the stem into the soil while the shoot continues to grow and produce leaves.

In practice, the cut end of the stem is treated with a rooting hormone (*see* p. 42) to promote root growth, and evaporation from the shoot is reduced by covering it with polythene or a glass jar. Cassava, *Impatiens*, *Hibiscus* and sugar cane are commonly propagated by cuttings.

(*b*) **Grafting.** The bud or shoot from one plant is inserted under the bark on the stem of another, closely related variety so that the cambium layers of both are in contact. The rooted portion is called the *stock* and the bud or shoot being grafted is the *scion* (Fig. 6.7). Rubber trees are propagated by grafting. A bud from the desired variety is grafted on to the stem of a plant grown from seed. The bud then grows using water and nutrients supplied by the stock, and later the stock is cut off above the graft.

One of the characteristics of sexual reproduction (Chapter 7) is that the offspring are very variable (*see* Chapter 33 for an explanation of this). Seeds are the product of sexual reproduction, and in certain crops the plants grown from seed exhibit wide variations in yield and quality. Once a good variety has been bred it is possible to maintain its desirable characteristics by artificial propagation because the grafts or cuttings retain all the parental characteristics with little or no variation.

New varieties of citrus fruits, mango, cocoa and rubber plants are propagated by grafting. The new varieties may have a higher yield or be resistant to disease.

(*see* p. 42)

Plate 7. CLEFT GRAFT OF FRUIT TREE 6 WEEKS AFTER GRAFTING

(*Reprinted from* Span **15**, *Shell International*)

QUESTIONS

1. Which plant organs are modified for storage of food in (*a*) a potato, (*b*) an onion?
2. Plants can often be propagated from stems but rarely from roots. What features of shoots account for this difference?
3. In a bulb-forming plant, what is the principal source of food (*á*) early in the growing season, (*b*) late in the growing season?
4. In bulb-forming plants you usually see a flower stalk but not a stem (i.e. the leaves seem to emerge from the ground). Why is this?
5. Why do bulb-forming plants frequently form dense clumps?
6. Annual plants classed as "weeds" can be controlled by hoeing them before they flower. Perennial weeds, such as *Imperata* grass cannot be controlled in this way. What biological principles underly this difference?

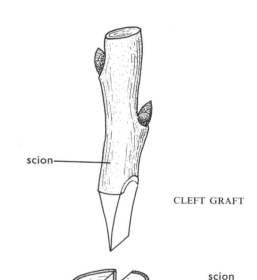

scion

CLEFT GRAFT

a 'T' slit is made in the bark of the stock and the bud graft with its own piece of bark is slipped inside.
In both cases the graft is held in place with tape or twine and the wound covered with grease to exclude fungi and reduce evaporation.

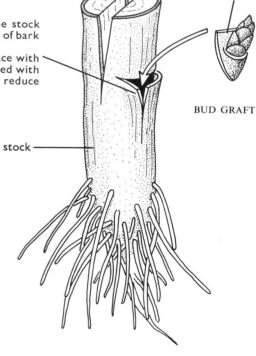

scion

stock

BUD GRAFT

Fig. 6.7   Two types of grafting

7 | Sexual Reproduction in Flowering Plants

FLOWER STRUCTURE

A flower is a reproductive structure of a plant. Most flowers have both male and female reproductive organs, though some are of a single sex. The floral parts are arranged in whorls or spirals with short internodes, often borne at the end of a flower stalk whose end is expanded to form a *receptacle*. The outer whorl is called the *calyx*, the next, the *corolla*. Within the corolla is the *androecium* and, finally, the *gynoecium*.

An **inflorescence** is a group of flowers borne on the same main stalk.

The **calyx** consists of *sepals*, which are usually green and small. They enclose and protect the rest of the flower while it is in the bud.

The **corolla** consists of *petals*, which are often coloured and scented. They attract insects which visit the flowers and collect nectar and pollen, pollinating the flowers as they do so. Small grooves or darker lines in the petals called "honey guides" are thought to direct the insect to the nectaries within the flower. The calyx and corolla are collectively known as the *perianth*. The term is important in those cases, e.g. many monocotyledons, where there is no obvious distinction between petals and sepals or simply one whorl of members.

The **androecium** is the male part of the flower and consists of *stamens*. The stalk of the stamen is the *filament*. At the end of the filament is an *anther* which contains pollen grains in four pollen sacs. The pollen grains contain the male reproductive cells or *gametes*.

The **gynoecium** is the female part of the flower. It consists of *carpels*, which may be either single and solitary, many and separate from each other, or few and joined together. In all of them, the *ovules* which contain the female gametes are enclosed in a case, the *ovary*. Extending from the ovary is a *style*, expanded or divided at one end into a *stigma*, which will receive pollen from another flower. The ovules when fertilized will become seeds, while the whole ovary will become the fruit. The wall of the ovary develops into the *pericarp* of the fruit.

Nectaries are glandular swellings, often at the base of the ovary or on the receptacle, which produce a sugary solution called nectar. Insects visit the flower and drink or collect this nectar.

Number of parts

In many species of flowering plant, the structures described above occur in definite numbers. For example, if there are five sepals there are likely to be five petals and five or ten stamens.

Whorls may be repeated; for example, there may be two whorls of five petals or two whorls of five stamens. In some genera of the Malvaceae, e.g. *Hibiscus*, and of the Mimosaceae, e.g. *Acacia*, the stamens are numerous, the numbers varying from one plant to another. The floral parts usually alternate so that petals do not come opposite sepals but between them. Likewise, stamens are borne between petals, and so on.

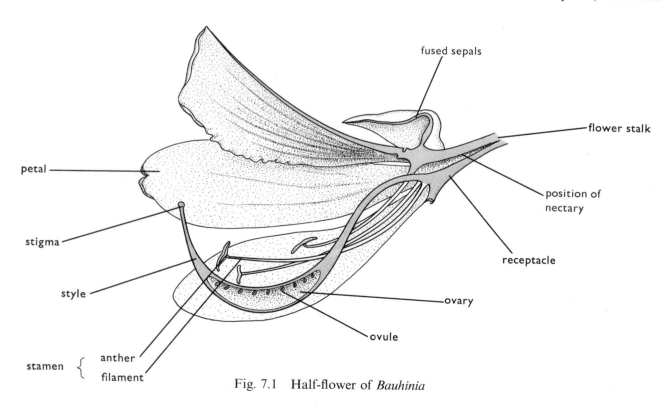

Fig. 7.1 Half-flower of *Bauhinia*

Variations

In many flowers, petals or sepals are joined or "fused" for part of or all of their length, forming tubular structures as in *Thunbergia* and *Tecoma*. In flowers like *Cassia* all the petals are the same size and are not joined, but in many others which have joined or free petals, some petals differ in size and shape from others, as in *Delonix* and *Crotalaria*.

The half-flower

A drawing of a half-flower is a convenient method of representing flower structure. The flower is cut in halves with a razor blade, the outline of the cut surfaces drawn, and the structures visible behind these filled in. A longitudinal section shows only the cut surfaces.

Bauhinia (Figs. 7.1 and 7.2). Five sepals fused into a single leaf-like structure; five petals, not joined, the uppermost petal having more pronounced markings; five stamens; a single pod-shaped carpel forms the ovary which contains a single row of ovules and bears a style and stigma.

Crotalaria (Figs. 7.3 and 7.4). Five fused sepals; five petals, not all joined but of different shapes and sizes. The uppermost petal is called the standard, and the two partly joined petals at the side are the wings. Within the wings are two partly joined petals forming a boat-shaped keel. Inside the keel are ten stamens, five with rounded anthers and five with elongated anthers. The filaments are fused to form a sheath round the ovary. The ovary is long, narrow and pod-shaped, and consists of one carpel with about ten ovules. The style ends in a stigma, just within the pointed end of the keel.

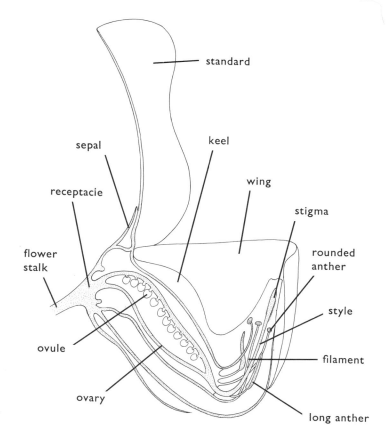

Fig. 7.3   Half-flower of *Crotalaria*

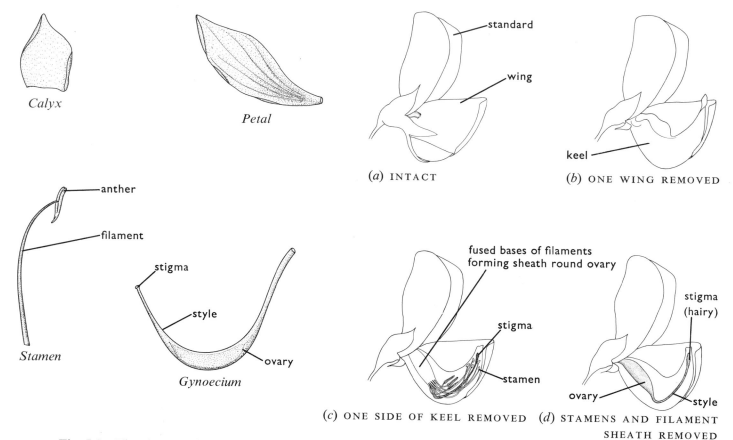

Fig. 7.2   Floral parts of *Bauhinia*

Fig. 7.4   *Crotalaria* flower dissected

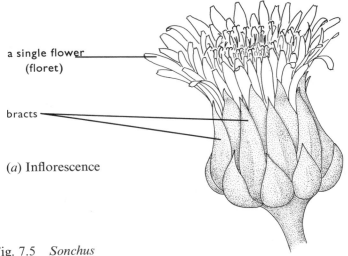

a single flower (floret)

bracts

(a) Inflorescence

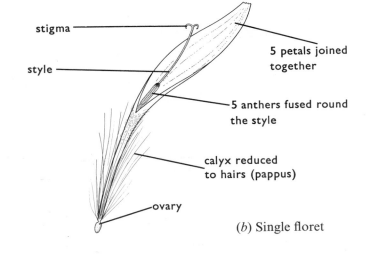

stigma

style

5 petals joined together

5 anthers fused round the style

calyx reduced to hairs (pappus)

ovary

(b) Single floret

Fig. 7.5   *Sonchus*

Sonchus. The flowers of the Compositae family such as marigolds and sunflowers are arranged in dense inflorescences (Fig. 7.7a). What at first appears to be a petal in the flower head is actually a complete flower, often called a *floret* (Fig. 7.7b). The florets of *Sonchus* consist of five petals joined together to form a tube at their base and a flat ribbon at the outer end. The sepals are reduced to fine hairs which form a "parachute" when the seeds are dispersed. Inside the base of the corolla tube is an ovary with a single ovule and a long style ending in a forked stigma. Five long anthers are grouped together round the style.

In some Compositae, the outer florets with conspicuous petals have no reproductive organs and are therefore sterile; the inner florets with corollas of tiny, fused petals carry the reproductive organs. The sunflower, *Helianthus*, and the wild marigold, *Aspilia*, are examples of this type of inflorescence.

Zea mays: **maize** (Figs. 7.6 and 7.7). The flowers are uni-sexual, containing either stamens or ovary but not both, and the long, crowded inflorescences bear flowers of only one sex, the male flowers on terminal branches and the female flowers lower down on axillary branches. The male flowers are small with no petals or sepals in the usual sense, but green, leaf-like *bracts*. The flowers are in pairs; each pair is called a *spikelet* and is enclosed by two of these bracts. Two smaller bracts enclose each androecium of three stamens. When mature, the anthers hang outside the bracts (Figs. 7.6 b to d).

The female inflorescence is completely wrapped in a small number of leaves and forms the cob (Fig. 7.7a). The female spikelets are arranged spirally on the inflorescence stalk. Each fertile flower is enclosed by thin, transparent bracts. The flower has a gynoecium consisting of an ovary with a single ovule, and a long style which protrudes from the top of the cob (Figs. 7.7 a and b). Also inside the spikelet is a small sterile female flower.

Maize is a cereal of considerable economic importance. It is, however, closely related to wild grasses whose flowers differ from it by having both male and female organs.

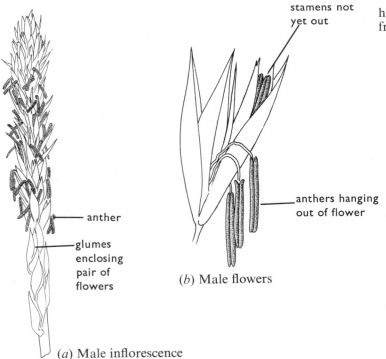

stamens not yet out

anthers hanging out of flower

anther

glumes enclosing pair of flowers

(b) Male flowers

(a) Male inflorescence

Fig. 7.6   *Zea mays*

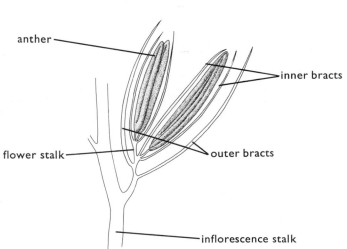

anther

inner bracts

flower stalk

outer bracts

inflorescence stalk

(c) Section through two male flowers

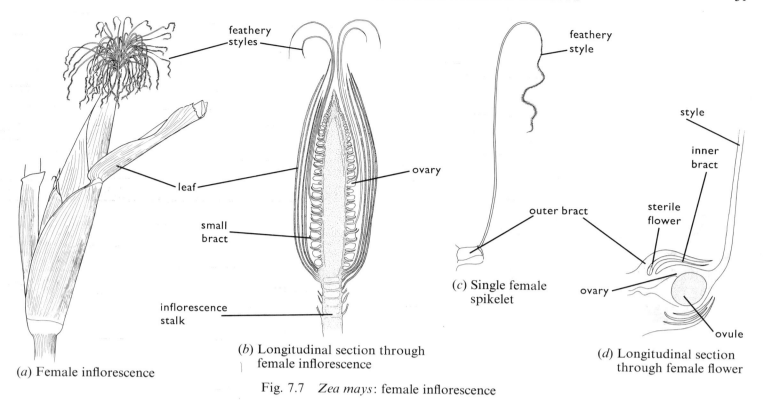

(a) Female inflorescence

(b) Longitudinal section through female inflorescence

(c) Single female spikelet

(d) Longitudinal section through female flower

Fig. 7.7 *Zea mays*: female inflorescence

POLLINATION

The transfer of pollen from anthers to stigma is called pollination. Cross-pollination is the transfer of pollen from the anthers of one flower to the stigma of another flower of the same species. In some species self-pollination occurs either regularly, as in the groundnut, or when cross-pollination has failed to take place, as in *Tridax*. In cross-pollination pollen is usually transferred on the bodies of insects entering the flowers, or by chance air-currents carrying the pollen from one flower to the next. The structures of many flowers are closely adapted to the method of insect or wind pollination. The table, p. 34, gives the main differences between these two kinds of flower.

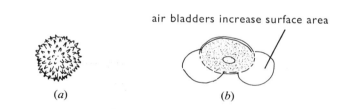

Fig. 7.8 (a) Pollen of an insect-pollinated flower
(b) Pollen of pine (wind pollinated)

Insect pollination mechanisms

Essentially, these mechanisms involve an insect's visiting one flower, becoming dusted with pollen from the ripe stamens, and then visiting another flower where some of the pollen on its body adheres to the stigma.

When ripe, the pollen sacs of the anther split open and expose the pollen which can then be dislodged (Fig. 7.9 *a* and *b*).

Self-pollination is prevented in various ways. In some flowers the anthers have shed all their pollen and have shrivelled before the stigma is receptive. In other cases the pollen of one flower simply will not germinate and produce a pollen tube on the stigma of its own flower. In certain species, the position of the stamens and style alter as the flower ages so that the visiting insect will come into contact with either the anthers, or the stigma but not both.

Bauhinia is pollinated by moths which hover in front of the flower while their extended proboscides (p. 152) take up nectar from the nectary. The anthers of young flowers are above the stigma and the moth's body becomes dusted with pollen. When the moth visits an older flower, the pollen will adhere to the sticky stigma which is now higher than the anthers.

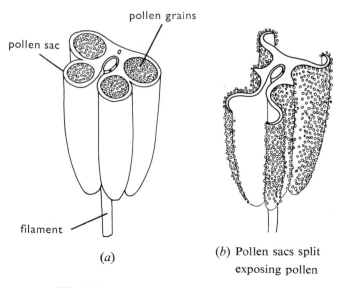

(a)

(b) Pollen sacs split exposing pollen

Fig. 7.9 Structure of anther (top cut off)

Thunbergia. The colour and scent attract bees which enter the flower in search of nectar. As the bee crawls through the corolla tube the anthers brush the insect's back (Fig. 7.10), dusting it with pollen. Similarly, on its way in, the bee encounters the stigma whose sticky surface picks up pollen which has been deposited on the insect from another flower.

Frequently a bee, e.g. a carpenter bee, gains access to the nectary by biting through the corolla tube from the outside and inserting its proboscis ("tongue"). This robs the plant of its nectar without bringing about pollination.

Crotalaria **and other bean family flowers.** Some members of this family have no nectar, and the bees or moths which visit them collect only pollen from the flowers. Other members including *Crotalaria* do produce nectar.

The weight of the insect depresses the "wings" of the flower as it alights on them. Near their bases, the wings are linked to the petals of the keel so that these too are forced down (Fig. 7.11). Pollen from the long anthers has collected at the tip of the keel and as the latter is forced down, the accumulated pollen is forced out of a hole in its tip by the rounded anthers

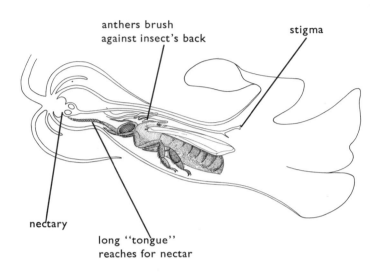

Fig. 7.10   Pollination of *Thunbergia*

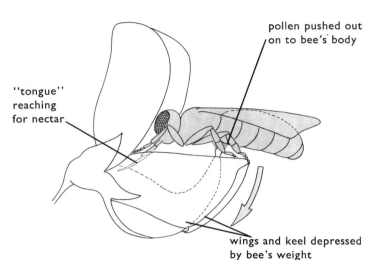

Fig. 7.11   Pollination of *Crotalaria*

WIND AND INSECT POLLINATED FLOWERS COMPARED

WIND POLLINATED	INSECT POLLINATED
1 Small, inconspicuous flowers; petals often green. No scent or nectar.	*1* Relatively large flowers or conspicuous inflorescences. Petals brightly coloured and scented; mostly with nectaries.

Insects respond to the stimulus of colour and scent and are "attracted" to the flowers. When in the flower, they collect or eat the nectar from the nectaries, or pollen from the anthers.

2 Anthers large and loosely attached to filament so that the slightest air movement shakes them. The whole inflorescence often dangles loosely, and the stamens hang out of the flower exposed to the wind (Fig. 7.6 *a* and *b*).	*2* Anthers not so large and firmly attached to the filament. They are not usually carried outside the flower but are in a position within the petals where insects are likely to brush against them (Fig. 7.10).

The wind is more likely to dislodge pollen from exposed, dangling anthers than from those enclosed in petals.

3 Large quantities of smooth, light pollen grains produced by the anthers.	*3* Smaller quantities of pollen produced. The grains often have spiky patterns or stick together in clumps (Fig. 7.8).

With wind pollination, only a very small proportion of pollen grains is likely to land on a ripe stigma. If large quantities of pollen are not shed, the chances of successful pollination become very poor. Smooth, light grains are readily carried in air currents and do not stick together.
In pollination by insects, fewer of the pollen grains will be wasted. The patterned or sticky pollen grains are more likely to adhere to the body of the insect.

4 Feathery style or stigmas hanging outside the flower (Fig. 7.7 *a* and *b*).	*4* Flat or lobed, sticky stigmas inside the flower (Fig. 7.10).

The feathery stigmas of grasses form a "net" of relatively large area in which flying pollen grains may be trapped.

and hairy stigma. Thus a ribbon of pollen is extruded on the under-surface of the bee.

In the nectar-producing members of this family, the sheath of filaments round the ovary is open at the top, enabling the insect's "tongue" to reach the nectaries.

When an insect visits a flower from whose keel all pollen has been expelled, only the stigma will emerge, touch the underside of the insect and collect any pollen that has adhered from previous visits to *Crotalaria* flowers. Clearly, a great deal of pollen from the same flower will come into contact with the stigma, and in *Crotalaria* probably results in self-pollination. In many other species, however, chemicals in the stigma prevent the growth of the pollen; the pollen and stigma are *self-incompatible*.

Zea mays. When mature, the filaments in the male flowers elongate so that the anthers hang outside the glumes (Fig. 7.6 *a* and *b*). The pollen sacs split open and pollen is carried away in air-currents, some of it becoming trapped on the feathery styles of the female flowers (Fig. 7.7a) which present a large surface area. Since in any one maize plant the anthers are ripe before the styles are receptive, pollination is unlikely to occur between the flowers of the same plant, while cross-pollination between neighbouring plants is favoured.

Incompatibility

In both wind- and insect-pollinated flowers, pollen from a certain species may reach the stigma of a different species. Usually the chemicals present in the cells of the stigma prevent further development of the "foreign" pollen grains.

Importance of pollination to agriculture

After fertilization the ovary of a plant develops into a fruit. Fruit formation therefore depends on fertilization, which can follow only after pollination.

Farmers and fruit growers are well aware that a good yield of fruit will occur only if most of the available flowers have been pollinated. Many of the cereals are self-pollinated or wind-pollinated, and the fact that the plants grow close together makes the latter effective.

FERTILIZATION

The following four generalizations apply to both plants and animals.

1. A *gamete* is a reproductive cell. A male gamete is usually small with a nucleus and little cytoplasm it is the gamete which leaves the male organ and moves about, either by its own power or by external agencies like wind or insects.

2. The female gamete is larger, with a nucleus and more cytoplasm than the male; it sometimes contains food reserves. Often it does not leave the female organ or body in which it is produced until after it is fertilized. The male gamete in a flowering plant is a nucleus in the pollen grain; in most animals it is the sperm. The female gamete in plants is a large egg-cell in the ovule, while in animals it is the ovum.

3. The product of the fusion of male and female gametes is called a *zygote*.

4. *Fertilization* is the fusion (joining together) of the nuclei of male and female gametes to form a zygote. After fertilization the zygote undergoes cell division and growth, developing into a new individual or a preliminary form which may be an embryo, a seed, or a larva.

Fertilization in plants

Fertilization follows pollination, but the interval of time between the two events varies in different species from sixteen hours to twelve months. The pollen grain absorbs nutriment secreted by the stigma, and the cytoplasm in the grain grows out as a tube This tube grows down through the style between the cells (Fig. 7.12) absorbing a nutritive fluid from them. On reaching the ovary it grows to one of the ovules and enters it through a hole, the micropyle (Fig. 7.13). The tip of the pollen tube breaks open in the ovule, and the male nucleus, which has been passing down the tube, enters the ovule and fuses with the female nucleus there.

Each egg-cell of an ovule can be fertilized only by a male nucleus from a separate pollen grain.

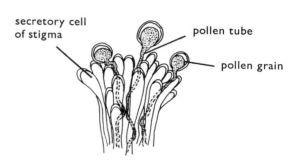

secretory cell of stigma — pollen tube — pollen grain

Fig. 7.12   Pollen grains growing on a stigma

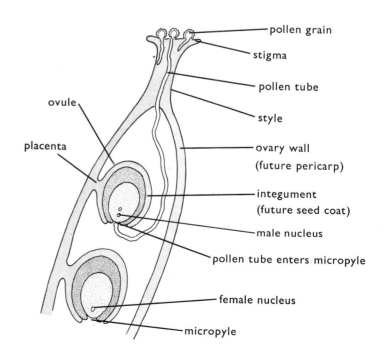

pollen grain
stigma
pollen tube
style
ovary wall (future pericarp)
integument (future seed coat)
male nucleus
pollen tube enters micropyle
female nucleus
micropyle
ovule
placenta

Fig. 7.13   Diagram of fertilization

Result of fertilization

Fruit and seed formation. After fertilization the petals, stamens, style and stigma wither and usually fall off (Fig. 7.14). The sepals may persist in a dried and shrivelled form. Food made in the leaves reaches the fertilized ovules and the ovary, which grow rapidly. Inside the ovule, cell division and growth produce a seed containing a potential plant or embryo. The embryo consists of a miniature root or radicle, a small shoot

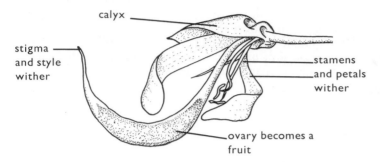

Fig. 7.14   *Bauhinia* flower after fertilization

or plumule, and one or two leaves, the cotyledons, which usually contain food reserves. The integuments of the ovules become thicker and harder, forming the testas of the seeds, and finally, water is withdrawn from the seeds, making them dry and hard. In this condition they are best able to withstand drought and other adverse conditions.

The ovary wall may become dry and hard, forming a capsule, e.g. Mexican poppy (*Argemone*), or pod, e.g. *Crotalaria*, or it may become succulent and fleshy as in the tomato, pawpaw and mango.

Fruits. In a strictly biological sense, the term *fruit* means the fertilized ovary of a flower and in only a small number of cases is such a fruit edible. The products of flowering plants which are grown, eaten and sold as fruits may be single ovaries as in the mango and pawpaw, in which case at least part of the ovary

wall is fleshy and edible. Sometimes, however, the flesh of the "fruit" is derived from much more than a single ovary wall, as in the soursop, *Anona muricata*, where a large number of fused ovaries contribute to the edible fruit. This fruit is still the product of a single flower whereas the flesh of the pineapple is derived from the fused ovaries of a large number of individual flowers, their receptacles, the flower stalks and even the inflorescence stalk (Fig. 7.18).

A *dehiscent* fruit is one which opens to release its seeds, e.g. *Phaseolus* (Fig. 7.23), and *Tecoma* (Fig. 7.17). An *indehiscent* fruit does not open; it falls from the plant as a whole and may have to decay at least partially before the seeds are able to germinate, e.g. pawpaw and tomato (Fig. 7.16). The part of the fruit or ovary to which the seeds are attached is called the *placenta*.

Parthenocarpy. Strictly, parthenocarpy means the development of a fruit from an ovary without fertilization. In some cases the stimulus of pollination is needed for fruit development, in others, e.g. banana, pollination is unnecessary. Parthenocarpic fruits are often seedless, e.g. certain pineapples, and since it is not always easy to tell if fertilization has occurred, the term *parthenocarpic* is often applied to all seedless fruits.

Fruit formation. Examples of the formation of fruits from fertilized flowers are shown in Figs. 7.15–7.18.

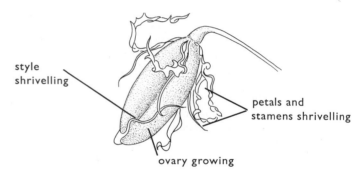

(*b*) AFTER FERTILIZATION

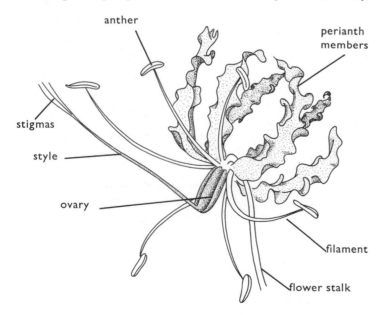

(*a*) GLORIOSA FLOWER (sepals have dropped)

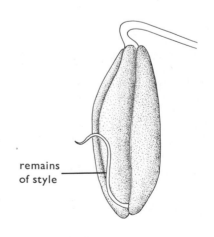

(*c*) MATURE FRUIT BEFORE DEHISCENCE

Fig. 7.15   *Gloriosa superba*

FRUIT FORMATION

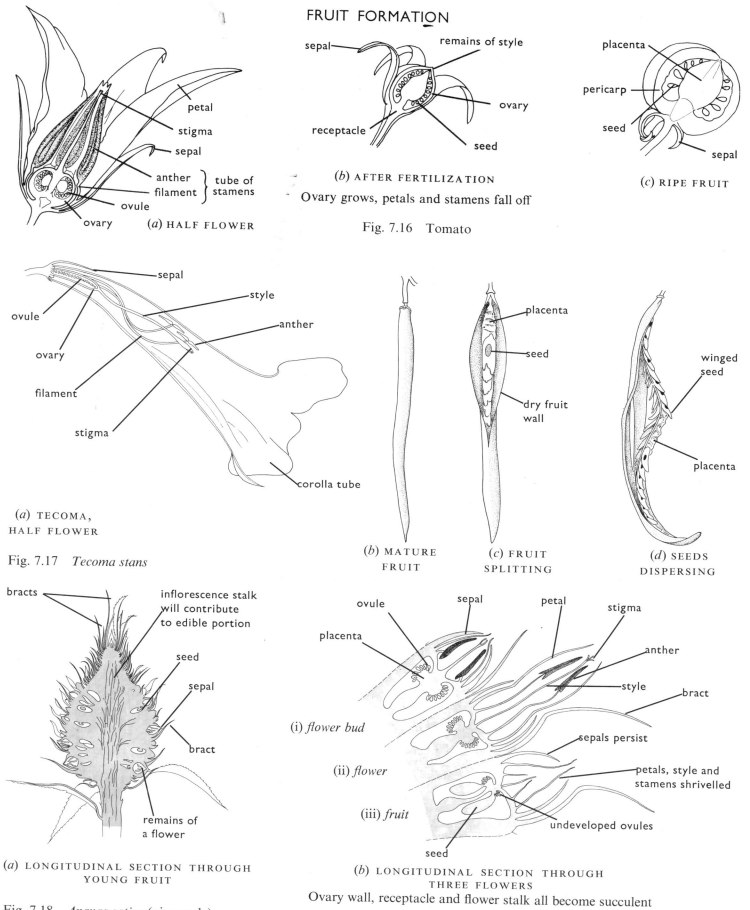

(a) HALF FLOWER

petal
stigma
sepal
anther
filament } tube of stamens
ovule
ovary

(b) AFTER FERTILIZATION
Ovary grows, petals and stamens fall off

sepal
remains of style
receptacle
ovary
seed

Fig. 7.16 Tomato

(c) RIPE FRUIT

placenta
pericarp
seed
sepal

(a) TECOMA, HALF FLOWER

sepal
ovule
style
anther
ovary
filament
stigma
corolla tube

Fig. 7.17 *Tecoma stans*

(b) MATURE FRUIT

(c) FRUIT SPLITTING

placenta
seed
dry fruit wall

(d) SEEDS DISPERSING

winged seed
placenta

(a) LONGITUDINAL SECTION THROUGH YOUNG FRUIT

bracts
inflorescence stalk will contribute to edible portion
seed
sepal
bract
remains of a flower

Fig. 7.18 *Ananas sativa* (pineapple)

(b) LONGITUDINAL SECTION THROUGH THREE FLOWERS
Ovary wall, receptacle and flower stalk all become succulent

ovule
sepal
petal
stigma
placenta
anther
style
bract
sepals persist
petals, style and stamens shrivelled
undeveloped ovules
seed

(i) *flower bud*
(ii) *flower*
(iii) *fruit*

DISPERSAL OF FRUITS AND SEEDS

When flowering is over and the seeds are mature the whole ovary, or the individual seeds, fall from the parent plant to the ground, where if conditions are suitable germination will subsequently take place. In many plants, the fruits or seeds are adapted in such a way that they are distributed away from the parent plant; this helps to reduce overcrowding among and competition between members of the same species for light, air, water and mineral salts, and results in the colonization of new areas.

Wind dispersal

(a) **Censer mechanism.** The ovary becomes a dry capsule which partially opens at the top. The capsule is at the end of a long stalk which is shaken to and fro by the wind. The seeds that have become detached from the placenta are shaken out and scattered. Examples are the Mexican poppy (*Argemone*) (Fig. 7.19), *Nicotiana* and *Sesamum*.

(b) **"Parachute" fruits and seeds.** Feathery hairs projecting from the fruit or seed increase its surface area so much that air resistance to its movements is very great. In consequence it sinks to the ground very slowly and is likely to be carried great distances from the parent plant by slight air-currents. The hairs of the cotton seed (*Gossypium*) are outgrowths from the seed coat. In the Compositae, e.g. *Sonchus* (Figs. 7.5 and 7.20), the pappus of hairs on the fruit is formed by the calyx.

(c) **Winged seeds.** Seeds of *Jacaranda*, *Tecoma* (Fig. 7.17) and *Spathodea* (Fig. 7.21) have papery extensions formed from the placenta or testa making wing-like structures. The extra surface area of these wings offers increased air resistance, so delaying the fall of the seed and increasing its chances of being blown away from its parent plant by the wind.

Animal dispersal

(a) **Mammals: hooked fruits.** In *Triumfetta* and *Desmodium*, hooks develop on the ovary wall. In *Bidens* (Fig. 7.22) there are hooks on the calyx. These hooks catch in the fur of passing mammals or in the clothing of people. The seeds may fall from the fruit during the animal's wanderings or the whole fruit may be brushed off or scratched off some distance from the parent plant. If the seeds fall in a situation where there is adequate soil, moisture and light, they will germinate to new plants.

(b) **Mammals and birds: succulent fruits.** The succulent texture and in some cases the bright colour of these fruits may be regarded as an adaptation to this method of dispersal. Sometimes, as in the guava (*Psidium*), the fleshy part of the fruit is eaten and the seeds with their resistant seed coats pass undigested through the animal's alimentary canal, to be dropped with the faeces some distance from the parent plant. In the case of the mango and avocado, the fruit may be carried away from the parent tree by rats, for example, the flesh eaten and the seed discarded.

Self-dispersal

The pods formed by the flowers of the bean (*Phaseolus*) dry in the sun or a dry wind and shrivel. The tough diagonal fibres in the pericarp shrink and set up a tension. When the carpel splits in half down two lines of weakness, the two halves twist up (Fig. 7.23) trapping the seeds between the coils. As the coils tighten the seeds are suddenly squeezed out and projected away from the parent. There are many quite different methods of self-dispersal; in the ripe fruits of *Impatiens*, for example, osmotic forces are set up which cause the intake of water and the sudden splitting of the pericarp into five lobes which curl up suddenly and flick out the seeds.

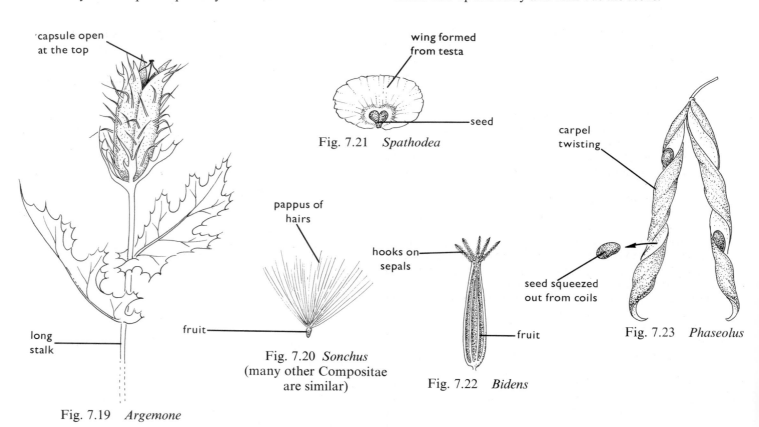

capsule open at the top

Fig. 7.19   *Argemone*

long stalk

fruit

pappus of hairs

Fig. 7.20 *Sonchus* (many other Compositae are similar)

wing formed from testa

seed

Fig. 7.21   *Spathodea*

hooks on sepals

fruit

Fig. 7.22   *Bidens*

carpel twisting

seed squeezed out from coils

fruit

Fig. 7.23   *Phaseolus*

(The drawings are *not* to scale)

(After R. Scholes)

PRACTICAL WORK

Pollen on stigma. If the stigmas of a number of flowers are examined dry and by reflected light under the low power of the microscope, pollen grains may be seen adhering to them. If the stigmas are crushed with water between two slides, pollen tubes may be seen growing between the cells (*see* Fig. 7.12).

Pollen tubes. By placing pollen grains in a 10 per cent solution of cane sugar in a cavity slide and covering them with a glass cover slip the growth of pollen tubes may be seen after a day or two. *Crotalaria* pollen has proved satisfactory.

Pollen. Pollen can be examined microscopically by dusting or squashing ripe anthers on to a slide.

QUESTIONS

1. What do you understand by the term "gamete"? What are the male and female gametes in a flowering plant?
2. What is "fertilization" and where does it occur in a flowering plant?
3. Pollination may occur without fertilization taking place but fertilization will not occur without pollination. Explain why this is so.
4. What part in reproduction is played by (*a*) petals, (*b*) stamens, (*c*) carpels?
5. Only large insects such as bees are likely to effect pollination in *Thunbergia* or *Tecoma*. Why are smaller insects unlikely to do so?
6. Most flowering plants produce many more seeds than are ever likely to grow to maturity. (*a*) What kind of adverse circumstances are likely to prevent successful germination and growth? (*b*) How does seed dispersal contribute to the survival of the species despite these hazards?
7. What kind of competition is likely to take place between seedlings growing closely together?
8. Distinguish between wind pollination and wind dispersal.

8 | Seeds, Germination and Tropisms

SEEDS

Seed structure

A seed develops from an ovule after fertilization. It consists of a tough coat or *testa* enclosing an *embryo* which is made up of a *plumule*, a *radicle* and one or two *cotyledons*. In favourable conditions the seed can grow and become a fully independent plant, bearing flowers and seeds during its life cycle. In the embryo of the seed are all the potentialities of development and growth to a mature plant resembling other members of its species in almost every detail of leaf shape, cell distribution and flower colour and structure.

The **testa.** The integuments (p. 33) round the ovule form the testa, a tough, hard coat which protects the seed from fungi, bacteria and insects. It has to be split open by the radicle before germination can proceed.

The **hilum** is a scar left by the stalk which attached the ovule to the ovary wall.

The **micropyle** is the opening in the integuments through which the pollen tube entered at fertilization (p. 33). It remains as a tiny pore in the testa opposite the tip of the radicle and admits water to the embryo before germination.

The **radicle** is the embryonic root which grows and develops into the root system of the plant.

The **plumule** is the leafy part of the embryonic shoot. These leaves are attached to the embryonic stem, of which the part above the attachment of the cotyledons is called the *epicotyl* and the part below, the *hypocotyl* (Fig. 8.3*b*).

Cotyledons. Monocotyledons such as grasses and cereals have seeds with only one cotyledon. The other flowering plants all have two cotyledons. They are leaves attached to the plumule and radicle by short stalks, and they often contain food reserves which are used during the early stages of germination. In most plants the cotyledons are brought out of the

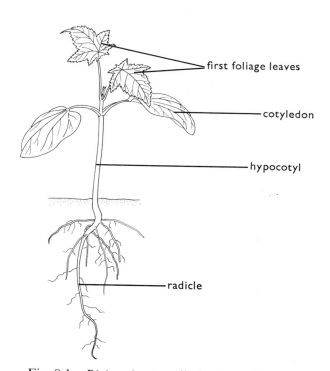

Fig. 8.1 *Ricinus* (castor oil plant) seedling

testa and above ground, whereupon they become green and make food by photosynthesis. The cotyledons eventually fall off, usually after the first foliage leaves have been formed. The cotyledon leaves bear no resemblance to the ordinary foliage leaves, the shape of which is first apparent when the plumule leaves open and grow (Fig. 8.1).

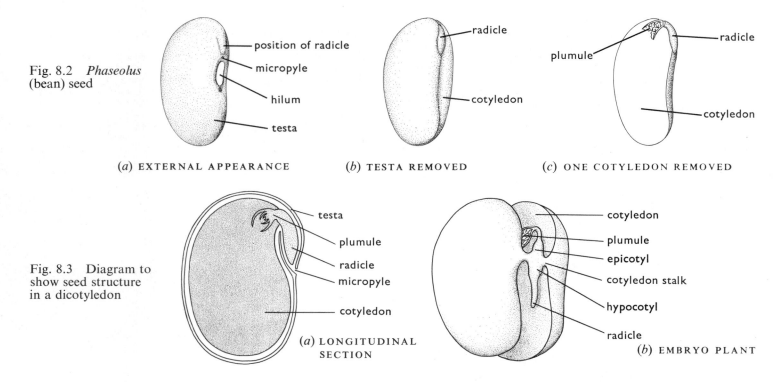

Fig. 8.2 *Phaseolus* (bean) seed

(a) EXTERNAL APPEARANCE   (b) TESTA REMOVED   (c) ONE COTYLEDON REMOVED

Fig. 8.3 Diagram to show seed structure in a dicotyledon

(a) LONGITUDINAL SECTION   (b) EMBRYO PLANT

Structure of types of seed. This is best shown by the diagrams and drawings in Figs. 8.2–8.5. One important point of difference is that maize has only one cotyledon, and a separate food store, called the *endosperm*, that is not present in the others. The plants have been selected because they show two of the different ways in which germination can take place, and their seeds are large enough for the structure to be examined and the course of germination followed in some detail.

GERMINATION

The course of germination

Phaseolus vulgaris (Fig. 8.4). The seed absorbs water, and swells. After about three days, depending on temperature, the radicle grows and bursts through the testa. It grows down between the soil particles, its tip protected by a root cap (*see*

p. 21). Root hairs appear in the region where elongation has ceased. Water and salts from the soil are absorbed by the root hairs on the radicle and pass to the rest of the seedling. Later, lateral roots develop from the radicle. Once the radicle is firmly anchored in the soil, the hypocotyl starts to grow. The rapid growth of the hypocotyl pulls the cotyledons out of the testa and through the soil. The plumule is still between the cotyledons and thus protected from damage during its passage through the soil. Sometimes the testa, still partly enclosing the cotyledons, is brought above the soil and pushed off later as the cotyledons separate. Once above the soil, the hypocotyl straightens and the cotyledons separate, exposing the plumule.

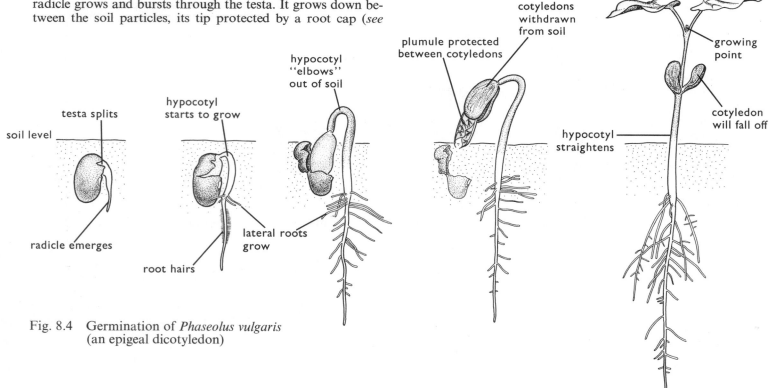

Fig. 8.4 Germination of *Phaseolus vulgaris* (an epigeal dicotyledon)

The cotyledons become green and, presumably, photosynthesize for a day or two before shrivelling and falling off. Meanwhile, the epicotyl has extended and the plumule leaves have expanded and begun to photosynthesize, making the seedling independent. The germination of a seedling such as *Phaseolus* which brings its cotyledons above the ground is called *epigeal*.

In the early stages of germination, the food reserves in the cotyledons, mostly starch and protein, have been acted upon by enzymes and converted to soluble products which pass to, and are used by, the actively growing regions where new cells and new protoplasm are being made, and energy for these processes is being released. Glucose is formed from the stored starch, being utilized in various ways. Some is built up into cellulose and incorporated into new cell walls, and part is oxidized by respiration and releases energy which may be used in the many chemical activities taking place in the growing regions.

The conversion of starch to glucose (a form of sugar) also results in a fall of osmotic potential (*see* p. 61), which may assist the seedlings to take in water and their newly formed cells to extend during growth. When the first foliage leaves are above soil and their chlorophyll properly developed, the seedling can make its own food and is independent of the cotyledons.

Maize. (Fig. 8.6). The maize grain is really a fruit containing one seed, but the thin ovary wall does not interfere with germination. The fruit absorbs water, swells, and a radicle bursts through the *coleorhiza* (Fig. 8.5b) and fruit wall. Root hairs grow on the upper regions of the radicle. The plumule grows straight up and through the fruit wall, but the growing point and first leaves are protected by a sheath, the *coleoptile*, with a hard, pointed tip. From the base of the plumule grow adventitious roots. Once above the soil, the first leaves burst out of the coleoptile which remains as a sheath round the leaf bases. The cotyledon remains below the soil, absorbing food from the endosperm and transmitting it to the growing root and shoot. Eventually, both the cotyledon and the exhausted endosperm rot away.

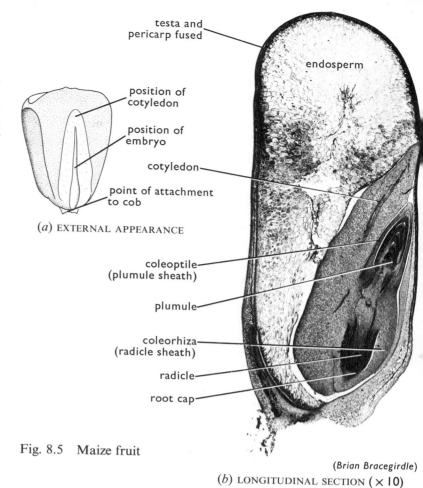

(a) EXTERNAL APPEARANCE

Fig. 8.5   Maize fruit

(Brian Bracegirdle)

(b) LONGITUDINAL SECTION (× 10)

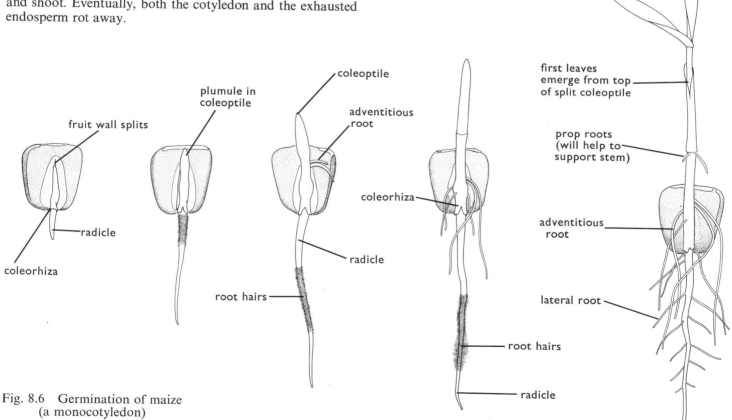

Fig. 8.6   Germination of maize
   (a monocotyledon)

Dormancy

Most seeds when shed contain only about 10 per cent of water by weight. In this dry condition all the chemical processes of living are very slow and little food is used. The seed may remain alive in this state for long periods without germinating, though still able to do so when conditions are favourable. The seed is said to be *dormant*. If properly stored, wheat can still be germinated after about fifteen years, but the pará rubber seed loses the power of germination after only a few days. The percentage of seeds which will germinate usually decreases with the length of time they are kept dormant. In many tropical plants there is no dormancy period and in the mangrove, for example, germination of seeds occurs while they are still on the parent plant.

Controlled experiments

A controlled experiment is one in which the experimenter controls the conditions. By this method he can be sure of the way in which these conditions influence the animal or plant. If, out of 50 seeds shed by a wild flower, only 20 germinate and only 10 of these produce mature flowers, it is possible only to guess at the factors that might have been responsible. These could include dead seeds, attack by fungus or bacteria, unfavourable conditions of light, temperature, moisture or air.

All these conditions are beyond the control of an observer because he is unable to influence them in the plant's natural environment and he does not know the variations in them that have already taken place during the development of the plants.

To find out the importance of a particular condition to the normal development and existence of an animal or plant, the usual experimental practice is to exclude or vary this particular condition, keeping all others constant, and observe the effect on the plant or animal. Most experiments involve placing the plant or animal in an unusual situation, in boxes, jars or cages, when it can be argued that the peculiar experimental conditions are responsible for the observed results. For this reason, it is necessary to set up two almost identical experiments, the one with normal conditions and the other with the single eliminated or varied factor; any difference can then be attributed to the latter. The first experiment is called the *control*.

The control also enables the researcher to be sure that the "results" of his experiment would not have occurred quite irrespective of the experimental conditions.

CONDITIONS NECESSARY FOR GERMINATION

Experiment 1. **To find whether oxygen is necessary for germination** (Fig. 8.7)

The principle of the experiment is to deprive the seeds of oxygen and see how many of them germinate compared with others having a normal oxygen supply.

A piece of wet cotton wool is rolled on some small seeds which will stick to it. The cotton wool is suspended from a

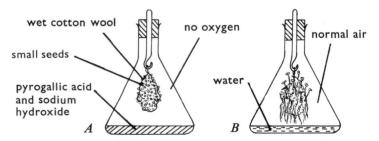

Fig. 8.7 To find out if oxygen is needed for germination

thread inside a tightly corked flask, *A*, which contains a solution of pyrogallic acid and sodium hydroxide.* This mixture absorbs oxygen from the air. The cotton wool must not touch the chemicals. It could be objected that seeds sown in such abnormal surroundings could hardly be expected to germinate anyway. To check on this a second apparatus is set up using the same size flask, *B*, seeds from the same source, but with water in the flask instead of the chemicals. This is the control, in which the experimental situation is the same except that the seeds in it are not deprived of oxygen. Both flasks are placed in the same conditions of light and temperature.

Result. After a few days most of the seeds in flask *B* will have germinated, while those in flask *A* will not, or if they have, they are fewer in number and much less advanced.

Interpretation. Without oxygen, germination cannot take place. To show that the chemicals have not killed the seeds the cotton wool from flask *A* can be transferred to *B*, when, after a few days the seeds will germinate successfully.

Note. Since sodium hydroxide absorbs carbon dioxide, flask *A* will lack both oxygen and carbon dioxide. Strictly speaking the control flask should contain sodium hydroxide solution and not water.

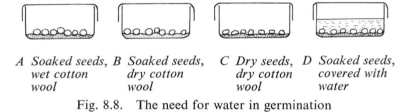

A Soaked seeds, B Soaked seeds, C Dry seeds, D Soaked seeds, wet cotton wool   dry cotton wool   dry cotton wool   covered with water

Fig. 8.8.   The need for water in germination

Experiment 2. **To find whether water is necessary for germination** (Fig. 8.8)

Four Petri dishes, or similar containers that can be covered to prevent evaporation, are labelled *A*, *B*, *C* and *D*. Cotton wool or blotting paper is placed in the bottom of each. In *A* are placed seeds that have been soaked overnight, and the blotting paper is moistened. In *B*, soaked seeds are also placed but the blotting paper is not moistened. In *C*, unsoaked seeds are placed on dry paper. In *D*, soaked seeds are placed and completely covered with water. There should be equal numbers of seeds from the same source in each container and these should be left in the same conditions of light and temperature for a few days, water being added to *A* and *D* if necessary.

Result. Only in *A* do the seeds germinate properly. Those in *B* may start and then shrivel and die. The ones in *D* will probably go rotten, though some may begin to germinate.

Interpretation. Adequate water must be present for germination to start and continue; excess water prevents germination, probably by excluding oxygen.

Experiment 3.   **To investigate the effect of temperature on germination**

Equal numbers of soaked seeds are placed on moist cotton wool in three labelled dishes and the dishes placed in situations which differ only in temperature, e.g. incubator (30°C), refrigerator (4°C), cupboard in the laboratory (20°C). They are left for a week, the temperature being noted daily, after which the extent of germination in the seeds is compared, e.g. length of radicle or plumule.

* Dissolve 1 g pyrogallic acid in 10 cm³ 10 per cent sodium hydroxide. The solution is very caustic and attacks skin, clothing and wooden bench tops. If spilt it should be neutralized at once with dilute hydrochloric acid.

Result. It will be found that extremes of temperature do not favour germination. Low temperatures prevent it altogether. Higher temperatures accelerate it up to the point where either the protoplasm is killed, drying up is too rapid, or fungal growth is promoted.

Interpretation. Each species of seed probably has an optimum temperature for germination, but in this experiment the intervals between temperatures are too widely spaced to determine this optimum.

The seeds from the refrigerator should subsequently be allowed to germinate in a warm place to demonstrate that failure to germinate in the refrigerator was due to the retarding effect of a low temperature, and not to their being killed by the cold.

EXPERIMENTS ON THE SENSITIVITY OF PLANTS: TROPISMS

Seedlings are good material for experiments on sensitivity because their growing roots and shoots respond readily to the stimuli of light and gravity. Growth movements of this kind, in which the direction of growth is related to the direction of the stimulus, are called *tropisms*.

Experiment 4. *The effect of one-sided lighting on growing shoots*

Two potted seedlings, e.g. sunflower, at about equivalent stages of growth are selected. After watering, one is placed under a cardboard box with a window cut in one side so that the light reaches its shoot from one direction only (Fig. 8.9). The other is placed in an identical situation, but on a slowly rotating *clinostat*. This consists of an electric or clockwork motor which rotates a turntable about four times per hour, thus exposing all sides of the shoot equally to the source of light. This is a control.

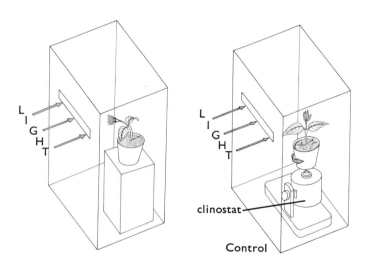

Fig. 8.9 Phototropism in shoots

Result. After a few days, the two plants are removed from the boxes and compared, when it will be found that the stem of the plant with one-sided illumination has changed its direction of growth and is growing towards the light.

Interpretation. The results suggest that the young shoot has responded to one-sided lighting by growing towards it. This tendency to grow in response to the direction of light is called *phototropism* and the shoot is *positively phototropic* because it grows towards the direction of the stimulus.

However, the results of an experiment with a single plant cannot be used to draw conclusions which apply to green plants as a whole. The experiment described is more of an illustration than a critical investigation. To investigate phototropisms thoroughly a large number of plants from a wide variety of species would have to be used.

Effect of light on growth of radicles. Most roots are unaffected by one-sided illumination. Where they are influenced they are negatively phototropic, i.e. they grow away from the light.

Experiment 5. *The effect of gravity on shoots*

Two equivalent potted seedlings are selected as for Experiment 4. One is placed on its side so that the shoot is horizontal, while the other is placed in a clinostat so that, although the shoot is horizontal, all sides are exposed equally to the "pull" of gravity (Fig. 8.10). The lighting conditions should be the same for each shoot or else both experiments should be covered by cardboard boxes.

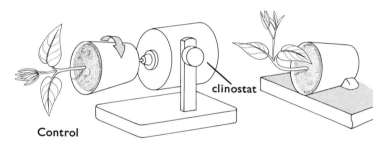

Fig. 8.10 Geotropism in shoots

Result. After about 24 hours, the shoot in the clinostat will still be growing horizontally while that of the stationary plant will have changed its direction of growth to vertically upwards.

Interpretation. The result illustrates that growing shoots tend to grow away from the direction of gravitational pull. A response of this kind to gravity is called a *geotropism* and since the shoots grow away from the direction of the stimulus, the response is said to be negative, i.e. shoots are *negatively geotropic*. As with Experiment 4, the number of specimens used does not permit a general conclusion about plants as a whole.

Experiment 6. *The effect of gravity on roots*

Bean or pea seedlings with straight radicles are pinned to a large cork as shown in Fig. 8.11. The cork is then placed in the mouth of a jar which is left on its side for 48 hours: The radicles being horizontal are subjected to a gravitational force perpendicular to their length. A control with a clinostat is arranged as shown, so that gravity acts equally on all sides of the radicles in turn. In both cases, moist blotting paper lines the container to saturate the air with water vapour, and the apparatus is left in darkness to eliminate the possibility of a phototropic response.

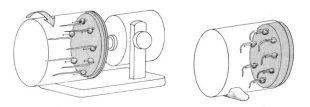

Fig. 8.11 Geotropism in roots

Result. The radicles of the seedlings on the clinostat continue to grow horizontally while those in the stationary jar have grown downwards.

Interpretation. If light, humidity and temperature are uniform in the containers and identical in each experiment, the radicles showing a growth curvature must have responded to the one-sided pull of gravity. This growth movement is *geotropism* and the roots are *positively geotropic*. Lateral roots, however, growing more or less horizontally, are clearly not positively geotropic.

Experiment *A* 1 offers an alternative method of investigating geotropism in roots.

Hydrotropism, the response to water. Experiments are sometimes quoted which purport to show that radicles respond positively to the "direction" of water by growing towards it. In practice it is difficult to design an experiment with a moisture gradient and the results are often susceptible to more than one interpretation. A root system in a soil which was not uniformly moist might well show a lop-sided distribution because the dry soil has inhibited the root growth while this would have been promoted in moist soil, but such an effect could not be attributed to a directional growth response by the growing root tips. (For a critical review of this subject, *see* I. A. Dodd, *The School Science Review*, 156, **45**, 396 and 162, **47**, 476.)

Experiment 7. *The effect of light on plants*

Two equivalent groups of seedlings are selected. The plants of one group are grown in darkness while those in the other grow in normal lighting conditions. After two days the seedlings are compared. Those growing in total darkness will have taller, thinner stems with long internodes between the leaves. The leaves will be few, small and yellowish in colour. Seedlings in this condition are said to be *etiolated*. The plants growing in the light will have shorter, stouter, stems with short internodes between leaves which will be larger, more numerous and greener in colour. Light, therefore, seems to (*a*) reduce the rate of growth of stems, (*b*) promote the production of chlorophyll and expansion of leaves. The phototropic response of shoots is an outcome of this effect of light on growth rate; the side of the stem receiving more illumination will grow more slowly, so producing a curvature towards the light.

These growth responses to light can be seen to be advantageous to green plants. The shoots of seedlings which are partially obscured by other vegetation will grow rapidly until they reach the light, whereupon the leaves will expand, chlorophyll will be activated and photosynthesis will proceed.

Experiment 8. *Indoleacetic acid on wheat coleoptiles* (Fig. 8.12)

Ten soaked wheat grains are placed in each of four shallow dishes containing moist cotton wool. The fruits are allowed to germinate in darkness for six days after which the coleoptiles will be about 20 mm long. The dishes are labelled *A* to *D*. The seedlings in dishes *A*, *B* and *C* have 2 mm cut from the coleoptile tips and then the lengths of all the coleoptiles are measured and recorded. The average length in each dish is calculated. To the cut tips of the coleoptiles in *A* is added a small quantity of lanolin containing 0·1 per cent IAA. To the tips of the coleoptiles in *B* is added plain lanolin, while *C* and *D* are left untreated. The seedlings are allowed to continue growing for a further two days after which the coleoptiles are cut off and measured. By subtracting the original average length in each case from the new average length, the average increase in length can be found.

Result. In general it is found that there is little difference between the untreated coleoptiles in *C* and the lanolin-treated shoots in *B*, neither of them having grown as much as those in *A* and *D*. The decapitated coleoptiles treated with IAA in *A* may well have grown more than those in *D*.

Interpretation. Removal of the coleoptile tip seems to cause retardation of growth in *C*. This might be attributed to the damage inflicted on the growing point. Since, however, growth is normal or above normal in *A* in which IAA is supplied, it looks as if removal of the tip in *C* deprived the coleoptile of IAA or a similar growth-promoting substance. That the active agent in the experiment is IAA and not the lanolin in which it is dissolved, is shown by the failure of the controls in *B* to grow significantly longer than those in *C*.

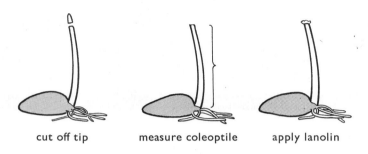

cut off tip　　　measure coleoptile　　　apply lanolin

Fig. 8.12　　IAA on wheat coleoptiles

The auxin theory of tropistic response

There is evidence to suggest that the cells near the tip of some growing shoots produce a chemical, an auxin or growth substance, which in certain concentrations accelerates growth in length. The auxins achieve this effect probably by delaying the loss of plasticity in the walls of the cells in the region of extension so that at a time when the cells are osmotically active and taking in water, the increased pressure of the vacuole forces the cell wall to extend. (*See* Fig. 4.5, p. 12 and Plate 6, p. 22). The kind of evidence supporting this hypothesis is outlined in Fig. 8.13.

Assuming that the results with coleoptiles are applicable to other plants it looks as if one-sided lighting alters the production or distribution of auxin from the growing point so that the illuminated side of the shoot receives less auxin than the darker side. It is not yet known how this redistribution of auxin is brought about.

The same reasoning can be applied to geotropism in shoots and roots. The lower side of a shoot placed horizontally might receive more auxin than the upper side, resulting in a curvature upwards in the growing region. With roots, it is assumed that the higher concentration of auxin on the lower side retards rather than accelerates extension so producing a downward curvature.

One of the growth substances isolated from plants is indoleacetic acid (IAA). The term auxin is often applied specifically to this compound but there are many other substances which are known to influence not only growth but, for example, flowering, bud sprouting, leaf shedding and seed dormancy.

Indoleacetic acid promotes the growth of shoots in concentrations of about 10 parts per million. Roots respond to lower concentrations and different species of plants vary in their response to specific concentrations of auxin. When compounds related to IAA, e.g. 2–4 D, are sprayed on lawns as selective weed killers, the concentrations are chosen so that the broad-leaved plants are killed but the grasses are unaffected.

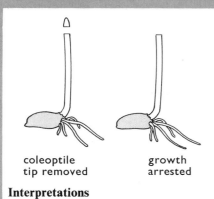

coleoptile tip removed   growth arrested

Interpretations
(a) *Coleoptile tip provides the cells for growth*
(b) *Coleoptile tip produces growth-promoting chemicals*
(c) *Desiccation of or damage to cut coleoptile stops growth*

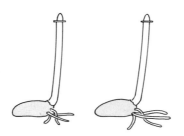

tip replaced but separated from shoot by mica   growth arrested

Interpretation. *Mica prevents both cells and chemicals getting to shoot, but desiccation is ruled out now as a cause of arrested growth*

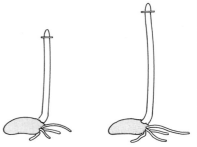

tip replaced but separated from shoot by agar jelly   growth resumed

Interpretation. *Cells still cannot pass from tip to shoot but chemicals can. A growth-promoting chemical from the tip has passed through the agar and caused the shoot to extend*

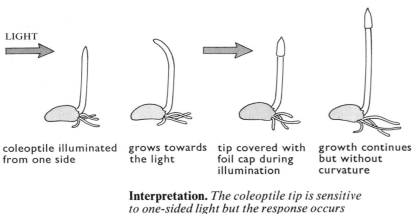

coleoptile illuminated from one side   grows towards the light   tip covered with foil cap during illumination   growth continues but without curvature

Interpretation. *The coleoptile tip is sensitive to one-sided light but the response occurs below the tip. There must be some form of communication between the tip and the rest of the shoot*

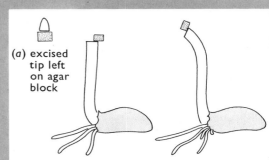

(a) excised tip left on agar block

(b) agar block placed asymmetrically on decapitated coleoptile

(c) coleoptile grows and bends as shown

Interpretation. *A growth-promoting chemical has diffused from the coleoptile tip into the agar. In (b) the right side of the coleoptile receives more chemical than the left. The extra extension on the right side produced the curvature*

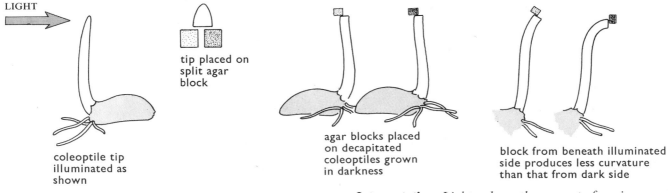

coleoptile tip illuminated as shown   tip placed on split agar block   agar blocks placed on decapitated coleoptiles grown in darkness   block from beneath illuminated side produces less curvature than that from dark side

Interpretation. *Light reduces the amount of auxin reaching shoot from coleoptile tip. Therefore illuminated side grows less than dark side so producing curvature*

Note. The coleoptile is a short-lived and specialized structure in grass and cereal seedlings. Its response to auxin may not be typical of flowering plants as a whole. There is a good deal of evidence which does not support the auxin theory of tropisms.

(*After Went & Thimann, Phytohormones, Macmillan, 1937*)

Fig. 8.13   Some classical experiments to test the auxin theory

To obtain seedlings with straight radicles, soaked seeds are rolled in blotting paper or newspaper as shown in Fig. 8.14, placed in a beaker and kept moist. If several sets are started at daily intervals there will be abundant material from which to select for experiments on tropisms.

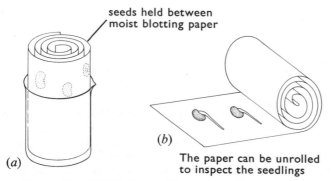

Fig. 8.14   To obtain seedlings with straight radicles

ADDITIONAL EXPERIMENTS

*Experiment A 1. **Positive geotropism in growing roots***

A few germinating seeds at equivalent stages and with straight radicles are selected and placed between two strips of moist cotton wool in a Petri dish, as shown in Fig. 8.15. The seedlings are arranged with the radicles horizontal and the lid of the dish is replaced and held in position with an elastic band. The dish is then placed on its edge as illustrated, in a dark cupboard or container and marked at the top to show which way up it is left. After two days the lid is removed and the seedlings examined.

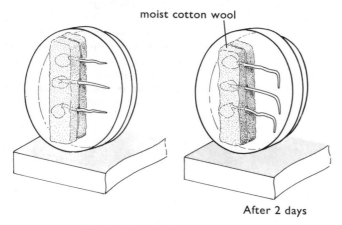

Fig. 8.15   Geotropism in roots

Result. The radicles will be seen to have grown and to have changed their direction of growth from horizontal to vertically downwards.

Interpretation. The experiment is not controlled and illustrates rather than investigates the response of radicles to unilateral gravity. A partial control is to set up an identical experiment but to leave the radicles directed vertically downwards. If the controls show no growth curvature, it is reasonable to attribute the response made by the experimental seedlings to the position in which the radicles were held.

*Experiment A 2. **To find the region of most rapid growth in radicles***

Straight radicles of bean seedlings after a few days' germination are marked with indian ink lines 2 mm apart. They are then arranged as in Fig. 8.15 but with radicles vertically downward and allowed to continue growth. The region of most rapid elongation will be shown by the subsequent spacing of the lines (Fig. 8.16).

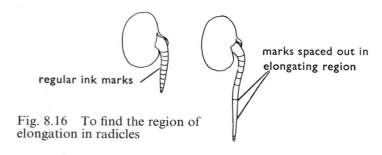

Fig. 8.16   To find the region of elongation in radicles

*Experiment A 3. **To find the region of response in the radicle*** (Fig. 8.17)

Straight radicles are marked as in *A* 2 and placed horizontally in Petri dishes as in *A* 1. Some of the radicles have 1 mm cut from their

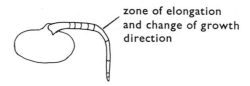

Fig. 8.17   Response to one-sided gravity

tips. After a day or two, the lines will be more spaced out in the bent region than elsewhere. The radicles with the tips removed may continue to grow horizontally.

*Experiment A 4. **Food tests on seeds***

To investigate the kind of food stored in the cotyledons or endosperm of seeds, the seeds should be crushed and heated with water. The food tests described on p. 85 can then be applied.

QUESTIONS

1. Flowering plants are made up principally of root, stem and leaf. In what form are these structures represented in a dicotyledonous seed?
2. How do the functions of cotyledons differ in a dicotyledon such as the bean and a monocotyledon such as maize?
3. (*a*) How is the food stored in the cotyledons of a bean seed made available to the growing region? (*b*) How is the food utilized by the seedling? (*c*) At what stage of development does the seedling become independent of this stored food?
4. Explain why the experiment to show that oxygen is needed for germination is a good example of a controlled experiment. Why is experiment *A* 1 not a controlled experiment?
5. In terms of the auxin hypothesis explain why (*a*) shoots deprived of light grow very tall and (*b*) shoots illuminated from one side grow towards the light source.

9 | Respiration

RESPIRATION in living organisms is the series of chemical changes which release energy from food material. It involves a complicated chain of chemical breakdowns, accelerated by *enzymes* (*see* p. 85), but it can be regarded, for experimental purposes, as the breakdown of carbohydrates to form carbon dioxide and water, with a corresponding release of energy.

The energy released from food is used firstly to combine a phosphate group (PO_4) with a compound called *adenosine diphosphate* (*ADP*) and so form *adenosine triphosphate* (*ATP*). ATP then serves as a store of energy. When it breaks down to ADP and phosphate, it releases energy which can be used for almost any living process, such as muscular contraction, nervous conduction, secretion of enzymes and driving a great many chemical reactions in the living cell. Respiration is one of the most important aspects of the vital chemistry of living matter.

A distinction is usually made between two forms of, or stages in, respiration called *aerobic* and *anaerobic*. Aerobic respiration involves the use of oxygen in the breakdown of carbohydrates or fats which are eventually oxidized completely to carbon dioxide and water. Anaerobic respiration is the breakdown of carbohydrates to release energy without the use of oxygen. This is discussed more fully on p. 47.

The term "respiration" is also often used loosely in reference to breathing, as in "artificial respiration", "pulse and respiration rate" or in connexion with gaseous exchange, e.g. "organs of respiration". For this reason, the "respiration" described in this chapter is sometimes called *tissue respiration* or *internal respiration* to distinguish it from either the breathing movements (ventilation) or the intake of oxygen and output of carbon dioxide (gaseous exchange).

From the equation above, it is apparent that for respiration to occur food and oxygen must be taken in and react together. Also, carbon dioxide and water, which are the end-products of the reaction, must constantly be removed.

Methods of demonstrating respiration. A demonstration of respiration in material is one indication that the material is living, and measurements of the rate of respiration in cells, tissues, organs or organisms give some idea of the rate of chemical activity. Consequently, to the biologist, methods of measuring respiration rates are important.

The equation (Fig. 9.1) suggests that if an organism is respiring it will (*a*) use up carbohydrate, (*b*) take in oxygen, (*c*) give out carbon dioxide, (*d*) produce water or water vapour, and (*e*) release energy. With the exception of (*d*) (*see* p. 47), if one or more of these changes are taking place the material is likely to be living and respiring.

(*a*) Decrease in dry weight (using up carbohydrate)

If living material is converting carbohydrate to carbon dioxide and water, which escape into the air, its weight will decrease. However, it is the dry weight which must be measured since any material, living or non-living, may lose weight by the evaporation of water into the atmosphere.

One hundred seeds are soaked in water for 12 hours. Half

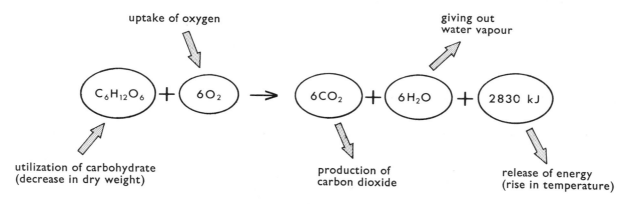

Fig. 9.1   Ways of detecting respiration

Aerobic respiration

The following equation summarizes the process of aerobic respiration, i.e. respiration which uses oxygen (the formulae represent the molecular weights of the substances in grams):

$$C_6H_{12}O_6 + 6O_2 \rightarrow 6CO_2 + 6H_2O + 2830 \text{ kJ} *$$

glucose   oxygen   carbon   water   energy
dioxide

of them are killed by boiling (controls). The 50 living seeds are placed in one dish with moist cotton wool and the 50 dead seeds in identical conditions. Every day for 5 days, 10 seeds or seedlings are selected from each dish and heated in an oven at $120°C$ for 12 hours to evaporate all the water. The two samples of 10 seeds are then weighed. In this way only the solid matter in the seeds is weighed and, if the seeds are respiring, the solids in the food reserve of the endosperm or cotyledons should be decreasing as the food is used to provide energy.

* A *joule* (J) is a unit of energy. A thousand joules are called a *kilojoule* (kJ).

(b) *Uptake of oxygen* (Fig. 9.2)

The apparatus is arranged as shown in Fig. 9.2. After five minutes the tubes will have acquired the temperature of the water in the beaker and the screw clips are closed. If the seeds are respiring they will give out carbon dioxide and take in oxygen so there may be no effective change in the volume of gas in the tube. However, soda lime will absorb all the carbon dioxide produced so that any volume change may be attributed to the uptake of oxygen. If oxygen is absorbed by the seeds, the level of liquid in the capillary should be seen to rise within 20 minutes or so. Any change in the temperature of the tubes will cause the air in them to expand or contract and produce corresponding movements of the liquid in the capillary, which could be confused with the movements due to oxygen uptake.

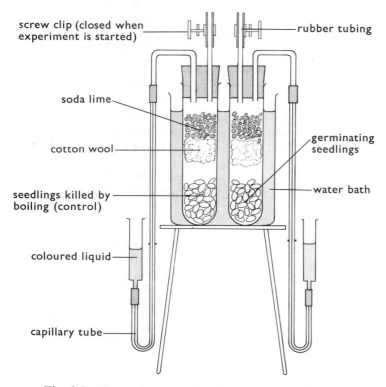

screw clip (closed when experiment is started)

rubber tubing

soda lime

cotton wool

germinating seedlings

seedlings killed by boiling (control)

water bath

coloured liquid

capillary tube

Fig. 9.2   To see if oxygen is taken up in respiration

The water in the beaker, however, should minimize temperature fluctuations and since these will affect both tubes to the same extent, the change in volume due to oxygen uptake alone can be determined by *comparing* the levels of liquid in the experiment and the control. The control thus allows for changes due to temperature variation and also serves to show that oxygen uptake results from a living process in germinating seeds and is not merely due to physical absorption by the seeds.

(c) *Production of carbon dioxide*

(i) *Germinating seeds* (Fig. 9.3)

Wet cotton wool is placed in two flasks A and B. Soaked seeds are added to A and an equal number of boiled seeds to B. Both groups of seeds are soaked for 15 minutes in sodium hypochlorite solution to prevent fungal or bacterial growth which might produce carbon dioxide. The flasks are securely corked and left in the same conditions of light and temperature until germination is clearly perceptible in A. The seeds in B should not germinate. The gases in each flask are then tested by removing the cork and tilting the flask over a test-tube of lime water and shaking up the test-tube.

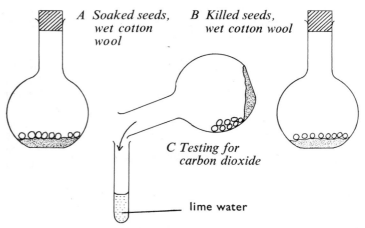

A Soaked seeds, wet cotton wool

B Killed seeds, wet cotton wool

C Testing for carbon dioxide

lime water

Fig. 9.3   Carbon dioxide production in germinating seeds

Result. The air from flask A should turn the lime water milky showing carbon dioxide is present. Air from B should have no effect.

Interpretation. The carbon dioxide must have been produced by the germinating seeds. B is a control and proves that it is not the cotton wool or anything other than germinating seeds that give carbon dioxide.

(ii) *Animals and plants* (Fig. 9.4)

This experiment is suitable for giving fairly quick results with small animals but will also work, over a longer period, with plant material.

The animal or plant is placed in the vessel C. If it is a plant, the vessel must be "blacked out" to prevent photosynthesis occurring. If a potted plant is used, the pot must be enclosed in impermeable material so that the respiration of organisms in the soil does not affect the result. A stream of air is drawn slowly through the apparatus by means of a filter pump at E. In A, soda lime absorbs the carbon dioxide from the incoming air; the lime water in B should stay clear and so prove that carbon dioxide is absent from the air going into vessel C. If carbon dioxide is given out by the organism, the lime water in D will go milky after a time.

If the rates of respiration of different animals or plants are to be compared, the time taken for the lime water to go milky should be noted.

For an experiment to show carbon dioxide production in man, *see* p. 105.

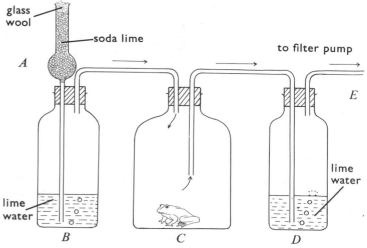

glass wool

soda lime

to filter pump

A

E

lime water

lime water

B   C   D

Fig. 9.4   Carbon dioxide production in an animal

(d) **Production of water vapour**

Since non-living matter may give off water vapour by evaporation, this is not a reliable test of respiration.

(e) **Release of energy in germinating seeds** (Fig. 9.5)

Heat production is a good indication of energy release. Sufficient seeds to fill two small vacuum flasks are soaked in water for 24 hours and half of them killed by boiling for 10 minutes. Both lots of seeds are soaked for 15 minutes in a solution of sodium hypochlorite (e.g. commercial hypochlorite diluted 1:4) to kill fungal spores on the grains. The seeds are rinsed with tap water; the living seeds are placed in one flask, the dead seeds in the other. Thermometers are inserted and the mouths of the flasks plugged with cotton wool.

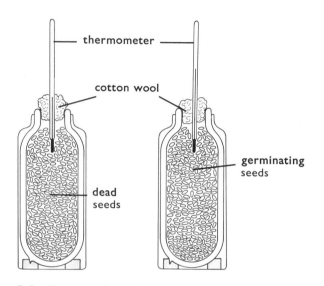

Fig. 9.5   Energy release in germinating seeds

Result. After a few days the temperature in the flask with living seeds will be considerably higher than in the control.

Interpretation. During the germination of seeds, heat energy is released. The results, however, do not justify the conclusion that the heat is the result of respiration rather than any other chemical process.

Anaerobic respiration

This is the release of energy from food material by a process of chemical breakdown which does *not* require oxygen. The food, e.g. carbohydrate, is not broken down completely to carbon dioxide and water but to intermediate compounds such as lactic acid or alcohol. The incomplete breakdown of the food means that less energy is made available during anaerobic respiration than is released during aerobic respiration.

Both processes may be taking place in cells at the same time. Indeed, the first steps in the breakdown of glucose in respiration are anaerobic.

$$\text{glucose} \xrightarrow{\textit{anaerobic}} \text{lactic acid} \xrightarrow{\textit{aerobic}} \text{carbon dioxide and water}$$

During vigorous activity, the oxygen supply to the muscles may not be sufficient to meet their energy demands. Consequently the products of the initial, anaerobic, stages accumulate, e.g. lactic acid. These products are oxidized or converted back to carbohydrate so that even after vigorous activity has ceased, the uptake of oxygen continues at a high rate. The organism is said to have incurred an "oxygen debt" as a result of its excess of anaerobic respiration.

Certain bacteria and fungi derive all or most of their energy from anaerobic respiration and the end products are frequently alcohol and carbon dioxide; the process in this case is called fermentation.

Fermentation

The term fermentation is not applied exclusively to anaerobic respiration in which alcohol is produced; a variety of organic acids, e.g. citric, butyric, oxalic may be formed by the anaerobic respiration of micro-organisms and such fermentations are exploited commercially to produce these compounds.

The yeasts (unicellular fungi) and bacteria which bring about fermentation are able to employ their enzyme systems to release energy anaerobically from carbohydrates, particularly starch and sugar. Alcoholic fermentation on a commercial scale is usually brought about by yeasts (*see* p. 77) acting on sugar solutions such as the malt sugar prepared from germinating barley. The equation below summarizes the reactions:

$$C_6H_{12}O_6 \rightarrow 2CO_2 + 2\underset{\textit{alcohol}}{C_2H_5OH} + 118 \text{ kJ}$$

If this equation is compared with the one on p. 45 it can be seen that far less energy is obtained from a gramme molecule of glucose during anaerobic respiration than is released when the sugar is completely oxidized. Unless the products of fermentation, in this case ethanol, are removed, they will reach a concentration which will eventually kill the organism producing them.

(f) **To show carbon dioxide production during anaerobic respiration (fermentation) in yeast**

Some water is boiled to expel all the dissolved oxygen and when cool is used to make up a 5 per cent solution of glucose and a 10 per cent suspension of dried yeast. 5 cm³ of the glucose solution and 1 cm³ of the yeast suspension are placed in a test-tube and covered with a thin layer of liquid paraffin to exclude atmospheric oxygen from the mixture. A delivery tube is fitted as shown in Fig. 9.6 and allowed to dip into clear lime water. After 10–15 minutes, with gentle warming if

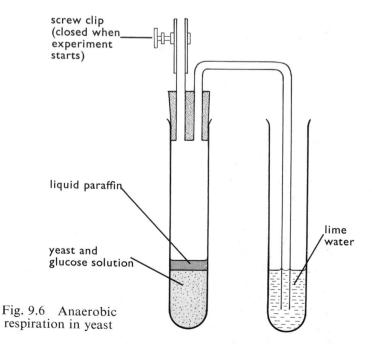

Fig. 9.6   Anaerobic respiration in yeast

necessary, there should be signs of fermentation in the yeast-glucose mixture and the bubbles of gas escaping through the lime-water turn it milky. The gas is therefore carbon dioxide.

A control can be set up in the same way but using a boiled yeast suspension which will not ferment. The fact that the living yeast produces carbon dioxide despite being deprived of oxygen is evidence to support the contention that anaerobic respiration is taking place.

If the experiment is repeated on a larger scale using 500 cm^3 glucose solution and left for several days in a warm place, the alcohol can be distilled off, collecting the fraction that vaporizes between $70-80°C$. The distillate can be identified as alcohol by its taste, odour and the fact that it can be ignited.

Metabolism

The thousands of enzyme-controlled chemical changes which take place in organisms and the cells of which they are composed are often referred to collectively as metabolism. The reactions concerned may be changing one compound into another more useful or more reactive, combining simple substances into more complex ones which can be built into the tissues, breaking down complex compounds to release their energy or to make them more easily transportable. Respiration is one manifestation of metabolism.

QUESTIONS

1. (a) Where does respiration occur? (b) What is the importance of respiration? (c) What materials does respiration (i) need, (ii) produce?
2. List the differences between aerobic and anaerobic respiration. Are these two forms of respiration mutually exclusive? Explain.
3. Which aspects of respiration can be measured or demonstrated?
4. In the mammal, which classes of food can be used to provide energy? Which ones provide the most energy? (See p. 82.)
5. An organism in the course of respiration takes in 50 cm^3 oxygen. It is quite likely to give out 50 cm^3 carbon dioxide in the same period so that there is no volume change in the gas surrounding it. In such a case how can one, in principle, design an experiment to show that oxygen is being taken up?

10 | Photosynthesis and the Nutrition of Green Plants

PHOTOSYNTHESIS

The process by which green plants build up carbohydrates from carbon dioxide and water is called photosynthesis. The energy for this synthesis is obtained from sunlight which is absorbed by chlorophyll. Oxygen is given off as a by-product. In land plants the water is absorbed from the soil by the root system and the carbon dioxide from the air through the stomata.

Photosynthesis goes on principally in the leaves, though any green part of the plant can photosynthesize.

The process may be represented by the equation:

$$6CO_2 + 6H_2O \xrightarrow[\text{absorbed by chlorophyll}]{\text{energy from sunlight}} C_6H_{12}O_6 + 6O_2$$

though it must be realized that this shows only the beginning and end of a very complicated chain of chemical reactions involving many intermediate compounds and numerous enzymes which promote the different chemical changes.

Photosynthesis in a leaf (see Figs. 5.9 and 5.10, pp. 19 and 20). The leaves of most green plants are well adapted to the process of photosynthesis taking place within them.

(a) Their broad, flat shape offers a large surface area for absorption of sunlight and carbon dioxide.

(b) Most leaves being thin, the distances across which carbon dioxide has to diffuse to reach the mesophyll cells from the stomata are very short.

(c) The large intercellular spaces in the mesophyll provide an easy passage through which carbon dioxide can diffuse.

(d) Numerous stomata on one or both surfaces allow the exchange of carbon dioxide and oxygen with the atmosphere.

(e) In the palisade cells the chloroplasts are more numerous than in the spongy mesophyll cells. The palisade cells being on the upper surface will receive most sunlight and this will be available to the chloroplasts without being absorbed by too many intervening cell walls. The elongated shape of many palisade cells may confer the same advantage.

(f) The branching network of veins provides a ready water supply to the photosynthesizing cells.

Photosynthesis in a palisade cell (Fig. 10.1). Water passes into the cell by osmosis (see Chap. 12) from the nearest vein; carbon dioxide from the adjacent air spaces diffuses through the cellulose wall and into the cytoplasm. In the chloroplast, molecules of carbon dioxide and water are combined by a series of chemical changes. For some of these changes the energy is provided in the chloroplast from sunlight absorbed by the chlorophyll. One of the final and easily recognizable products of photosynthesis is starch, and during daylight starch grains may be built up inside the chloroplast.

Oxygen is released during the process and diffuses out of the cytoplasm, through the cell wall into the air spaces and, finally, out of the stomata into the atmosphere.

When photosynthesis is rapid, starch will accumulate in the cells, but enzymes are acting on the starch all the time, turning it into soluble carbohydrates like sucrose which pass out of the cells and are carried off in the sieve tubes of the phloem. The sucrose may travel to storage organs and be changed back into starch or pass to actively growing regions where it can be

(a) oxidized in respiration to provide energy for chemical reactions in the cell,

(b) concentrated in the cell sap, lowering the water

potential (*see* p. 61) of the vacuole which enables the cell to take in more water, increase its turgor and so extend,

(*c*) converted to cellulose to be built into new cell walls or to thicken existing ones,

(*d*) used as a basis for the synthesis of many other compounds, proteins, fats, pigments etc.

In darkness all the starch in the leaf is converted to sugar and removed.

During rapid photosynthesis the production of sugars faster than they could be removed by the sieve tubes could result in the osmotic potential of the cells being lowered to a harmful or disruptive level. Starch, being insoluble, can accumulate without causing osmotic disturbances.

From the explanations given above, it is apparent that if starch is accumulating in a leaf, photosynthesis is probably going on and in the experiments which follow, a positive result to the iodine test on a leaf is regarded as evidence of photosynthesis. Some plants, e.g. those in the iris and lily family, do not form starch in their leaves and in these cases the starch test would prove nothing.

Gaseous exchange and compensation point. It can be seen that the simplified equation given above is the reverse of that on p. 45 representing respiration. During respiration, oxygen is used up, carbohydrates are broken down and water and carbon dioxide are excreted. In photosynthesis carbon dioxide and water are taken in, carbohydrates are built up and oxygen is excreted. In green plants, as in all living organisms, respiration goes on all the time.

In dim light, e.g. at dawn and dusk, the rate of photosynthesis may become equal to the rate of respiration so that all the carbon dioxide produced by respiration is used in photosynthesis and all the oxygen produced by photosynthesis is used in respiration. The rate of carbohydrate breakdown in respiration is equalled by the rate of carbohydrate build-up by photosynthesis and there is no net gaseous exchange with the atmosphere. In this state, the plant is said to have reached its *compensation point*.

In bright light, respiration continues but will be exceeded by the rate of photosynthesis so that more oxygen will be produced than is used and more carbon dioxide used than is produced.

The net gaseous exchange with the atmosphere will thus be carbon dioxide taken in and oxygen given out. In darkness there will be no photosynthesis and the plant will take in oxygen and give out carbon dioxide as a result of continuing respiration.

EXPERIMENTS ON PHOTOSYNTHESIS

Destarching. Since the presence of starch is regarded as evidence of photosynthesis, the experimental plants must have no starch in their leaves at the start of the experiment. If they are potted plants, they are destarched by leaving them in a dark cupboard for two or three days. Experiments conducted on plants in the open should be set up the day before, since during the night most of the starch will be removed from the leaves. Preferably, the selected leaves should be destarched by wrapping in aluminium foil for two days and one such leaf tested to ensure that no starch is present.

Testing a leaf for starch.

1. The leaf is detached and dipped in boiling water for half a minute. This kills the protoplasm by destroying the enzymes in it, and so prevents any further chemical changes. It also makes the cell more permeable to iodine solution.

2. The leaf is boiled in methylated spirit, using a water-bath (Fig. 10.2), until all the chlorophyll is dissolved out. This leaves a white leaf and makes colour changes caused by interaction of starch and iodine much easier to see.

3. Alcohol makes the leaf brittle and hard, but it can be softened by dipping it once more into boiling water, then spreading it flat on a white surface such as a glazed tile.

4. Iodine solution is placed on the leaf. Any parts which turn blue have starch in them. If no starch is present the leaf is merely stained brown by iodine.

The controlled experiments on p. 50, can be used to investigate or verify the conditions necessary for photosynthesis.

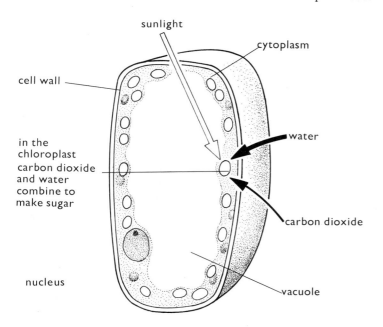

Fig. 10.1   Photosynthesis in a palisade cell

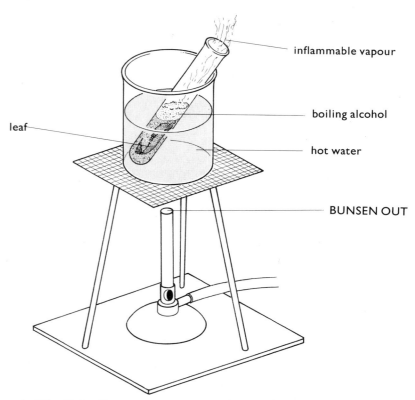

Fig. 10.2   To remove chlorophyll from a leaf

Experiment 1. *Is chlorophyll necessary for photosynthesis?*

As with the experiments on germination, the basis of these experiments is to eliminate the condition under investigation to see if photosynthesis can take place without it.

It is not possible to remove chlorophyll from a leaf without killing it, and so a leaf, or part of a leaf, which has chlorophyll only in patches is used. Such variegated leaves are found in varieties of *Tradescantia, Croton* and *Caladium*, for example. After a period of destarching, the leaf on the plant is exposed to daylight for a few hours. It is then detached, drawn carefully to show the distribution of chlorophyll, and tested for starch as described above.

Result. Only the parts that were previously green turn blue with iodine. The parts that were white stain brown (Fig. 10.3*b*).

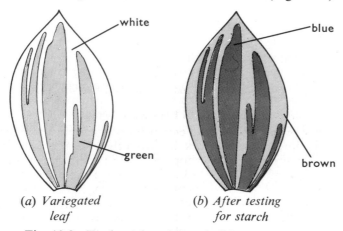

(a) *Variegated leaf*

(b) *After testing for starch*

Fig. 10.3   To show that chlorophyll is necessary

Interpretation. Since starch is present only in the parts which were green, it seems reasonable to suppose that photosynthesis goes on only in the presence of chlorophyll. It must be remembered, however, that there are other possible interpretations which the experiment has not eliminated, e.g. starch is made in the green parts and sugar in the white parts. Such alternative explanations can be tested by further experiments.

Experiment 2. *Is light necessary for photosynthesis?*

A simple shape is cut out from a piece of aluminium foil making a stencil which is attached to a previously destarched leaf (Fig. 10.4). After 4 to 6 hours of daylight, the leaf is detached and tested for starch.

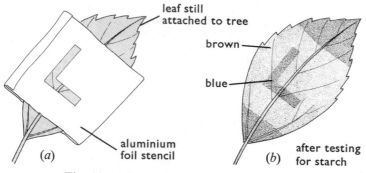

Fig. 10.4   To show that light is necessary

Result. Only areas which received light go blue with iodine.
Interpretation. As starch has not accumulated in the areas without light, it may be assumed that light plays an essential part in starch formation and hence in photosynthesis. It may

be objected, however, that the aluminium foil prevented carbon dioxide from reaching the leaf and that it was shortage of this gas rather than absence of light which prevented photosynthesis. Against this it can be argued that a leaf produces carbon dioxide by its own respiration but a control may be designed using a transparent material, e.g. polythene, instead of the aluminium foil stencil.

Experiment 3. *Is carbon dioxide needed for photosynthesis?*

Two destarched potted plants are watered and the shoots enclosed in polythene bags, one of which contains soda-lime to absorb carbon dioxide from the air and the other sodium hydrogencarbonate (bicarbonate) solution to produce extra carbon dioxide (Fig. 10.5). Both plants are placed in sunlight or under a fluorescent light for several hours and a leaf from each is then detached and tested for starch.

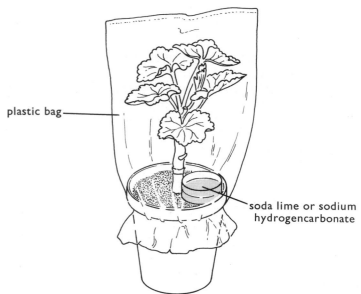

Fig. 10.5   To show that CO_2 is necessary

Result. The leaf deprived of carbon dioxide will not turn blue, while that from the carbon dioxide enriched atmosphere will turn blue.
Interpretation. The fact that no starch is made in the leaf deprived of carbon dioxide suggests that the latter must be necessary for photosynthesis. The control rules out the possibility that high humidity or temperature in the plastic bag prevents normal photosynthesis.

Experiment 4. *Is oxygen produced during photosynthesis?*

A short-stemmed funnel is placed over some *Elodea* in a beaker of water, preferably pond water, and a test-tube filled with water is inverted over the funnel-stem (Fig. 10.6). The funnel is raised above the bottom of the beaker to allow free circulation of water. The apparatus is placed in sunlight, and bubbles of gas soon appear from the cut stems, rise and collect in the test-tube. When sufficient gas has collected, the test-tube is removed and a glowing splint is inserted. A control experiment should be set up in a similar way but placed in a dark cupboard. Little or no gas should collect.
Result. The glowing splint bursts into flames.

Interpretation. The relighting of a glowing splint does not prove that the gas collected is *pure* oxygen but it does show that in the light, this particular plant has given off a gas which is considerably richer in oxygen than is atmospheric air.

*Experiment 5. **Gaseous exchange during photosynthesis***

Three test-tubes are washed with tap water, distilled water and hydrogencarbonate indicator before placing 2 cm³ hydrogencarbonate indicator* in each. A green leaf is placed in tubes 1 and 2 so that it is held against the walls of the tube and does not touch the indicator (Fig. 10.7). The three tubes are closed with bungs, tube 1 is covered with aluminium foil and all three are placed in a rack in direct sunlight or a few centimetres from a bench lamp for about 40 minutes.

Result. The indicator (which was originally orange) should not change colour in tube 3, the control; that in tube 1, with the leaf in darkness, should turn yellow; and in tube 2 with the illuminated leaf, the indicator should be scarlet or purple.

Interpretation. Hydrogencarbonate indicator is a mixture of dilute sodium hydrogencarbonate solution with the dyes cresol red and thymol blue. It is a pH indicator in equilibrium with the atmospheric carbon dioxide, i.e. its original colour represents the acidity produced by the carbon dioxide in the air. Increase in atmospheric carbon dioxide makes it more acid and it changes colour from orange to yellow. Decrease in atmospheric carbon dioxide makes it less acid and causes a colour change to red or purple.

Thus, the results provide evidence that in darkness (tube 1) leaves produce carbon dioxide (from respiration), while in light (tube 2) they use up more carbon dioxide in photosynthesis than they produce in respiration. Tube 3 is the control, showing that it is the presence of the leaf which causes a change in the atmosphere in the test-tube.

The experiment can be criticized on the grounds that the hydrogencarbonate indicator is not a specific test for carbon dioxide but will respond to any change in acidity or alkalinity. In tube 2 there would be the same change in colour if the leaf produced an alkaline gas such as ammonia, and in tube 1, any acid gas produced by the leaf would turn the indicator yellow. However, a knowledge of the metabolism of the leaf suggests that these are less likely events than changes in the carbon dioxide concentration.

* *See* p. 239.

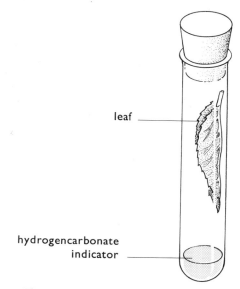

Fig. 10.7   Gaseous exchange during photosynthesis

PROTEIN SYNTHESIS IN PLANTS

Green plants use the sun's energy for only certain stages in the build-up of carbohydrates, but from these all the other compounds necessary for protoplasm and cell walls can be made. The sugar molecules are linked up into longer molecules to make cellulose. Additional elements such as nitrogen and sulphur are combined with carbohydrates to make proteins. The necessary energy for these processes comes from respiration, and they go on continuously in the plant, day and night.

Essential elements. Besides carbon, hydrogen and oxygen assimilated during photosynthesis, the plant takes up other elements from the soil. The chlorophyll molecule needs magnesium; many enzyme systems need phosphorus; calcium is used in the material between cell walls and potassium plays some part in controlling the rates of photosynthesis and respiration. These elements and the nitrogen and sulphur used in making proteins are obtained in the form of soluble salts from the soil. They are absorbed in very dilute solution by the root system. The plant must be able to collect these salts from the soil and concentrate them. The following are examples of soluble salts containing the essential elements mentioned above, but these are not necessarily the ones that occur in the soil:

Potassium nitrate contains potassium and nitrogen.
Magnesium sulphate contains magnesium and sulphur.
Potassium phosphate contains potassium and phosphorus.
Calcium nitrate contains calcium and nitrogen.

Many other elements, e.g. copper, manganese, boron, in very small quantities are also needed for healthy growth. These are often referred to as *trace elements*.

Water cultures. Since a plant can make all its vital substances from carbon dioxide, water and salts, it is possible to grow plants in water containing the necessary salts. These solutions are called water cultures, and by carefully controlling the salts present it is possible to find out the relative importance of particular elements in the growth of the plant.

*Experiment 6. **To demonstrate the importance of certain elements in normal plant growth*** (Fig. 10.10)

A suitable culture solution can be made from the salts listed above by dissolving 2 g of calcium nitrate, 0·5 g of the others

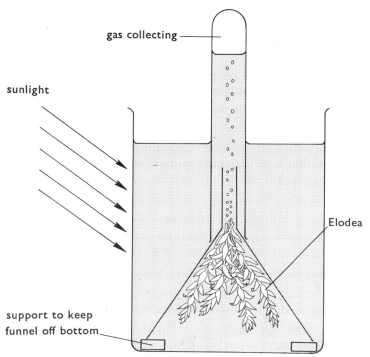

Fig. 10.6   To show that oxygen is set free

gas collecting

sunlight

Elodea

support to keep
funnel off bottom

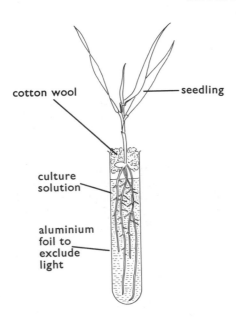

Fig. 10.10   To set up a water culture

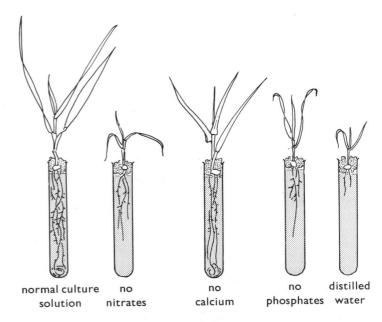

Fig. 10.11   Result of water culture experiment

and a trace of ferric chloride in 2000 cm³ of distilled water. To make a solution lacking sulphur, magnesium chloride replaces sulphate; for one deficient in calcium, potassium nitrate is used instead of calcium nitrate; to eliminate phosphorus, potassium sulphate replaces the phosphate; ferric chloride is omitted to exclude iron; the nitrates are replaced by chlorides for a nitrogen-free solution; calcium salts replace potassium salts to eliminate potassium; potassium sulphate instead of magnesium sulphate excludes magnesium.

Five test-tubes are labelled and filled with experimental solutions as follows: (a) complete culture solution, (b) distilled water, (c) culture solution lacking nitrate, (d) a solution lacking phosphate, and (e) one lacking calcium. Other solutions, deficient in different elements can be used instead of, or in addition to, those listed.

Seedlings are germinated as suggested on p. 44 and five of these at about equivalent stages of development are selected and placed, one in each of the culture solutions, supported by cotton wool as shown in Fig. 10.10. It is best to select seeds with only a little food reserve in their cotyledons or endosperm, e.g. sorghum, so that the reserves are quickly exhausted and the plants come to depend on the culture solution for their minerals. Light is excluded from the solutions to prevent growth of algae which might affect the mineral content. The tubes are placed where the shoots receive sunlight equally, and the solutions kept topped-up with distilled water.

Result. After a few weeks the seedlings are compared by counting and measuring their leaves and roots as far as possible. The one in distilled water will have grown hardly at all and is stunted and weak; the one in complete culture solution will be large and sturdy with dark green leaves. The others are all likely to be smaller than that in complete culture, with fewer and smaller leaves, frequently with a much paler green colour (Fig. 10.11).

For various reasons, e.g. impurities in the chemicals used to prepare the culture solutions, the results may not be so clear-cut as predicted above. However, all the seedlings from the class experiments can be collected together in batches, i.e. all seedlings from complete culture together, all seedlings from distilled water together, etc. The sorted batches of seedlings

are then placed in labelled beakers and heated in an oven at 120 °C for twelve hours to dry them. The dried seedlings are then weighed and the dry weights compared. The dry weights represent the amount of new matter synthesized by the seedling and it is very likely that the seedlings provided with the full range of minerals will show the greatest increase in dry weight.

Interpretation. A supply of mineral salts containing the elements listed above is necessary for the normal growth and existence of green plants.

Note. Although nitrogen is abundant in the atmosphere it cannot be utilized directly by green plants.

Source of salts, particularly nitrates

Since plants are continually removing salts from the soil, and rain-water washes out those that are soluble, it follows that the salts must be replaced or all vegetation would die.

Rock consists of minerals, some of which are dissolved out by the action of slightly acid rain-water containing dissolved carbon dioxide. The salts from these weathered rocks soak into the soil and are eventually washed into streams and rivers and, finally, into the sea

A great proportion of the essential salts in the soil comes from the excretory materials of animals and the decomposition products of dead plant and animal remains. It is possible to trace the cycle of events which constantly adds nitrogenous matter to the soil and removes it (*see* Nitrogen Cycle p. 54).

QUESTIONS

1. What are the requirements for photosynthesis? How are these requirements met in (a) a land plant, (b) an aquatic plant?
2. What is meant by "destarching" a plant? In what circumstances can the presence of starch in a leaf be regarded as evidence that photosynthesis has occurred?
3. If a plant was producing carbon dioxide and taking in oxygen why would you *not* be justified in assuming that no photosynthesis was taking place?
4. It can be claimed that the sun's energy is indirectly used to produce a muscle contraction in your arm. Trace the steps in the conversion of energy which would justify this claim.
5. Proteins contain carbon, hydrogen, oxygen, nitrogen and often sulphur. Name the source, for green plants, of each of these elements.

11 | The Interdependence of Living Organisms

Food chains

ALL animals derive their food either directly or indirectly from plants. Carnivorous animals feed on other animals which themselves feed on smaller animals but sooner or later in such a series we come to an animal which feeds on vegetation. For example, guppies eat mosquito larvae, and mosquito larvae feed on microscopic plants in the pond or lake. This kind of relationship is called a *food chain*. The basis of food chains on land is vegetation in general, but particularly grass and other leaves. In water, the basis is the *phytoplankton* (Plate 10)—the millions of microscopic plants living near the surface of the sea, ponds and lakes. These need only the water round them, the dissolved carbon dioxide and salts and sunlight to make all their vital substances. Feeding on these microscopic plants are tiny animals, *zooplankton* (Plate 11) such as crustacea and the larvae of many kinds of animal.

The small animals of the zooplankton are eaten by surface-feeding fish, which may then be eaten by larger fish or by man.

$$\text{diatoms} \rightarrow \text{crustacea} \rightarrow \text{fish} \rightarrow \text{man}$$

A comparable food chain on the land might be

$$\text{grass} \rightarrow \text{insect} \rightarrow \text{lizard} \rightarrow \text{bird}$$

The green plants at the beginning of a food chain are sometimes referred to as the *producers*, while the animals which eat them are called *consumers*. A *first order* consumer such as an antelope eats vegetation; a *second order* consumer such as a lion eats animals which feed on vegetation. Consumers such as fungi which are involved in the process of decay are classed as *decomposers*.

The plants at the start of a food chain are frequently small in size and very numerous. At the end of a food chain the animals are often large and relatively few in numbers. The food chain can thus be represented as a pyramid of numbers in which the horizontal width of the bands represents the numbers or, sometimes, the mass (*biomass*) of the organisms (Figs. 11.1 and 11.8).

In reality, food "chains" are not so straightforward as described since a given animal, particularly a predator, does not live exclusively on one type of food; e.g. lions may hunt gazelle or zebra, young crocodiles eat water bugs, while older crocodiles eat fish. This more complex relationship can be shown as a food "web" (Fig. 11.2) but even this is greatly simplified and generalized. (See also p. 219.)

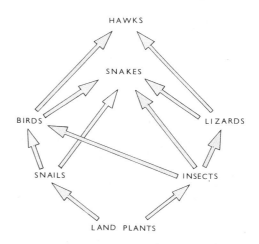

Fig. 11.2   A food web

If the population of one of the animals in a food web is altered, all the others are affected. When the rabbits in Britain were almost exterminated by the disease myxomatosis in 1954–5, the vegetation in what had been rabbit-infested areas changed; sheep could graze where rabbits had previously eaten all the available grass and trees that were hitherto nipped off as seedlings began to grow to maturity, with the result that what had once been grassland, e.g. chalk downs, started to become scrub and eventually woodland. Foxes ate more voles, beetles and blackberries than before and attacked more lambs and poultry. Similarly, in Uganda, protection of the hippopotamus resulted in their multiplying to a point where they began to destroy their habitat and threaten their source of food.

Fig. 11.1   Examples of food chains

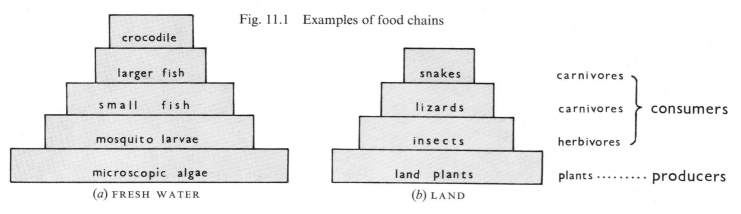

(a) FRESH WATER   (b) LAND

53

Ecosystems

The examples above illustrate the dependence of animals upon plants and each other for their sources of food; they also indicate that plant communities are influenced by the activities of animals. The soil, on which plant life depends, is affected by the plants growing on it, the small animals, plants and bacteria living in it and the activities of the larger animals moving about on its surface. The plant roots modify the crumb structure of the soil (p. 78); the larger soil organisms such as termites and beetle larvae make tunnels which affect the drainage; bacteria and fungi decompose the dead remains of plants and animals and so make their chemicals available for plant nutrition.

The study of the interaction of plants and animals with each other and their environment is called *ecology*. A self-supporting system of plants and animals in, for example, a pond, an ocean or a forest is called an *ecosystem* and the interdependent groups of plants and animals are referred to as *communities*. In a stable ecosystem on the land, the producers (i.e. the green plants) will use carbon dioxide from the air and water and salts from the soil for their growth. Animals will eat the plants and each other. The dead remains of both will return to the soil and provide food for the decomposers, i.e. the fungi and bacteria, which will thus replace the organic matter needed for a good soil structure and the mineral salts needed by the plants. Thus, the materials in a stable ecosystem are not lost but recycled (Fig. 11.3). The recycling of two elements, nitrogen and carbon, will now be described in more detail. In this case, the ecosystem is the entire Earth or, rather, that part of it which contains living organisms, *the biosphere*.

The nitrogen cycle (Fig. 11.4)

Food chains and food webs are but one link in the constant use and re-use of the Earth's chemical resources. The carbon cycle described on p. 56 is one example of this and the nitrogen cycle, described below, is another.

When a plant or animal dies its tissues decompose, largely as a result of the action of enzymes and bacteria. One of the important products of this decomposition is ammonia, which is washed into the soil where it forms ammonium compounds.

Nitrifying bacteria. In the soil are many other bacteria and certain of these oxidize the ammonium compounds to nitrites. Other bacteria further oxidize nitrites to nitrates, and these can be taken up in solution by plants. The faeces of animals contain organic matter that is similarly broken down, while their urine

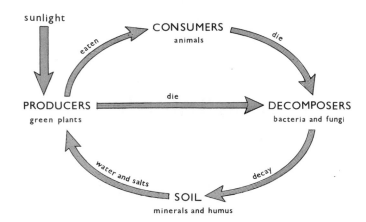

Fig. 11.3   Recycling in an ecosystem

is rich in nitrogenous waste products such as ammonia that can be oxidized to nitrates by soil bacteria.

The nitrifying bacteria derive energy from these oxidative processes in much the same way as plants and animals derive energy from respiration by oxidizing carbohydrates to form carbon dioxide and water.

Nitrogen-fixing organisms. Although green plants cannot utilize the nitrogen in the atmosphere, there are bacteria and blue-green algae in the soil which absorb and combine it with other elements, so making nitrogen compounds. This is called the *fixation of nitrogen*. Some nitrogen-fixing bacteria, as well as existing free in the soil, are also found in special root swellings, or *nodules* (*see* Plate 12), in plants of the pea family such as *Crotalaria* and ground-nut.

Denitrifying bacteria. There are also bacteria in the soil that obtain energy by breaking down compounds of nitrogen to gaseous nitrogen which consequently escapes to the atmosphere.

There are similar cycles for other minerals, e.g. phosphates. The process of bacterial decay releases these minerals slowly into the soil at a rate which, in a stable ecosystem, matches the rate at which they are taken up by plants.

Crop rotation

Different crops make differing demands on the soil, so by changing the crop grown on a particular field from year to year the soil is not depleted of one particular group of minerals.

Plate 10.   PHYTOPLANKTON (×100)
These microscopic plants are diatoms (the producers)
(Dr. D. P. Wilson)

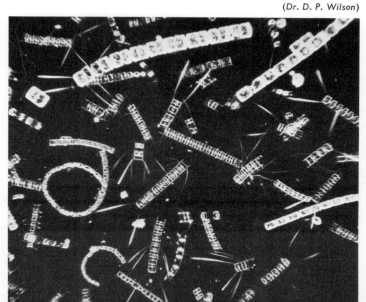

Plate 11.   ZOOPLANKTON (×15)
Adult and larval crustacea (1st order consumers)
(Dr. D. P. Wilson)

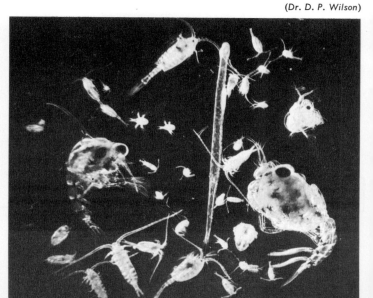

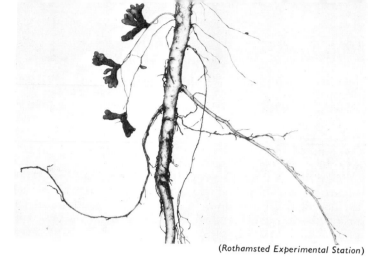

(Rothamsted Experimental Station)

Plate 12. ROOT NODULES

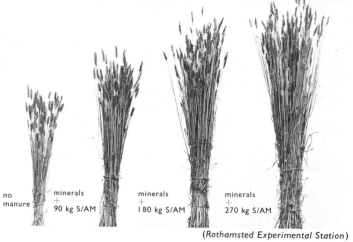

(Rothamsted Experimental Station)

Plate 13. WHEAT HARVESTED FROM EQUAL AREAS OF DIFFERENT PLOTS (S/AM=sulphate of ammonia)

Leguminous crops such as clover and beans may help to restore the nitrogen content of the soil with their root nodules containing nitrogen-fixing bacteria. In addition, a year or two of grass improves the soil's crumb structure.

Rotating the crops also reduces the hazards from infestation e.g. successive crops of potatoes on a soil will increase the population of the fungus causing the disease "potato blight". A field freed for a few years from potatoes will show a reduced incidence of this disease.

Manure and artificial fertilizers in agriculture

If plants are continually cropped from the soil, this, and the constant washing out of soluble salts by the rain, will reduce the soil's content of nitrogen and other elements. If these are not replaced by artificial fertilizers such as ammonium nitrate, ammonium sulphate, compound fertilizers, or by farmyard manure, the yield of crops become less and the soil deteriorates. Wheat has been grown and harvested on an experimental strip at an agricultural experimental station for over one hundred years without anything being added to the soil. The yield has dropped in this time from 14·7 kg to 6·9 kg

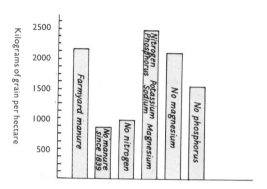

Fig. 11.6 Rothamsted experimental station, Broadbalk Field: average yearly wheat yields from 1852 to 1925

per 100 m². The soil nitrogen, however, has remained at a steady concentration over the last eighty years, and this is probably attributable to the nitrogen-fixing bacteria and other micro-organisms present in the soil. (*See* Plate 13.)

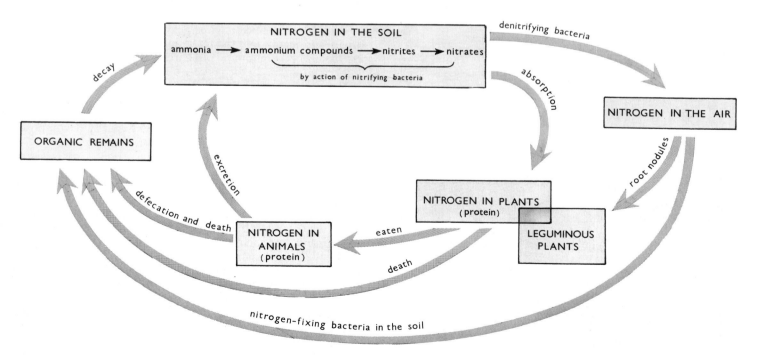

Fig. 11.4 Nitrogen cycle

Hazards of using chemical fertilizers

Long-term experiments show that by applying to the soil a programme of crop rotation and using farmyard manure, the yield of crops can be increased over a fifty-year period. The long-term effects of using chemical fertilizers, in particular soluble salts of nitrogen, are far less satisfactory. Whereas organic manure contributes to the humus content of the soil (*see* p. 78), helping to maintain its crumb structure and hence its porosity and permeability to air, the continued exclusive use of chemicals leads to a loss of organic humus, a deterioration of crumb structure and an increase in permeability. As a consequence the soluble salts are washed by rain from the soil and eventually drain into rivers and lakes where they cause eutrophication (*see* below).

In the short term, heavy application of nitrates to crops has raised the level of free nitrates in the food plants to a point where it may constitute a hazard to health.

Another harmful long-term effect of exclusive use of chemical fertilizers, particularly on light soils, is that in destroying the crumb structure, the soil is much more likely to become dry and powdery and be blown away by the wind, when it is not protected by a plant cover. This leads to loss of valuable top-soil or in extreme cases to dust-bowls and deserts.

Two possible solutions to these problems are (*a*) the development of chemical fertilizers which are less soluble and release their nitrogen slowly into the soil at a rate to suit the demands of the plants and (*b*) more efficient use of organic manure to help to conserve the humus and maintain the soil structure.

Eutrophication. This is the overgrowth of microscopic aquatic plants resulting from an excess of salts reaching rivers. The salts may come from farmland where heavy application of soluble nitrogenous fertilizers is taking place or from the sewage effluents of cities, intensive animal rearing units and the phosphates present in certain detergents. When the nitrates and phosphates reach lakes and rivers they provide abundant nutrients for microscopic green plants whose populations are usually limited by a shortage of these nutrients. As a result, the algae grow and reproduce at a tremendous rate, much faster than they can be eaten by the first order consumers. The algae eventually die and decompose but the vast numbers of aerobic bacteria (p. 71) which are responsible for their decay take so much oxygen from the water that the oxygen supply is depleted and fish and other aquatic animals suffocate and die. The semi-decomposed organic remains of the algae form an oxygen-deficient mud.

Lake Erie in America receives water draining from 30,000 square miles of farmland and the effluents of large cities such as Detroit and Cleveland. In its waters eutrophication has produced an organic mud with a large oxygen deficit. A layer of iron oxide separates the organic mud from the water above but some scientists think that further removal of oxygen could dissolve this layer, allowing the organic matter to mix with the water and so produce anaerobic conditions which could not support life.

The carbon cycle

The carbon cycle describes, in essence, the processes which increase or decrease the carbon dioxide in the environment (Fig. 11.5).

Removal of carbon dioxide from the atmosphere. Green plants, by their photosynthesis (p. 48) remove carbon dioxide from the atmosphere or from the water in which they grow. The carbon of the carbon dioxide is incorporated at first into carbohydrates such as sugar or starch and eventually into the cellulose of cell walls, and the proteins, pigments and other organic compounds which comprise living organisms. When the plants are eaten by animals the organic plant matter is digested, absorbed and built into compounds making the animals' tissues. Thus the carbon atoms from the plant become an integral part of the animal.

Addition of carbon dioxide to the atmosphere.

(*a*) *Respiration.* Plants and animals obtain energy by oxidizing carbohydrates in their cells to carbon dioxide and water (*see* p. 45). These products are excreted and the carbon dioxide returns once again to the environment.

(*b*) *Decay.* The organic matter of dead animals and plants is used by bacteria and fungi as a source of energy. The micro-organisms decompose the plant and animal material, converting the carbon compounds to carbon dioxide.

(*c*) *Combustion.* In the process of burning carbon-containing fuels such as wood, coal, petroleum and natural gas, the carbon is oxidized to carbon dioxide. The hydrocarbon fuels originate from communities of plants such as prehistoric forests or deposits of marine algae which have only partly decomposed over the millions of years since they were buried.

Thus, an atom of carbon which today is in a molecule of carbon dioxide in the air, may tomorrow be in a molecule of cellulose in the cell wall of a blade of grass. When the grass is eaten by a cow, the carbon atom may become one of many in a protein molecule in the cow's muscle. When the protein molecule is used for respiration the carbon atom will enter the air once again as carbon dioxide. The same kind of cycling applies to nearly all the elements of the Earth. No new matter is created but it is repeatedly rearranged. A great proportion of the atoms of which you are composed will, at one time, have been an integral part of many other organisms.

Today, man's activities affect these cycles. For example, the nitrogen present in his excretory products is not usually re-cycled to the land producing his food; the carbon fuels are being burned in ever-increasing quantities, depleting their sources and adding more carbon dioxide to the atmosphere.

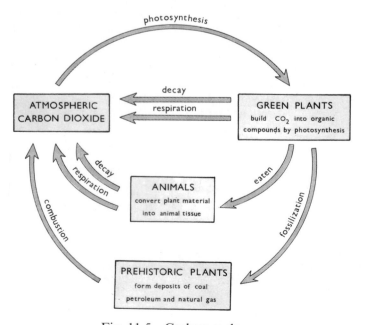

Fig. 11.5 Carbon cycle

Energy flow in an ecosystem

With the exception of atomic energy and tidal power, all the energy released on Earth is derived from sunlight. The energy released by animals is derived ultimately from plants that they or their prey eat and the plants depend on sunlight for making their food (p. 48). The energy in organic fuels also comes ultimately from sunlight trapped by plants. Coal is formed from fossilized forests and petroleum comes from the cells of ancient marine plants.

To estimate just how much life the Earth can support, it is necessary to examine how efficiently the sun's energy is utilized. The amount of energy from the sun reaching the Earth's surface in one year ranges from 2 million to 8 million kilojoules* per square metre (2–8 × 10⁹ J m⁻² per year) depending on the latitude. When this energy falls on to grassland, about 20 per cent is reflected by the vegetation, 39 per cent is used in evaporating water from the leaves (transpiration), 40 per cent warms up the plants, the soil and the air, leaving only about 1 per cent to be used in photosynthesis for making new organic matter in the leaves of the plants. This figure of 1 per cent will vary with the type of vegetation being considered and with climatic factors such as the availability of water and the soil temperature. Sugar cane grown in ideal conditions can convert 3 per cent of the solar energy into photosynthetic products, and sugar beet at the height of its growth has nearly a 9 per cent efficiency. Tropical forests and swamps are far more productive than grassland, but it is difficult, at the moment, to harvest and utilize their products effectively.

In order to allow crop plants to approach their maximum efficiency they must be provided with sufficient water and mineral salts. This can be achieved by irrigation and the application of fertilizer. In some cases the small amount of carbon dioxide in the air may limit the rate of photosynthesis, but little can be done about this except in an artificially enclosed ecosystem such as a greenhouse.

Having considered the energy conversion from sunlight to plant products, the next step is to study the efficiency of transmission of energy from plant products to first order consumers. On land, first order consumers eat only a small proportion of the available vegetation. In a deciduous forest only about 2 per cent is eaten; in grazing land, 40 per cent of the grass may be eaten by cows. In open water, however, where the producers are microscopic plants (phytoplankton) and swallowed whole by the first order consumers in the zooplankton, 90 per cent or more may be eaten. In the land communities, the vegetation not eaten by the first order consumers will die and be used as a source of energy by the decomposers.

A cow is a first order consumer; of the grass it eats, over 60 per cent passes through its alimentary canal (p. 85) without being digested. Another 30 per cent is used in the cow's respiration to provide energy for its movement and other life processes. Less than 10 per cent of the plant material is converted into new animal tissue to contribute to growth (Fig. 11.6). This figure will vary with the diet and the age of the animal. In a fully grown animal all the digested food will be used for energy and replacement and none will contribute to growth. Economically it is desirable to harvest the first order consumers before their rate of growth starts to fall off.

The transfer of energy from first to second order consumers is probably more efficient since a greater proportion of the animal food is digested and absorbed than is the case with plant material. The transfer of energy at each stage in a food chain may be represented by classifying the organisms in a

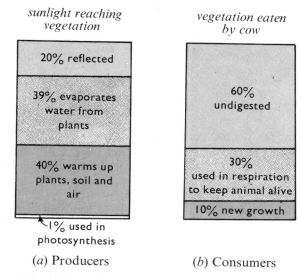

sunlight reaching vegetation

20% reflected

39% evaporates water from plants

40% warms up plants, soil and air

1% used in photosynthesis

(a) Producers

vegetation eaten by cow

60% undigested

30% used in respiration to keep animal alive

10% new growth

(b) Consumers

Fig. 11.6   Utilization of energy by producers and consumers

community as producers, first, second and third order consumers, and showing their relative masses in a pyramid such as the one shown in Fig. 11.1 but on a more accurate scale. In Fig. 11.7 the width of the horizontal bands is proportional to the masses (dry weight) of the organisms in a shallow pond.

In human communities, the use of plant products to feed animals which provide meat, eggs and dairy products is very wasteful because only 10 per cent of the plant material is converted to animal products. It is far more economical for man to eat bread made from wheat than to feed the wheat to hens and then eat the eggs and chicken meat, because it avoids using any part of the energy in the wheat to keep the chickens alive and active. Energy losses can be reduced by keeping hens indoors in small cages where they lose little heat to the atmosphere and cannot use much energy in movement. The same principles can be applied in "intensive" methods of rearing calves, but many people feel these methods are less than humane, and the saving of energy is far less than if the plant products were eaten directly by man.

It is estimated that about 50 g protein is needed each day by an adult. Since animal protein contains more essential amino acids (p. 83) than plant protein, about half this amount should come from animal sources. Animal protein eaten in excess of about 40 g per day is wasteful of food resources.

In Europe, much of the animal protein harvested from a dwindling fish population is used not to feed man but to provide fish meal for animal feed stuffs.

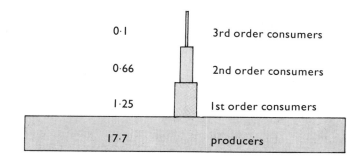

0·1   3rd order consumers

0·66   2nd order consumers

1·25   1st order consumers

17·7   producers

Fig. 11.7   Dry weight of living organisms in a shallow pond (in g/m²)

(After R. H. Whittaker, Communities and Ecosystems, Macmillan)

*See p. 45.

Consideration of the energy flow in a modern agricultural system reveals other sources of inefficiency. To produce one tonne of nitrogenous fertilizer takes energy equivalent to burning five tonnes of coal. Calculations show that if the energy needed to produce the fertilizer is added to the energy used to produce a tractor and to power it, the energy derived from the food so produced is less than that expended in producing it.

Man's effect on the ecosystems

Most ecosystems must have taken hundreds or thousands of years to establish a dynamic balance between the plant and animal communities and their environment. The balance is very easily disturbed: sometimes intentionally, as in agriculture, and sometimes unwittingly, as with excessive hunting or fishing. Described below are just a few of the ways man has interrupted the natural cycles and disturbed the balance of the ecosystems he exploits for food.

(a) **Deforestation.** Trees may be cut down to make way for agriculture or to use the timber. If carried out in the right areas to the correct extent and with provision for reafforestation, a balanced community can be maintained.

The soil on sloping ground, however, is often thin and once the tree cover is removed, it is no longer protected by the leaf canopy from wind and rain. The topsoil is washed away, silting up rivers and lakes and causing floods (see Fig. 16.2, p. 80).

In temperate forests the decomposition of organic matter in the soil is slow. This is due probably to the low average temperature and also perhaps to the absence of termites. In tropical forests, the higher temperatures and the activities of termites in removing and eating dead vegetation results in a low level of organic matter in the soil. Although the two ecosystems contain about the same amount of organic carbon compounds, in the tropical forest about 75 per cent of the carbon is in the wood of the trees and only 20 per cent in the soil. In the temperate forest, 50 per cent of the organic carbon is in the soil as decaying organic matter. When a temperate forest is cut down there is thus a fair amount of nutrient matter left in the soil. When a tropical forest is cut down and the trees removed, the remaining soil is poor in nutrients, and those that are present are soon dissolved out by the increased rain now reaching the exposed soil.

(b) **Erosion.** Repeated ploughing of soils, exclusive use of artificial fertilizers, overgrazing of pastures can, in certain areas, lead to soil erosion as described on p. 80, ultimately making the land incapable of supporting life of any kind.

(c) **Eutrophication.** This is the overgrowth of aquatic plants resulting from an excess of nitrogenous salts reaching rivers. The nitrates may come from farmland where heavy application of nitrogenous fertilizers is taking place or from the effluent of treated sewage. Its effects are discussed on p. 56.

(d) **Monoculture.** A natural environment usually has a wide variety of vegetation at different levels, flowering and fruiting at different times. This vegetation is exploited in different ways by the animals living there, e.g. giraffe browse on the leafy branches, antelopes crop the turf, birds take berries and nuts from the trees, and worms consume the leaves which fall from them. Agricultural practice involves removal of the natural plant and animal community and its replacement with large populations of a single species of plant or animal: arable fields given over to cereals, pastures supporting cattle exclusively. This practice obviously makes the environment unsuitable for the majority of its original inhabitants, indeed it is meant to; a mixed population of cereal and "weeds" is commercially

undesirable. The practice of monoculture, however, has its disadvantages.

Parasites and pests, which in a mixed community find their hosts well spaced, in a monoculture can spread rapidly since suitable hosts are growing closely together. In many parts of Africa there is evidence to suggest that more protein could be obtained by harvesting the mixed populations of wild animals living in a natural environment than is derived from the herds of sickly cattle which replace them and destroy their habitat.

(e) **Pesticides.** To protect the plants in a monoculture from the depredations of insects the crops are often sprayed with insecticides such as the chlorinated hydrocarbon DDT. This prevents the loss of hundreds of tonnes of food but in some cases it upsets the dynamic balance of life in unexpected ways. For example, the chemicals affect harmful and beneficial insects alike, so that after spraying fruit trees to eliminate a moth whose larvae burrow into apples, enormous numbers of red mites appeared because the spray had also killed the spiders which normally preyed upon them.

For a few years after it had been discovered and developed, DDT seemed to be the perfect insecticide. Used to kill body lice and mosquitoes it must have saved thousands of lives by eradicating typhus and malaria, spread respectively by these insects in certain areas and conditions. The concentrations used seemed harmless to man and other animals though, in higher concentration, it was known to be poisonous, particularly to fish. Unfortunately, however, when DDT is taken in with food and water, it is not all eliminated from the body, a proportion being retained and accumulated in the fat deposits of the body. When, in some animals, the fat is mobilized for respiration, harmful quantities of DDT may be released into the blood.

The animals at the end of food chains are particularly vulnerable when DDT is used to kill insect pests on a large scale. In America, DDT was used to kill the beetle which transmits dutch elm disease. The spray and the sprayed leaves reached the soil where the DDT was taken up by worms. When birds, notably the American robin, ate the worms, they accumulated lethal doses of DDT and whole populations of birds were wiped out.

A similar event occurred when an insecticide was used to kill gnat larvae in Clear Lake, California. At a concentration of 0·015 part per million of insecticide in the lake water the fish were unharmed. After five years, however, the western grebes on the lake were dying in large numbers. Although the water contained only 0·015 ppm, the plankton living in the waters had accumulated the compound to a level of 5 ppm. The small fish which fed on the plankton contained 10 ppm and the predatory fish even higher concentrations. The grebes which fed on the larger fish had as much as 1600 ppm in their body fat.

DDT is a stable compound and its effects last for a long time; a good property for an insecticide but potentially disastrous for the balance of nature. When applied to the crops, it reaches the soil and destroys the insect life there. Eventually it reaches the rivers, lakes and oceans where, if sufficient accumulated, it could begin to poison the fish and other marine life.

There is no end to the examples of man's wilful or unwitting depredation of the Earth: the excessive killing of animals for food or profit, to a point where they are exterminated; irrigation schemes which make dry areas more productive but spread the water snails which carry the disease bilharziasis; clearing tropical forests for agriculture and so providing conditions in which the tsetse fly can breed and spread sleeping sickness. Most of these effects can be attributed ultimately to the rapidly increasing human population with its consequent demand for more food and living space.

TYPES OF NUTRITION AND LIFE STYLES

A great many different terms are used to describe the ways in which living organisms get their food and how they depend on each other. The following is an attempt to put these terms into some kind of order.

Autotrophic

Autotrophic organisms are those which can build up all the organic substances they need from simple inorganic chemicals. Plants, for example, need only carbon dioxide, water and salts to make all their essential substances (p. 48). In any ecosystem it is the autotrophs which are the *producers*. Autotrophs may be either *photo-autotrophs* or *chemo-autotrophs*.

(*a*) **Photo-autotrophs.** These are organisms which have chlorophyll or similar pigments. The pigments absorb energy from sunlight and make it available for synthesis of their organic molecules. Green plants, algae (p. 172) and some bacteria and other micro-organisms are photo-autotrophic. Sometimes the word *holozyphytic* is used to describe this kind of nutrition.

(*b*) **Chemo-autotrophs.** These are bacteria which derive energy from chemical changes involving simple, inorganic compounds. This energy is then used to build up their organic substances. Nitrifying bacteria (p. 54) derive energy from oxidizing ammonium compounds in the soil, to nitrates. They use the energy from this process to build up carbohydrates from carbon dioxide. Chemo-autotrophic bacteria may also be called *chemosynthetic*.

Heterotrophic

Heterotrophic nutrition refers to organisms which must use complex organic compounds as a source of food. These organic compounds will have been made by the autotrophs. The heterotrophs digest the organic compounds and absorb the products into their bodies. In an ecosystem, the heterotrophs are the *consumers* or the *decomposers*.

(*a*) **Holozoic.** The term refers to the feeding method of animals which eat plants or other animals and digest them internally.

(i) *Carnivores* eat other animals and may be called *predators* if they catch and kill other animals. If their diet consists mainly of animals killed by other carnivores, they may be called *scavengers*, but the distinction may not always be clear-cut.

(ii) *Herbivores* are animals which eat plants and their products. *Grazing* animals eat mainly grass and small plants. *Browsing* animals eat the leaves and branches of trees and shrubs.

(iii) *Omnivores* eat plant and animal material.

(*b*) **Saprophytic.** Many bacteria and fungi feed saprophytically (p. 75). They secrete enzymes into the dead and decaying remains of animals and plants and absorb the soluble, digested products back into their bodies.

(*c*) **Parasitic.** A parasite is an organism which derives its food from another organism, called the host, while the host is still alive. *Ecto-parasites* live on the surface of their host; *endo-parasites* live inside the host.

A flea is an ecto-parasite which lives in the fur or feathers of mammals or birds and sucks blood from the skin. An aphid (greenfly) is an ecto-parasite on plants and sucks food from the veins in their leaves or stems. A tapeworm is an endo-parasite living in the intestine of a vertebrate host and absorbing the host's digested food. In some cases the parasite will harm the host by weakening it or upsetting its metabolism by the parasite's excretory products. In many cases, however, the host appears to suffer no serious disadvantage. Often, this will depend on how many parasites the host is carrying.

Many bacteria and fungi are parasitic and may cause diseases in their hosts. Bacteria often live on or in their hosts without apparently causing any harm. In this case they might be called *commensals* rather than parasites. Sometimes the host is thought to benefit from the activities of the bacteria which may then be called *symbionts*.

Symbiosis and commensalism

Symbiosis originally referred to two unrelated organisms living more or less permanently together, irrespective of whether one of them was a parasite. More commonly, however, it implies that both organisms derive some benefit from the association.

For example, in the stomachs of cattle and sheep there live large numbers of bacteria. They cause no symptoms of illness and they are thought to be of value to the animals because they help to digest the cellulose in its food. The cow benefits from the relationship because it is better able to digest grass. The bacteria are thought to benefit by having an abundant supply of food, though they are themselves digested when the grass moves along the cow's digestive tract.

The nitrogen-fixing bacteria in root nodules (p. 54) provide a further example of symbiosis. The plant benefits from the extra nitrates that the bacteria provide, while the bacteria are protected in the plant's cells and can also use the sugars made by the plant's photosynthesis.

Where both organisms clearly benefit from their association, the term *mutualism* is sometimes used instead of symbiosis.

Commensalism is a close association between two unrelated organisms in which one partner is assumed to derive some benefit and the other partner is not harmed. For example, a large population of bacteria live on our skin as commensals. They feed on the secretions of our sebaceous glands (p. 110) and other substances and they do us no harm. If the skin is damaged, however, they may invade the tissues and cause infection. In this case they are acting as parasites.

It is not always easy to decide whether a relationship is symbiotic (mutualistic), commensal or parasitic. For example, there are bacteria living in our large intestine which normally do us no harm. Are they parasites or commensals? It appears that they produce a substance called vitamin K, which we need, so perhaps they are symbionts. However, there is little evidence that we actually absorb or use this vitamin and so the relationship is difficult to classify.

QUESTIONS

1. Trace the food chains involved in the production of the following articles of man's diet: eggs, cheese, bread, meat, wine. In each case show how the energy in the food originates from sunlight.
2. Discuss the advantages and disadvantages of man's attempting to exploit a food chain nearer to its source, e.g. the algae of Fig. 11.1*a*.
3. Construct a diagram, on the lines of the carbon cycle (Fig. 11.5) to show the cycling process for hydrogen.
4. How do you think evidence is acquired in order to assign animals to their position in a food web?
5. What would be the desirable qualities of an insecticide to control an insect pest living on the leaves of a crop plant? What might be the disadvantages of total eradication of an insect pest?

12 | Diffusion and Osmosis

Diffusion

All substances are made up of minute particles called *molecules*, e.g. the smallest particle of carbon dioxide is a molecule consisting of one atom of carbon joined to two atoms of oxygen. In a solid the molecules are packed relatively closely together with little or no freedom to move; in liquids the molecules are also close together but are free to move; the molecules of a gas are very much further apart and are moving about at random colliding with each other and the walls of whatever contains the gas. Because of this constant random movement the molecules of a gas tend to distribute themselves evenly throughout any space in which they are confined. The same principle holds true for substances which dissolve in a liquid, e.g. if a crystal of copper sulphate is placed at the bottom of a beaker of water the blue colour of the solid will eventually spread throughout the water as the copper sulphate dissolves. This molecular movement in gases or liquids which tends to result in their uniform distribution is called *diffusion*.

The following experiments illustrate the process of diffusion in air and water.

Experiment 1. *Diffusion of a gas*

Squares of wetted red litmus paper are pushed with a glass rod or wire into a wide glass tube, corked at one end, so that they stick to the side and are evenly spaced out (Fig. 12.1). The open end of the tube is closed with a cork carrying a plug of cotton wool saturated with a strong solution of ammonia. The alkaline ammonia vapour diffuses along inside the tube at a rate which can be determined by observing the time when each square of litmus paper turns completely blue. If the experiment is repeated using a more dilute solution of ammonia the rate of diffusion is seen to be slower.

Experiment 2. *Diffusion in a liquid*

Diffusion in a liquid is very slow and liable to be affected by convection currents or other physical disturbances in the liquid. In this experiment the water is "kept still" so to speak, by dissolving gelatin in it. 10 g gelatin is dissolved in 100 g hot water and the solution is poured into test-tubes to half fill them. Some of the liquid gelatin remaining is coloured with methylene blue and when the first layer of gelatin in the test-tube has set firmly, a narrow layer of blue gelatin is poured into it. When the blue layer of gelatin is cold and firm, the test-tube is filled with cool but liquid gelatin and cooled quickly so that the blue gelatin is sandwiched between two layers of clear gelatin (Fig. 12.2). After a week, the blue dye is seen to have diffused into the clear gelatin, upwards and downwards to equal extents.

The rate of diffusion of a substance depends to a large extent on the size of the molecule, the temperature of the substance and its concentration. The larger the molecule, the more slowly it diffuses and the warmer the substance, the more rapidly it diffuses. Experiment 1 shows that the more concentrated the source of a substance, the more rapidly it diffuses and that the direction of diffusion is from the region of high concentration to the region of low concentration. The difference in concentration which results in diffusion is called a *diffusion gradient* and the "steeper" the diffusion gradient the more rapid is the resulting diffusion. For example, when rapid photosynthesis is going on in a palisade cell of a leaf (p. 49) carbon dioxide is being removed from the cytoplasm and incorporated into carbohydrate. The carbon dioxide concentration in the cell falls and so sets up a diffusion gradient between the air in the intercellular spaces and the cell. As a result, carbon dioxide diffuses into the cell from the intercellular space. The same cell will be producing oxygen in the course of photosynthesis, creating an oxygen gradient in the opposite direction to that for carbon dioxide. Oxygen consequently diffuses out of the cell into the intercellular space.

cotton wool soaked with ammonia solution

wet litmus paper

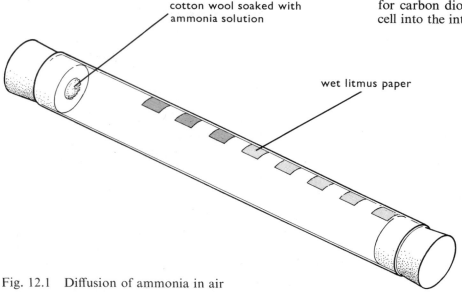

Fig. 12.1   Diffusion of ammonia in air

clear gelatin

gelatin with methylene blue

clear gelatin

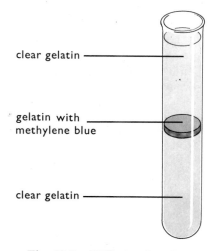

Fig. 12.2   Diffusion in a liquid

Diffusion in living organisms. Diffusion plays a part in most cases of uptake or expulsion of substances within an organism or between the organism and the environment. Sometimes, as in microscopic single-celled organisms, diffusion may be rapid enough to account entirely for the uptake of oxygen and the removal of carbon dioxide and other excretory products (*see* p. 176). In many cases, however, diffusion is too slow to meet the demands of the living tissues and is superseded by, on a large scale, such processes as the circulation of blood and, on a cellular scale, "active transport" whereby substances are moved by some form of chemical activity into, across or out of cells.

Specific instances of diffusion in plants and animals are mentioned in the appropriate chapters or they can be sought out by referring to the index.

Osmosis

Osmosis can be regarded as a special case of diffusion; the diffusion of water from a dilute to a concentrated solution. When a substance (a solute) dissolves in water, the solute molecules attract water molecules, forming a kind of loose chemical bond with them. The water molecules bonded to the solute molecules in this way can no longer move freely in the solution. This means that a concentrated solution of sugar in water would have more "bound" water molecules, and therefore fewer "free" water molecules than would the same volume of a dilute sugar solution.

If these two solutions were in contact, the diffusion gradient for sugar molecules would be from the concentrated solution to the dilute solution. The gradient for water molecules, on the other hand, would be from the dilute solution (more free water molecules) to the concentrated solution (fewer free water molecules). If the two solutions were separated from each other by a membrane which allowed water molecules to pass through

it but not sugar molecules, then the diffusion of sugar molecules would be prevented but the diffusion of water molecules would continue. Thus, water would pass across the membrane from the dilute to the concentrated solution.

This movement of water across a membrane, from a dilute to a concentrated solution is called *osmosis* and a membrane with these properties is said to be *partially permeable* (sometimes called "semi-permeable").

Experiment 3. **Demonstration of osmosis** (Fig. 12.3)

A length of dialysis tubing (cellophane) is filled with a concentrated solution of syrup or sugar and fitted over the end of a capillary tube with the aid of an elastic band. The dialysis tube is lowered into a beaker of water and the tube clamped vertically. In a few minutes, the level of liquid is seen to rise up the capillary tube and may continue to do so for a metre or more according to the length of the tube.

Interpretation. The most plausible interpretation is that water molecules have passed through the cellophane tubing into the sugar solution, increasing its volume and forcing it up the capillary tube. This movement should theoretically continue until the hydrostatic pressure of the column of syrup in the capillary is equal to the diffusion pressure of water entering the dialysis tube.

The partially permeable membrane. It is not very clear what the properties are that make a membrane partially permeable. One theory supposes that the membrane acts as a molecular sieve, having tiny pores in it that are too small to allow large molecules like sugar to pass through, but large enough to let the small water molecules go through (Fig. 12.4). In fact, most artificial membranes allow some large molecules to pass through but at a much slower rate than water molecules do.

Water potential. The results of Experiment 3 show that pressure builds up in the syrup solution and forces liquid up the capillary. If the capillary were blocked, the pressure would

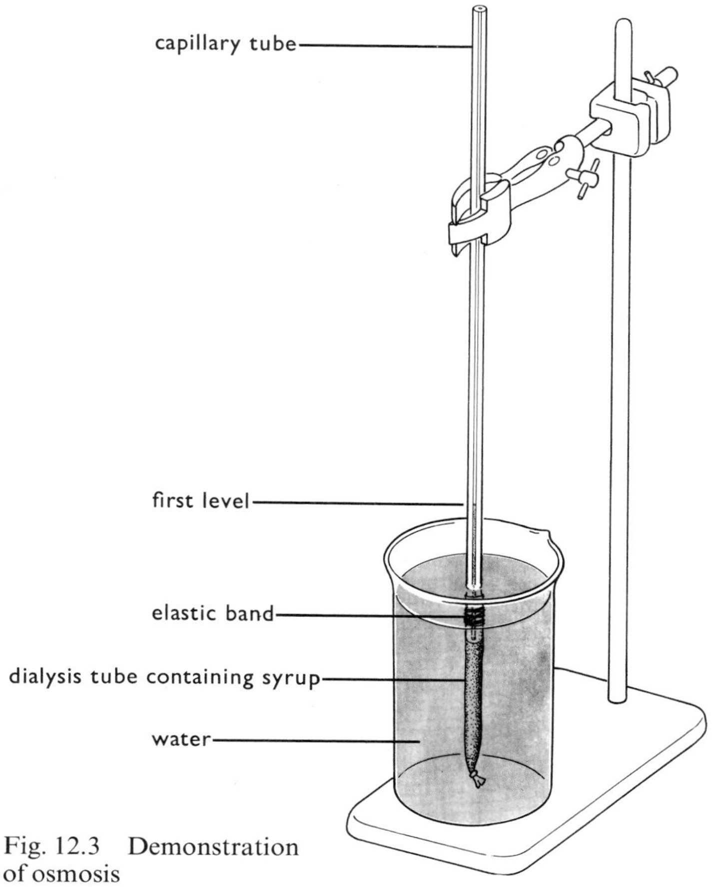

capillary tube—

first level—

elastic band—

dialysis tube containing syrup—

water—

Fig. 12.3   Demonstration of osmosis

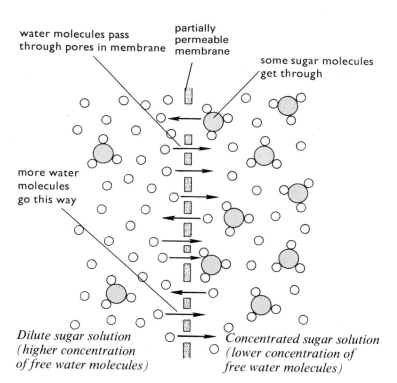

water molecules pass through pores in membrane

partially permeable membrane

some sugar molecules get through

more water molecules go this way

Dilute sugar solution (higher concentration of free water molecules)

Concentrated sugar solution (lower concentration of free water molecules)

Fig. 12.4   The diffusion theory of osmosis

burst the dialysis tubing. The syrup solution is thus said to exert an osmotic pressure.

A dilute solution has relatively more free water molecules than a concentrated solution and so is said to have a higher water potential than a concentrated solution; i.e. if the solutions are separated by a partially permeable membrane, water will flow from the dilute to the concentrated. Pure water has the highest possible water potential.

OSMOSIS IN PLANTS

The surfaces of plants and animals and the membranes in their cells frequently have partially permeable properties. When these organisms or their individual cells are surrounded by fluids weaker or stronger than their own, osmotic forces are set up.

Turgor

The cellulose wall of plant cells is freely permeable to water and dissolved substances. The cytoplasm, however, behaves as a partially permeable membrane, while the cell sap in the vacuole, since it contains salts and sugars, has a water potential less than pure water. If an isolated plant cell is surrounded by water, osmosis would cause water to enter the cell sap. The vacuole would expand, pushing the cytoplasm

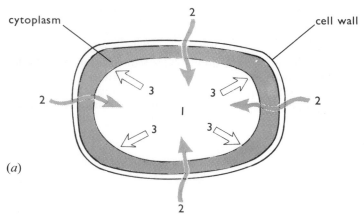

(a)

Turgor
1. Dissolved salts and sugars in cell sap give it a low water potential
2. Water enters by osmosis passing through the permeable cell wall and the partially permeable cytoplasm
3. The cell sap volume increases and pushes outwards on the cell wall making the cell turgid

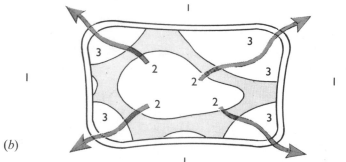

(b)

Plasmolysis
1. The solution outside the cell is more concentrated than the cell sap
2. Water passes out of the vacuole by osmosis
3. The vacuole shrinks, pulling the cytoplasm away from the cell wall and leaving the cell flaccid

Fig. 12.5   Turgor in plant cells

against the cell wall (Fig. 12.5a). Eventually the outward pressure of the vacuole would be equalled by the resistance of the inelastic cell wall and the cell could take in no more water. Such a cell is *turgid* and the vacuole is exerting *turgor pressure*. The normal source of water for producing turgidity in cells is the xylem vessels or neighbouring cells.

A plant structure made of turgid cells is resilient and strong; the plant stem stands upright and the leaves are held out firmly. Many young plants depend entirely upon this turgidity for their support but in older plants, woody and fibrous tissues take over this function.

Growth. In the growing regions of plants, the cell walls are still fairly plastic. After new cells have been produced by division at the growing point, vacuoles begin to form in their cytoplasm (*see* Fig. 4.5, p. 12). Water enters the cell by osmosis and the vacuoles join up and increase in volume. Since the cell wall is plastic, the cell is extended as the vacuole pushes outwards on the walls. Hundreds of cells extending in this way produce expansion growth (*see* pp. 21 and 42).

Wilting. When plants are exposed to conditions in which they lose water to the atmosphere faster than it can be obtained from the soil, water is lost from the vacuoles. The turgor pressure of the vacuoles decreases and they no longer push out against the cell wall. The cell becomes limp or *flaccid* (like a deflated football). A plant structure made of such cells is weak and flabby, the stem droops and the leaves are limp: in other words, the plant is *wilting*.

Plasmolysis. If a plant cell is surrounded by a solution more concentrated than the cell sap, water passes out of the vacuole to the outside solution. Loss of water causes the vacuole to shrink and pull the cytoplasmic lining away from the cell wall (Fig. 12.5b). There is now no pressure outwards on the cell wall and the cell is flaccid. This condition, called *plasmolysis*, can be induced experimentally in living cells without necessarily harming them, but it is an extreme condition and rarely occurs in nature.

Stomata (*see* p. 20). Although the details of the stomatal mechanism are not fully worked out, it seems that when a leaf is illuminated and photosynthesis is rapid, there is a fall in the carbon dioxide concentration in the leaf. This triggers off changes which produce a rise in the concentration of solutes in the guard cells with a corresponding fall of osmotic potential in their vacuoles. The higher osmotic potential of the neighbouring epidermal cells forces water into the guard cells, increasing their turgor. Since the inner walls, bounding the stoma, are thicker than the others (Fig. 12.6) the increase in turgor

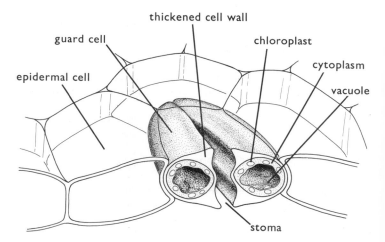

Fig. 12.6   Structure of guard cells

pressure causes the guard cells to curve and open the stoma between them. Thus the stomata are usually open in daylight when carbon dioxide is needed for photosynthesis and closed at night when photosynthesis ceases.

Movement of water in a plant

Cells. Osmosis plays a part in the passage of water from one cell to another in a plant. Imagine two adjacent cells A and B (Fig. 12.7). A has a lower concentration of sugar in its cell sap and hence a higher water potential than B. The more dilute cell sap in A will thus force water by osmosis into cell B. The water entering cell B will dilute its cell sap and raise both its water potential and its turgor pressure so tending to force water out into the next cell in line. Thus water passes from cell to cell down an osmotic gradient.

However, if cell B is fully turgid it is unable to expand and so can take in no more water even though it has a lower water potential than its neighbour A. In fact, if cell A is not fully turgid and still capable of expansion, the high wall pressure of cell B will force water out into cell A against the osmotic gradient. The movement of water between plant cells depends, therefore, not only on the water potential of their vacuoles but also on how turgid they are.

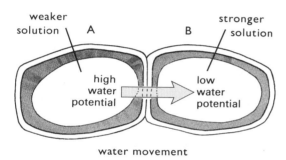

Fig. 12.7   Movement of water through cells

Roots. In this way, water may be absorbed from the soil by the roots, though this is not established fact, but rather one of the more widely held theories. Fig. 12.8 shows the general direction of water-flow, and Fig. 12.9 represents a few cells along the radius of the root.

The root hairs are thin-walled extensions from the cells of the outer layer of a root (*see* p. 21). They grow out, pushing between the soil particles to which they adhere closely. The film of water which surrounds the soil particles also surrounds the root hairs. Although soil water has mineral salts dissolved in it, they make only a very dilute solution, and the cell sap of the root hair is more concentrated than this. Water passes from the soil through the cell wall and its thin cytoplasmic lining into the vacuole of the root hair. This extra water raises the turgor pressure of the vacuole and so forces water out into the cell walls towards the inside of the root. If the cell next to the root hair, on the inside, has a lower turgor pressure than the root hair, water may pass into it by osmosis. Thus, some of the water absorbed by the root hairs will pass from cell to cell across the root to the xylem vessels in the centre.

In fact, it is now thought that only a small amount of water passes through the cells in this way and that the bulk of it travels inwards *along* or between the cell walls, from cell to cell, without actually entering the cytoplasm or vacuole of each cell (Fig. 12.9).

Once it reaches the xylem vessels, the water is drawn up the root to the stem by the "suction" effect of the transpiration stream, described in the next chapter.

The water passing along the cell walls will also carry dissolved salts from the soil. The process of osmosis by which root hairs take up water from the soil and by which some of the water passes through the root, cannot account for salt uptake by the cells since, by definition, osmosis is the movement of water. Salts may enter cells by diffusion or, more likely, by active transport.

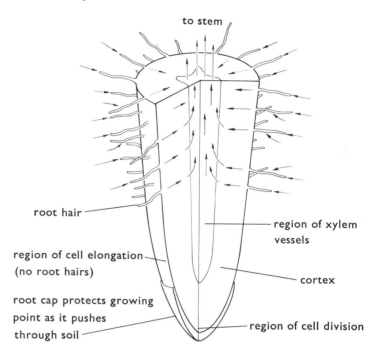

Fig. 12.8   Diagrammatic section of root to show passage of water from the soil

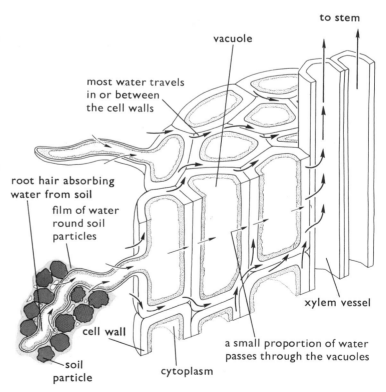

Fig. 12.9   Diagram to show the probable pathway of water from soil to xylem vessel in a root

In some plants at certain times of the year, it is possible to demonstrate a positive pressure, *root pressure*, in the xylem. For example, sap oozes from the stump of a tree if it is cut down in the wet season. If a glass tube containing a little water is fitted to the cut stem of a well-watered potted plant, as shown in Fig. 12.12, the water can be seen to rise several centimetres in the tube. There is some evidence that this root pressure derives from the sort of osmotic activity described above but its significance is not certain. In some plants, root pressure is thought to be responsible for the exudation of drops of water, *guttation*, from the tips of the leaves.

The partially permeable properties of cytoplasm depend on its being alive. Anything which kills the cytoplasm also destroys its selective permeability. At the same time, of course, it will destroy all transport systems which depend on living processes such as active transport or movements of solutes in the phloem.

Leaves. Fig. 12.10 shows a few adjacent cells in a leaf. The palisade cell (*a*) is losing water by evaporation from its surface into the intercellular spaces. This loss of water results in a reduction of turgor pressure and an increase in the concentration of the sugars and salts in its vacuole. The cell sap in the vacuole becomes more concentrated and its water potential falls. The cell will therefore absorb water, firstly from its own cell walls which are touching the neighbouring cells such as (*b*). Some water will flow from cell (*b*)'s vacuole to replace this loss but a greater proportion of the water will come from (*c*)'s cell wall. Water will then pass from (*d*) to (*c*) with cell (*d*) absorbing it from the water vessels in the vein.

The amount of water which travels along the cell walls or through the cells will vary with the rate of transpiration and the availability of water. It is thought, however, that most of the water passes along the cell walls without entering the cell as shown in Fig. 12.11.

Experiment 4. ***To demonstrate root pressure*** (Fig. 12.12)

A piece of glass tubing is connected by rubber tubing to the freshly cut stem of a potted plant. A little coloured water is placed in the tube and its level marked. If the roots are kept well watered, the coloured water will rise a few cm in the tube. This demonstrates root pressure.

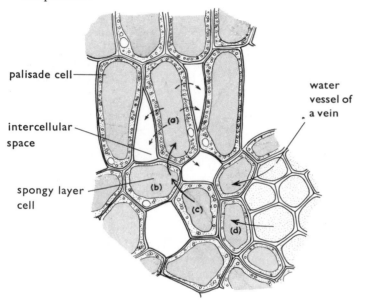

palisade cell

intercellular space

spongy layer cell

water vessel of a vein

(a)
(b)
(c)
(d)

Fig. 12.10   Diagram of a few leaf cells to show how water movement could occur by osmosis

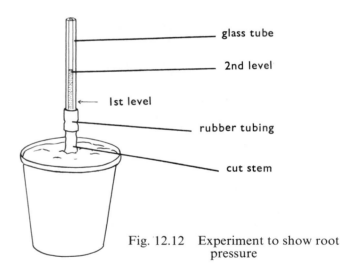

glass tube

2nd level

1st level

rubber tubing

cut stem

Fig. 12.12   Experiment to show root pressure

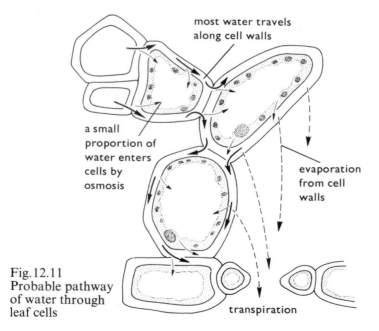

most water travels along cell walls

a small proportion of water enters cells by osmosis

evaporation from cell walls

Fig.12.11 Probable pathway of water through leaf cells

transpiration

Experiment 5. ***To demonstrate osmosis in living tissue***

Peel a very thin strip of the purple epidermis from a *Rheo* leaf. Place a small piece of this tissue in a drop of water on a microscope slide and cover it with a cover slip. Examine the slide with the microscope to find an area of epidermis where the cells are distinct and the cell sap is purple. With a pipette, place two drops of sugar solution on the slide at the left-hand edge of the cover slip with a small piece of blotting paper. Watch the cells for 2 or 3 minutes.

Result. The purple vacuoles will shrink and pull the lining of cytoplasm away from the cell walls (Fig. 12.5, p. 62), although it may not be possible to see the thin cytoplasmic layer. The cells are now plasmolysed.

Interpretation. The sugar solution is more concentrated than the cell sap and so water passes by osmosis from the vacuole to the sugar solution, causing the vacuole to shrink. It can be seen that the cell sap also becomes darker as it gets more concentrated. The procedure can be reversed by drawing water under the cover slip. The vacuoles should expand to fill the cells again.

OSMOSIS IN ANIMALS

The skins of many aquatic animals are more or less partially permeable and this results in osmotic effects between them and their surroundings.

Fresh-water animals. The blood of fishes and amphibians and the body fluids of invertebrates that live in fresh water are more concentrated than the pond or stream water that surrounds them. Water tends to enter their bodies by osmosis, through their skins or such patches of skin as are exposed. If this water were not removed continually, the animal's blood would be diluted and the whole creature would swell and become water-logged. Vital processes in the body would be interfered with and the animal would die. In a great many fresh-water animals it has been possible to show that certain organs are able to eliminate the excess water, or *osmo-regulate* (*see* p. 175) and keep the concentration of the body fluids constant. In frogs and fish the kidneys extract excess water from the blood as it passes through them, and it is passed out of the body as a dilute urine.

Impermeable coverings, like the cuticle on the exoskeleton of beetles and other aquatic insects, greatly reduce the surface over which water might be absorbed. In some fresh-water animals it is not clear how osmosis affects them or how their osmo-regulation is carried out.

Salt-water animals. Sea water is a more concentrated solution than the blood of many marine fish, in consequence there is a tendency for water to pass out of their bodies and into the sea, by osmosis. Sea-water fish swallow water and in some way absorb it through their alimentary canals. There is also evidence that they can eliminate the excess salts taken in.

Animals in estuaries have to withstand extreme osmotic changes, being alternately covered with fresh and salt water.

Land animals. Osmotic effects occur within the bodies of all animals (*see* p. 98), but in general, land animals lose water from their body surfaces by evaporation and gain it from their food and drink. The concentration of the blood is nevertheless kept very constant by the regulatory action of the kidneys and other organs (*see* pp. 106 and 108). The impermeable cuticle of insects, the fur of mammals and the feathers of birds reduce water-loss by evaporation and contribute to the success of these groups on land.

PRACTICAL WORK

1. *To show turgor pressure in cells.* A 50-mm piece of young onion leaf is cut along its length into strips about 2 mm wide. The outer epidermis is inelastic while the thin-walled inner cells, freed from the restraint of the epidermis, tend to expand. Thus the strips curl outwards, with the epidermis on the inner circumference.

One strip is placed in a watch glass containing water, another in sugar solution, and a third left as a control. The first strip will absorb water by osmosis; the inner cells will expand while the inelastic epidermal cells will not, and the strip will curl up more. In the sugar solution, water will escape from the cells, which will lose their turgor; the unequal stresses in the strip will disappear and it will straighten.

By placing the strips in a range of solutions from 5 to 15 per cent in strength, an estimate can be made of the water potential of the cell.

The solution which only just produces some curling must approximate in strength to the water potential of the cell sap.

2. *Turgor in potato tissue.* Two cylinders of potato tissue are prepared as follows: a no. 4 or no. 5 cork borer is pushed into a large potato, the core of tissue extracted by pushing with the flat end of a pencil and the ends trimmed square with a scalpel or razor blade. Both cylinders should be the same length and as long as possible (50 mm or more). The length of the potato cylinders are measured and recorded. One cylinder is placed in a test-tube of water and the other in a test-tube of strong sugar solution. After 24 hours the cylinders are removed and measured again.

The cells from the potato were probably not fully turgid, so that the tissue which has been in water will have taken up water by osmosis, increased its length by 2 mm or more and will feel firm. The tissue in sugar solution will lose water by osmosis and shrink slightly; it will also feel limp and flabby.

3. *Dialysis.* This involves the diffusion of soluble substances through a selectively permeable membrane and can occur in similar circumstances to osmosis.

A 15 cm length of dialysis tubing is soaked in water and knotted securely at one end. A dropping pipette is used to fill the tubing with a mixture of 30 percent glucose and 3 percent starch solutions. The dialysis tubing is now placed in a test-tube. The open end of the tubing is folded over the test-tube rim and secured by an elastic band. After washing away any traces of solution from the outside of the tubing, the test-tube is filled with water and left for 15 minutes or more.

After this time, the water in the test-tube is tested for glucose and starch as described on p. 85. It will be found that the glucose has "leaked" out of the tubing into the water by dialysis but the starch has not.

The usual interpretation is that the relatively small molecules of glucose can pass through the "pores" in the dialysis tubing but the large starch molecules cannot.

The experiment is sometimes used to illustrate the uptake of dissolved food in the small intestine (p. 89) but it is misleading in that absorption of food is more likely to be the result of some form of active transport (p. 61) than simple dialysis.

QUESTIONS

1. A solution of salt is separated by a partially permeable membrane from a solution of sugar of equal concentration (equimolecular).* Discuss whether osmosis would take place and justify your conclusions.
2. If too much artificial fertilizer, e.g. ammonium sulphate, is spread on a pasture, the grass will wither and die. Suggest an explanation for this in terms of osmosis.
3. What features in a fish gill would help to maintain a steep diffusion gradient of oxygen between it and its immediate environment?
4. In an actively photosynthesizing cell, the sugars being formed are quickly converted to starch. What is the biological advantage of this in terms of osmosis?
5. What activities in man are likely to increase and decrease the water potential of his blood and body fluids?
6. What osmotic problems confront the salmon, which is hatched in a river, grows to maturity in the sea and returns to the river to lay its eggs?

* The same number of gram molecules per litre.

13 | Translocation and Transpiration

TRANSLOCATION is the movement of dissolved substances through a plant. Transpiration is the evaporation of water from the leaves and the subsequent movement of water through the xylem.

Translocation

In very general terms, water and dissolved salts from the soil travel upwards through the xylem vessels while food made in the leaves passes downwards or upwards in the sieve tubes of the phloem. (*See* Figs. 4.8*c*, p. 14 and 5.3*b*, p. 16.)

The sucrose produced by photosynthesis in the leaves is carried in the phloem out of the leaf and into the stem. It may then travel up the stem to actively growing regions or maturing fruits and seeds or downwards to the roots and underground storage organs. It is quite possible for substances to be travelling both upwards and downwards at the same time in the phloem.

Mechanism of translocation in the phloem. The mechanism, in fact, is not known though it does depend on the fact that the sieve tubes, unlike the xylem vessels, contain living cells. Anything which kills the phloem cells, severely interferes with the movement of food. This is illustrated by the experiment in Fig. 13.1. The leaf makes sucrose (*see* p. 48) from the radio-active carbon dioxide. When the phloem of the stem below the leaf is killed by a jet of steam the substances containing radio-active carbon are found to move up the stem. When the phloem above the leaf is killed, conduction is down the stem. If the phloem above and below the leaf is killed, the radio-active substances do not appear anywhere in the stem. Similarly if the oxygen supply to the phloem is cut off, translocation of sugars ceases.

Xylem vessels consist of dead cells which are unaffected by heat or oxygen shortage. If transport of sucrose took place in the vessels, heat treatment of the stem would not be expected to interfere with the movement of sugar.

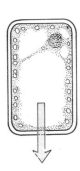

(1) LEAF CELL

(a) Accumulation of sugar
(b) Fall in water potential of cell sap
(c) Intake of water by osmosis
(d) High turgor pressure

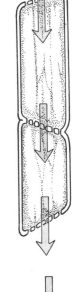

(3) SIEVE TUBES

Liquid forced from region of high turgor pressure to region of low turgor pressure

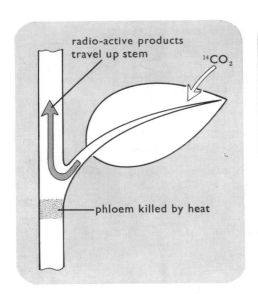
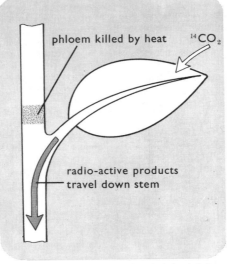

Fig. 13.1   Experimental evidence for transport in phloem

(After Rabideau & Burr, Amer. J. Bot. **32** 1945)

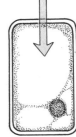

(2) ROOT CELL

(a) Sugar used up in respiration or stored as starch
(b) Rise in water potential of cell sap
(c) Low turgor pressure

Fig. 13.2

One of the most widely held theories to account for the movement of solutes in the phloem is the *mass flow hypothesis* depicted diagrammatically in Fig. 13.2. The "root cell" could, in practice, be any cell in which sucrose is being used up in respiration or converted to starch and removed from solution.

There are several objections to the mass flow hypothesis. For example, how can it account for the simultaneous movement of substances both up and down the phloem and why must the sieve tube cells be alive for the process to go on?

Movement of salts in the xylem. It can be shown that if a ring of bark and phloem (*see* Fig. 5.7, p. 18) is removed from a stem, the upward movement of salts is little affected. If a core of xylem is removed, however, the upward movement of salts is arrested. Similarly, killing the phloem by heat treatment does not significantly affect the upward movement of salts.

The forces moving the salts through the xylem in the transpiration stream are described below under "Transpiration".

Uptake of salts by the roots. There is, as yet, no wholly convincing explanation of the uptake of mineral salts from the soil by roots. It may be that diffusion from a relatively high concentration in the soil to a lower concentration in the root cells accounts for some uptake of salts, but it has been shown (a) that salts can be taken from the soil even when their concentration is below that in the roots and (b) that anything which interferes with respiration impairs the uptake of salts. It looks, therefore, as if "active transport" plays an important part in the uptake of salts.

"Active transport" is itself only a hypothetical process. By expenditure of energy in respiration it is thought that enzyme-like substances, *carriers*, might combine with the salts, carry them across the cytoplasm and release them into the vacuole.

Transpiration

Transpiration is the process by which plants lose water as water vapour into the atmosphere. Most of this loss takes place through the leaves but evaporation also occurs from the stem and flowers.

Turgor pressure in the mesophyll cells (*see* p. 20) forces water outwards through the cell walls. From the outer surface of the cell walls, the water evaporates into the intercellular spaces and diffuses out of the stomata into the atmosphere (Fig. 13.3). Closure of the stomata greatly reduces, but does not entirely prevent, evaporation from the leaf.

Significance of transpiration. The transpiration is probably an inevitable consequence of photosynthesis. For adequate photosynthesis to take place, a large surface area must be exposed to the atmosphere to absorb sunlight and carbon dioxide. A leaf which is permeable to carbon dioxide will also be permeable to water vapour. It seems, therefore, that evaporation of water must inevitably accompany photosynthesis. Nevertheless, transpiration produces effects which may be regarded as beneficial to the plant.

(a) *Transpiration stream.* Evaporation of water from the leaf cells causes their turgor to fall and the concentration of their cell sap to rise and consequently produces a decrease in osmotic potential (*see* p. 63). Cells in this condition will absorb water from their neighbours and eventually from the xylem vessels in the leaf. Withdrawal of water by osmosis from the xylem vessels produces a tension, i.e. the water is submitted to pressures below atmospheric. This tension draws water up the vessels of the stem from the roots. This flow of water is called the transpiration stream and is dependent on the rate of evaporation from the leaves (Fig. 13.4).

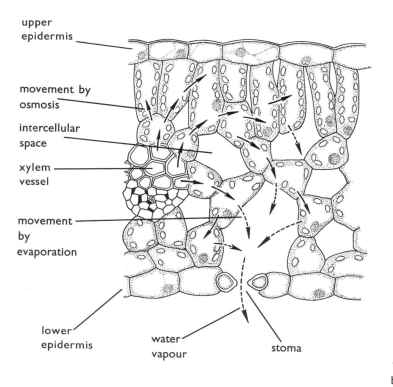

Fig. 13.3 Movement of water through a leaf blade as seen in section

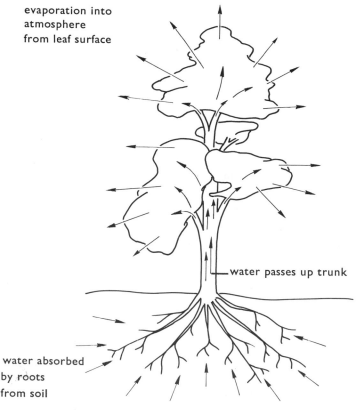

Fig. 13.4 The transpiration stream

It is easy to envisage a wire or a string being subjected to tension along its length without breaking but one would expect a column of water under tension to break up, leaving gaps filled with water vapour. The *cohesion theory* outlined above, however, supposes that the cohesive forces between water molecules in very thin columns of water are not so easily overcome. This theory, then, offers an explanation of the movement of water up the stems of plants, including trees nearly 100 metres high.

A tree on a hot day may evaporate hundreds of litres of water from its leaves. Of all the water passing through the plant, only a tiny fraction is retained for photosynthesis and to maintain the turgor of the cells.

(*b*) *Transport of salts*. The transpiration stream undoubtedly carries mineral salts from the roots to the leaves but the rate of uptake of salts from the soil is not directly dependent on the rate of transpiration.

(*c*) *Cooling*. The rapid evaporation of water from the leaf surface and the consequent absorption of latent heat from the leaf tissues is almost certainly of value in keeping the temperature of a leaf below harmful levels in the direct rays of the sun.

Conditions affecting transpiration rate

(*a*) **Light intensity.** When light intensity increases, the stomata open and allow more rapid evaporation.

(*b*) **Humidity.** When the atmosphere is saturated with water vapour, little more can be absorbed from the plants, and transpiration will be reduced. In a dry atmosphere, transpiration will be rapid.

(*c*) **Temperature.** A high temperature increases the capacity of the air for water vapour; hence transpiration increases. When the leaf itself becomes warm, evaporation from it occurs more rapidly. Direct sunlight even without a warm atmosphere will have this effect, since the leaf absorbs radiant energy and its temperature rises.

(*d*) **Air movements.** In still air, the region round a transpiring leaf will become saturated with water vapour so that no more can be absorbed from the leaf; in consequence transpiration is much reduced. In moving air, the water vapour will be swept away from the leaf as fast as it diffuses out, so that transpiration continues rapidly.

Control of transpiration

(*a*) **Stomata.** Since most of the water vapour is lost through the stomata, the closure of these will greatly reduce transpiration. However, there is little or no evidence to suggest that a high rate of evaporation results in the stomata closing, although in extreme conditions where loss of water greatly exceeds uptake, the plant wilts, the cells of the leaf become flaccid (flabby) and the stomata close, preventing further evaporation. Usually the movements of the stomata depend on the light intensity, so that they are generally open during the day and closed at night. Less water vapour is lost during darkness, therefore, when photosynthesis is impossible and carbon dioxide is not needed.

(*b*) **Leaf fall.** In temperate climates, deciduous trees shed their leaves in winter; those in the tropics may shed theirs in the dry season. If the leaves were retained, transpiration would still tend to go on even though the supply of water would be limited by low temperatures or drought respectively.

(*c*) **Leaf shape and cuticle.** Leaves with a small surface area will transpire less rapidly than the broad, flat deciduous leaves. Waxy cuticles and stomata sunk below the epidermis level, e.g.

oleander, are also modifications thought to be associated with reduced transpiration. They are often found in plants which grow in dry or cold conditions or in situations where water is difficult to obtain. Most evergreen plants have one or more of these leaf characteristics and this probably plays a part in their retention of leaves during the winter months in temperate climates and dry period in the tropics.

EXPERIMENTAL WORK

Experiment 1. ***To measure rate of transpiration by loss of weight***

(*a*) **Cut shoot or uprooted small plant** (Fig. 13.5). The only direct method of measuring transpiration is to determine what weight of water the plant loses in a given time.

Both test-tubes will lose water vapour from their open ends

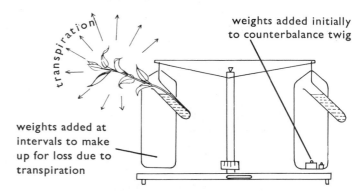

Fig. 13.5   To measure rate of transpiration in a cut shoot or small plant

but this will be the same for both sides. The one with the cut shoot or dug plant will lose more by transpiration. By adding weights at regular intervals to the scale pan on this side to maintain the balance, the weight of water lost by transpiration in a given time can be found. By setting up the experiment in various atmospheric conditions the effect of these on the transpiration rate can also be found, but such a comparison is more easily shown by the potometer.

(*b*) **Potted plant.** After the soil has been watered, the plant and pot are weighed at intervals to find the loss of weight due to transpiration. To prevent evaporation directly from the soil or pot, some impermeable material, polythene or rubber sheet, is wrapped round the pot and tied firmly round the plant's stem. In both experiments, it is assumed that increases of weight resulting from photosynthesis or decreases from respiration are small compared with losses from transpiration.

Experiment 2. ***To show uptake of water by a cut leafy shoot*** (Fig. 13.6)

This is done by the potometer. The type of potometer shown has the advantage of using only very small volumes of water, so that changes in temperature are likely to produce in the water only negligible contractions or expansions which otherwise would confuse or falsify the results.

To set up the potometer a shoot is cut from a shrub or herbaceous plant and at once placed in water to prevent air being taken into the water vessels of the stem. The potometer is filled with water, and the cut end of the shoot fitted into the rubber tubing, care being taken to avoid the inclusion of any air bubbles.

As water evaporates from the leaves, more is drawn from the stem which, in turn, draws it from the potometer tubes. The tap below the funnel is closed so that this water will be withdrawn from the capillary tube. Here, the meniscus at the air/water boundary can be seen moving quite rapidly as water is withdrawn and air is drawn in behind the retreating water column. By timing this water-column movement over a fixed distance on the scale the rate of water uptake can be determined. When the water column reaches the end of the capillary it can be sent back by momentarily opening the tap below the funnel. Any air that is drawn into the apparatus by allowing it to work too long will collect in the stem of the funnel and will not reach the cut shoot.

It must be emphasized that the potometer does not measure water lost by transpiration but only water taken up as result of it. Not all the water taken up will escape into the atmosphere. Some of it will be combined with carbon dioxide to make starch during photosynthesis. Since, in conditions of constant light intensity, this will be a fixed weight, the potometer can be used most effectively for comparing rates of transpiration of the same shoot in different situations.

Experiment 3. *Comparing rates of transpiration*

In various atmospheric conditions increase or decrease in the rate of water uptake will relate directly to changes in the rate of evaporation. By placing the potometer in different situations, e.g. in a warm room with still air, in front of a fan, in a cold room, etc., the difference in rate of water uptake can be measured, and this will indicate the difference in transpiration rate. The intensity of the light should not vary greatly.

Before readings are taken in any situation, the apparatus should be left for several minutes in the new conditions to allow the new rate of transpiration to become established.

Further experiments can be tried to find out more about transpiration. Different shoots of approximately the same leaf area can be compared, say mango and oleander. Leaves and flowers can be removed one by one, or their surfaces smeared with petroleum jelly.

Experiment 4. *To show that water vapour is given off during transpiration* (Fig. 13.7)

The shoot of a recently watered potted plant, or a plant in the garden, is completely enclosed in a transparent, polythene bag which is tied round the base of the stem. The plant is allowed to remain for an hour or two in direct sunlight. The water vapour transpired by the plant will soon saturate the atmosphere inside the bag and drops of water will condense on the inside. The bag is removed and all the condensed water shaken into a corner so that it can be tested with anhydrous copper sulphate. A control experiment is set up using a shoot in a similar situation but from which all the leaves and flowers have been detached.

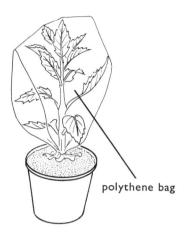

polythene bag

Fig. 13.7   To show that water is given off during transpiration

Experiment 5. *To find which surface of a leaf loses more water vapour* (Fig. 13.8)

Small squares of cobalt chloride paper taken straight from a desiccator are stuck as quickly as possible to the upper and lower surfaces of a leaf blade by means of transparent adhesive tape, avoiding prominent veins to ensure an air-tight seal. In damp conditions, cobalt chloride paper changes from blue to pink, and by comparing the time needed for such a change in both squares, the difference in the loss of water vapour between the two surfaces can be estimated.

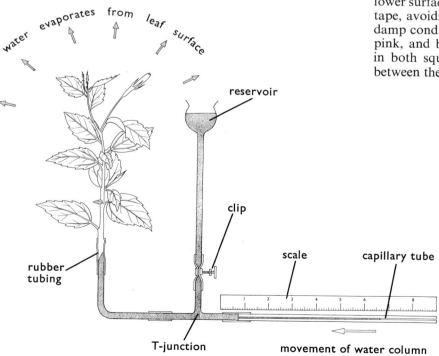

Fig. 13.6   The potometer

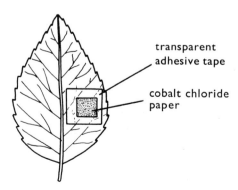

transparent adhesive tape

cobalt chloride paper

Fig. 13.8   To find which surface of a leaf loses more water vapour

*(From J. F. Eggleston, The School Science Review, 1962, 151, **43**, 723)*

*Experiment 6. **Transport in the vascular bundles***

Several small leafy plants are picked and the cut ends of their stems placed in a coloured solution such as neutral red or methylene blue. One of the plants is removed after five minutes, one after ten minutes and so on. By slicing across the base of the stem with a razor blade the water vessels will be seen to have been stained by the coloured solution. By cutting sections higher and higher up the stem until the colour can no longer be seen in the vessels, the height to which the solution has risen in the stem can be determined.

*Experiment 7. **To investigate the distribution of stomata in a leaf***

A small leaf, or a piece of a large leaf is held in forceps and plunged into a beaker of hot water (about 80° C). The rise in temperature expands the air inside the leaf and this will escape through the stomata. The numbers of bubbles appearing on the upper and lower surfaces should be compared and the results related, as far as possible, to the relative numbers of stomata seen under the microscope in comparable pieces of epidermis stripped from the upper and lower surfaces.

A control should be devised to try and eliminate the possible claim that the air bubbles come not from inside the leaf but from the air dissolved in the water merely collecting on the leaf surface.

QUESTIONS

1. Why should cutting a deep ring of bark from a tree cause its death in view of the facts that (*a*) water and salts can travel up to the leaves in the xylem and (*b*) the leaves can still manufacture food by photosynthesis?
2. Explain how it could come about that a plant could (*a*) take in more water than it is losing by transpiration and (*b*) lose more water by transpiration than it is taking in from the roots, at least for a time.
3. Outline the path taken by water from the soil through the roots, stem and leaves of a plant and into the atmosphere as vapour. Explain briefly the forces causing its movement at each stage.
4. Outline the path taken and changes undergone by a nitrogen atom in a solution of nitrate in soil-water as it passes into a plant, is built into an amino acid in a leaf and is finally stored in the cotyledon of a developing seed.

14 | Bacteria and Man

Structure (Fig. 14.1*a*)

Bacteria are very small organisms consisting of single cells, rarely more than 0·01 mm in length and visible only under the higher powers of the microscope. Unlike plant cells they do not have cellulose walls or chloroplasts. Their cell walls are of proteinaceous and fatty substances, and the single chromosome (p. 177) is not enclosed in a nuclear membrane. Granules of glycogen, fat and other food reserves may be present. Bacteria reproduce rapidly by cell division, as often as once in 20 minutes, and may form chains of individuals, clumps or films over the surface of static water. The individuals may be spherical, rod-shaped, or spiral (Fig. 14.2) and some have filaments protruding from them called *flagella*, the

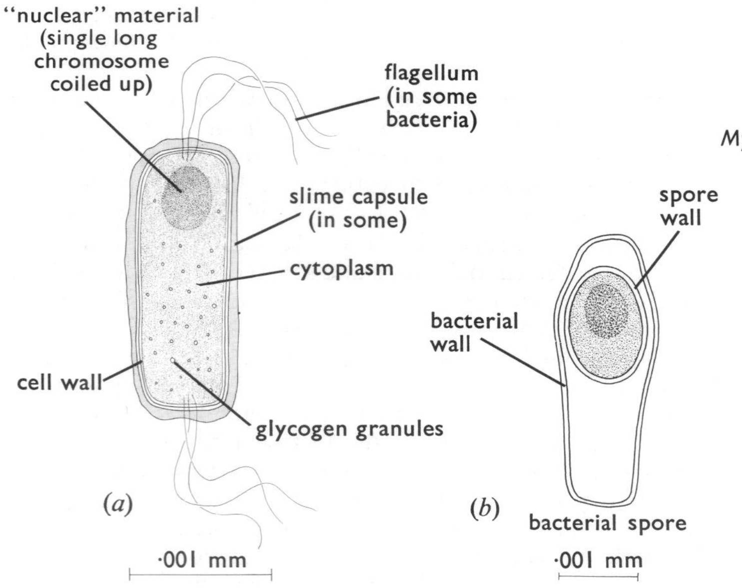

SPHERICAL BACTERIA
[cocci]

Diplococcus
[pneumonia]

Staphylococcus
[boils, blood
poisoning]

Streptococcus
[sore throat,
scarlet fever]

ROD-LIKE BACTERIA
[bacilli]

Mycobacterium tuberculosis
[tuberculosis]

Clostridium tetani
[lock jaw]

Salmonella typhi
[typhoid fever]

SPIRAL FORMS
[not always classified as bacteria]

Treponema [syphilis]

Spirillum [free living]

Vibrio [cholera]

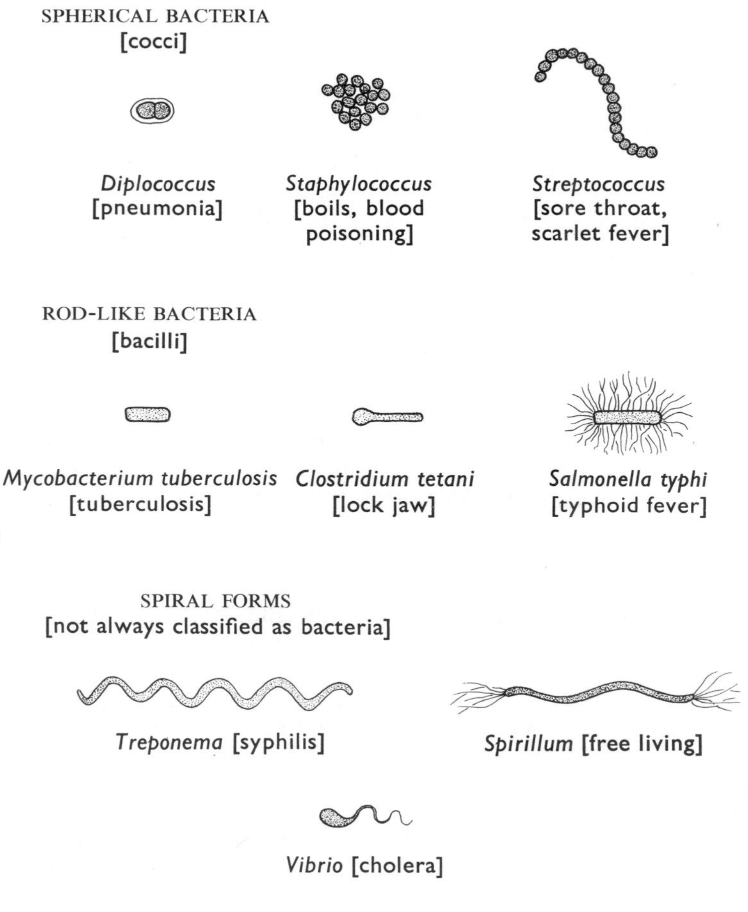

Fig. 14.2   Bacterial forms

"nuclear" material
(single long
chromosome
coiled up)

flagellum
(in some
bacteria)

slime capsule
(in some)

cytoplasm

spore
wall

bacterial
wall

cell wall

glycogen granules

(*a*)

·001 mm

(*b*)

bacterial spore

·001 mm

Fig. 14.1   Generalized diagram of a bacterium

lashing action of which moves the bacterium about. Some bacteria need oxygen to respire while others can respire anaerobically, that is, obtain their energy by breaking down compounds without using oxygen (p. 47).

Spores (Fig. 14.1*b*). Some bacteria can form spores, a resting stage in which the protoplasm is concentrated in one part of the cell and surrounded by a thick wall. Bacterial spores are very widespread, being easily distributed by air currents, and occur on the surface of most objects, in soil, in dust and in the air. These spores are very resistant to extremes of temperature, and some can withstand the temperature of boiling water for long periods. Most normal bacteria can, however, be killed by temperatures above 50°C although they can live at very low temperatures. In favourable conditions, the spores break open and the bacteria reproduce and grow in the normal way.

The part played in nature by bacteria

Most bacteria live freely in the soil, in water and in decaying organic matter where they obtain their food saprophytically (p. 48), bringing about the decay of dead material. Enzymes made in the bacterial cells are secreted into the food, dissolving it to form soluble organic compounds such as amino acids which can be absorbed through the cell wall. Some bacteria obtain their energy by converting these organic compounds to inorganic substances, such as ammonia, which can then be absorbed by different bacteria and oxidized further to nitrates, releasing energy for their metabolism.

Thus the dead remains of plants and animals are converted once more to simpler substances which can be taken in by plants and used to synthesize food. In this way the resources of the Earth are re-cycled and made available for re-use by living organisms. (*See also* Nitrogen Cycle, p. 54 and Carbon Cycle, p. 56.)

The activities of decay bacteria are harnessed in the sewage works. Anaerobic bacteria (*see* below) act on the organic solids in the settling tanks and release soluble organic compounds from them. By spraying this liquid from the tanks over filter beds or by agitating it with paddles, it is oxygenated sufficiently for aerobic bacteria to flourish and convert the soluble organic compounds to inorganic salts such as nitrates and phosphates which are released with the effluent into rivers. Any industrial wastes which harm the bacteria in the sewage plant severely interfere with the effective treatment of sewage. Similarly, substances which cannot be used as a source of food by the bacteria will pass unchanged through the sewage works and contaminate the effluent. Hence the urgent need to use, for example, *bio-degradable* detergents which can be metabolized by the bacteria.

Even the "harmless" mineral salts in the sewage effluent can create hazards (*see* Eutrophication, p. 56).

Some types of bacteria live in the alimentary canals of animals. A few of these cause diseases such as cholera and typhoid but the majority are harmless or even beneficial. For example, in the intestine of man there are bacteria which appear to play a part in the synthesis of vitamin K and the vitamins of the B_2 complex (p. 84). In the alimentary canals of many herbivorous animals there is a dense population of bacteria which play a part in digestion. Few animals can produce an enzyme which digests cellulose, yet many herbivores feed exclusively on vegetation, the most nourishing part of which is enclosed in cellulose cell walls. These walls are broken open partly by efficient chewing and partly by the enzymes of the bacteria and single-celled animals in the gut; in the *caecum* and *appendix* of the rabbit, for example, and the *rumen* (or paunch) of cows and sheep.

Certain bacteria are able to produce food by photosynthesis and some of these bacteria can use H_2S (hydrogen sulphide) instead of H_2O as a source of hydrogen atoms.

Anaerobic bacteria can live in situations where no free oxygen is present. They obtain their energy either by processes similar to fermentation (p.47) or by using inorganic chemicals. The denitrifying bacteria (p. 54) in the soil can use the oxygen from the nitrate ($—NO_3$) present in the soil to oxidize carbohydrates. *Aerobic* bacteria are those which normally use free oxygen for their respiration.

Parasitic bacteria live in or on living animals or plants and are often harmful to the organism.

Harmful bacteria. Some bacteria which live parasitically in plants and animals do a great deal of harm on account of the damage to tissues and highly poisonous proteins, *toxins*, that they produce, e.g. diptheria and tetanus. For example, five millionths of a gram of dried tetanus toxin will kill a mouse and 0·00023 g is fatal for a man. Certain bacteria are the causes of major diseases such as typhoid, cholera, plague and tuberculosis. The diseases are caught as a result of the bacteria being passed directly or indirectly from one person to another. Since bacteria can reproduce so rapidly, a single bacterium may give rise to a million offspring in a few hours.

For a person to catch a bacterial disease, bacteria must enter the body either through the natural openings such as the mouth, nose or vagina, or through the skin via a wound caused by accident or by a blood-sucking insect. The body has natural defences to bacteria (*see* below) but if a sufficient number of bacteria penetrate these defences and multiply in the body, they may become numerous enough to cause the symptoms of a disease.

Transmission of diseases

Food and drink may become contaminated by bacteria in a variety of ways. If the faeces of a person suffering from an intestinal disease such as cholera or typhoid are deposited in or near a source of drinking water, it is likely that the bacteria present in the faeces will enter the water and be drunk by, perhaps, hundreds of other people. Since it is possible for a person to have these bacteria in his intestine without experiencing any symptoms of ill-health, great care should be taken by *all* individuals to see that their excreta cannot contaminate drinking water (Fig. 14.3).

Disease bacteria may get into food when it is washed in contaminated water or be deposited from the feet of flies (p. 155) which have recently walked on human faeces.

After urinating or defaecating, the hands may be contaminated with urine or faeces so that if the unwashed hands come in contact with food, harmful bacteria from the intestine may be transferred to the food and so infect those who eat it. It has been known for one carrier of typhoid working in a restaurant or canteen to infect hundreds of others.

Droplet infection. The acts of coughing, sneezing, talking or merely breathing, discharge into the atmsphere tiny droplets of moisture from the lungs, trachea, mouth and nose. If a person has a disease of the respiratory tract, such as tuberculosis, these droplets will contain bacteria. The droplets remain suspended for some time in the air, to be breathed in by other people. Crowded, humid, confined situations are very favourable to the spread of disease by droplet infection and unchecked coughing and sneezing propel the droplets over considerable distances.

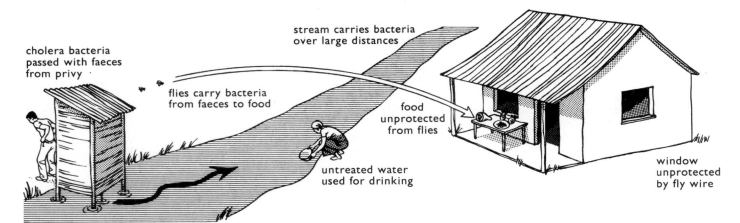

cholera bacteria
passed with faeces
from privy

stream carries bacteria
over large distances

flies carry bacteria
from faeces to food

food
unprotected
from flies

untreated water
used for drinking

window
unprotected
by fly wire

Fig. 14.3   How cholera is spread   (*Brian Jones*)

Contagion. This is the spread of disease by contact with an infected person as is the case with leprosy. The venereal diseases such as syphilis and gonorrhoea are spread only by sexual contact. The sexual organ of an infected person will carry the spirochaete *Treponema* (syphilis), or the gonococcus *Neisseria* (gonorrhoea). During sexual intercourse the bacteria will be transferrred to the sexual organ of the healthy partner and set up an infection. In the case of gonorrhoea, the infection is usually confined to the reproductive organs but syphilis, if untreated, may spread throughout the body producing ulcers, heart disease and mental degeneration. A baby born to a mother with a venereal disease may be infected in the uterus or as it passes through the vagina.

Infection by insects. The possibility of house-flies transmitting diseases has already been mentioned and is described more fully on p. 153. There are many biting insects which, if themselves infected with bacteria or other harmful organisms, may introduce them into the blood stream of Man. Bubonic plague is caused by a bacterium transmitted from infected rats to Man by the bites of fleas which feed on both. The transmission of sleeping sickness and malaria (caused by protozoa, not bacteria) is described on pp. 222–3.

Resistance to disease

The invasion of harmful bacteria is counteracted by the blood of healthy mammals in two ways.

(*a*) The skin forms a defence against the invasion of the blood and body cavities by bacteria. This is effected partly by the physical barrier of the dead, cornified, outer layer of the skin and partly by production of chemicals which destroy bacteria (*see* Vitamins, p. 84). The eyes, for example, are protected by an enzyme present in normal tears. The lining of the alimentary canal and respiratory passages also resist the entry of bacteria.

(*b*) The white cells, *leucocytes*, engulf the bacteria and secrete chemicals that kill them (p. 93). Other chemicals, *antitoxins*, made in the blood, effectively neutralize the poisonous proteins that the bacteria give out. Once an animal has recovered from a bacterial disease, its blood is much better able to combat the bacteria and neutralize its toxins; it is said to have acquired *immunity* (p. 94).

Prevention of infection

Food. Most uncooked food contains bacteria, but not usually in sufficient numbers to cause disease, and the lining of the gut and the hydrochloric acid in the stomach will often prevent their development. The techniques of food preservation, involving the destruction of bacteria whose activities would cause the food to decay, also serve to destroy disease bacteria, e.g. typhoid, which could be transmitted by food. *Refrigeration* does not kill bacteria but prevents their multiplication. The high temperatures of *cooking* kill most bacteria and their spores, if continued long enough. *Bottling* and *canning* kill bacteria by the high temperature used and then prevent their access to the food by sealing it in a vacuum. Poisons such as sulphur dioxide may be added to canned or bottled fruit in a concentration sufficient to kill bacteria but too weak to harm the consumer.

Today, experiments are being conducted on food exposed to radiation from radio-active cobalt. This seems to destroy bacteria effectively without harming the food. Drying, curing, smoking and salting are all methods of food preservation.

In the case of salting and preservation with sugar, the preservation depends on the low water potential of the food which plasmolyses (p. 62) any bacteria which arrive in it.

Food should be eaten soon after it has been cooked or removed from a container and so give invading bacteria, or any not destroyed during cooking, little opportunity to multiply. Flies, notorious carriers of bacteria, should never be allowed to settle on food, and people who handle food that is to be eaten without subsequent cooking should take great care that their hands do not carry harmful bacteria.

Clean water. To ensure that water is free from harmful bacteria it is necessary (*a*) to dispose of human sewage in such a way that it cannot contaminate water supplies, and (*b*) to subject the water to treatment that removes or destroys any harmful bacteria which may be present. These processes are discussed more fully below.

Ventilation. To reduce the chances of droplet infection, buildings need to be adequately ventilated, i.e. provision is made to exchange the air frequently with that from outside so that the suspended droplets with their bacteria and viruses are removed before they reach harmful proportions. In houses this can normally be achieved by windows and ventilators. In public buildings, the normal exchange of air through windows, doors and ventilators may be enhanced by some form of air conditioning which not only exchanges the air but cools it and reduces its humidity.

Venereal and other contagious diseases. The venereal diseases can only be contracted by sexual contact with an infected person. The symptoms of infection are not necessarily obvious, so casual sexual intercourse with a person whose habits and sexual health are not known could lead to infection. The people most likely to be infected are prostitutes who have sexual relations with a large number of people, some of whom are bound to be infected. Gonorrhoea and, in its early stages, syphilis can be treated by antibiotic drugs but treatment must be administered by a properly qualified person immediately an infection is suspected. (*See also* p. 221.)

Other contagious diseases such as tinea (caused by a fungus) can be caught by touching an infected person or his clothing. So even a person suffering from a mild, contagious skin disease spread in this way should avoid contact with other people as far as possible and ensure that his clothing, bed clothes and washing materials are kept separate from others.

Control of insects. Flies which may carry disease bacteria on their legs or proboscos should be prevented from walking on food for human consumption, especially food which is to be eaten without further cooking. Control of house-flies and insects such as mosquitoes which carry malaria is discussed more fully in chapters 28 and 37.

Personal hygiene. Bacteria and their spores are present all over the surface of a person's skin. They cannot be totally removed but their numbers can be reduced by regular washing with soap. Thus there is less chance of the person being infected should the skin be damaged. The hands in particular should be washed frequently, especially after using the toilet and before handling food so that intestinal bacteria cannot be taken in with the food. For the same reason, cooking utensils, plates, cups and cutlery should be kept as clean as possible. The bacteria present in an infected wound can cause acute poisoning if they get into food. Therefore, food should not be prepared by anybody with a septic wound, particularly on the hands, unless strict precautions are taken to avoid contamination.

Regular washing of the body and clothing not only keeps down the bacterial population on the skin but also reduces the possibility of harbouring lice and fleas which can transmit serious diseases.

Isolation. People carrying a disease which can be transmitted by touch or droplet infection should not mix with others if the disease is serious and as little as possible if the disease is mild. In particular they should not mingle with crowds where they could pass on the bacteria to a great many people.

Immunization and vaccination. By deliberately infecting a person with a mild form of disease, antibodies are formed in his blood and these will protect him against later infections. This is described more fully on p. 94.

Antiseptics and antibiotics. Antiseptics are chemicals which act against bacteria. Some antiseptics kill all bacteria and their spores, others kill the bacteria but not the spores and some merely prevent the bacteria from multiplying. Antiseptic chemicals are present in disinfectants which can be used to kill bacteria on the floors, walls and equipment in buildings such as hospitals where high standards of hygiene are necessary. They can be used to reduce the bacterial population in lavatories, wash-basins and drains. In general, they should not be used on the skin or for treatment of wounds because they may destroy cells of the skin and tissue as well as the bacteria. Thorough washing with clean water is usually adequate for cleansing skin wounds.

Antibiotics such as penicillin are chemicals extracted from bacteria or fungi (p. 77). They destroy many forms of harmful bacteria and can be used internally against infections of the tissues where they kill the bacteria without harming the cells of the body. For example, an antibiotic like penicillin can be used to control an infection of the middle ear either by the patient's eating the antibiotic or having it injected into the circulatory system.

Pure water

Fig. 14.4 compares a shallow well and a deep well. In the former, bacteria from faeces, urine and other organic matter can be washed through the pervious top-soil into the water. In the latter case, surface water cannot reach the deep well because its sides are enclosed in concrete and the water comes from beneath the pervious layer.

In small quantities water can be made safe to drink by boiling it to kill the bacteria or filtering it through special porcelain filters to remove the bacteria. When water is supplied to towns, it is first filtered through beds of sand. The sand particles become covered with a gelatinous film of micro-organisms which feed on the bacteria and so remove them from the water. Any bacteria which escape the filters are killed by exposing the water to chlorine gas before it reaches the storage tanks.

Sewage disposal

In small isolated communities it is safe to dispose of faeces and urine in deep pits provided that the soil is permeable and there is no source of drinking water within 100 metres to become contaminated by seepage. In a small village or a house with flushing toilets, the sewage can be rendered harmless by

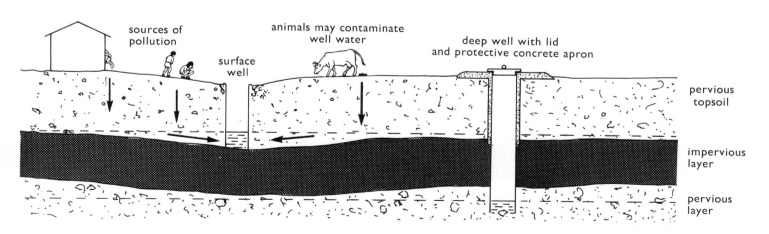

Fig. 14.4   Comparison between a shallow surface well and a protected deep well

(*Brian Jones*)

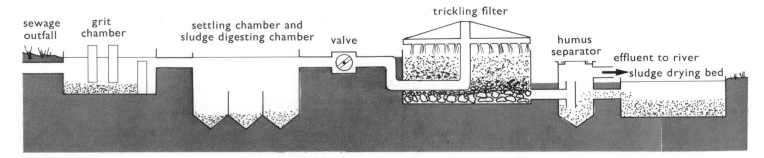

Fig. 14.6   Layout of plant for the biological filter treatment of sewage   (Brian Jones)

letting it run into a septic tank (Fig. 14.5). In the first compartment the solid matter settles to the bottom. In the second chamber a film of protozoa and bacteria growing on the broken bricks traps and digests the suspended organic matter so making it harmless. The sludge has to be removed and buried periodically.

One method of large-scale treatment of sewage from a town is shown diagrammatically in Fig. 14.6. The largest solid particles settle out first and the remaining fluid with fine suspended organic matter is passed through a filter bed packed with coke or broken stones. This is similar to the second compartment of the septic tank. A gelatinous film of protozoa and other micro-organisms grows on the stones, the spaces between the stones allowing circulation of air for the aerobic organisms. The suspended organic particles are eaten and digested by the micro-organisms in the film so that only water and soluble salts escape to the river. The sludge and "humus" are dried and can be used as fertilizer on crops other than those which are eaten without cooking.

The water from a sewage works should be free from any bacteria and organic particles but it may contain nitrates and phosphates in solution and so cause problems of eutrophication (*see* p. 56).

PRACTICAL WORK

Bacteria can be obtained by allowing cooked cassava or yam to rot in water. After a few days, drops of the water examined under the high power of the microscope should show bacteria. Gentian violet will stain bacteria.

Bacteria culture. In order to identify and investigate the bacteria it is necessary to culture them. This is done by mixing fruit juice, meat extract or other nutritious substances with gelatine or *agar* jelly which then forms a medium in or on which the bacteria can grow and reproduce. The bacteria multiply and form visible colonies whose

colourful and chemical reactions make them identifiable. By including or excluding certain substances from the culture medium, the essential conditions for the growth and reproduction of a particular bacterium can be found, and the effects of chemicals and antiseptics in various concentrations can be investigated.

Sterilization. The removal of bacteria from an object by killing them, using high temperatures such as steam under pressure in an *autoclave*, or by chemicals, is termed "sterilization".

Culturing bacteria from the environment. The apparatus must be sterilized by superheated steam in an autoclave or pressure cooker for 15 minutes at 1000 N/m^2 (15 lb per sq.in.), so that unwanted bacteria on the glassware are destroyed.

Fifteen grammes of agar are stirred into 1000 cm^3 hot distilled water and 3 g beef extract, 2 g yeast extract, and 5 g peptone added. The mixture is sterilized in an autoclave or pressure cooker as before and poured into sterile Petri dishes which are covered at once and allowed to cool.

Each dish is then exposed to bacteria in one of various ways; for example, A is left open outside for 5 minutes, B is placed in a classroom for the same length of time, C is coughed into, in D a fly is allowed to walk once over the medium, E is left open in a dust-bin for 5 minutes. One, the control, is left covered to prove that sterilization has been effective. After they have all been covered they are incubated at $36°C$ for two days, or simply left in a warm place, when colonies of bacteria and fungi will appear. No growth should appear on the control.

Since the cultures may contain thousands of potentially harmful bacteria, the plates must be examined *without removing* the lids, and before the cultures are discarded, they must be autoclaved again in the closed dishes to kill all the bacteria present.

QUESTIONS

1. Give some examples of bacteria and their activities which may be considered to be directly or indirectly beneficial to man.
2. Substances such as wood, paper and cloth will rot away in time. Materials like polythene and polystyrene will not. Why should there by this difference and why is it a cause for concern in industrialized countries?
3. During a surgical operation, the surgeon and his team wear sterile clothing and face masks. Why are such measures adopted in this case but not during a routine medical examination?
4. Exposure to mild infectious diseases such as measles is considered to be a normal hazard of communal living. Cases of serious infectious diseases such as typhoid are kept in isolation so that they cannot infect other people and yet an injection of dead typhoid bacteria can produce resistance to the disease. Discuss the biological principles underlying these social activities and attitudes.
5. Why is sewage sludge used as a fertilizer only on crops that are cooked before they are eaten?
6. What kind of health checks are desirable on people who are preparing and serving food to large numbers of others, or working in food processing factories?
7. To sterilize substances which would be decomposed by the temperatures in an autoclave, the substances are heated to 100°C for one hour on three successive days and incubated at 25–30°C between each steaming.
   What is the biological basis for this method of sterilization?

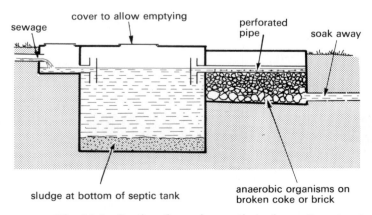

Fig. 14.5   Section through a septic tank   (Brian Jones)

15 | Fungi

Structure. The fungi are included in the plant kingdom but in many ways they are quite different from green plants. The basic unit of a fungus is a *hypha* (Figs. 15.1 and 15.2), not a cell, although in some species the hollow tubes of the hyphae may be divided by cross-walls. Some fungal hyphae have walls containing cellulose but in most, the wall consists mainly of an organic nitrogenous compound, *chitin*. The composition may vary with age and environmental conditions. Cytoplasm fills the tips of the growing hyphae but in older regions there may be a central vacuole. Many very small nuclei are present in the cytoplasm.

There are no chloroplasts or chlorophyll in the fungi and the food particles in the cytoplasm may be oil droplets or glycogen, but not starch. The hyphal threads spread out over and into the food material making a visible mesh or *mycelium* (Fig. 15.2). In some fungi they are massed together to make the familiar "fruiting bodies" of mushrooms and toadstools, though the organization and division of labour in the hyphae is never so complex as in the flowering plants.

Feeding. The absence of chlorophyll means that fungi cannot synthesize food from simple substances such as carbon dioxide and water, as is done in photosynthesis, but must take in organic matter derived from other living organisms. Fungi are either saprophytic or parasitic. The parasitic ones live on or in the tissues of another living organism, the host, absorbing nourishment from its body. Some of the most devastating diseases of crops are due to parasitic fungi, e.g. potato blight.

The saprophytes derive their food from dead and decaying materials. Examples are the moulds which develop on stale, damp food and the many fungi which live in the soil and feed on the humus there. Both parasitic and saprophytic fungi can produce enzymes at the growing tips of the hyphae. These enzymes enable the parasitic hyphae to penetrate the cell walls of the host and, in both parasites and saprophytes, to break down the organic matter externally by digestion. The simpler, soluble substances so formed can be absorbed into the protoplasm through the cell walls.

Reproduction is typically of two kinds, asexual and sexual. In asexual reproduction, a great many tiny spores are produced and scattered into the air. If they land in a suitable situation they grow out into new hyphae and mycelia. Sexual reproduction involves the fusion of nuclei in special hyphal branches. The product sometimes represents a resting rather than a dispersive stage.

Rhizopus

Rhizopus is the name given to a genus of moulds which grow on the surface of decaying fruit, bread and other organic matter. The fungus grows rapidly, and in a few days covers the surface of its food with a dense, white or grey mass of hyphae. The young hyphae have no cross-walls but branch repeatedly and give rise to the mycelium.

Reproduction. Asexual reproduction takes place rapidly after the establishment of a mycelium. Long hyphae, "stolons", grow out from the mycelium, at first into the air and then as they get longer, they bend over and touch the food material again. At this point they produce a number of branching hyphae which penetrate into and absorb nutriment from the food material. Also from this point, a small number of vertical hyphae grow out. These become swollen at their ends, the swellings containing dense cytoplasm with many nuclei (Fig. 15.2). The swelling becomes the sporangium and the protoplasm inside breaks up into elliptical spores, each with several nuclei and forming its own wall. In most species the sporangium wall breaks open so that the spores are freed and may be blown away in slight air-currents. The wall of the spore breaks open when a suitable situation is reached, and the protoplasm inside grows out into a new hypha and eventually a new mycelium. The germination of spores is greatly favoured by warm, damp conditions. The spores are said to be very resistant to adverse conditions and can remain dormant for years.

In sexual reproduction, two short, hyphal branches grow out and meet each other. Where they touch, the ends swell and are cut off from the rest of the mycelium by cross-walls. The nuclei within divide repeatedly and the walls between the two swollen hyphae break down so that the contents mix. In the *zygospore* so formed, the nuclei pair up and fuse and the zygospore wall becomes thickened and dark with rough pyramidal patterns on it. Eventually, the connecting hyphae shrivel leaving the zygospore to germinate, after a dormant period of a few months, into a single, vertical hypha, bearing at its tip a sporangium which produces spores as described above.

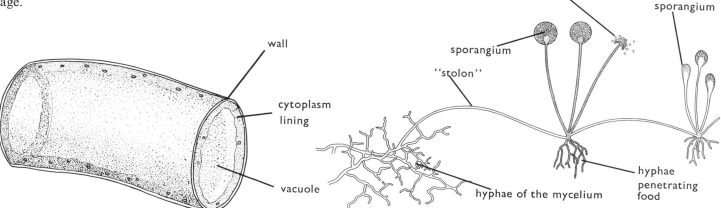

Fig. 15.1   Part of fungal hypha

Fig. 15.2   *Rhizopus*: asexual reproduction
(Note: sporangium is shown in section)

Parasitic fungi

Parasitic fungi are the principal disease-causing organisms in plants, and fungal attacks can result in devastating agricultural losses. For example, black pod, a fungus disease of cocoa, has sometimes caused a 90 per cent loss of crop in Nigeria. There are many forms of disease fungi known, for example, as rust, smut, mildew or blight.

The spores of the fungi gain entry to the plant in various ways. The spore germinates and produces a hypha which enters the stoma of a leaf stem, or penetrates the cuticle directly, or —with tough tissues such as tree bark or yam epidermis— through a wound. The hyphae penetrate the internal tissues, dissolving the cell walls with an enzyme and absorbing the soluble products of the cell contents. This destruction of tissue causes visible patches of discoloration on the leaves and stems and, as the mycelium spreads throughout the plant, kills the leaf and stem. At some stage, hyphae emerge from the host plant and produce spores which are blown or washed on to new host plants. These spore-bearing hyphae projecting from the leaves give rise to the powdery appearance of some of the mildews.

Parasitic fungi survive in the interval between crops in a variety of ways. The spores may persist in the soil as they do in potato blight and possibly in the brown spot disease of rice, or the plant seeds may be covered with a fungus mycelium which invades and kills the seedlings at germination as does the fungus *Pythium* with sorghum seedlings.

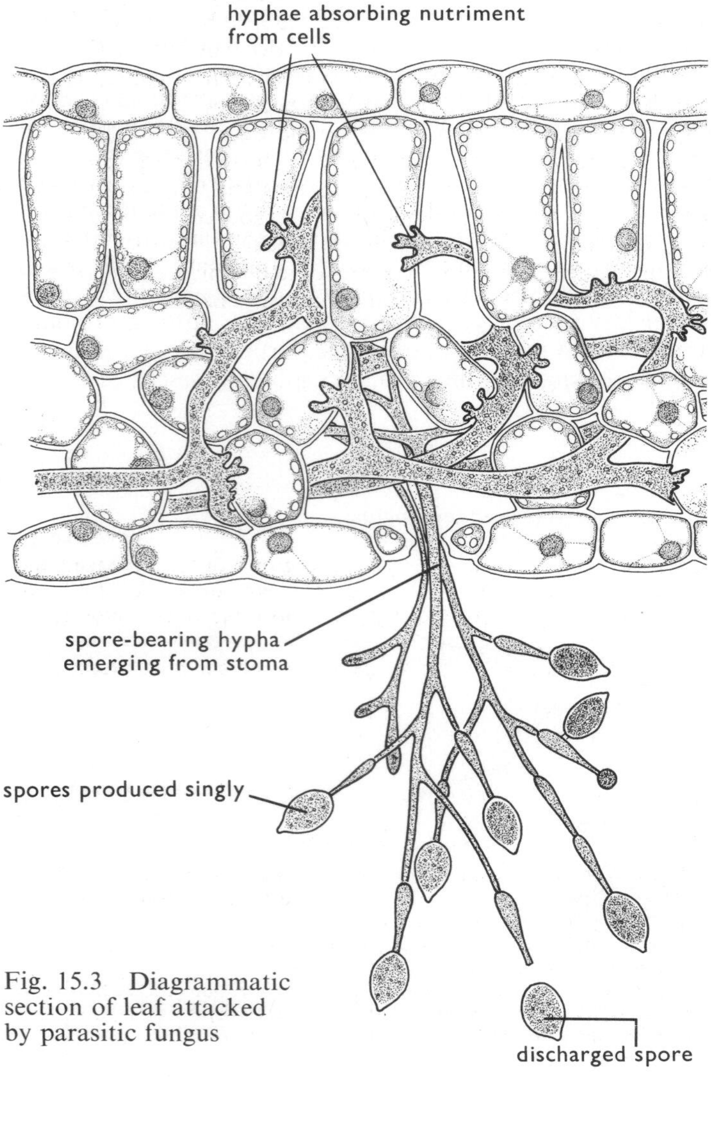

hyphae absorbing nutriment from cells

spore-bearing hypha emerging from stoma

spores produced singly

Fig. 15.3 Diagrammatic section of leaf attacked by parasitic fungus

discharged spore

Methods of control. It is clearly necessary to understand the methods of transmission of fungus diseases in order to exercise control over them. The most effective measure is to find or to breed varieties of crop plant which are resistant to the fungus (*see* p. 199). This resistance is sometimes the result of a tough cuticle which the fungus cannot penetrate, or a chemical secreted by the plant which destroys the germinating spores. In other cases the plant variety completes its life cycle and yields its crop at a time when the fungus is not abundant.

Control of fungus diseases on a small scale is best done by uprooting and burning infected plants, as with downy mildew of sorghum, or removing and destroying the infected parts at an early stage as with black pod of cocoa. In this way, the spores cannot reach the remaining healthy plants. On a large scale, the crop can be sprayed or dusted with a chemical which kills the fungus (a *fungicide*) while leaving the crop unharmed. Unfortunately, such fungicides often contain copper or mercury compounds which are poisonous to humans and are very expensive to apply.

When a fungus is known to be carried on the seed as with sorghum, a very effective method of control is by seed dressing, i.e. the seeds are dipped in a mercurial solution which destroys the fungus.

If the spores are thought to survive in the soil during the non-growing season then crop rotation is an effective method of control (*see* p. 54) since the spores which affect, say, sorghum will not affect maize or beans.

Potato blight. The hyphae of the parasite fungus *Phytophthora infestans*, which causes the disease potato blight, spread internally through the leaves. Short branches from the hyphae penetrate the cell walls, presumably with the aid of enzymes, and absorb nutriment from the cell contents (Fig. 15.3). The cells are eventually killed and then the leaves and finally the whole shoot dies. Before this happens, branching hyphae grow out of the stomata and the tips of the hyphae constrict to cut off individual spores which are blown away in air currents. If a spore lands on a leaf of a healthy potato plant, in warm moist conditions a new hypha grows out from it and penetrates the leaf via a stoma (Fig. 15.4). When spores fall on the ground, they may be washed into the soil by rain, so reaching and infecting the potato tubers, causing them to rot. The close proximity of the plants in the potato field allows very rapid spread of the fungus from one individual to the next.

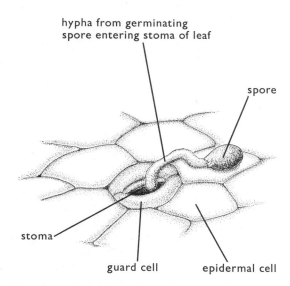

hypha from germinating spore entering stoma of leaf

spore

stoma

guard cell

epidermal cell

Fig. 15.4 One method of infection

Antibiotics

Certain moulds, notably species of *Penicillium*, have become of economic importance owing to the anti-bacterial substances, *antibiotics*, they produce. These moulds are grown on nutrient broths, and the antibiotic chemicals such as penicillin are extracted from the fluid and purified.

Many antibiotics, e.g. *streptomycin*, come from soil-dwelling micro-organisms, *actinomycetes*, which exhibit characteristics of both fungi and bacteria. It may be that by producing antibiotic chemicals in their natural environment these actinomycetes restrict the growth of bacterial colonies in the soil and so reduce the competition for food. There is little direct evidence, however, to support this assumption.

Penicillin seems to attack the bacterial cell wall but the mode of action of antibiotics in general against bacteria has not been elucidated.

Yeast

The yeasts are a rather unusual family of fungi. Only a few of the several species can form true hyphae; the majority of them consist of separate, spherical cells, which can be seen only under the microscope. They live in situations where sugar is likely to be available, e.g. the nectar of flowers or the surface of fruits.

Structure. The thin cell wall encloses the cytoplasm, which contains a vacuole and a nucleus. In the cytoplasm are granules of glycogen and other food reserves.

Reproduction. The cells reproduce by budding, in which an outgrowth from a cell enlarges and is finally cut off from the parent as an independent cell. When budding occurs rapidly the individuals do not separate at once, and as a result, small groups of attached cells may sometimes be seen (Fig. 15.4b).

In certain conditions, two cells may *conjugate*, that is, they join together and their cell contents fuse. Later, the cell contents divide into four individuals, each developing a thick wall. These are spores and may constitute a resting stage. When the old cell wall enclosing them breaks open, the spores are set free and can germinate to form normal, budding cells. Such spores often arise without any previous conjugation.

Fermentation. Yeasts, in nature, live on the surface of fruits and in other similar situations. They are of economic importance, however, in promoting alcoholic fermentation. Yeast cells contain many enzymes, one group of them being called, collectively, *zymase*. By means of these enzymes they can break down sugar into carbon dioxide and alcohol. This chemical change makes available energy which the yeast cells can use for their vital processes in a way similar to respiration, only far less energy is set free in this case:

$$C_6H_{12}O_6 \rightarrow 2CO_2 + 2\underset{alcohol}{C_2H_5OH} + 118 \text{ kJ}$$

Alcoholic fermentation is in fact similar to anaerobic respiration (p. 47), but unless the yeast is supplied with sugar, oxygen is necessary for the preliminary conversion of other carbohydrates to a suitable form for releasing energy.

Many fruit juices will ferment of their own accord if the crushed fruit is left in suitable conditions and the yeasts present on the skin allowed to develop. If too much oxygen is admitted or the wrong species of yeasts, together with fungi and bacteria, allowed to enter, the oxidation of the alcohol may be continued until acetic (ethanoic) acid is produced, as in vinegar.

In baking, yeast is added to uncooked dough to make the dough "rise", as a result of the carbon dioxide bubbles given off, before the bread is baked.

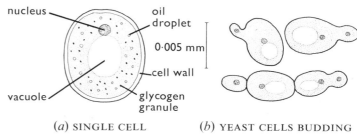

(a) SINGLE CELL   (b) YEAST CELLS BUDDING

Fig. 15.5   Yeast

Yeast as food. Yeasts are becoming important as a source of food for man and his farm animals. Given only sugar and inorganic salts, these micro-organisms will grow and reproduce very rapidly, converting the sugar and salts to make their protein. As one eminent biologist has expressed it, "In 24 hours, half a tonne of bullock will make a pound of protein; half a tonne of yeast will make 50 tonnes and needs only a few square metres to do it on." Yeasts contain most of the essential amino acids and vitamins (p. 83) needed by man, and at present the yeasts produced on a commercial scale are used to supplement diets inadequate in these respects. Yeast is also used specifically to remedy vitamin B deficiency diseases.

Economic importance of fungi

From the information in this chapter it can be seen that fungi are of considerable importance in a variety of ways. Their harmful effects include the crop losses caused by parasitic fungi and, to a much smaller extent, the harm done by fungal diseases in man (p. 222) and his domestic animals. Mould fungi cause damage to stored food, and those species which can digest wood bring about decay and rot in buildings.

On the positive side, the digestive activities of fungi on organic matter break down dead remains and help in recycling nutrients (p. 54). Fungi are important sources of antibiotic drugs and are used increasingly in industrial processes, apart from baking and brewing, to bring about chemical changes, e.g. the large scale production of citric acid and enzymes.

PRACTICAL WORK

Mucor and related species of fungi can be grown in the laboratory by placing moistened pieces of bread, banana, etc., on a Petri dish and covering them with a beaker. In the humid atmosphere colonies of mould grow in a few days.

For an experiment on the fermentation of sugar by yeast, *see* Experiment *f*, p. 47.

QUESTIONS

1. When something "goes mouldy" what is actually happening to it?
2. Suggest why bread, wood and leather are to be seen going mouldy while metal, glass and plastic are not.
3. Suggest why toadstools may be found growing in very dark areas of woodland where green plants cannot flourish.
4. The fungi are not easy to classify as plants but they bear little resemblance to animals. Discuss the ways in which they (a) resemble, (b) differ from green plants and animals.

16 | Soil

Components

Soil consists of a mixture of: (*a*) particles of sand or clay, (*b*) humus, (*c*) water, (*d*) air, (*e*) dissolved salts, (*f*) bacteria.

(*a*) **Inorganic particles** are formed from rocks which have been weathered and broken down. Particles from 2 to 0·02 mm diameter constitute sand, 0·02 to 0·002 mm form silt and less than 0·002 mm clay. Chemically, sand is silicon oxide while clay may be various complexes of aluminium and silicon oxides. Iron oxide may give a red or brown coating to the particles.

Aggregates of these inorganic particles together with humus produce *crumbs* up to about 3 mm in diameter, which form the "skeleton" of the soil. The crumb structure of a soil depends on the proportion of clay, sand and humus and the activities of plant roots; a good crumb structure is one of the most important attributes of a soil.

(*b*) **Humus** is the finely divided organic matter incorporated into the crumbs; it originates mainly from decaying plant remains. The presence of humus in the crumbs affects the colour and physical properties of the soil. Humus is black, structureless, often forms a coating round sand particles and may be important in "glueing" particles together to form soil crumbs. A sandy soil deficient in humus tends to have a poor crumb structure and is easily blown away if exposed by ploughing. The exclusive use of chemical fertilizers on certain soils in dry climates may lead to the formation of dust bowls or the advance of desert margins. (*See* p.79.)

The bacterial decay of humus and the organic matter from which it originates produces the nitrates and other mineral salts needed for plant growth.

(*c*) **Water** is spread over the sand particles or clay aggregates as a thin film which adheres by capillary attraction. It may also penetrate the aggregates and be held to the clay particles by chemical forces. When a soil contains as much water as it can hold by capillary and chemical attraction (i.e. any more would drain away by the force of gravity), it is said to be at *field capacity*. Capillary attraction will tend to distribute water from regions above field capacity to drier regions. The forces holding water in the soil also set up considerable opposition to the "suction" of plant roots when the soil begins to dry out.

(*d*) **Air** occurs in the spaces between the aggregates or sand particles unless the soil is water-logged, in which case the air spaces are blocked up. A supply of oxygen is essential for the respiration of roots and some soil organisms, e.g. bacteria.

(*e*) **Mineral salts.** Salts in the soil water are dissolved out either from the surrounding rock or from the humus in the soil. They make a very dilute solution with the soil water but are vital for plant growth as explained on page 51.

(*f*) **Bacteria.** Many microscopic plants, fungi and animals live in the soil, but among the most important to plant life are the bacteria which break down the organic matter and humus to form soluble salts which can be taken up in solution by roots. Other bacteria convert atmospheric nitrogen to organic compounds of nitrogen. For further details, *see* p. 54.

Soil types

Heavy soils. A soil in which clay particles predominate and which has a poor crumb structure will be sticky and difficult to dig or plough. This results partly from chemical and capillary forces acting on the very large surface area of the minute clay particles, making them difficult to separate. When dry, the soil forms hard clods which do not break up readily during cultivation.

The small distances between particles tend to produce poor aeration and drainage, but the large surface presented by the particles retains a high proportion of water in conditions of drought. There is also less tendency for soluble minerals to be washed away as they are held chemically to the clay particles.

A heavy soil can be made lighter, more workable and permeable to water and air by adding organic matter or lime. The lime makes the particles clump together or *flocculate*, the clumps of particles behaving as the larger particles of a light soil. The crumb structure of a clay soil can be improved by growing grass on it for a year or two.

Light soils. The large inorganic particles of a light soil give it its sandy texture (Fig. 16.1*b*). The wider separation of the particles leads to better aeration and drainage but there is a smaller surface for the water film. Such a reduced surface lessens the surface forces of the water and makes it easier to separate the

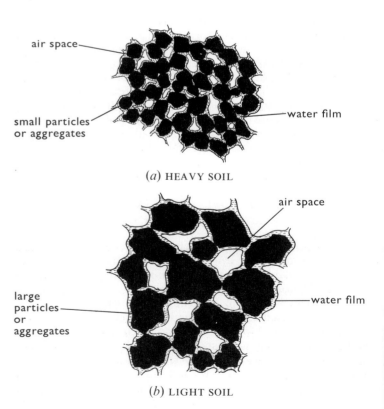

(*a*) HEAVY SOIL

(*b*) LIGHT SOIL

Fig. 16.1   Structure of light and heavy soils

particles in ploughing and digging, and the clumps break up easily when dry.

The mineral salts are more liable to be washed out from a lighter soil and it loses water rapidly in dry conditions. Its water-holding properties and nitrogen content can be improved by adding farmyard manure or compost.

Loam. A soil with a balanced mixture of particle sizes, a good humus content and stable crumb structure is called a loam. Loams are the most productive soils in agriculture.

Laterite soils. A laterite soil is formed in tropical conditions where, at high temperatures, decomposition of organic matter goes on very rapidly and the heavy rain washes out many of the minerals including much of the silica. The soil is mainly of alumina particles coloured red with iron oxide and is deficient in humus and mineral nutrients. When it dries, the alumina and iron oxide particles stick together, forming a hard layer which is poorly aerated and difficult to plough or dig.

Soil pH (acidity). The pH of soil varies. A soil on limestone or chalk may be alkaline, up to pH 8. Some clay soils and soils containing much organic matter may be acid, down to pH 4·5. Acid conditions in the soil often lead to a deficiency of minerals by making them more soluble and easily washed out by rain. Alkaline conditions, on the other hand, may make some minerals so insoluble that they cannot be taken up in solution by the plant.

A pH of about 6·5 is considered favourable for most crops and cultivation methods can be used to adjust the pH. For example, application of lime (calcium hydroxide or carbonate) will raise the pH of an acid soil, while addition of ammonium sulphate will lower the pH of an alkaline soil.

Soil erosion (Fig. 16.2a)

Soil erosion means the removal of top-soil, usually by the action of wind and rain.

(a) **Deforestation.** The soil cover on steep slopes is usually fairly thin but can support the growth of trees. If the forests are cut down to make way for agriculture, the soil is no longer protected by a leafy canopy from the driving rain. Consequently, some of the soil is washed away into the rivers which tend to become choked with silt and overflow their banks.

(b) **Poor farming methods.** Ploughing loosens the soil and destroys its natural structure. Failure to replace humus after successive crops, and burning the stubble or weeds, reduces the water-holding properties, so that the soil dries easily and may be blown away as dust. On sloping ground, such soil may be eroded by water.

(i) *Sheet* erosion is the imperceptible removal of thin layers of soil but usually leads to:

(ii) *Rill* erosion, in which the water cuts channels. The channels deepen as the volume of run-off increases and so become gulleys.

(iii) *Gulley* erosion. The gulleys so formed reach enormous proportions so that thousands of hectares of top-soil are carried off. Gulley erosion is often accentuated by careless ploughing and may follow the tracks made by vehicles, goats, cattle and other farm animals.

(c) **Over-grazing.** Too large a population of animals on a given area will not make economic use of the food they eat, since its scarcity will make their growth rate too slow. In addition, sheep and goats graze the vegetation very closely, leaving little plant cover on the soil, while their hooves trample and compact the soil into a hard layer. Consequently there is less absorption of rain; the soil dries out quickly and may eventually be blown away.

(Agricultural Information Section, Ministry of Agriculture, Enugu, Eastern Nigeria)

Plate 14. CONTOUR STRIP CROPPING IN THE FACULTY OF AGRICULTURE FARM, UNIVERSITY OF NSUKKA, EASTERN NIGERIA

Methods of reducing erosion (Fig. 16.2b)

(a) **Terracing.** This is cultivation along the line of the contours, in horizontal strips supported by walls, so breaking up the steep downward rush of the surface run-off. Terracing is a useful temporary measure against water erosion, but is a rather costly and difficult method of farming.

(b) **Contour ploughing.** Ploughing at right angles to the slope, i.e. along the contours instead of up and down the hill, allows the furrows to trap water rather than channel it away and start gulley erosion.

(c) **Strip cropping.** This consists of alternate bands of tilled and untilled soil following the contours (Plate 14). Grass and cover crop strips, between strips of ploughed land carrying grain, prevent the soil being washed away from the tilled portions. By alternating the grass and grain each year, the soil is allowed to rebuild its structure while under grass. Strip cropping is also effective against wind erosion if the strips are planted at right angles to the direction of the prevailing wind.

(d) **Correct crops for the soil.** Steep slopes which should not or cannot be ploughed are covered with pasture crops. The foliage reduces the run-off, and the roots hold the soil in place and preserve its structure. The following Table illustrates this point.

Indicated time necessary to remove 18 cm of topsoil from a 10 per cent slope, sandy clay loam, Southern Piedmont

Type of ground cover	kg of soil removed annually per 1000 m²	Number of years needed to erode 18 cm topsoil at this rate
Virgin forest	5	500,000
Grass	775	3,225
Rotation	35800	70
Cotton	79000	32
Bare ground	166000	15

(From Bennett, *Elements of soil conservation*, McGraw Hill, 1947, Table 5.)

(e) **Reafforestation.** Mountainous areas which have suffered from erosion are replanted with trees, so reducing the run-off and controlling floods. Controlled thinning of forests is also desirable, since thickly afforested areas may prevent too large a proportion of water from ever reaching the ground.

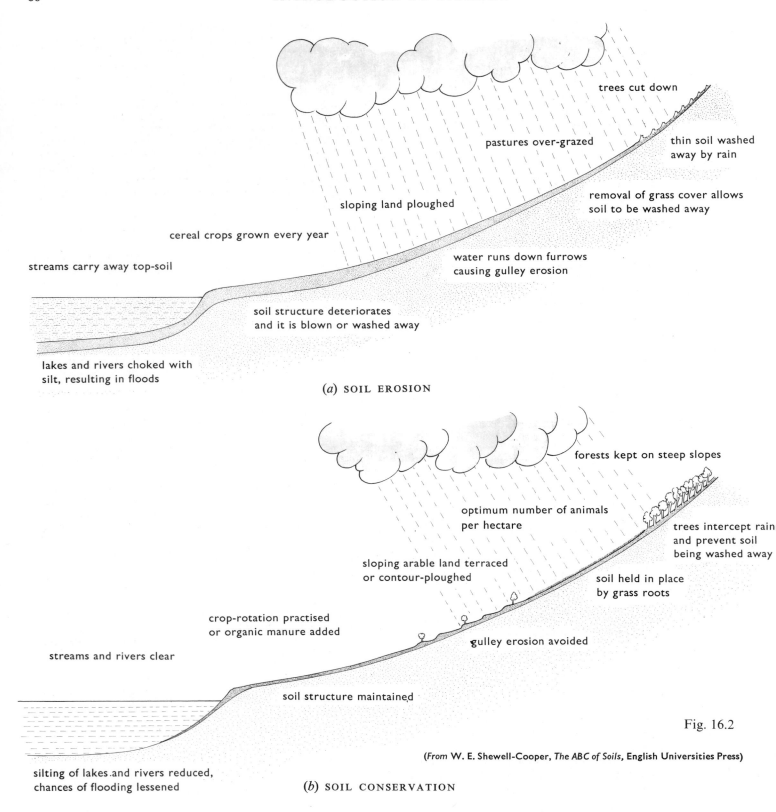

trees cut down

pastures over-grazed

thin soil washed away by rain

removal of grass cover allows soil to be washed away

sloping land ploughed

cereal crops grown every year

streams carry away top-soil

water runs down furrows causing gulley erosion

soil structure deteriorates and it is blown or washed away

lakes and rivers choked with silt, resulting in floods

(a) SOIL EROSION

forests kept on steep slopes

optimum number of animals per hectare

trees intercept rain and prevent soil being washed away

sloping arable land terraced or contour-ploughed

soil held in place by grass roots

crop-rotation practised or organic manure added

gulley erosion avoided

streams and rivers clear

soil structure maintained

Fig. 16.2

(From W. E. Shewell-Cooper, The ABC of Soils, English Universities Press)

silting of lakes and rivers reduced, chances of flooding lessened

(b) SOIL CONSERVATION

Methods of conserving and renewing soil fertility

In natural conditions soil fertility is maintained by the activity of the organisms living on it or in it. For example, the plant roots maintain the soil's crumb structure and the burrows of arthropods enhance its drainage. Although plants remove mineral salts, these are replaced by the death and decomposition of plant and animal bodies. The practice of agriculture interrupts natural cycles by removing the crops at harvest but not returning to the soil the dead remains of either the plants or the animals which eat them. This practice and the loss of soluble salts washed out by rain greatly reduces the yield from crops.

In Kenya the yield of maize from an experimental plot dropped from 5800 kg per hectare to 2240 kg per hectare in only three years.

To make good the losses from the soil, the farmer adds either manure, compost or artificial fertilizers.

Manure. The grass bedding used for domestic animals such as chickens, goats and cattle collects their faeces and urine, and when dug into the soil it provides organic matter which (*a*) decays to give the nutrient salts needed by plants and (*b*) provides the material needed to form humus. Compost, i.e. rotting plant remains, such as vegetable peelings or uprooted weeds, can also provide humus. Untreated human sewage, although it would help to complete the nitrogen cycle, is not used on crops because of the dangers of spreading intestinal diseases such as cholera, typhoid and dysentery, but treated sewage and sewage sludge which has been fermented at a high temperature can be a safe and useful fertilizer for the soil.

Artificial fertilizers. Although small mixed farms may produce enough manure to maintain soil fertility, large-scale arable farms do not and the minerals must be replaced by more direct chemical means. The artificial fertilizers are made in factories from sulphuric acid, ammonia, lime, slag from steel processing, and other industrial wastes.

Ammonium nitrate, NH_4NO_3, is used as a source of nitrogen; ammonium sulphate, $(NH_4)_2SO_4$, supplies nitrogen and sulphur. There are many other commercially prepared fertilizers which contain various mixtures of minerals specially suited to particular crops or soil conditions. Most of them contain varying proportions of nitrate, phosphate and potassium (NPK fertilizers).

Crop rotation helps to conserve fertility (*a*) by changing the demands made on the mineral resources of the soil, (*b*) by improving crumb structure and (*c*) by reducing the density of harmful fungi and other parasites which affect particular crops (see p. 54).

PRACTICAL WORK

Experiment 1. *Observation of mineral particles in soil*

Some dry soil is sieved to remove stones and particles larger than about 3 mm. The soil is crushed lightly to break up aggregates of particles and 50 g is placed in a small, flat-sided bottle. The bottle is filled with water almost to the top, the cap screwed on and the bottle shaken for at least 30 seconds to disperse the soil throughout the water. The bottle is then allowed to stand for 10 to 15 minutes so that the soil settles down. The large particles will fall most rapidly and form the bottom layer. Smaller particles will contribute to successively higher layers and much of the clay will remain in suspension in the water. The larger particles of organic matter will float to the top. If the layers are distinct enough to be measured, the results can be used to compare soils from different areas.

Experiment 2. *The weight of organic matter in the soil*

A sample of soil is placed in a weighed evaporating basin which is then reweighed. The basin is heated over a water-bath for some hours or days, according to the weight and nature of the sample, to drive off the soil water. The basin is then allowed to cool in a desiccator and weighed again. Heating and reweighing are continued until two weighings give identical results, showing that all the soil water has evaporated.

The difference between the first and final weighings gives the weight of water that was originally present. Higher temperatures than the water-bath cannot be used as they will cause the burning of the organic matter in the soil and so give an additional loss of weight.

Experiment 3. *Weight of organic matter in the soil*

The dry soil from the previous experiment is heated in the same evaporating basin, but this time on a sand-tray or gauze, until it loses no further weight. All the organic matter has now been burned and oxidized to carbon dioxide and water so that the loss of weight represents the weight of organic matter originally present.

Experiment 4. *Demonstration of erosion*

Obtain two metal or plastic trays about 5 cm deep. Fill one with soil and press it down tightly. Pour water on it carefully till it is saturated and then leave the tray tilted on end to let the surplus water drain away. Cut a rectangle of turf to fit exactly into the second tray. Water this in the same way as the soil.

Place the tray with the turf at an angle of about 45° in a plastic bowl or similar container and water the soil from a watering can with a fine "rose" fitted, for 30 seconds. Empty the bowl and repeat the experiment with the soil. Compare the quantity of soil washed into the bowl in each case. A further comparison can be made by cutting all the grass blades from the turf and watering it again. If a quantitative comparison is wanted, the soil washed into the basin can be collected by allowing it to settle, decanting the excess water, collecting, drying and weighing the soil.

Experiment 5. *A comparison of water retaining properties in soils*

Two equal-sized plastic cups have their bases perforated and lined with glass fibre. One cup is partially packed with dry sand and the other is packed to the same depth with dry soil rich in organic matter. The cups are supported in turn over a beaker and a known volume of water is poured through the soil from a measuring cylinder. When all the water has drained through it is returned to the measuring cylinder to see how much is retained by the soil. The experiment is repeated with the other sample using the same volume of water as before.

It is expected that the soil rich in organic matter will retain a greater proportion of water than the sand, thus illustrating one of the advantages of organic matter in the soil.

Experiment 6. *Permeability of soil to water*

Two glass funnels are plugged with glass wool and half-filled with equal volumes of sandy and clay soils respectively. Both are then covered with water, the level of which is kept constant by topping up throughout the experiment so that there is no difference in pressure between the two. The water that runs through in a given time is collected in a measuring cylinder.

Alternatively, two tins of equal volume or the plastic cups from Experiment 5 are perforated at the bottom, half-filled with soil samples and kept filled to the top with water. The water coming through in a given time is collected in a beaker and transferred to a measuring cylinder.

At first sight, this experiment may seem to make the same comparisons as in Experiment 5. Retention of water and permeability are not the same thing, however, since a soil may retain a large amount of water while still allowing the excess to drain through rapidly.

Experiment 7. *To show the presence of micro-organisms in the soil*

Prepare two Petri dishes of sterile, nutrient agar as described on p. 74. In one of them sprinkle some particles of soil and in the other, as a control, some particles of clean sand that have been sterilized by heating. If bacteria or fungi are present in the soil, they will appear as colonies in the surface of the agar within two days. The absence of such colonies from the control will prove that the bacteria were in the soil and did not come from the air, the dish, the medium or the instrument used to introduce the soil.

QUESTIONS

1. What are the conditions in the soil which make it a suitable environment for microscopic animals and plants?

2. What do you suppose is the biological significance of the following agricultural practices: (i) ploughing farmyard manure (animal faeces and straw) into the soil, (ii) adding lime to the soil, (iii) spreading sulphate of ammonia on the land?

3. Outline the ways in which careless agricultural practices can lead to rapid erosion of a light sandy soil.

4. When the properties of soils are compared in Experiments 2 and 6 the soil samples should be at field capacity if the comparisons are to be valid. Explain why this is necessary.

17 | Food and Diet in Humans

FOOD made by plants and taken in by animals is utilized in three ways: (a) it may be oxidized to produce energy that is expended in work and physical exercise; (b) it may be incorporated into new cells and tissue to produce growth; or (c) to renew and replace parts of tissue that are constantly being broken down by the chemical changes that occur during life.

Most animals, particularly humans, need a diet providing:

(a) a sufficient quantity of energy,
(b) the correct proportion of *carbohydrates*, *proteins* and *fats*,
(c) mineral salts,
(d) *vitamins*,
(e) water,
(f) fibre (roughage)

Energy value of food

A *joule* is a unit of energy and the number of kilojoules* which can be obtained from a sample of food is a measure of its possible value as a source of energy in the body. Only about 15 per cent of the energy in the food can be obtained as mechanical energy, but the additional heat energy set free is important in maintaining body temperature.

The number of kilojoules needed by human beings varies very greatly according to age, sex, occupation and activity, but a general indication of the daily requirement of normal people can be obtained by considering estimates given for adults engaged in different occupations, e.g. a lumberjack doing eight hours' work per day requires from 23,000 to 25,000 kJ, a tailor needs between 10,000 and 11,000 kJ and a child of six years about 8000 kJ.

Clearly, heavy manual work, rapid growth and vigorous activity will require a greater supply of energy. The following Table indicates roughly how the energy requirements during the day depend on activity:

	kJ
8 hours asleep	2400
8 hours awake; relatively inactive physically	3000
8 hours physically active	6600
Total	12,000

If the daily intake of food does not provide sufficient energy, a human being will lose weight as the existing food stores and tissues of the body are oxidized to release energy, and the capacity for work will fall off. An intake of less than 6300 kJ per day, if maintained for a long period, would probably produce wasting and death, though the conditions in which this is likely to occur would probably give rise to malnutrition through lack of certain vitamins in the first instance.

The energy value of food is calculated by burning a known weight of it completely to carbon dioxide and water. The

* 1000 joules = 1 kilojoule (kJ).

burning takes place in a special apparatus, a bomb calorimeter, designed to ensure that all the heat given out during the combustion is transmitted to a known weight of water whose temperature rise is measured. Since 4·2 joules of heat raise the temperature of 1 g water by 1°C, the number of joules given out by the burning food can be calculated. Whether the body can obtain the same quantity of energy depends on the efficiency of digestion, absorption and the chemical processes undergone by the food.

Carbohydrates

Carbohydrates are substances containing the elements carbon, hydrogen and oxygen. Examples are *glucose*, $C_6H_{12}O_6$; *cane sugar*, $C_{12}H_{22}O_{11}$; *starch*, $(C_6H_{10}O_5)_n$; and *cellulose*. The formula for starch means that the molecule is a large one, made up of repeated $C_6H_{10}O_5$ units. The "n" may be equivalent to 300 or more. Foods relatively rich in carbohydrates are milk, fruit, jam and honey, all of which contain sugar, and bread, potatoes and yams, all of which contain starch.

Carbohydrates are principally of value as energy-giving foods, each gramme of which can provide 16 kJ of energy. In mammals, excess carbohydrate is stored as *glycogen* in the liver and the muscles, or converted to fat and stored in fat cells beneath the skin.

Proteins

Proteins contain the elements carbon, hydrogen, oxygen, nitrogen, usually sulphur and, possibly, others according to their source. Examples of foods containing protein are lean meat, eggs, beans, groundnuts, fish and milk and its products such as cheese.

Proteins are broken down by digestion to substances called amino acids which are absorbed into the blood stream and eventually reach the cells of the body. In the cells the amino acids are re-assembled to form the structural proteins of the cytoplasm and its constituent enzymes. There are only about twenty different kinds of amino acids but there are hundreds of different proteins. The difference between one protein and the next depends on which amino acids are used to build it, how many of each there are, their sequence and their arrangement as shown below.

A-B-C-D-E-F-G-H-I-J-K

(a) Representation of a small protein molecule. The letters are the amino acids

(b) The protein is digested and the amino acids are set free

B-J-K-D-A-F
|
E-C-G-H-I

(c) The same amino acids are built up into a different protein

82

Plants can build all the amino acids they need from carbohydrates, nitrates and sulphates but animals cannot. They must therefore obtain their amino acids from proteins already made by plants or present in other animals and the diet must therefore include a minimum quantity of protein of one sort or another. A diet with a sufficient energy content of fats and carbohydrates and rich in vitamins and salts will lead to illness and death because of its lack of proteins. Proteins are particularly important during periods of pregnancy and growth when new cytoplasm, cells and tissues are being made.

Although animals cannot make amino acids they can, in some cases, convert one amino acid into another. There are, however, ten or more amino acids which animals cannot produce in this way and these *essential amino acids* must be obtained directly from proteins in the diet. Animal proteins generally contain more essential amino acids than do plant proteins but since milk and eggs contain the highest proportion of all, a vegetarian who includes these in his diet should not lack essential amino acids.

Proteins must be included in the diet because it is from proteins alone that new cells and tissues can be built for growth and replacement. If proteins are eaten in excess, there will be more amino acids in the body than are needed to produce or replace cells. The excess amino acids are converted in the liver to carbohydrates which are then oxidized for energy, or converted to glycogen and stored. The energy value of protein is 17 kJ/g.

Kwashiorkor. For a long time it was thought that kwashiorkor was the result of a shortage of protein in the diet. It is when babies are weaned from protein-rich breast milk to protein-deficient yam and cassava that they tend to develop kwashiorkor. They become listless and miserable; their skin cracks and becomes scaly; their abdomens swell and their hair takes on a reddish colour. Because kwashiorkor occurs mainly in children whose diets are deficient in quantity as well as in protein, the disease has also been described as protein-calorie, or protein-energy malnutrition (PEM). In many cases it has been possible to cure the disease by providing more food and increasing the protein content of the diet.

However, there are many cases where some children develop kwashiorkor and others do not, even though they all have the same low-protein, low-energy diet. Also, kwashiorkor occurs mainly in hot, humid regions rather than in hot dry regions despite the fact that diets in the two regions differ very little.

Recent studies point to the possibility that the disease might be caused by poisons produced by a mould which grows in certain types of food. These poisons, are called *aflatoxins*, and they have been found in ground-nuts, chick peas and dried okra and affected children have higher levels of aflatoxins in their blood than normal. Aflatoxins are known to cause liver damage. It seems likely that some children are able to break down the aflatoxins in their bodies better than others, which would explain why they do not develop kwashiorkor even though they eat the same food. If this theory is correct, one way to combat the disease would be to improve the methods of storing and marketing the suspect food, to prevent the growth of mould.

Fats

Like carbohydrates, fats contain only carbon, hydrogen and oxygen but in different proportions. They are present in milk, butter and cheese, fat, egg-yolk, groundnuts and margarine.

Although fats are less easily digested and absorbed than carbohydrates, they have more than double the energy value, providing 38 kJ/g. Fat can be stored in the body.

Mineral salts

A wide variety of salts is essential for the chemical activities in the body and for the construction of certain tissues. The red pigment in the blood contains iron; bones and teeth contain calcium, magnesium and phosphorus; sodium and potassium are essential in nearly all cells, in the blood fluid and in nerves; iodine is necessary for the proper functioning of the *thyroid gland*. In addition to the sulphur and nitrogen in the body, traces of copper, cobalt and manganese are required.

Salts of these elements are present in small quantities in a normal diet and the body can absorb and concentrate them.

Anaemia is a shortage of red cells or haemoglobin in the blood. It may result from the failure of the red bone-marrow to make enough cells or sufficient pigment, or from an excessive rate of destruction of red cells, or simply a shortage of iron in the diet. In the latter case, iron-deficiency anaemia, the condition can be cured by eating meat, liver, or green vegetables such as the leaves of spinach or groundnuts, which contain iron, or by taking tablets containing compounds of iron.

Vitamins

Vitamins are complex chemical compounds which, although they have no energy value, are essential in small quantities for the normal chemical activities of the body.

It has long been known that certain diseases could be prevented or cured by making alterations in the diet. In about 1750, James Lind, a naval doctor, cured scurvy in seamen by providing them with citrus fruits. Christiaan Eijkman, a Dutch doctor working in Java, in 1896, was searching for the "germ" which he thought transmitted the disease beriberi, but found that the disease could be caused by feeding chickens with polished (de-husked) rice and cured by feeding them unpolished rice. Although Eijkman concluded from this result that the disease was caused by a poisonous substance in the polished rice, which was normally neutralized by something present in the husk of the unpolished grain, it was realized in the next ten years by Eijkman and other scientists, notably the English biochemist Gowland Hopkins, that the husk contained an *accessory food factor* whose absence led to the disease. Many similar accessory food factors have been identified and although their composition varies widely they are usually listed under the general heading of *vitamins*.

Fifteen or more vitamins have been isolated and most of them seem to act as catalysts in essential chemical changes in the body, each one influencing a number of vital processes. Vitamins A, D, E and K are the *fat-soluble vitamins*, occurring mainly in animal fats and oils and absorbed along with the products of fat digestion. Vitamins B and C are the *water-soluble vitamins*.

If a diet is deficient in one or more vitamins, this results in a breakdown of normal bodily activities and produces symptoms of disease. Such diseases can usually be effectively remedied by including the necessary vitamins in the diet.

Plants can build up their vitamins from simple substances, but animals must obtain them "ready-made" directly or indirectly from plants.

Some of the important vitamins are set out in the Table overleaf together with their properties. It must be emphasized that nearly all normal, mixed diets will include adequate amounts of vitamins, and deficiency diseases are most likely to occur where, as in rice-eating countries, the bulk of the diet consists of only one or two kinds of food.

Vitamins and their Characteristics

NAME AND SOURCE OF VITAMIN	DISEASES AND SYMPTOMS CAUSED BY LACK OF VITAMIN	NOTES
Retinol (vitamin A; fat-soluble) Liver, cheese, butter, margarine, milk, eggs. **Carotene** (vitamin A precursor; water-soluble) Spinach, red palm oil, carrots.	Reduced resistance to disease, particularly those which enter through the epithelium. Poor night vision. Cornea of eyes becomes dry and opaque leading to *keratomalacia* and blindness.	The yellow pigment, carotene, present in green leaves, carrots, red peppers and palm oil, is turned into retinol by the body. Modified retinol forms part of the light-sensitive pigment in the retina (page 131). Retinol is stored in the liver.
Vitamin B complex Ten or more water-soluble vitamins usually occurring together. Four are described here.	The B vitamins are present in most unprocessed food. Deficiency diseases usually arise only in populations living on restricted diets.	Many of the B vitamins act as catalysts in the oxidation of carbohydrates during respiration. Absence of these catalysts upsets the body chemistry and leads to illness.
Thiamine (vitamin B_1) Whole grains of cereals, beans, groundnuts, green vegetables, meat, yeast and "Marmite".	Wasting and partial paralysis, or water-logging of the tissues and heart failure. These are symptoms of the two forms of *beriberi*.	
Nicotinic acid or **Niacin** (vitamin B_3) Beans, lean meat, liver, yeast and "Marmite". Nicotinic acid can be made in the body from the essential amino acid *tryptophan* which is present in most cereals.	Skin eczema on exposure to sunlight, diarrhoea, wasting and mental degeneration; all symptoms of *pellagra*.	Rice husks contain both thiamine and tryptophan, so highly milled rice is deficient in both. Populations living largely on milled rice are very prone to beriberi. Maize lacks tryptophan, so a diet which consists mainly of maize can lead to pellagra.
Cobalamin (vitamin B_{12}) From animal products only, e.g. meat, milk, eggs, cheese, fish.	*Vitamin deficiency anaemia* (pernicious anaemia).	This vitamin contains cobalt and is made by the bacteria in the intestines of herbivorous animals.
Folic acid Liver, spinach, fish, beans, peas.	*Vitamin deficiency anaemia* Not enough red blood cells are made.	Likely to affect pregnant women on poor diets, and people suffering from malaria and hookworm.
Ascorbic acid (vitamin C; water-soluble) Oranges, lemons, guava, pawpaw, mango, tomatoes, fresh green vegetables.	Vitamin C is needed for the formation of collagen fibres in connective tissues, e.g. in the skin. If ascorbic acid is deficient, wounds do not heal properly; bleeding occurs under the skin, particularly at the joints; the gums become swollen and bleed easily. These are all symptoms of *scurvy*.	Possibly acts as a catalyst in cell respiration. Scurvy is only likely to occur when fresh food is not available. Milk contains little ascorbic acid so babies need additional sources. Cannot be stored in the body; daily intake needed.
Calciferol (vitamin D; fat-soluble) Butter, milk, cheese, egg-yolk, liver, fish-liver oil.	Calcium is not deposited properly in the bones, causing *rickets* in young children because the bones remain soft and are deformed by the child's weight. Deficiency in adults causes *osteomalacia*; fractures are likely.	Calciferol helps the absorption of calcium from the intestine and the deposition of calcium salts in the bones. Natural fats in the skin are converted to a form of calciferol by sunlight.

There are several other substances classed as vitamins, e.g. **riboflavin** (B_2), **tocopherol** (E), **phylloquinone** (K), but these are either (a) unlikely to be missing from the diet, or (b) not known to be important in the human diet. Vitamin K is synthesized by bacteria in the colon (p. 89). If it is absorbed, this might explain why dietary deficiency is unimportant.

Water

Water makes up a large proportion of all the tissues in the body and is an essential constituent of normal protoplasm.

In the intestine, water is needed to digest and dissolve the food, and water in the blood plasma carries the dissolved food all round the body. Nitrogenous waste products are removed from the body in a water solution, called urine. Water is present in all kinds of food but a water balance in the body (*see* p. 108) is maintained by drinking.

Dietary fibre (roughage)

Fibre consists largely of plant-cell walls which cannot be digested by man but are digested by bacteria in the colon. The fibre is thought to be important in maintaining a healthy digestive system in a variety of ways. It adds bulk to the food and enables the muscles of the alimentary canal to grip it and keep it moving by peristalsis (p. 86).

Cereals, vegetables and fruits contain a high proportion of fibre.

Milk

The sole article of diet during the first few weeks or months of a mammal's life, milk is an almost ideal food since it contains proteins, fats, carbohydrates, mineral salts, particularly those of calcium and magnesium, and vitamins. For adults, however, it is less satisfactory because of its high water content and lack of iron. Large volumes would have to be consumed if it were the principal article of diet for an adult, and serious blood deficiencies would result from the lack of iron. In the body of the embryo mammal, iron is stored while the embryo develops inside its mother, and this supply must suffice until the young mammal begins to eat solid food.

PRACTICAL WORK

Food tests. Test for starch. A little starch powder is shaken in a test-tube with some cold water and then boiled to make a clear solution. When the solution is cold, 3 or 4 drops of *iodine solution** are added. The dark blue colour that results is characteristic of the reaction between starch and iodine. This test is very sensitive.

Test for glucose. A little glucose is heated with some Benedict's solution* in a test-tube. The solution changes from blue to opaque green, yellow, and finally a red precipitate of copper(I) oxide appears. If the liquid is allowed to boil, the mouth of the test-tube must be directed away from people as the solution tends to "bump" out of the tube. Sucrose is recognized by its failure to react with Benedict's solution until after it has been boiled with dilute hydrochloric acid and neutralized with sodium hydrogencarbonate.

Test for protein. (Biuret test). To a one per cent solution of albumen is added 5 cm³ dilute sodium hydroxide (CARE: this solution is caustic) and 5 cm³ one per cent copper sulphate solution. A purple colour is indicative of protein.

Test for fats. Two drops of cooking oil are thoroughly shaken with about 5 cm³ ethanol in a dry test-tube until the fat dissolves. The alcoholic solution is poured into a test-tube containing a few cm of water. A cloudy white emulsion is formed.

Application of the food tests. These tests can be applied to samples of food such as milk, pineapple, potato, onion, beans, egg-yolk, ground-nuts, to find out what food materials are present in them.

They can also be carried out in connexion with work on seeds and storage organs. The seeds are crushed in a mortar and shaken with warm water to extract soluble products. The solution and suspension of crushed seed is subjected to the tests given above.

QUESTIONS

1. What principles must be observed when working out a diet in order to lose weight? What dangers are there if such diets are not scientifically planned?
2. Kwashiorkor is a protein deficiency disease which affects young children in parts of Asia and Africa. Its onset is usually most severe when a child is weaned from the mother's milk to the starchy plant foods, e.g. yam, cassava, of the adults. Why should weaning mark the onset of the disease?
3. It is a common fallacy that manual workers need much more protein than sedentary workers. Suggest why this idea is fallacious.
4. Eating a large amount of protein at one sitting is wasteful. It is better to take in a little protein at each meal. Why do you think this is the case?
5. What dietary problems confront (*a*) people living predominantly off rice or maize, (*b*) strict vegetarians?

* Methods of preparing the reagents are given on p. 250.

18 | The Digestion, Absorption and Metabolism of Food

To be of any value to the body, the food taken in through the mouth must enter the blood stream and be distributed to all the living regions.

Digestion is the process by which insoluble food, consisting of large molecules, is broken down into soluble compounds having smaller molecules. These smaller molecules, in solution, pass through the walls of the intestine and enter the blood stream. Digestion and absorption take place in the *alimentary canal* (Fig. 18.1 and Plate 15), digestion being brought about by means of active chemical compounds called *enzymes*. The alimentary canal is a muscular tube, with an internal glandular lining, running from mouth to anus. Some regions have particular functions and, accordingly, different structures. Juices are secreted in the alimentary canal from glands in its lining or are poured into it through ducts from glandular organs outside it. As the food passes through the alimentary canal it is broken down in stages until the digestible material is dissolved and absorbed. The indigestible residue is expelled through the anus.

Enzymes

Enzymes are chemical compounds, protein in nature, made in the cells of living organisms. They act as catalysts – substances which accelerate the rate of most chemical changes in the organism without altering the end-products. They occur in great numbers and varieties in all protoplasm and without them the chemical reactions would be too slow to maintain life. The vast majority of enzymes are *intracellular*, that is, they carry out their functions in the protoplasm of the cell in which they are made. Some enzymes, however, are secreted out of the cells in which they are made, to be used elsewhere. These are called *extracellular* enzymes. Bacteria (p. 73) and fungi (p. 75) secrete such extracellular enzymes into the medium in which they are growing. The higher organisms secrete extracellular enzymes into the alimentary tract to act on food taken into it.

These digestive enzymes accelerate the rate at which insoluble compounds are broken down into soluble ones. Enzymes which act on starch are called *amylases*, those acting on proteins are *proteinases*, and *lipases* act on fat.

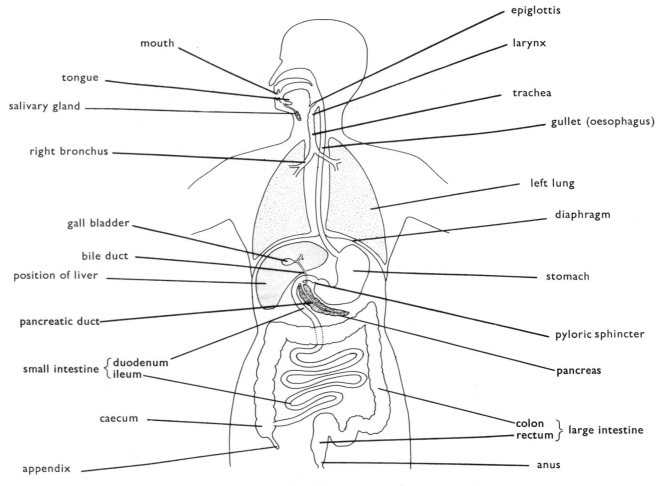

Fig. 18.1   The alimentary canal

Every enzyme has the following characteristics:

    (a) it is destroyed by heating, since it is a protein,

    (b) it acts best within a narrow temperature range,

    (c) it acts most rapidly in a particular degree of acidity or alkalinity (pH),

    (d) it acts on only one kind of substance,

    (e) it always forms the same end-product or products, since an enzyme affects only the rate of reaction.

Movement of food through the alimentary canal

Ingestion is the act of taking food into the alimentary canal through the mouth.

Swallowing (*see* Fig. 18.3). In swallowing, the following actions take place: (a) the tongue presses upwards and back against the roof of the mouth, forcing the pellet of food, called a *bolus*, to the back of the mouth, or *pharynx*; (b) the *soft palate* closes the opening between the nasal cavity and the pharynx; (c) the *laryngeal cartilage* round the top of the trachea, or wind-pipe, is pulled upwards by muscles so that the opening of the larynx lies beneath the back of the tongue, and the opening of the trachea is constricted by the contraction of a ring of muscle; and (d) the *epiglottis*, a flap of cartilage, directs food over the laryngeal orifice. In this way food is able to pass over the trachea without entering it. The beginning of this action is voluntary, but once the bolus of food reaches the pharynx swallowing becomes an automatic or reflex action. The food is forced into and down the oesophagus, or gullet, by *peristalsis*.

This takes about six seconds with relatively solid food, and then the food is admitted to the stomach. Liquid travels more rapidly down the gullet.

Peristalsis (Fig. 18.2). The walls of the alimentary canal contain circular and longitudinal muscle fibres. The circular muscles, by contracting and relaxing alternately, urge the food in a wave-like motion through the various regions of the alimentary canal.

Egestion. The expulsion from the alimentary canal of the undigested remains of food is called egestion.

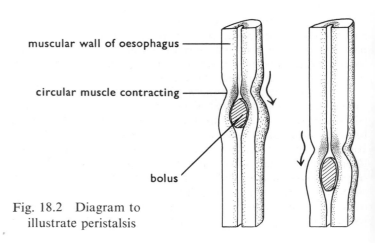

Fig. 18.2   Diagram to illustrate peristalsis

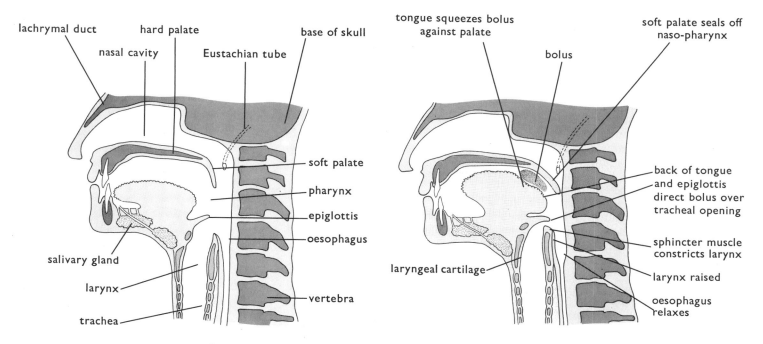

Fig. 18.3 Section through head to show swallowing action

Digestion in the mouth

In the mouth the food is chewed and mixed with saliva. Chewing reduces the food to suitable sizes for swallowing and increases the available surface for enzymes to act on.

Saliva is a digestive juice secreted by three pairs of glands the ducts of which lead into the mouth (Fig. 18.3). It is a watery fluid, not particularly acid or alkaline and containing a little mucus, which helps to lubricate the food and makes the particles adhere to one another. An adult may secrete from 1 to 1·5 litres of saliva per day. One enzyme, *salivary amylase*, is present in saliva. Salivary amylase acts on cooked starch and begins to break it down into *maltose*, a soluble sugar.

The longer food is retained in the mouth, the further this starch digestion proceeds and the more finely divided does the food become as a result of chewing. In fact even well-chewed food does not remain in the mouth long enough for much digestion of starch to take place, but saliva will continue to act for a time even when food is passed into the stomach.

Digestion in the stomach

This part of the alimentary canal has flexible walls and so can be extended as food accumulates in it. This enables food from a particular meal to be stored for some time and released slowly to the rest of the alimentary canal.

Very little absorption takes place in the stomach, but its glandular lining (Fig. 18.4) produces *gastric juice* containing the enzyme *pepsin*, and it may also contain, in young children, an enzyme called *rennin*. Pepsin acts on proteins and breaks them down into more soluble compounds called *peptides*. Rennin, if present, clots protein in milk. The stomach wall also secretes *hydrochloric acid* which makes a 0·5 per cent solution in the gastric juice. The acid provides the best degree of acidity (optimum pH) for pepsin to work in, and probably also kills many of the bacteria taken in with the food. The

salivary amylase from the mouth cannot digest starch in an acid atmosphere, but it seems likely that it continues to act within the bolus of food until this is broken up and the hydrochloric acid reaches all its contents.

The rhythmic, peristaltic movements of the stomach, about every twenty seconds, help to mix the food and gastric juice to a creamy liquid called *chyme*. Each wave of peristalsis also pumps a little of the chyme from the stomach into the first part of the small intestine, called the *duodenum*. The pyloric sphincter is usually relaxed but contracts at the end of each wave of peristalsis, so limiting the amount of chyme which escapes. Even when relaxed, the pyloric opening is narrow and only liquid is allowed through. When the acid contents of the stomach enter the duodenum, they set off a reflex action (p. 139), which closes the pyloric sphincter until the duodenal contents have been partially neutralized.

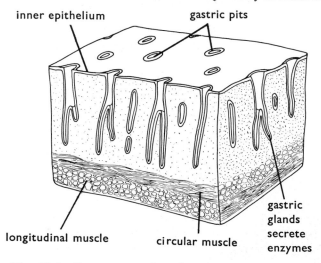

Fig. 18.4 Stereogram of section through stomach wall

Digestion in the duodenum

An alkaline juice from the *pancreas*, and *bile* from the liver, are poured into the duodenum. The pancreas is a cream-coloured gland lying below the stomach (Fig. 18.5). Its cells make enzymes which act on carbohydrates, proteins and fats respectively. Three of these enzymes, including *trypsin*, break down proteins to peptides, and peptides to soluble *amino acids*. Starch is broken down to *maltose* and fats are split up into *fatty acids* and *glycerol*. Pancreatic juice also contains sodium hydrogencarbonate which partly neutralizes the acid chyme from the stomach, and so creates a suitable environment (pH) for the pancreatic and intestinal enzymes to work in.

Bile is a green, watery fluid made in the liver, stored in the gall bladder and conducted to the duodenum by the bile duct. Its colour is derived largely from breakdown products of the red pigment from decomposing red blood cells. It contains sodium chloride, sodium hydrogencarbonate and organic bile salts but no enzymes.

Bile dilutes the contents of the intestine, and the bile salts reduce the surface tension of fats, so emulsifying them. This results in fats forming a suspension of tiny droplets, the increased surface so presented allowing more rapid digestion. Many of the bile salts are reabsorbed in the ileum.

Digestion in the ileum

In the small intestine, digestion is continued by the action of the pancreatic enzymes. All the digestible material is changed to soluble compounds which pass into the cells lining the ileum. In these cells, peptides are broken down to amino acids, and maltose and sucrose are broken down to glucose and fructose. These substances then enter the blood capillaries.

The glandular lining of the alimentary canal is continually secreting mucus which helps to lubricate the passage of food between its walls but which also prevents the digestive juices from reaching and digesting the alimentary canal itself. The cells which make the protein-digesting enzymes would themselves be digested by these chemicals were it not for the fact that the enzymes are made in an inactive form and cannot work until they reach the cavity of the alimentary canal, where they are activated by the chemicals present. Pepsin, for example, is made and secreted as an inactive substance, *pepsinogen*. When

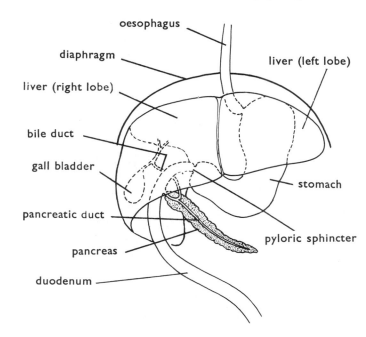

Fig. 18.5   Diagram to show relation of stomach, liver and pancreas

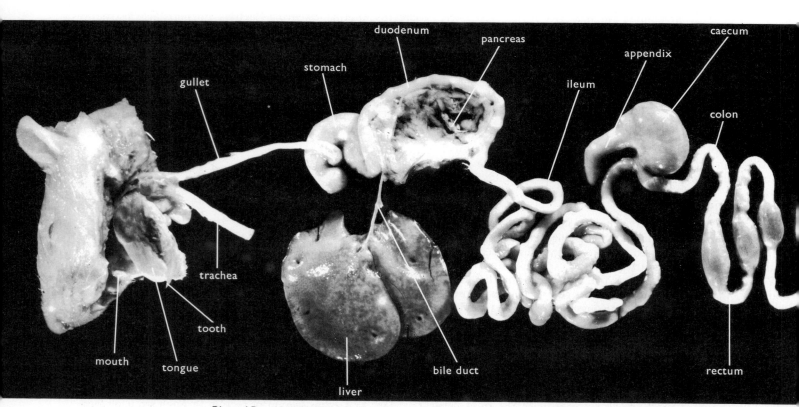

Plate 15.   ALIMENTARY CANAL OF A RAT UNRAVELLED

(Dissection by Griffin & George Ltd, Gerrard Biological Centre)

pepsinogen is set free in the stomach the hydrochloric acid present converts it to active pepsin. This pepsin cannot now digest the stomach walls because of their protective coating of mucus.

Absorption in the ileum

Nearly all the absorption of digested food takes place in the ileum, and certain of its characteristics are important adaptations to its absorbing properties:

(a) it is usually fairly long and presents a large absorbing surface to the digested food,

(b) its internal surface is greatly increased by thousands of tiny, finger-like projections about 1 mm long called *villi* (Fig. 18.6 and Plate 16),

(c) the lining epithelium is very thin and the fluids can pass fairly rapidly through it,

(d) there is a dense network of blood capillaries in each villus (Fig. 18.7).

The small molecules of the digested food, principally amino acids and glucose, pass through the epithelium and the capillary walls and enter the blood plasma. They are then carried away in the capillaries which unite to form veins and eventually join up to form one large vein, the *hepatic portal* vein. This carries all the blood from the intestine to the liver, which may retain or alter any of the digestion products. The digested food then reaches the general circulation.

Some of the fatty acids, and glycerol from the digestion of fats, enter the blood capillaries of the villi but a large proportion may be recombined in the intestinal lining to form fats once again and then these fats pass into the *lacteals*. It may be that some of the finely emulsified fat is absorbed directly, i.e. without digestion, as minute droplets which subsequently enter the lacteals. The fluid in the lacteals enters the *lymphatic system* which forms a network all over the body and eventually empties its contents into the blood stream (p. 100).

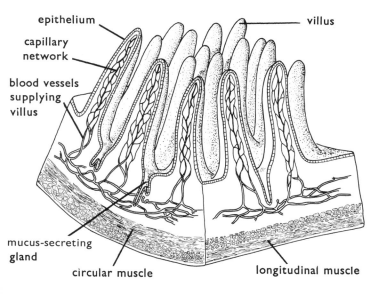

Fig. 18.6   Stereogram to show structure of ileum

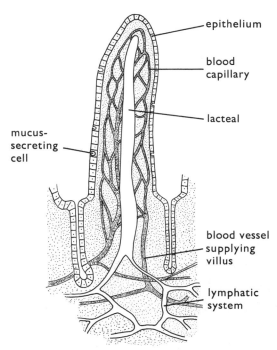

Fig. 18.7   Villus structure

The large intestine (colon and rectum)

The material passing into the large intestine consists of water with undigested matter, largely cellulose and vegetable fibres (roughage), mucus and dead cells from the lining of the alimentary canal. The large intestine secretes no enzymes but the bacteria in the colon digest part of the fibre. The colon absorbs much of the water from the undigested residues. This semi-solid waste, *the faeces*, is passed into the *rectum* by peristalsis and is expelled at intervals through the *anus*. The residues may spend from 12 to 24 hours in the intestine.

The caecum and appendix

In humans the caecum and appendix are small structures possibly without digestive functions. In herbivores like the rabbit and the horse they are much larger, and it is here that most of the cellulose digestion takes place, largely as a result of bacterial activity. The appendix has lymph nodes (p. 100).

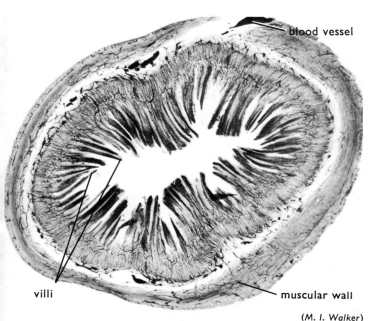

(M. I. Walker)

Plate 16.   TRANSVERSE SECTION THROUGH ILEUM OF CAT, SHOWING VILLI (× 12)

Digestive Action

REGION OF ALIMENTARY CANAL	DIGESTIVE GLAND	DIGESTIVE JUICE PRODUCED	ENZYMES IN THE JUICE	CLASS OF FOOD ACTED UPON	SUBSTANCES PRODUCED	NOTES
MOUTH	Salivary glands	Saliva	Salivary amylase	Starch	Maltose	Slightly acid or neutral. Mucus helps form bolus. Water lubricates food.
STOMACH	Gastric glands (in stomach lining)	Gastric juice	Pepsin	Proteins	Peptides	0·5% hydrochloric acid also secreted, provides acid medium for pepsin and kills most bacteria. No absorption except of alcohol.
			(Rennin)	(Milk protein)	(Clots it)	
DUODE-NUM	Pancreas	Pancreatic juice	Trypsin	Proteins and peptides	Amino acids	Two other protein-digesting enzymes are present. Bile emulsifies fats and aids their absorption. Duodenum contents slightly acid.
			Amylase	Starch	Maltose	
	(Liver)	(Bile)	Lipase	Fats	Fatty acids and glycerol	
ILEUM	The glands between the villi produce mucus but few, if any, digestive enzymes	Intestinal juice contains an enzyme which activates pancreatic trypsin	Pancreatic enzymes still active	Peptides	Amino acids	These final stages of digestion take place in the ileum with the aid of pancreatic enzymes. Some digestion occurs in the epithelial cells of the villi.
				Fats	Fatty acids and glycerol	The main function of the ileum is the absorption of the digested products.
				Maltose	Glucose	
				Sucrose	Glucose and fructose	
				Lactose	Glucose and galactose	
COLON						Absorption of water

Utilization of digested food

The products of digestion are carried round the body in the blood plasma. From the blood, most living cells are able to absorb and metabolize glucose, fats and amino acids.

(a) *Glucose*. During respiration in the protoplasm, glucose is oxidized to carbon dioxide and water (*see* p. 47). This reaction releases energy to drive the many chemical processes in the cell, and in specialized cells produces, for example, contraction (muscle cells) and electrical changes (nerve cells).

(b) *Fats*. Fats are incorporated into cell membranes and other structures in cells. The fats not used for growth and maintenance in this way are oxidized to carbon dioxide and water, releasing energy for the vital processes of the cells. Twice as much energy can be obtained from fats as from glucose.

(c) *Amino acids* are absorbed by cells and reassembled to make proteins (p. 82). These proteins may form visible structures such as the cell membrane and other components of the protoplasm or the proteins may be enzymes which control and co-ordinate the chemical activity within the cell.

Amino acids not required for building proteins are *de-aminated* in the liver, that is, their nitrogen is removed and the residue is used in the same way as carbohydrate, namely oxidized, or converted to glycogen and stored.

Storage of digested food

If the quantity of food taken in exceeds the energy requirements of the body or the demand for structural materials, it is stored in one of the following ways:

(a) *Glucose* (Fig. 18.8). The concentration of glucose in the blood of a person who has not eaten for eight hours is usually between 90 and 100 mg/100 cm^3 blood. After a meal containing carbohydrate, the blood sugar level may rise to 140 mg/100 cm^3 but two hours later, the level returns to about 95 mg.

The sugar not required immediately for the energy supply in the cells is converted in the liver and in the muscles to glycogen. The glycogen molecule is built up by combining many glucose molecules in a long branching chain rather similar to the starch molecule. About 100 g of this insoluble glycogen is stored in the liver and about 300 g in the muscles. When the blood sugar level falls below 80 mg/100 cm^3, the liver converts its glycogen back to glucose and releases it into the circulation. The muscle glycogen is not normally returned to the circulation but is used by active muscle as a source of energy in much the same way as glucose.

The glycogen in the liver is a "short-term" store, sufficient for about only six hours if no other glucose supply is available. Excess glucose not stored as glycogen is converted to fat and stored in the fat cells of the fat depots. (*See* below.)

(b) *Fats*. Certain cells can accumulate drops of fat in their cytoplasm. As these drops increase in size and number, they join together to form one large globule of fat in the middle of the cell, pushing the cytoplasm into a thin layer and the nucleus to one side (Figs. 18.9 and 18.10). Groups of fat cells form *adipose tissue* beneath the skin and in the connective tissue of most organs. (Plate 22, p. 110.)

Unlike glycogen, there is no limit to the amount of fat stored and because of its high energy value it is an important reserve of energy-giving food.

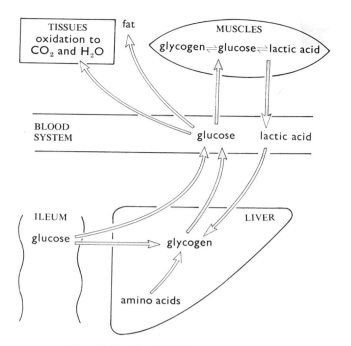

Fig. 18.8   Carbohydrate metabolism

(Figs. 18.8 and 18.11 by kind permission of Bell, G. H., Davidson, J. N., Scarborough, H. (1959) Textbook of Physiology and Biochemistry, 4e, Edinburgh, Livingstone)

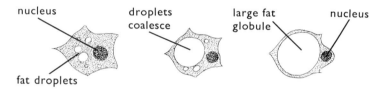

Fig. 18.9   Accumulation of fat in a fat cell

Fig. 18.10   Small section of adipose tissue

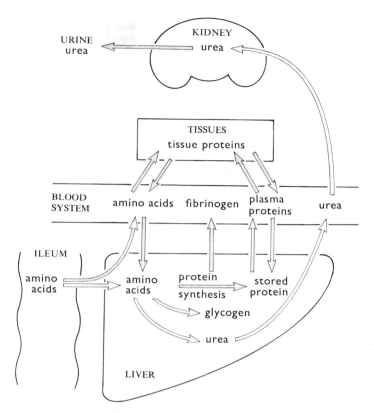

Fig. 18.11   Protein metabolism

(c) *Amino acids* (Fig. 18.11). Amino acids are not stored in the body. Those not used in protein formation are deaminated. The protein of the liver and tissues can act as a kind of protein store to maintain the protein level in the blood but absence of protein in the diet soon leads to serious disorders.

The rate of oxidation of glucose and its conversion to glycogen or fat is controlled by hormones (p. 144). When intake of carbohydrate and fat exceeds the energy requirements of the body, the excess will be stored mainly as fat. Some people never seem to get fat no matter how much they eat, while others start to lay down fat when their intake only marginally exceeds their needs. Putting on weight is unquestionably the result of eating more food than the body needs but it is not clear why individuals should differ so much in their reaction. The explanation probably lies in the hormonal balance which, to some extent, is determined by heredity. A slimming diet designed to reduce calorific intake must, nevertheless, always include the essential amino acids, vitamins, mineral salts and certain essential fatty acids.

The liver

The liver is a large, reddish-brown organ which lies just below the diaphragm and partly overlaps the stomach (Fig. 18.5). In addition to a supply of oxygenated blood from the *hepatic artery*, it receives all the blood which leaves the alimentary canal. It has a great many important functions, some of which are described below. (*See* also Figs. 18.8 and 18.11.)

1. **Regulation of blood sugar.** The liver is able to convert glucose, amino acids and other substances to an insoluble carbohydrate, *glycogen*. Some of the glucose so converted may be taken from the *hepatic portal* vein carrying blood, rich in digested food, from the ileum to the liver. About 100 g glycogen is stored in the liver of a healthy man. If the concentration of glucose in the blood falls below about 80 mg/100 cm³ blood, some of the glycogen stored in the liver is converted by enzyme action into glucose and it enters the circulation. If the blood sugar level rises above 160 mg/100 cm³, glucose is excreted by the kidneys. A blood glucose level below 40 mg/100 cm³ affects the brain cells adversely, leading to convulsions and coma. By helping to keep the glucose concentration between 80 and 150 mg the liver prevents these undesirable effects and so contributes to the homeostasis (*see* below) of the body. (*See* Fig. 19.2 for circulatory supply to liver.)

2. **Formation of bile.** Green and yellow pigments are formed when the red blood cells break down. These pigments are removed from the blood by the liver and excreted in the bile. The liver also produces bile salts which play an important part in the emulsification and subsequent absorption of fats (p. 88).

Bile is produced continuously by the liver cells, but stored and concentrated in the gall bladder. It is discharged through the bile duct into the duodenum when the acid chyme arrives there. Bile is reabsorbed with the fats they emulsify and eventually return to the liver.

3. **Storage of iron.** Millions of red blood cells break up every day. In the liver their decomposition is completed and the iron from the haemoglobin is stored.

4. **Deamination.** Excess amino acids are not stored in the body. Amino acids which are not built up into proteins and used for growth and replacement are converted to carbohydrates by the removal from the molecule of the *amino group*, —NH_2, which contains the nitrogen. The residue can be converted to glycogen, being stored or oxidized to release energy. The nitrogen of the amino group is converted in the liver to *urea*, an excretory product that is constantly eliminated by the kidneys.

5. **Manufacture of plasma proteins.** The liver makes most of the proteins found in blood plasma, including fibrinogen which plays an important part in the clotting action of the blood (p. 94).

6. **Use of fats in the body.** When fats stored in the body are required for use in providing energy, they travel in the blood stream from the fat depots. Some are used directly by the muscles and some are oxidized in the liver to substances which can be oxidized by other tissues to release energy.

7. **Detoxication.** Poisonous compounds, produced in the large intestine by the action of bacteria on amino acids, enter the blood, but on reaching the liver are converted to harmless substances, later excreted in the urine. Many other chemical substances normally present in the body or introduced as drugs are modified by the liver before being excreted by the kidneys. The hormones, for example, are converted to inactive compounds in the liver so limiting their period of activity in the body.

8. **Storage of vitamins.** The fat-soluble vitamins A and D are stored in the liver. This is the reason why animal liver is a valuable source of these vitamins in the diet. The liver also stores a product of the vitamin B_{12}. This product is necessary for the normal production of red cells in the bone marrow.

[*Note:* Contrary to statements made in previous impressions (prior to 1997), the liver is not a net exporter of heat. Although some of its chemical reactions release heat energy, many of these reactions require an input of energy.]

Homeostasis

A complete account of the functions of the liver would involve a very long list. It is most important, however, to realize that the one vital function of the liver, embodying all the details outlined above, is that it helps to maintain the concentration and composition of the body fluids, particularly the blood.

Within reason, a variation in the kind of food eaten will not produce changes in the composition of the blood.

If this *internal environment*, as it is called, were not so constant, the chemical changes that maintain life would become erratic and unpredictable so that with quite slight changes of diet or activity the whole organization might break down. The regulation of the internal environment is called *homeostasis* and is discussed again on pp. 93, 108 and 145.

PRACTICAL WORK

To investigate the action of pepsin on egg-white. The white of one egg is stirred into 500 cm^3 tap water. The mixture is boiled and filtered through glass wool to remove large particles. About 2 cm of the cloudy suspension is poured into each of 4 tubes labelled *A* to *D*. To *A* is added 1 cm^3 1 per cent pepsin solution, to *B* is added 3 drops of bench hydrochloric acid, to *C* 1 cm^3 pepsin solution and 3 drops of acid and to *D* 3 drops of acid and 1 cm^3 boiled pepsin solution. All four test-tubes are placed in a beaker of water at 35–40°C for 5–10 minutes, after which time the contents of tube *C* will be clear. The change from a cloudy suspension to a clear solution suggests that the solid egg-white particles have been digested to soluble products. This result, and those of the controls *A*, *B* and *D*, support the idea that pepsin digests egg-white in acid conditions.

The digestive action of saliva on starch. Saliva is collected in a test-tube after rinsing the mouth to remove traces of food, and about 1 cm^3 is added to each of two test-tubes containing approximately 2 cm^3 of 2 per cent starch solution. After 5 minutes, one tube is tested with iodine solution while the other is tested with Benedict's reagent as described on p. 85. Failure to obtain a blue colour with iodine indicates that starch is no longer present, while a red precipitate with Benedict's reagent shows that a sugar has been produced. A control is conducted by repeating the experiment using boiled saliva. The theory that saliva contains an enzyme which can change starch to sugar is supported by this experiment.

The effect of acidity and alkalinity on an enzyme reaction. Six test-tubes, labelled *A* to *F*, each have 5 cm^3 1 per cent starch solution placed in them. Acid or alkali is added as follows: 0·1 M sodium bicarbonate solution, *A* 10 drops, *B* 4 drops; 0·1 M hydrochloric acid, *F* 8 drops, *E* 7 drops, *D* 6 drops. Rows of drops of iodine solution are placed on a tile. Saliva is collected as before and 1 cm^3 is added to each tube. Samples are withdrawn at intervals from each tube in turn and added to the iodine drops. When a sample *fails* to give a blue colour, it is assumed that all the starch has been digested. In conditions of acidity or alkalinity most favourable to the enzyme, digestion will be most rapid and samples will cease to give a blue colour after a short time.

The effect of temperature on an enzyme reaction. Three test-tubes each containing 10 cm^3 2 per cent starch solution are placed separately in beakers of ice-water, cold tap water, warm water at about 40°C. After 5 minutes, 1 cm^3 saliva is added to each and samples tested as described above. The tube at the temperature most favourable to starch digestion will give the first sample which fails to turn iodine blue.

QUESTIONS

1. List the chemical changes undergone by (*a*) a molecule of starch from the time it is placed in the mouth to its ultimate use in providing energy, (*b*) a molecule of protein from the time it is swallowed to the time when its components are used in a cell (other than in the liver).

   In each case, state where the changes are taking place.

2. Write down the menu for your breakfast and lunch (or supper); indicate the principal food substances present in each component of the meal and state the final digestion product of each and the use your body is likely to have made of them.

3. What advantage is it to an animal to take food into its alimentary canal for digestion rather than digest it externally as do the fungi?

4. Herbivorous animals have very long intestines with a large caecum and appendix but carnivorous animals have a relatively shorter intestine with small caecum and appendix. In what ways are these differences related to the differences in diet. (*See* also p. 125.)

19 | Blood, its Composition, Function and Circulation

COMPOSITION

BLOOD consists of a suspension of cells in an aqueous solution. In an adult man there are five to six litres of blood in the body.

Cells

Red cells (erythrocytes) (Fig. 19.1a and Plate 17). Minute, biconcave discs, the red cells consist of spongy cytoplasm in an elastic membrane. They have no nuclei. In their cytoplasm is a red pigment, *haemoglobin*, which is a protein with iron in its molecule. It has an affinity for oxygen and readily combines

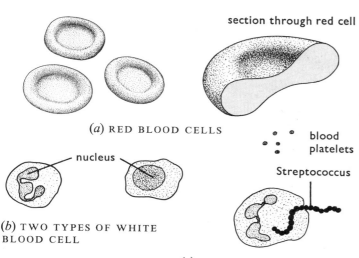

(a) RED BLOOD CELLS

(b) TWO TYPES OF WHITE BLOOD CELL

(c) WHITE CELL ENGULFING A STREPTOCOCCUS

Fig. 19.1   Blood cells

with it in conditions of high oxygen concentration. It forms an unstable compound called *oxy-haemoglobin* which, however, in conditions of low oxygen concentration readily breaks down and releases the oxygen. This property makes it most efficient in transporting oxygen from the lungs to the tissues.

The red cells are made in the red bone-marrow of the short bones such as the sternum, ribs and vertebrae. There are about five-and-a-half million in a cubic millimetre of blood. A red blood cell lasts for about four months, after which it breaks down and is disintegrated in the liver or spleen. About 200,000,000,000 are formed and destroyed each day, which means that about 1 per cent of the total is replaced daily.

White cells (leucocytes) (Fig. 19.1b and Plate 17). There are about 600 red cells to every white cell. The actual numbers vary between 4000 and 13,000/mm³. Various kinds of white cell occur; they are made in the bone marrow, the lymph nodes or the spleen. Some are irregular in shape, can change their form, and all have a nucleus. Most of them are of a type called *phagocytes* which can move by a flowing action of their cytoplasm and can pass out of blood capillaries by squeezing between the cells of the capillary wall. They ingest and destroy bacteria and dead cells by flowing round, engulfing and digesting them (Fig.

19.1c). They accumulate at the site of an injury or infection and devour invading bacteria and damaged tissue, so preventing the spread of harmful bacteria as well as accelerating the healing of the infected region.

Platelets are cell fragments budded off from special, very large cells in the red bone marrow and they play an important part in the clotting action of the blood. There are about 400,000 of them in a cubic millimetre of blood and they appear as tiny, round or oval structures.

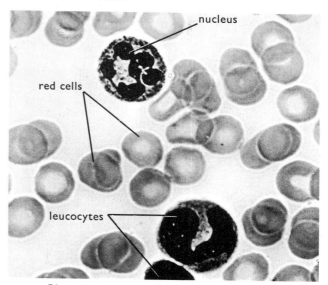

Plate 17.   RED AND WHITE CELLS   *(Gene Cox)*
FROM THE HUMAN BLOOD (×1500)

Plasma. The liquid part of the blood is called plasma, which is a solution in water of many compounds. Some of the most important of these compounds are sodium chloride, sodium hydrogencarbonate, glucose, amino acids and proteins including *albumin*, *fibrinogen* and the *globulin antibodies*; *hormones*, *urea* and other nitrogenous compounds. In the plasma, digested food, carbon dioxide and excretory products are carried round the body.

Serum is blood plasma from which the fibrinogen has been removed.

FUNCTIONS OF THE BLOOD

It will be convenient at this point to distinguish between (a) the functions of the blood as the agent replenishing the tissue fluid surrounding the cells, and (b) the circulation of blood.

(a) **Homeostatic functions of the blood**

All the cells of the body are bathed by a fluid, tissue fluid, derived from plasma, which supplies them with the food and oxygen necessary for their living chemistry, and removes the products of their activities which, if they accumulated, would poison the cells.

The composition of the blood plasma is very precisely regulated by the liver and kidneys so that, within narrow limits, the living cells are soaked in a liquid of unvarying composition. This provides them with the environment they need and enables them to live and grow in the most favourable conditions. By delivering oxygen and nutrients to the tissue fluid and removing the excretory products, the blood fulfils a homeostatic function (p. 108), maintaining the constancy of the internal environment. (*See* p. 98 for further details.)

(b) Circulation

The movement of the blood in vessels round the body constantly changes the fluid surrounding the living cells so that fresh supplies of oxygen and food are brought in as fast as they are used up and poisonous end-products are not allowed to accumulate. The following account is concerned principally with the circulation as a transport system, rather than with the chemical properties of blood fluid as an internal environment.

On the average, a particular red cell would complete the circulation of the body in 45 seconds.

1. **Transport of oxygen from lungs to tissues.** When exposed to the relatively high oxygen concentration in the lungs (p. 103) the haemoglobin in the red cells combines with oxygen forming *oxy-haemoglobin*. Oxy-haemoglobin decomposes when it reaches an active tissue where oxygen is being used up, and sets free oxygen which diffuses out of the capillary wall and so reaches the cells. Oxy-haemoglobin is bright red, while haemoglobin is a dark red. The combination of oxygen with haemoglobin as soon as it enters the red cell, effectively removes oxygen from solution so that its concentration as a dissolved gas inside the cell is kept very low. Thus a steep diffusion gradient (*see* p. 60) is maintained between the source of oxygen and the red cell and, as a result, the rate of diffusion of oxygen into the erythrocyte is rapid.

2. **Transport of carbon dioxide from the tissues to the lungs.** Carbon dioxide produced from actively respiring cells diffuses through the capillary wall and dissolves in the plasma. Some of it enters the red cells and some of it forms sodium hydrogen-carbonate in the plasma. In the lungs (p. 103) it is released, diffuses into the air sacs, and is expelled.

3. **Transport of nitrogenous waste from the liver to the kidneys.** When the liver changes amino acids into glycogen (p. 92), the amino ($-NH_2$) part of the molecules is changed into the nitrogenous waste product, *urea*. This substance is carried away in the blood circulation. When the blood passes through the kidneys, the urea is removed and excreted (p. 107).

4. **Transport of digested food from the ileum to the tissues.** The soluble products of digestion pass into the capillaries of the villi lining the ileum (p. 89). They are carried in solution by the plasma and after passing through the liver enter the general circulation. Glucose and amino acids diffuse out of the capillaries and into the cells of the body. Glucose may be oxidized in a muscle, for example, and provide the energy for contraction; amino acids will be built up into new proteins and make new cells and fresh tissues.

5. **Distribution of hormones.** Hormones are chemicals which affect the rate of vital processes in the body. They are carried in the blood plasma, from the glands which make them, all round the body. When they reach certain organs such as the heart they affect the rate at which these organs work (p. 144).

6. **Distribution of heat and temperature control.** Muscular and chemical activity release heat. These processes occur more rapidly in some parts of the body than others; for example,

chemical activity in the abdominal organs and muscular action in the limbs. The heat so produced locally is distributed all round the body by the blood and in this way an even temperature is maintained in all regions.

The diversion of blood to or away from the skin also plays a part in keeping the temperature constant (*see* p. 110).

7. **Formation of clots.** When a blood vessel is cut open, or its lining damaged, the blood platelets and damaged tissue produce chemicals which help to convert the protein *fibrinogen* to *fibrin*. This makes a network of fibres across the wound within which red cells become entangled, forming a clot which stops further loss of blood and prevents entry of bacteria and poisons. The platelets also adhere to the damaged area and help to form a plug before causing the fibrin to precipitate. The dried clot eventually becomes a scab which protects the damaged area while new skin is forming.

8. **Prevention of infection.** (*a*) INFECTED WOUNDS. Normally the skin provides a barrier to the entry of any bacteria. The layer of dead cells on the skin provides a mechanical barrier while the mucus and chemicals of the alimentary canal offer a chemical defence. If the skin is broken, however, and bacteria enter the cut, certain of the white cells migrate through the capillaries in that region and begin to engulf and digest any bacteria that have invaded the tissues. Many dead white cells and self-digested, dead tissues may accumulate at the site of infection and form pus. In this way, and as a result of clot formation which prevents free circulation, the site of the infection is localized and most of the bacteria are destroyed before they can enter the general circulation. Those which escape into the lymphatic system are trapped by stationary white cells in the lymph nodes or in the spleen and liver. Certain virulent strains of bacteria cannot be ingested by the white cells until they have been acted upon by chemicals called *antibodies,* made in the blood by special white cells. If these antibodies are not already present in the blood or are not made quickly enough, the virulent bacteria or their products will invade the whole body and give rise to symptoms of disease.

(*b*) DISEASE AND IMMUNITY. Many diseases are caused by the presence of bacteria or viruses in the body, and the symptoms may be due to one or more of the following: (*a*) foreign proteins of the bacteria themselves; (*b*) the poisonous chemicals (usually proteins) called *toxins*, which are produced by the bacteria; (*c*) the breakdown products of the infected tissue. Recovery from the disease and subsequent immunity depend to a large extent on the production of *antibodies* in the blood. These antibodies are proteins released into the plasma and they may affect bacteria or their products in a number of ways:

(*a*) *opsonins* adhere to the outer surface of bacteria and so make it easier for the phagocytic white cells to ingest them,
(*b*) *agglutinins* cause bacteria to stick together in clumps; in this condition the bacteria cannot invade the tissues,
(*c*) *lysins* destroy bacteria by dissolving their outer coats, and
(*d*) *anti-toxins* combine with and so neutralize the poisonous toxins produced by bacteria.

The substances which stimulate the production of antibodies are called *antigens*.

When the organism recovers from the disease the antibodies remain for only a short time in the circulatory system but the ability to produce them is greatly increased so that a further invasion by bacteria or viruses is likely to be stopped at once and the person is said to be "immune" to the disease. People may possess this immunity from birth, they may acquire it after recovering from an attack as in measles, or it may be induced in them by vaccination or inoculation. Natural or acquired immunity may occur because disease bacteria are present in the body without being sufficiently numerous or suitably placed to produce disease symptoms.

A **vaccine** is a preparation of killed disease bacteria or viruses, or forms of these treated in such a way as to prevent their reproduction. When these are injected into the blood stream the organism undergoes a mild form of the disease and its cells manufacture an excess of antibodies. In this way immunity is artificially acquired. The period of immunity, during which antibodies can be produced rapidly, varies from a few months to many years, according to the nature of the infection.

Serum. The blood of a person or animal which has recently recovered from a disease will contain antitoxins and antibodies. If the cells and fibrinogen are removed from a sample of this blood a serum is obtained which, when injected into other people, may give temporary immunity or cure them if they already have the disease. Sera for treating tetanus and snake bites are prepared from horse's blood. The horse is injected with diluted poison which stimulates the formation of antitoxins in the blood. Samples of the blood are then taken from the horse, and serum prepared from the samples is used to treat cases.

CIRCULATORY SYSTEM (Figs. 19.2 and 19.3)
The blood is distributed round the body in vessels, most but not all of them tubular, and varying in size from about 1 cm to 0·001 mm in diameter. They form a continuous system, communicating with every living part of the body (Plate 18). Blood flows in them, always in the same direction, passing repeatedly through the heart, the muscular contractions of which maintain the circulation.

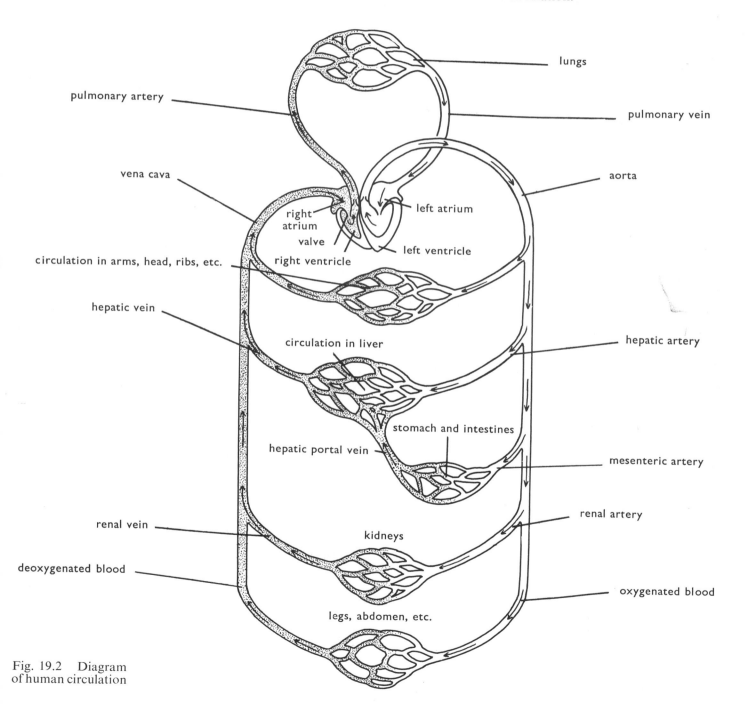

Fig. 19.2 Diagram of human circulation

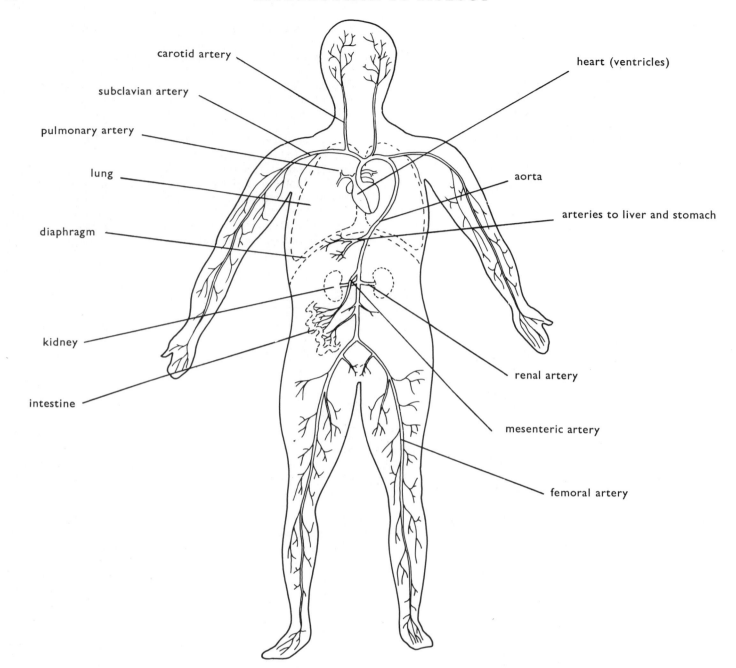

carotid artery

subclavian artery

pulmonary artery

lung

diaphragm

kidney

intestine

heart (ventricles)

aorta

arteries to liver and stomach

renal artery

mesenteric artery

femoral artery

Fig. 19.3   Diagram of human arterial system

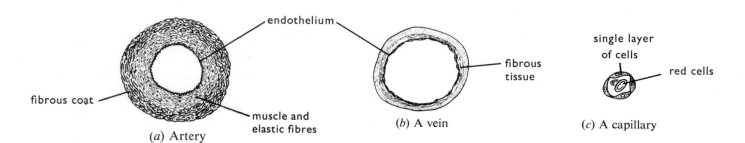

endothelium

fibrous coat

muscle and
elastic fibres

(a) Artery

fibrous
tissue

(b) A vein

single layer
of cells

red cells

(c) A capillary

Fig. 19.4   Blood vessels, transverse sections

There are three types of blood vessel, arteries, veins and capillaries, connected to form a continuous system (Plate 19).

Arteries (Fig. 19.4*a*) are fairly wide vessels which carry blood from the heart to the limbs and organs of the body. They are thick-walled, muscular and elastic and must stand up to the surges of high pressure caused by the heart-beat. The arteries divide into smaller vessels, called *arterioles*, which themselves divide repeatedly until they form a dense network of microscopic vessels permeating between the cells of every living tissue. These final branches are called *capillaries*.

Capillaries (Fig. 19.4*c* and 19.5) are tiny vessels with walls often only one cell thick. Although the blood seems to be

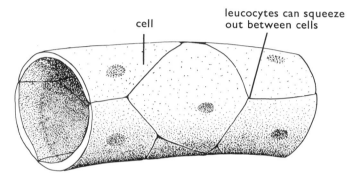

Fig. 19.5   Stereogram of blood capillary

physically confined within the capillary walls, the latter are permeable, allowing water and dissolved substances, other than proteins, to pass in and out. Through these thin walls, oxygen, carbon dioxide, dissolved food and excretory products are exchanged with the tissues round the capillary. The capillary network is so dense that no living cell is far from a supply of oxygen and food (p. 98). In the liver every cell is in direct contact with a capillary. Some capillaries are so narrow that the red cells are squeezed flat in passing through them. Eventually, the capillaries unite into larger vessels, *venules*, which join to form veins and these return blood to the heart.

Veins (Fig. 19.4*b*) return blood from the tissues to the heart. The blood pressure in them is steady and is less than in the arteries. They are wider and have thinner walls than the arteries. They also have valves (Fig. 19.6) in them which prevent blood

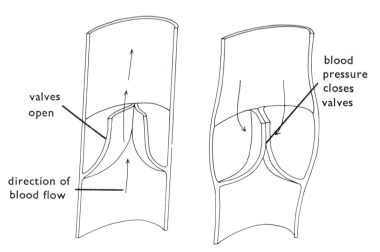

Fig. 19.6   Diagram to show the action of valves in a vein or the semilunar valves in the arteries leaving the heart

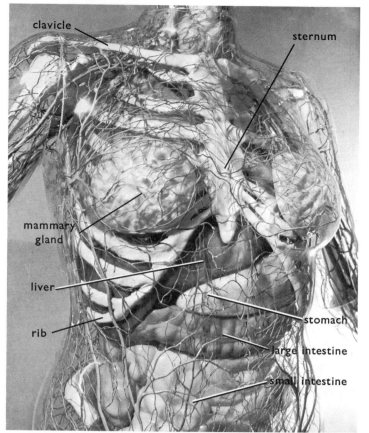

(A model in the Cleveland Health Museum, U.S.A.)

Plate 18.   "JUNO", THE TRANSPARENT WOMAN

flowing away from the heart. Contractions of skeletal muscles during activity compress the veins, so forcing blood along in a direction determined by the valves. This assists the return of blood to the heart. The blood in the veins will usually contain less oxygen and food, and more nitrogenous waste and carbon dioxide, while the arterial blood has a higher concentration of oxygen and dissolved food.

Exceptions to this are the *pulmonary artery* which carries deoxygenated blood to the lungs, the *pulmonary vein* which returns oxygenated blood to the heart, the *hepatic portal vein* to the liver from the alimentary canal which carries blood rich in glucose and amino acids, and the *renal vein* from the kidney where some water, salts and urea have been eliminated.

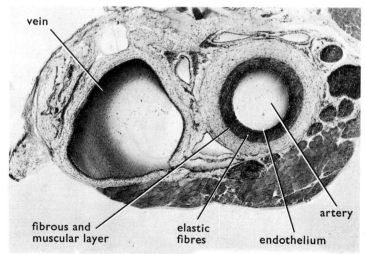

(G.B.I. Laboratories Ltd)

Plate 19.   TRANSVERSE SECTION THROUGH AN ARTERY AND VEIN (× 20)

The heart

The heart is a muscular pumping organ. It is thought that it has evolved from the highly muscular region of an artery. It is divided into four chambers; the left and right sides do not communicate. The upper chambers, the *atria*, which are relatively thin-walled, receive blood from the veins (Fig. 19.8). Oxygenated blood from the lungs enters the *left atrium* via the *pulmonary veins* and deoxygenated blood from the body enters the *right atrium* from the *venae cavae* (Fig. 19.9). Relaxation of the ventricular muscle allows the ventricles to expand and fill with blood which flows in from the atria and veins (Fig. 19.10). Simultaneous contraction of both atria forces the blood they contain into the corresponding ventricles and, about 0·1 sec. later, the ventricles contract simultaneously, expelling their blood into the arteries and round the body. Both ventricles have thick muscular walls but those of the left are thicker, having to pump blood all round the entire body via the *aorta*. The *right ventricle* pumps blood to the lungs through the *pulmonary arteries*. When the ventricles contract, blood is prevented from returning to the atria and veins by the closure of parachute-like valves between the atria and ventricles. Powerful contraction of the ventricles forces blood into the aorta and pulmonary arteries. When the ventricles relax, the pocket-like *semilunar valves* in these two arteries are closed and prevent the return of blood to the ventricles. The heart contracts about 70 times a minute when an adult person is at rest, but this rate increases to 100 or more during activity or excitement. In a sparrow the rate is nearly 500 a minute. The heart's rhythmic muscular contraction is basically automatic and needs no nervous stimulation to bring it about. If kept in the right solution of salts a frog's heart will continue to beat for some hours after removal from the body, and the same is true of a mammalian heart if an artificial circulation to the heart muscle is maintained. Nervous stimulation is, however, superimposed on the heart's natural rhythm and helps to maintain and control its rate. An increased heartbeat increases the speed with which the blood is supplied to the tissues and so allows a greater rate of activity. The *coronary arteries* shown in Fig. 19.7 carry oxygenated blood to the ventricular muscle whose constant activity demands an unceasing supply of food and oxygen.

Blood pressure. To force blood through a capillary system and to overcome atmospheric pressure, which tends to flatten the vessels, a fairly high pressure must be developed by the heart. This pressure varies according to the part of the body considered and the age of the individual, but an average pressure produced in the ventricle when it contracts is equal to 130 mm of mercury.

Exchange between capillaries, cells and lymphatics

At the arterial end of the capillary bed (Fig. 19.11) blood pressure is high and forces plasma out through the thin capillary walls. The fluid so expelled has a composition similar to plasma, containing dissolved glucose, amino acids and salts but has a much lower concentration of plasma proteins. This exuded fluid permeates the spaces between the cells of all living tissues and is called *tissue fluid*. From it the cells extract the glucose, oxygen, amino acids, etc. which they need for their living processes and into it they excrete their carbon dioxide and nitrogenous waste.

The narrow capillaries offer considerable resistance to the flow of blood. This slows down the movement of blood, so facilitating the exchange of substances by diffusion between the plasma and the tissue fluid (Fig. 19.12). The capillary resistance also results in a drop of pressure so that at the venous end of a capillary bed the blood pressure is less than that of the tissue fluid and the latter passes back into the capillaries.

The fact that the plasma contains more proteins than the tissue fluid gives the blood a low water potential (p. 61) which tends to cause water to pass from the tissue fluid into the capillary. At the arterial end of the capillary network, the blood pressure is greater than this osmotic pressure, so forcing water out, but at the venous end water from the tissue fluid enters the capillary by osmosis.

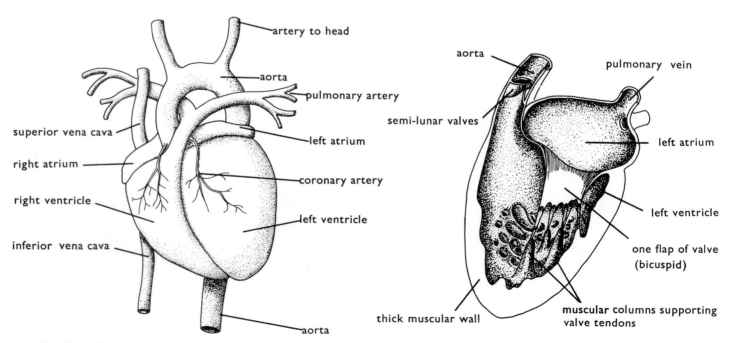

Fig. 19.7   External view of mammalian heart
(pulmonary veins not shown)

Fig. 19.8   Diagram of heart cut open
(left side)

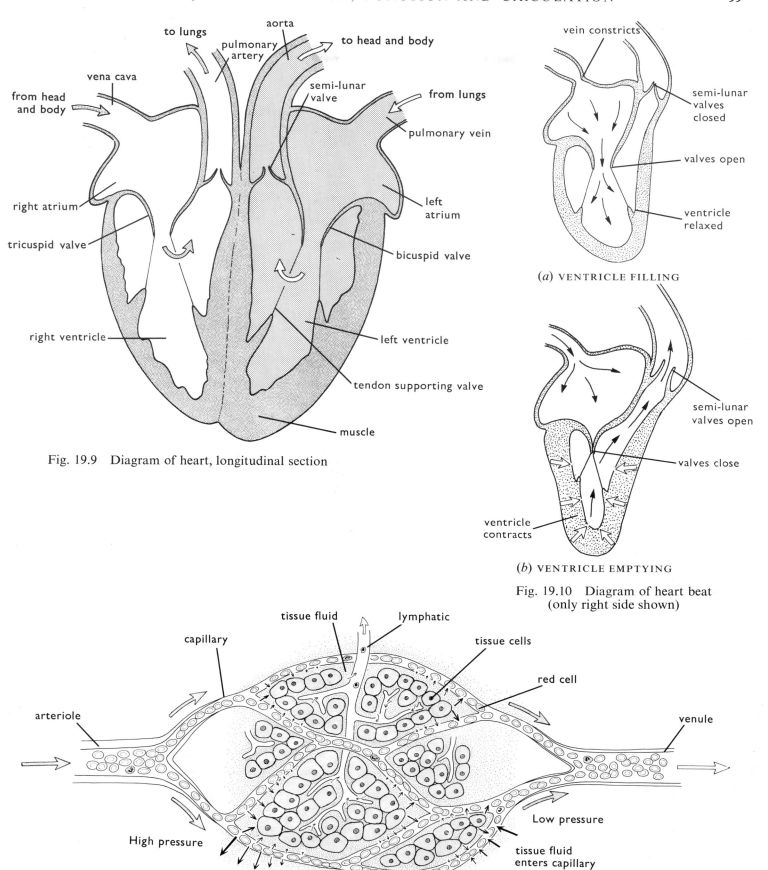

Fig. 19.9 Diagram of heart, longitudinal section

(a) VENTRICLE FILLING

(b) VENTRICLE EMPTYING

Fig. 19.10 Diagram of heart beat
(only right side shown)

CAPILLARY BED

Fig. 19.11 Relationship between capillaries, cells and lymphatics

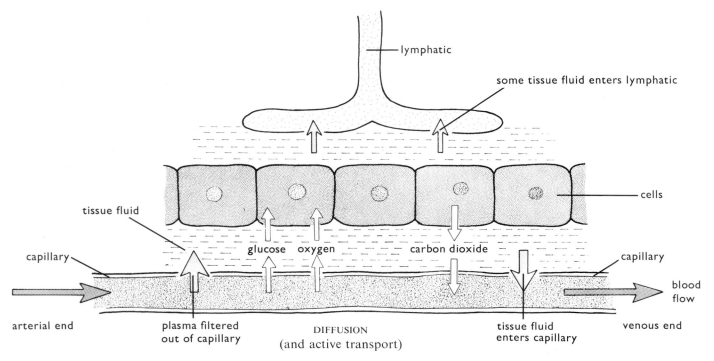

Fig. 19.12   Blood, tissue fluid and lymph

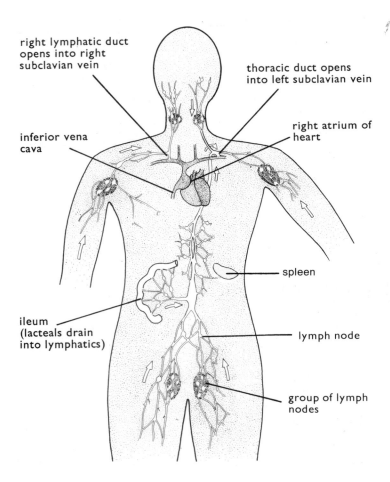

Fig. 19.13   Main drainage routes of
lymphatic system

Lymphatic system. The capillaries are not the only route by which the tissue fluid returns to the circulation. Some of it returns via the lymphatic system. The proteins in the tissue fluid are unable to re-enter the capillaries but can drain into blindly-ending, thin-walled vessels which are found between the cells. These *lymphatics* join up to form larger vessels which eventually unite into two main ducts and empty their contents into the large veins entering the right atrium.

The fluid in the lymphatic vessels is called *lymph*. Its composition is similar to plasma but it contains less proteins. It also contains a certain type of white cell, *lymphocyte*, which is made in the lymph nodes.

The larger of the two lymphatic ducts is the *thoracic duct* which collects lymph from the intestine and the lower half of the body (Fig. 19.13). The *lacteals* from the small intestine open into the lymphatic system. After a meal containing fats the lymph is a milky-white colour due to the fat droplets absorbed in the lacteals.

At various points along the lymph vessels are *lymph nodes*. In these nodes antibodies and new white cells are produced. Stationary white cells in the nodes ingest any bacteria which have gained access to the lymph.

The *spleen* is an important lymphoid organ, dark red in colour, lying just below the stomach. It makes lymphocytes and antibodies and also destroys worn out red cells.

The lymph flow takes place in only one direction, from the tissues to the heart, and there is no specialized pump. The flow is brought about partly by the pressure of the lymph that accumulates in the tissues, but one of the most important factors in the circulation of lymph is muscular exercise. Some of

Fig. 19.14   Deep lymphatic vessel cut open to show valves

the lymphatics have valves (Fig. 19.14) in them, pressure from the contracting muscles around them forcing the lymph along the vessels in one direction.

PRACTICAL WORK

1. *Blood smear.* Because of the risk of transmitting infections, such as hepatitis, it is best not to make blood smears from your own blood. Instead, use a microscope to study prepared slides which have been stained to show the red and white cells (Plate 17).

2. *Valves in the veins.* If a light tourniquet is applied to the upper arm the veins in the forearm can be made to stand out. The lower end of one of these is blocked off near the wrist by pressing it with a finger. The blood can be expelled from the vein by running a finger with light pressure along its length towards the elbow. When this has been done the vein will remain collapsed up to a certain point; above this the vein will fill up and swell once more. The boundary between the filled and collapsed regions indicates the position of a non-return valve.

3. *Effect of gravity on circulation.* Allow the left arm to hang straight down at the side of the body. Open and clench the hand repeatedly between once and twice a second. It should be possible to continue these movements for 3 or 4 minutes or up to 500 times without feeling acute discomfort. After a period of rest, hold the arm straight up and repeat the exercises. After about one minute, or 100 closures, the movement becomes almost impossible. One reason for this is the reduced blood supply resulting from the retarding effect of gravity on the circulation. It is interesting to speculate on which particular aspect of circulation, i.e. oxygen transport, waste removal, etc., is responsible for the fatigue.

4. *Capillaries.* These are best seen in the web of a frog's foot, tadpole's tail or external gills where the red cells can be seen streaming through the narrow vessels. (*See* p. 164, Fig. 30.9.)

Our own capillaries can be seen by soaking the back of the top joint of a finger in a clearing agent such as cedar-wood oil and examining, by reflected light under a microscope, the area below the nail cuticle. Capillary loops can usually be seen even with a good hand lens.

5. *Pulse rate.* The swelling of the arteries as a result of the surge of pressure from the heart can be felt in certain places and gives an indication of the rate of the heart's contractions. The pulse in the wrist is the most usual region for this. Count the number of pulsations over a period of 30 seconds and make a note of it. Then take some form of exercise, e.g. standing up and getting off a stool once in two seconds for about half a minute, and take the pulse rate again. Find out how long it takes to return to its original rate.

QUESTIONS

1. Although the walls of the left ventricle are thicker than those of the right ventricle, the volumes of the ventricles are the same. Why is this necessary?
2. State in detail the course taken by (*a*) a glucose molecule and a fat molecule from the time they are ready for absorption in the ileum, and (*b*) a molecule of oxygen absorbed in the lungs, to the time when all three reach a muscle cell in the leg.
3. Why is a person whose heart valves are damaged by disease unable to participate in active sport?
4. A system for transporting substances in solution might as well be filled with water. What advantages has the blood circulatory system over a water circulatory system?
5. What is the advantage to an animal of having capillaries which are (i) very narrow, (ii) repeatedly branched and (iii) very thin-walled?
6. How do you think microscopic animals can survive without having a circulatory system?

20 | Breathing

THE various processes carried out by the body, e.g. movement, growth and reproduction, require the expenditure of energy. In animals this energy can be obtained only from the food they eat. Before the energy can be used by the cells of the body it must be set free from the chemicals of the food. This process of liberating energy is called respiration (Chapter 9) and involves the use of oxygen and the production of carbon dioxide.

Oxygen enters the animal's body from the air or water surrounding it. In the less complex animals the oxygen is absorbed by the entire exposed surface of the body, but in the higher animals there are special respiratory areas such as lungs or gills. Excess carbon dioxide is usually eliminated from the same area. In the respiratory organ oxygen combines with the haemoglobin in the blood and is so carried to all living parts of the body where it is used in tissue respiration.

An efficient respiratory organ has a large surface area, a dense capillary network or similar blood supply, a very thin *epithelium* separating the air or water from the blood vessels and, in land-dwelling animals, a layer of moisture over the absorbing surface. In many animals there is also a mechanism which renews the air or water in contact with or near the respiratory surface, a process called *ventilation*. In mammals, the respiratory organs are lungs.

Lungs (Fig. 20.1)

The lungs are enclosed in the *thorax*. They have a spongy, elastic texture and can be expanded or compressed by movements of the thorax in such a way that air is repeatedly taken in and expelled. They communicate with the atmosphere through the wind-pipe or *trachea*, which opens into the *pharynx* (Fig. 18.3). In the lungs, gaseous exchange takes place; some of the atmospheric oxygen is absorbed and carbon dioxide from the blood is released into the lung cavities.

Lung structure. The trachea divides into two *bronchi* which enter the lungs and divide into smaller branches (Fig. 20.2). These divide further into *bronchioles* which terminate in a mass of little thin-walled, pouch-like air sacs or *alveoli* (Figs. 20.3, 20.4 and Plate 20).

(*a*) AIR PASSAGES. Rings of cartilage keep the trachea and bronchi open and prevent their closing up when the pressure inside them falls during inspiration. The lining of the air passages is covered with numerous *cilia*. These are minute, cytoplasmic hairs which constantly flick to and fro. Mucus is

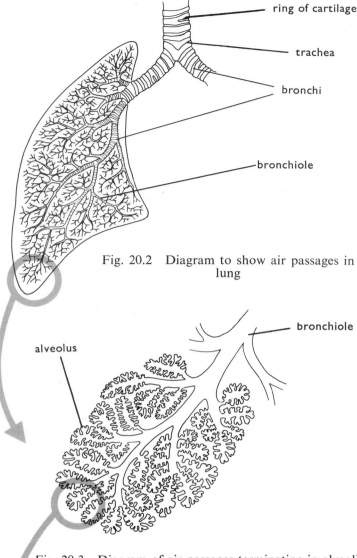

Fig. 20.2   Diagram to show air passages in lung

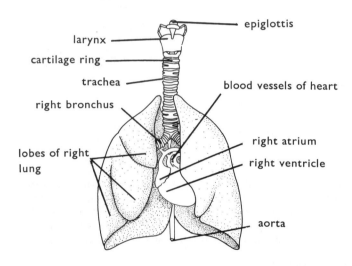

Fig. 20.1   Diagram of lungs showing position of heart

Fig. 20.3   Diagram of air passages terminating in alveoli

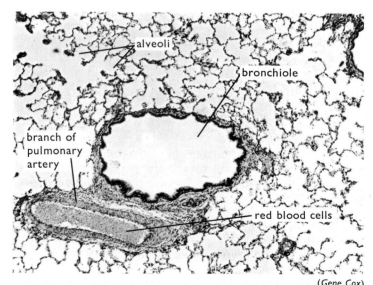

Plate 20.   MICROSCOPIC STRUCTURE OF LUNG TISSUE SEEN IN SECTION (×100)

(Gene Cox)

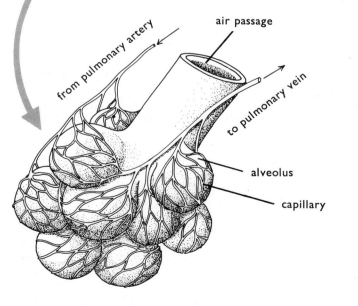

Fig. 20.4   Diagram to show relation of blood vessels to alveoli

secreted by glandular cells, also in the lining. Dust particles, bacteria, etc., which are carried in with the air during inspiration become trapped in the mucus film and, by the movements of the cilia, are swept away in it up to the larynx and into the pharynx where they are swallowed.

The epiglottis and other structures at the top of the trachea prevent food particles from entering the air passages, particularly during swallowing. Choking and coughing are reflex actions which tend to remove any foreign particles which accidentally enter the trachea or bronchi.

(b) ALVEOLI. The alveoli have thin, elastic walls consisting internally of a single cell layer, or epithelium, and beneath this, a dense network of capillaries (Fig. 20.4) supplied with de-oxygenated blood pumped from the right ventricle through the pulmonary artery. In one human lung there are about 350 million alveoli with a total absorbing surface of about 90 m².

Gaseous exchange (Fig. 20.5)

The lining of the alveoli is covered with a film of moisture. The oxygen concentration in the blood is lower than in the alveolus, hence oxygen in the air space dissolves in the film of moisture and diffuses through the epithelium, the capillary wall, the plasma and into a red cell, where it combines with the haemoglobin (see p. 94). The capillaries reunite and eventually form the pulmonary veins which return the oxygenated blood to the left atrium of the heart. The low concentration of carbon dioxide in the alveoli stimulates the enzyme, *carbonic anhydrase*, in the blood to break down the hydrogencarbonate salts and liberate carbon dioxide. This gas diffuses into the alveoli and is eventually expelled.

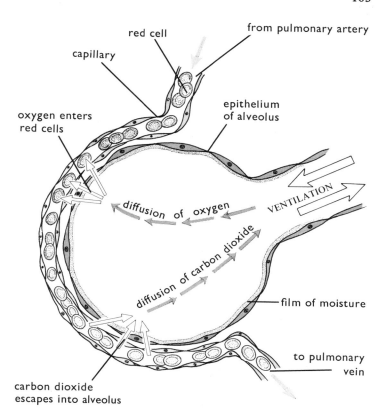

Fig. 20.5   Gaseous exchange in the alveolus

Approximate Composition of Inspired and Expired Air

	Inspired%	Expired%
Oxygen	21	16
Carbon dioxide	0·04	4
Nitrogen	79	79
Water vapour	varies	saturated

Although nitrogen does dissolve in blood plasma, it plays no part in the chemical reactions of the body so the rates of diffusion into and out of the blood are the same.

Diffusion gradient. A steep diffusion gradient (p. 62) of oxygen is maintained by (i) replenishment of air in the air passages by ventilation, (ii) the very short distance between the alveolar lining and the blood, (iii) the combination of oxygen with haemoglobin, so removing oxygen from solution, (iv) the blood flow which constantly replenishes oxygenated blood with deoxygenated blood. Similar factors work in the reverse direction for the diffusion of carbon dioxide. The conversion of hydrogencarbonate to carbon dioxide by carbonic anhydrase raises the concentration of carbon dioxide in the blood above that in the alveoli.

Rate of breathing

The rhythmical breathing movements are usually carried out quite unconsciously about 16 times a minute. They are controlled by a region of the brain which is very sensitive to the carbon dioxide concentration in the blood. If there is a rise in the carbon dioxide concentration of the blood reaching this region of the brain, nerve impulses are automatically sent to the diaphragm and rib muscles which increase the rate and depth of breathing. The concentration of carbon dioxide in the blood is most likely to rise during vigorous activity, and the accelerated rate of breathing helps to expel the rapidly accumulating carbon dioxide and to increase the amount of oxygen in the

blood, so meeting the demands of increased tissue respiration. By regulating the oxygen and carbon dioxide levels in the blood, the lungs are fulfilling a homeostatic function (p. 108). At most times the rate of breathing can be controlled voluntarily, as in singing or when playing a wind instrument.

Lung capacity

The total capacity of the lungs, when fully inflated in an adult man, is about 5½ litres, but during quiet breathing only about 500 cm³ of air is exchanged. This is called *tidal air*. During activity the thoracic movements are more extensive, and deep inspiration can take in another 2 litres while vigorous expiration can expel an additional 1½ litres. The thorax cannot collapse completely, so that 1½ litres of air can never be expelled. This *residual air*, which remains stationary in the alveoli, exchanges carbon dioxide and oxygen by diffusion with the tidal air that sweeps into the bronchi and air passages.

The nose

The ciliated epithelium and film of mucus which line the nasal passages help to trap dust and bacteria. The air is also warmed slightly before it enters the lungs. In addition, in the linings of the nasal cavity there are sensory organs which respond to chemicals in the air and confer a sense of smell.

Voice

The *vocal cords* are two folds protruding from the lining of the larynx. They contain ligaments which are controlled by muscles. When air is passed over them in a certain way they vibrate and produce sounds. The controlling muscles can alter the tension in the cords and the distance between them. In this way they vary the pitch and quality of the sounds produced.

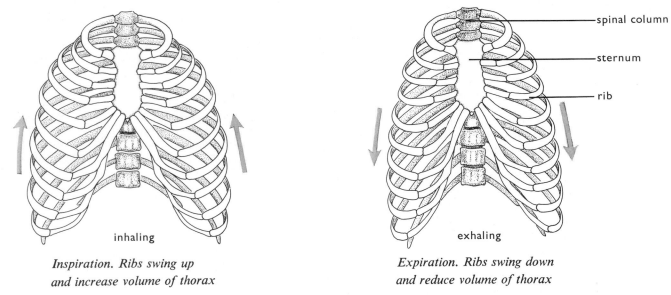

Inspiration. Ribs swing up
and increase volume of thorax

Expiration. Ribs swing down
and reduce volume of thorax

Fig. 20.6   Movement of rib cage during breathing

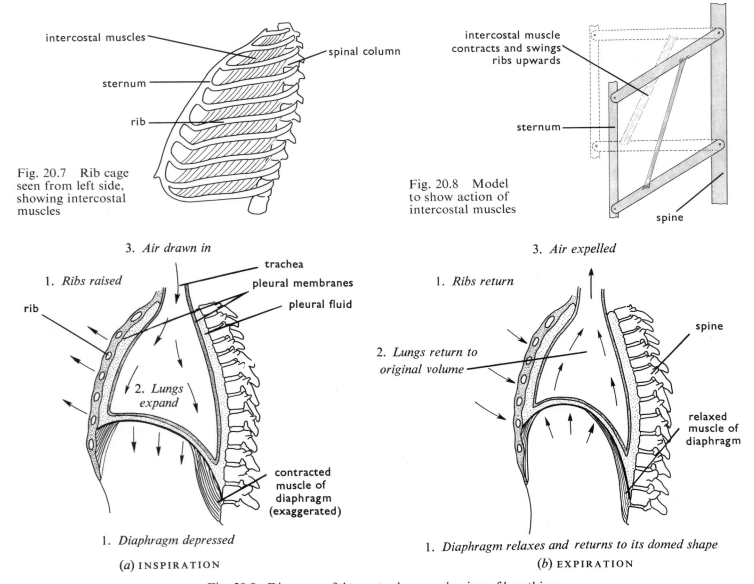

Fig. 20.7   Rib cage
seen from left side,
showing intercostal
muscles

Fig. 20.8   Model
to show action of
intercostal muscles

3. *Air drawn in*

1. *Ribs raised*

2. *Lungs
expand*

1. *Diaphragm depressed*

(*a*) INSPIRATION

3. *Air expelled*

1. *Ribs return*

2. *Lungs return to
original volume*

1. *Diaphragm relaxes and returns to its domed shape*

(*b*) EXPIRATION

Fig. 20.9   Diagrams of thorax to show mechanism of breathing

Ventilation of the lungs

The exchange of air in the lungs is brought about by muscular movements of the thorax which alter its volume. The thorax is an airtight cavity enclosed by the ribs at the sides and the *diaphragm* below. The diaphragm is a muscular sheet of tissue extending across the body cavity between the thorax and abdomen. At rest, it is dome-shaped, extending upwards into the thoracic cavity, with the liver and stomach immediately below it. Any change in the volume of the thorax is followed by the lungs, which are too thin to oppose the movements.

INSPIRATION. During inspiration the volume of the thorax is increased by two movements (Fig. 20.9).

(a) The muscles of the diaphragm contract and cause it to flatten from its domed position.

(b) The lower ribs are raised upwards and outwards (Fig. 20.6) by contraction of the intercostal muscles which run obliquely from one rib to the next (Figs. 20.7 and 20.8).

Both these movements increase the volume of the thorax and, consequently, the volume of the lungs which follow the movements. The increase in volume raises the capacity of the lungs so that atmospheric pressure forces air into them through the nose and trachea.

EXPIRATION. Expiration, or breathing out, results mainly from a relaxation of the muscles of the ribs and diaphragm. The ribs move down under their own weight, and the organs below the diaphragm, under pressure from the muscular walls of the abdomen, push the relaxed diaphragm back into its domed position. The lungs, as a result of these movements and by virtue of their elasticity, return to their original volume.

In this way air containing less oxygen and more carbon dioxide and water vapour than when it entered the lungs is expelled from them. Usually, in quiet breathing the movements of the diaphragm alone are responsible for the ventilation of the lungs.

Pleural membranes (Fig. 20.9). The pleural membrane is the lining which covers the outside of the lungs and the inside of the thorax. It produces pleural fluid which lubricates the surfaces in the regions of contact between the lungs and thorax. As a result, they can slide freely over one another with very little friction during the breathing movements.

Gaseous exchange in other organisms

(a) **Green plants.** The leaves and stem of a plant exchange oxygen and carbon dioxide with the atmosphere by diffusion (*see* pp. 16, 18, 51 and 62). Roots obtain their oxygen from the air dissolved in soil-water or in air spaces.

(b) **Micro-organisms.** The surface area of microscopic plants and animals is large in comparison with their volume and the distance from the cell surface to the centre of the protoplasm is very small. Consequently, simple diffusion of gases is rapid enough to meet the respiratory needs of the organism and the diffusion gradients are maintained by the consumption of oxygen and production of carbon dioxide in the protoplasm (*see* p. 176).

(c) **Insects** use their tracheal system for gaseous exchange (*see* p. 146).

(d) **Fish.** The respiratory surface of a fish is provided by the gills, and ventilation is achieved by passing a current of water over them (*see* p. 160).

(e) **Frog and tadpole.** Gaseous exchange takes place through the skin, gills and lungs at various stages of the life cycle and in different situations (*see* pp. 161–165).

PRACTICAL WORK

1. *Composition of exhaled air.* (Fig. 20.10). By placing tube T in the mouth and breathing gently in and out, air is made to pass into the lungs via test-tube A and out via B. After a few seconds the difference in the lime water of each test-tube will indicate one of the differences between the composition of inhaled and exhaled air.

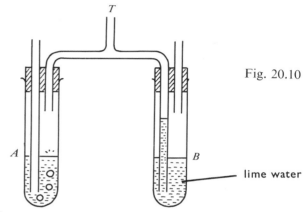

Fig. 20.10

lime water

2. *Oxygen concentration.* Exhaled air is collected in a gas jar by downward displacement of water. A lighted splint placed in the gas jar will give some indication of the oxygen concentration. The air exhaled first (tracheal and bronchial) and last (alveolar) should be collected separately and compared.

3. *Lung capacity.* A large plastic bottle is calibrated up to 5 litres by filling it with water 1 litre at a time and marking the levels. The bottle, full of water, is inverted in a trough or bowl of water, the stopper removed, and a rubber tube inserted through the neck. The experimenter takes a deep breath and exhales through the tube so that the exhaled air collects in the bottle, displacing the water. The level of water left in the bottle will give a measure of the lung capacity.

QUESTIONS

1. Outline the events which take place in the course of vigorous exercise which lead to a change in the rate and depth of breathing both during and after the activity. (See also Chapter 9.)

2. The lungs and ileum are adapted for absorption. Point out the features they have in common which facilitate absorption.

	Inhaled air	Exhaled air	Alveolar air
% Oxygen	21	16	14
% Carbon dioxide	0.03	4	5.5

3. The table above gives the approximate percentage volume composition of air inhaled, exhaled or retained in the lungs. Explain how these differences in composition are brought about by events in the lungs.

4. An artificial pneumothorax is a method of resting an infected lung. Air is injected into the pleural cavity and the lung collapses. After a few months, the air is absorbed and the lung works normally again. Try to explain why the introduction of air into the pleural cavity should cause the lung to stop working and say why it is possible for a person with a collapsed lung to lead a normal life.

21 | Excretion

THE processes that make a creature alive can be generally described as chemical reactions that perpetuate themselves. Many of these reactions, respiration for example, release energy that is used in setting off other reactions. All these reactions give rise to end-products, some of which are poisonous or could affect the normal chemical reactions in the body if they were allowed to accumulate.

Even the apparently permanent structures of the body such as the muscles, blood, skin and internal organs are, in fact, changing from day to day. The chemical units of living protoplasm are constantly being renewed. New molecules are being added, degenerate molecules or entire cells are being digested away. For example, an amino acid in some protein eaten one day may be built into the living protoplasm of a muscle fibre the next day. Later, the same amino acid may be broken down and the products carried off in the blood stream. The products of this kind of protein decomposition contain nitrogen, ammonia being one of the most common compounds. If nitrogenous compounds were allowed to accumulate in the body they would cause death in a matter of days or weeks. Excess amino acids absorbed after a meal containing protein are deaminated in the liver as described on p. 92, giving rise to urea and other nitrogenous compounds. Excretion is the process by which such harmful products are removed from the body as fast as they exceed a certain concentration.

Excretory products. The main excretory products in animals are carbon dioxide and water from respiration, and nitrogenous compounds from the breakdown of excess amino acids. The nitrogenous compounds such as ammonia are converted in the liver into *urea* and *uric acid* which are less poisonous.

Excretory organs. In man, the excretory organs are the lungs, the liver and the kidneys. The lungs excrete carbon dioxide; the liver excretes bile pigments derived from the decomposition of haemoglobin; the kidneys remove nitrogenous compounds from the blood and eliminate excess water and salts.

The kidneys

Gross structure. The two kidneys are fairly solid, oval structures, with an indentation on their innermost sides. They are red-brown, enclosed in a transparent membrane, and attached to the back of the abdominal cavity (Fig. 21.1). The *renal artery*, branching from the aorta, brings oxygenated blood to them, and the *renal vein* takes deoxygenated blood away to the vena cava. A tube, the *ureter*, runs from each kidney to the base of the *bladder* in the lower abdomen (*see* Plate 24).

The kidney tissue consists of many capillaries and tiny tubes, called *renal tubules*, held together with connective tissue. A section through a kidney shows a darker, outer region, the *cortex*, and a lighter inner zone, the *medulla*. Where the ureter leaves the kidney is a space called the *pelvis* and into this project cones or *pyramids* of kidney tissue (Fig. 21.2).

Detailed structure. The renal artery divides up into a great many arterioles and capillaries (Fig. 21.3), mostly in the cortex. Each arteriole leads to a *glomerulus*, which is a capillary repeatedly divided and coiled, making a little knot of vessels (Fig. 21.5). The glomerulus is almost entirely surrounded by a cup-shaped organ called a *Bowman's capsule*, which leads to a coiled renal tubule. This tubule, after a series of coils and loops, joins other tubules and passes through the medulla to

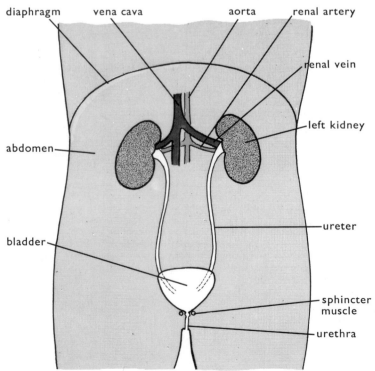

Fig. 21.1   Position of kidneys in the body

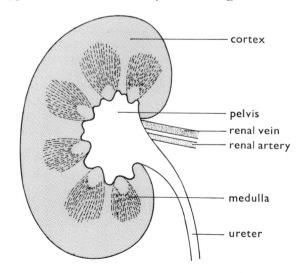

Fig. 21.2   Section through kidney to show regions

open into the pelvis at the apex of a pyramid (Fig. 21.4 and Plate 21).

Mechanism of excretion in the kidney. The tortuous capillaries of the glomerulus offer resistance to the flow of blood, so that a high pressure is set up. This pressure causes fluid to filter out through the capillary walls and collect in the Bowman's capsule. The filtered fluid, *glomerular filtrate*, contains a solution of glucose, salts, amino acids and urea, but

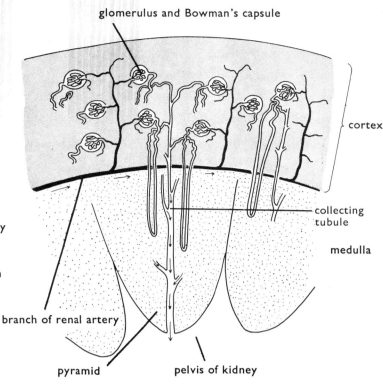

Fig. 21.4   Section through cortex and medulla

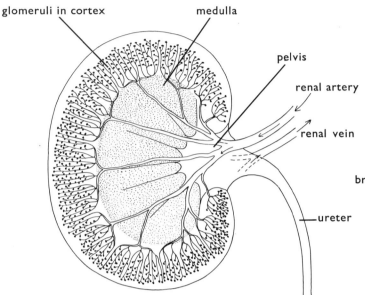

Fig. 21.3   Section through kidney to show distribution of glomeruli

fibrinogen and other proteins remain in the blood. In man, 180 litres per day of this filtrate, carrying 145 g glucose and 1100 g sodium chloride pass into the Bowman's capsules. As the filtered serum passes down the renal tubule, all the glucose and amino acids, some of the salts and much of the water are absorbed back into a network of capillaries surrounding the tubule (Fig. 21.5). This selective reabsorption prevents the loss of useful substances from the blood serum. The remaining liquid, now called *urine*, contains only the waste products such as inactive hormones, urea and excess salts and water. This liquid passes down the *collecting tubule* where more water is reabsorbed and the concentration of the blood is regulated. If the blood is too dilute, e.g. after drinking a great deal, less water is absorbed back into the blood and the urine is dilute. If the blood is too concentrated, e.g. after sweating profusely, more water is reabsorbed from the collecting tubule, making the urine more concentrated. From the collecting tubes, the urine enters the pelvis of the kidney where it collects and continues down the ureter to the bladder as the result of waves of contraction in the ureter.

The capillaries from the glomeruli and the renal tubules unite to form the renal vein. It is the cells of the kidney tubules which selectively reabsorb substances from the glomerular filtrate. They do this often against a diffusion gradient by methods which are not fully understood but which certainly need energy supplied by respiration within the cells. In consequence, the blood leaving the kidneys in the renal vein contains less oxygen and glucose, more carbon dioxide and, as a result of excretion, less water, salts and nitrogenous waste.

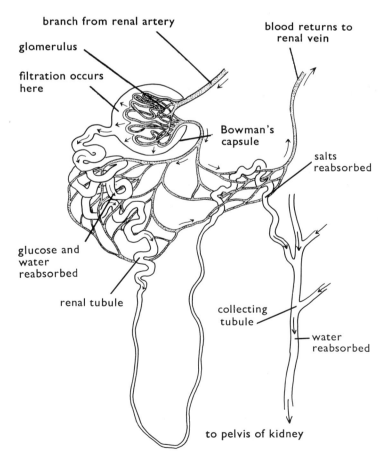

Fig. 21.5   Diagram of glomerulus and Bowman's capsule

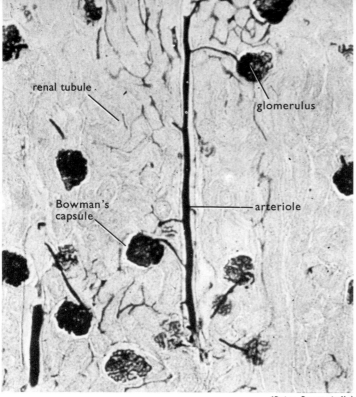

renal tubule

glomerulus

Bowman's capsule

arteriole

(Brian Bracegirdle)

Plate 21.   SECTION THROUGH CORTEX TO SHOW GLOMERULI (×80)

The following Table shows the main nitrogenous substances which are removed from the blood by the kidneys.

	Nitrogenous compounds in blood %	Nitrogenous compounds in urine %
Proteins	7–9	0
Urea	0·03	2
Uric acid	0·005	0·05
Ammonium compounds	0·0001	0·05
[Water	90–93	95]

The bladder

The bladder is an extensible sac with elastic and muscular tissue in its walls. The volume of accumulating urine entering the bladder from the ureters, extends its elastic walls to a volume of 400 cm³ or more. At intervals the sphincter muscle which closes the outlet to the bladder relaxes, and the bladder contracts, aided by the muscles of the abdomen, expelling the urine through a duct called the *urethra*. In babies, the sphincter muscle is controlled by a reflex action triggered off by nerve endings in the stretched walls of the bladder. After about two years or less the muscle can be controlled voluntarily.

Water balance and osmo-regulation

Water is lost from the body in urine, faeces, sweat and exhaled breath. It is gained by eating and drinking. These losses and gains will produce corresponding changes in the blood.

Changes in the concentration of the blood are detected by an area in the brain, the *hypothalamus* (p. 143). If the blood passing through the brain is too concentrated, the hypothalamus stimulates the *pituitary gland* beneath it to secrete into the blood a hormone (p. 144) called *anti-diuretic* hormone (ADH).

When this hormone reaches the kidneys, it causes the kidney tubules to absorb more water from the glomerular filtrate back into the blood. Thus the urine becomes more concentrated and the further loss of water from the blood is reduced. If blood passing through the hypothalamus is too dilute, production of ADH from the pituitary is suppressed and less water is absorbed from the glomerular filtrate.

The mechanism which produces the sensation of thirst is not well understood but it undoubtedly serves to regulate the intake of water and so maintain the concentration of the blood.

Homeostasis

The kidneys play a part in the homeostasis of the body, that is they help to regulate the composition of the internal environment.

If a mobile, single-celled organism such as Amoeba or Paramecium (p. 175) finds itself in conditions which are unfavourable, e.g. too acid, too warm or too light, it is capable of moving until it encounters conditions more amenable to its vital activities.

The cells in a multi-cellular organism cannot move to a fresh environment but are no less dependent on a suitable temperature and pH for the chemical reactions which maintain life. It is therefore crucial to their efficient functioning that the medium round them does not alter its composition very much. A fall in temperature will slow down the chemical reactions in the cell; a drop in pH may inhibit some enzyme systems; a rise in the concentration of solutes may withdraw water from the cell by osmosis. Homeostasis is the name given to the process by which such changes of the internal medium are kept within narrow limits and many organ systems of the body contribute to this control.

The internal medium of most animals is the tissue fluid (p. 98) which is in contact with all living cells in the body. The constitution of the tissue fluid depends on the composition of the blood from which it is derived and, therefore, the homeostatic mechanisms of many animals act by adjusting the composition of the blood.

The skin helps to regulate blood temperature (p. 110), the liver adjusts its glucose concentration (p. 91), the lungs keep the carbon dioxide concentration down to a certain level (p. 103) and the kidneys control its composition in three principal ways: (*a*) they eliminate harmful compounds such as urea, (*b*) they remove excess water and (*c*) they expel salts above a certain concentration. These activities are both excretory, in that they remove the unwanted products of metabolism, and osmo-regulatory, in that they keep the water potential of the blood more or less constant.

QUESTIONS

1. In an experiment, a man drank a litre of water. His urine output increased so that after two hours he had eliminated the extra water. When he drank a litre of 0·9 per cent sodium chloride solution, there was little or no increase in urine production. Explain the difference in these results.
2. In cold weather one may need to urinate frequently, producing a fairly colourless urine. In hot weather, urination is infrequent and the urine is often coloured. Explain these observations.
3. Consult pp. 89, 91 and 144 and then explain briefly why glucose does not normally appear in the urine.
4. Study the introduction to Chapter 12 and Experiment 3 (p. 63). In the artificial kidney a patient's blood is circulated through dialysis tubing immersed in a warm solution of sugar and salts. Explain how this results in the elimination from his blood of nitrogenous wastes without loss of essential glucose and salts.
5. Explain why the elimination of water by the kidneys may be considered to be both excretion and osmo-regulation.

22 | Skin, and Temperature Control

THE skin forms a continuous layer over the surface of the body. It has three principal functions:

(a) it protects the tissues beneath from mechanical injury, ultra-violet rays in sunlight, bacterial infection and desiccation;
(b) it contains numerous sense organs which are sensitive to temperature, touch and pain and so make the organism aware of changes in its surroundings (p. 128);
(c) it helps to keep the body temperature constant.

SKIN STRUCTURE

The skin consists of two main layers, (1) an outer *epidermis* and (2) an inner *dermis* (Fig. 22.1 and Plate 22). The relative thickness of the layers and abundance of structures within the dermis varies with the position on the body. For example, the skin on the soles of the feet has a very thick epidermis and no hair follicles. The account given below is a generalized one.

1. Epidermis

(a) The **Malpighian** layer is a continuous layer of cells which can divide actively and so produce new epidermis. Also in this layer are the pigment granules, melanin, that determine the skin colour and act as a screen against ultra-violet light.

(b) The **granular layer** contains living cells but towards the outside it gives way gradually to the *cornified layer*.

(c) **Cornified layer.** In this region the cells are dead and form a tough outer coat which offers resistance to damage and bacterial invasion and reduces the loss of water by evaporation. The cells of the cornified layer are continually being worn away and replaced from beneath. On the palms of the hand and soles of the feet it may become very thick, particularly when the hands are used for heavy manual work (Plate 23).

2. Dermis

The dermis is a thicker layer of connective tissue with many elastic fibres in it. There are also blood capillaries, nerve endings or sensory organs, lymphatics, sweat glands and hair follicles.

Capillaries. The capillaries supply the skin with the necessary food and oxygen and remove its excretory products. The sweat glands and hair follicles have a network of capillaries supplying

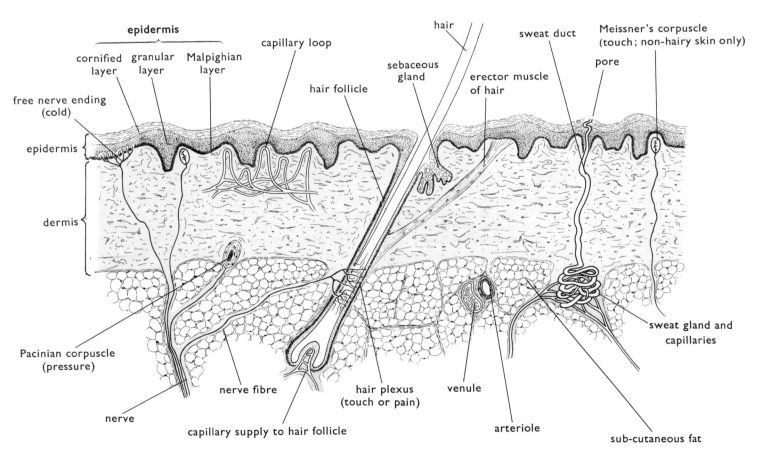

Fig. 22.1   Generalized section through skin

109

them. The capillaries beneath the epidermis play an important part in temperature control.

Sweat glands. The sweat gland is a coiled tube consisting of secretory cells which absorb fluid from the surrounding cells and capillaries and pass it into the duct through which it reaches the skin surface. The fluid is water with some salts, notably sodium chloride, dissolved in it and also small quantities of urea and lactic acid.

Although the body loses water vapour through the skin fairly constantly at most normal temperatures, the 2–3 million sweat glands do not operate until the body temperature rises about 0·2–0·5° C above normal. In a hot climate a man at work may lose about 1 kg per hour in sweat. Since salts, particularly sodium chloride and other solids, constitute up to 0·5 per cent of the sweat, these must be replaced by the food or in the drink of workers who lose much sweat; otherwise, if water alone is taken to replace that lost by sweating, the salt and water balance of the blood and tissues is upset leading to "heat cramp".

Hair follicle. The hair follicle is a deep pit of granular and Malpighian layers the cells of which multiply and build up a hair inside the follicle. The cells of the hair become impregnated with a horny substance, *keratin*, and die. The constant adding of new cells to the base of the hair causes it to grow. Growth continues for about four years; the hair then falls out and a new period of growth begins. The hairs of the body form a protective and heat-insulating layer in the regions where they grow thickly. The layer of stationary air held between the hairs reduces evaporation and heat loss. The follicle is supplied with sensory nerve-endings which respond to movements of the hair. This sensory function of the hair is well developed in the whiskers or *vibrissae* that grow on the sides of the face in mammals such as the cat or mouse.

Sebaceous glands. The sebaceous glands open into the top of hair follicles and produce an oily substance called **sebum**. The function of the sebum is not clear.

It has generally been thought to keep the skin supple and waterproof but there is not much evidence for this.

Sub-cutaneous fat. The layers beneath the dermis contain numerous fat cells (Fig. 18.9, p. 91) where fat is stored. The fat may also act as a heat-insulating layer.

TEMPERATURE CONTROL

Fish, amphibia, reptiles and all the invertebrates are *poikilothermic* (*see* p. 158), that is, their body temperature is the same as or only a few degrees above their surroundings, and varies accordingly. This makes them very dependent on temperature changes; for example, in cold conditions their low body temperature slows down all chemical changes and reduces the organism to a state of inactivity. Insects can be immobilized by a sudden fall in temperature.

Homoiothermic or constant-temperature animals are more independent of their surroundings because their body temperature is higher and does not alter with fluctuations in external temperature.

Heat loss and gain

Many of the chemical activities in living protoplasm release heat energy. Chemical changes in the abdominal organs and in contracting muscle produce a good deal of the body's heat which the circulatory system distributes round the body. At the same time the body loses heat from its surface to the atmosphere, mainly by convection and radiation. Evaporation of water from the surface of the skin also removes heat from the body. An outer layer of fur, feathers or clothing reduces the heat losses.

Normally a balance is maintained so that the rates of heat loss and gain are the same; hence man's body temperature, although varying in different parts of the body, remains at about 36·8° C, as shown by readings taken from under the tongue. There are regulating mechanisms in the body, under the control of the brain, that compensate for over-heating or cooling.

Over-heating

Vigorous activity, disease, absorption of radiation from the sun, and many other external causes may bring about over-heating. If the blood reaching the brain is a fraction of a degree higher than normal, nerve impulses are sent to the skin and produce two marked effects.

(1) **Vasodilation.** The dilating, or widening of the arterioles which supply the capillary network beneath the epidermis, causes more blood to flow near the surface. In consequence, more heat escapes into the air by convection and radiation

Plate 22.   SECTION THROUGH HAIRY SKIN (× 30)

(*Brian Bracegirdle*)

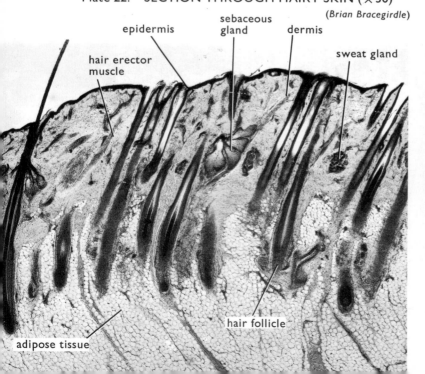

epidermis

sebaceous gland

dermis

hair erector muscle

sweat gland

hair follicle

adipose tissue

Plate 23.   SECTION THROUGH NON-HAIRY SKIN (× 80)
(The sweat ducts are contorted in passing through the cornified layer) (*Brian Bracegirdle*)

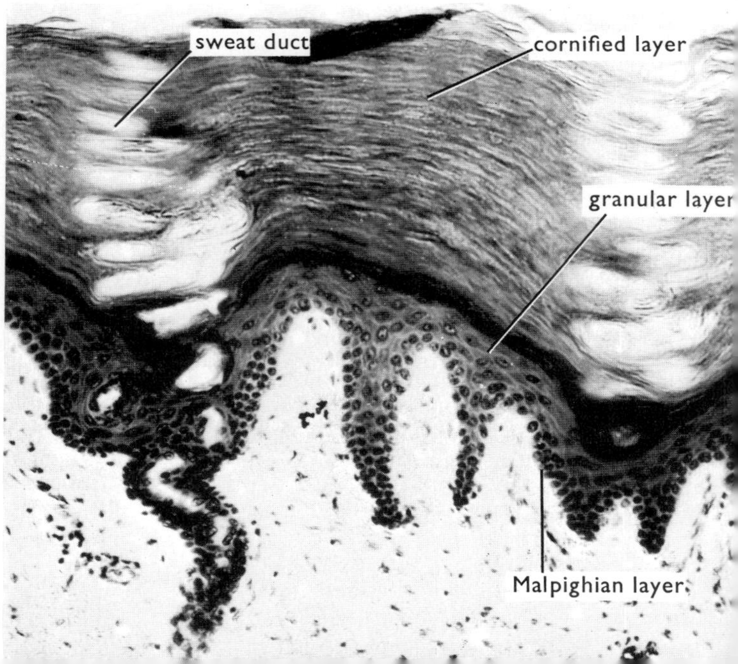

sweat duct

cornified layer

granular layer

Malpighian layer

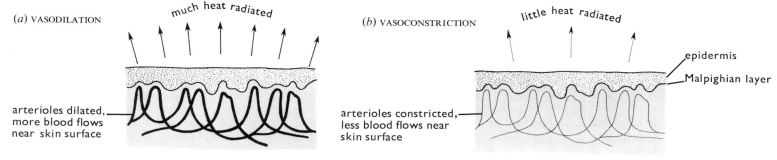

(a) VASODILATION — much heat radiated

arterioles dilated, more blood flows near skin surface

(b) VASOCONSTRICTION — little heat radiated

epidermis

Malpighian layer

arterioles constricted, less blood flows near skin surface

Fig. 22.2   Vasodilation and vasoconstriction

(Fig. 22.2). Vasodilation causes flushing of the skin because of the increased volume of blood beneath the epidermis.

(2) **Sweating.** Nerve impulses, starting mostly in the brain, increase the rate of sweat production so that a continuous layer of moisture may be produced on the skin surface. The latent heat absorbed by the sweat as it evaporates is taken from the body, so reducing the body's temperature. Any air movement over the body helps to speed up the evaporation of sweat which is why fans, while not necessarily reducing the temperature of a room, have a cooling effect on the body.

In humid conditions, the air contains so much water vapour that the sweat may not evaporate rapidly enough to produce an adequate cooling effect, and may lead to *heat stagnation* in which the body temperature rises to over 41°C, causing collapse and sometimes death. *Heat stroke* is a similar result of extreme over-heating when, after prolonged sweating due to vigorous activity at high temperatures, sweat production ceases and the body temperature rises to a lethal level. Both conditions may be called "*sun-stroke*" but it is not the effect of direct sunlight on the body so much as the high temperatures produced.

Over-cooling

If the body tends to lose more heat than it is generating the following compensatory changes may take place:

(1) **Decrease in sweat production,** thus minimizing heat lost by evaporation.

(2) **Vasoconstriction.** Constriction of the arterioles which supply the surface capillaries reduces the volume of blood flowing near the surface and hence diminishes heat losses. Vasoconstriction makes a person look pale or blue.

(3) **Shivering.** This reflex action operates when the body temperature begins to drop. It is a spasmodic contraction of the muscles. These contractions produce heat which helps to raise the body temperature.

Furry mammals and birds can fluff out their fur or feathers by contraction of the erector muscles which are attached to them in the skin. This increases the layer of trapped air round the skin and so improves insulation by reducing convection and conduction. In man, a similar contraction of the muscles of the hairs only produces "goose-pimples".

Hibernation

In cold climates or at high altitudes some small mammals pass the coldest months in a state of hibernation. When a mammal hibernates it falls asleep in some specially prepared burrow or nest and its body temperature falls well below normal, so that it may be only a few degrees above that of its surroundings. Breathing is often imperceptible, and all the chemical activities in the body go on very slowly, using food stored as fat and glycogen. The animal is quite insensible and cannot be awakened by touching it, in fact it is likely to die if such attempts are made. At the end of its hibernation period its temperature rises spontaneously to normal, starting from the innermost regions of the body. Hedgehogs and dormice are examples of hibernating mammals.

Hibernation allows the small mammal to survive the period when, because of the heat losses from its body, its energy requirements are high, but at the same time, food is scarce.

Surface area and heat loss

Consider the cube drawn in Fig. 22.3a. If it is cut in half as shown in 22.3b each portion has half the volume of the original cube but more than half its surface area because an extra surface "X" has been added to each half. Each time the solid is cut into smaller parts, the ratio $\frac{\text{surface area}}{\text{volume}}$ increases. This means that small animals have a relatively larger surface area per unit of volume than have larger animals and so the former lose heat more rapidly to the surroundings. This is thought to be one reason why the smallest homoiothermic vertebrates, e.g. humming birds, are restricted to areas with warm climates and why the polar regions are populated with relatively large mammals and birds.

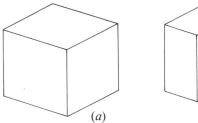
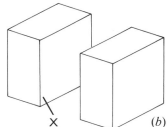

(a)   *(b)*   X

Fig. 22.3

QUESTIONS

1. Why is it more accurate to describe fish as "variable-temperatured" animals rather than "cold-blooded"?
2. When a dog is hot, it hangs its tongue out and pants. Why should this have a cooling effect?
3. Why do you think we experience more discomfort in hot humid weather than we do in hot dry weather?
4. You may "feel hot" after exercise or "feel cold" without your overcoat and yet your body temperature is not likely to differ by more than 0·5°C on the two occasions. Explain this apparent contradiction. (*See* also p. 128.)
5. Draw up a balance sheet showing all the possible ways in which the human body can gain and lose heat.

23 | Sexual Reproduction

SEXUAL reproduction involves the joining or fusing together of two cells. One of these reproductive cells comes from a male animal and the other comes from a female. The reproductive cells are called *gametes*. The fusing of two gametes is called fertilization and the resulting, composite cell is called a *zygote*. The most important aspect of fertilization is the fusion of the nuclei of the male and female gametes, because the factors which determine the characteristics of the individual that grows from the zygote are in these nuclei.

Fertilization, in short, is the fusion of the nuclei of male and female gametes to form a zygote, from which can develop a new individual.

In animals, the male gametes are *sperms*, which are produced in the reproductive organs called *testes*. The female gamete is an *ovum* which is produced in a reproductive organ called an *ovary*.

Some animals such as earthworms and snails are *hermaphrodite*, that is, they have both testes and ovaries, but in most animals the sexes are separate.

Internal and external fertilization. In most fish and amphibia fertilization is external. The female lays the eggs first and the male fertilizes them by placing sperms on them afterwards. A behaviour pattern which brings the sexes into proximity usually ensures that sperm is shed near the eggs and so increases the chances of fertilization.

In reptiles and birds, the eggs are fertilized inside the body of the female by the male's passing sperms into the egg ducts. A sperm meets the ovum and fertilizes it before it is laid. Very little development of the egg takes place before laying, however, and the embryo grows in the egg *after* it has left its mother's body.

In mammals, sperms are placed in the body of the female and the eggs are fertilized internally. They are not laid after fertilization but retained in the female's body while they develop to quite an advanced stage, after which the young are born more or less fully formed, being fed on a secretion of milk from the mammary glands and protected by their parents until they become independent.

Sexual reproduction in man

Female reproductive organs (Fig. 23.1 and Plate 24). The female reproductive organs are the *ovaries*, two cream-coloured, oval bodies lying in the lower part of the abdomen below the kidneys. They are attached by a membrane to the uterus and supplied with blood vessels. Close to each ovary is the expanded, funnel-shaped opening of the *oviduct*, the tube down which the ova pass when they are released from the ovary.

The oviducts are narrow tubes that open into a wider tube, the *uterus or womb*, lower down in the abdomen. When there is no embryo developing in it the uterus is only about 80 mm long. It communicates with the outside through a muscular tube, the *vagina*. The *cervix* is a ring of muscle closing the lower end of the uterus where it joins the vagina. There is normally only a very small aperture connecting these two organs at this point. The *urethra*, from the bladder, opens into the vulva in front of the vagina.

Male reproductive organs (Figs. 23.4 and 23.5). The two testes lie outside the abdominal cavity in man, in a special sac called the *scrotum*, consequently the testes remain at a temperature rather below that of the rest of the body, which is favourable to sperm production. The testes consist of a radiating mass of sperm-producing tubes. These tubes meet and join to form

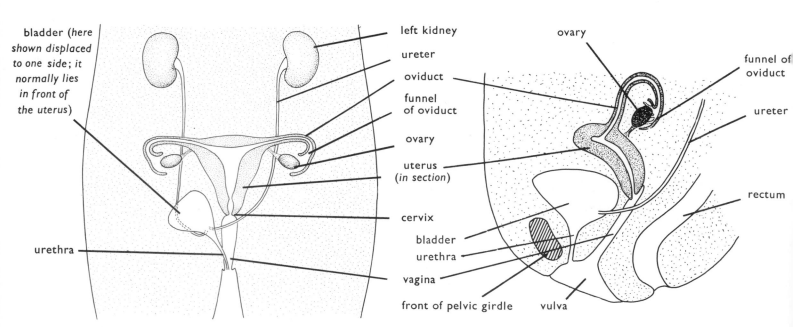

Fig. 23.1   Female reproductive organs

Fig. 23.2   Female reproductive organs (vertical section)

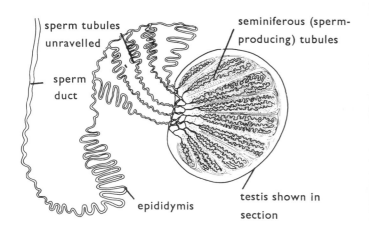

Fig. 23.3 Diagram to show relation of sperm ducts and testis

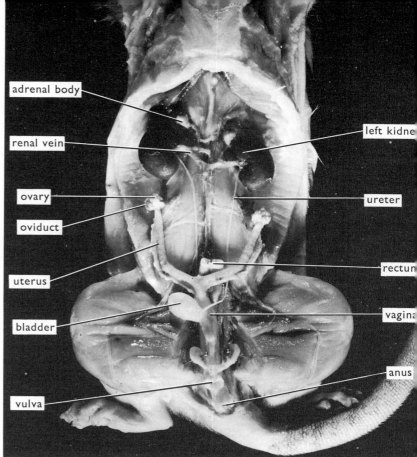

(Dissection by Griffin & George Ltd, Gerrard Biological Centre)

Plate 24. DISSECTION OF FEMALE REPRODUCTIVE
ORGANS OF A RAT
(Note that there are two uteri in the rat)

ducts leading to the *epididymis*, a coiled tube about 6 m long on the outside of each testis. The epididymis, in turn, leads into a muscular sperm duct. The two sperm ducts, one from each testis, open into the top of the urethra just after it leaves the bladder. A short, coiled tube, the *seminal vesicle*, branches from each sperm duct just before the latter enters the prostate gland. Surrounding the urethra at this point, is the *prostate gland* and farther down, *Cowper's gland*. The urethra conducts, at different times, both urine and sperms. In males the urethra runs through the *penis*, which consists of connective tissue with numerous small blood spaces in it.

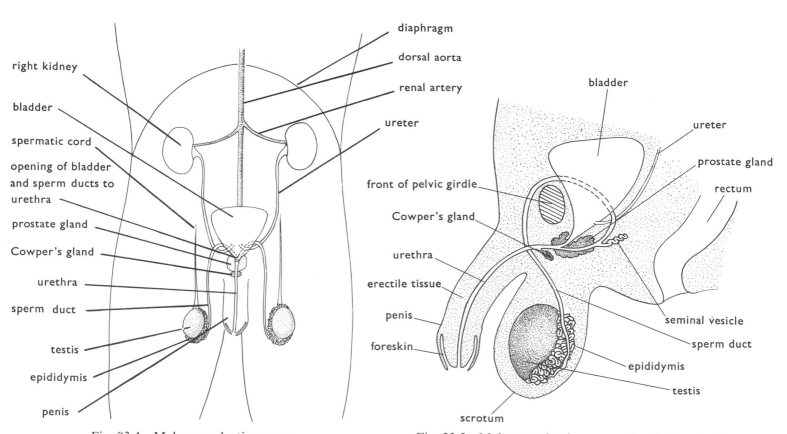

Fig. 23.4   Male reproductive organs

Fig. 23.5   Male reproductive organs (vertical section)

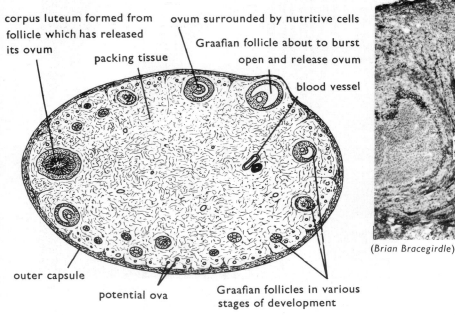

corpus luteum formed from follicle which has released its ovum

ovum surrounded by nutritive cells

Graafian follicle about to burst open and release ovum

packing tissue

blood vessel

outer capsule

potential ova

Graafian follicles in various stages of development

Fig. 23.6　Section through an ovary (as seen under the low power of a microscope)

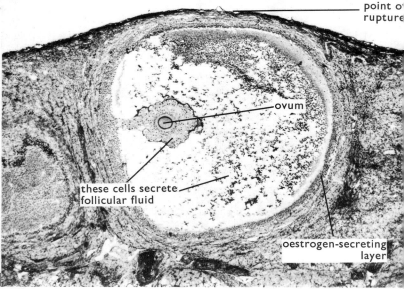

point of rupture

ovum

these cells secrete follicular fluid

oestrogen-secreting layer

(*Brian Bracegirdle*)

Plate 25.　MATURE GRAAFIAN FOLLICLE (× 40)

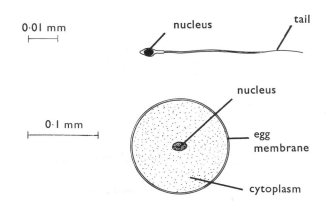

0·01 mm

nucleus

tail

0·1 mm

nucleus

egg membrane

cytoplasm

Fig. 23.7　Sperm and ovum of a mammal

Ovulation. The ovary consists of connective tissues, blood vessels and potential egg cells (Fig. 23.6). It is thought that 70,000 potential egg cells are already present at birth; they are not manufactured by the ovary during the lifetime. Of these 70,000 potential egg cells only about 500 will ever become mature ova (eggs). The ovaries also secrete hormones, *oestrogens*, which control the secondary sexual characters (p. 117) and initiate the thickening of the uterine lining which occurs each month.

Between the ages of about 11 and 16 years the ovaries become active and begin to produce mature eggs. The beginning of this period of life is called *puberty*. In the ovary some of the ova start to grow; the cells around them divide rapidly and become richly supplied with blood vessels. A fluid-filled cavity is eventually produced, and this partly encircles the ovum and its coating of nutritive cells. This region of the ovary is called a *Graafian follicle* (Plate 25). When the Graafian follicle is ripe it is about the size of a pea and projects from the surface of the ovary. Finally it bursts and releases the ovum into the funnel of the oviduct, the ciliated cells of which waft it into the tube. At this stage the ovum (Fig. 23.7) is a spherical mass of protoplasm about 0·13 mm in diameter, with a central nucleus and some of the follicle cells still adhering to it. An ovum is produced more or less alternately from the two ovaries every four weeks and it may spend about three days travelling down the oviduct to the uterus.

Sperm production (Fig. 23.3). The lining of the tubes making up the testis consists of actively dividing cells which give rise ultimately to sperms (Fig. 23.8). A sperm is a nucleus surrounded by a little cytoplasm which extends into a long tail (Fig. 23.7). Sperms are quite immobile when first produced; they pass into the epididymis where they are stored. During mating, muscular contractions of the epididymis, sperm duct and accessory muscles force the accumulated sperms through the urethra. Here, secretions of fluids from the prostate gland and seminal vesicles add nutrients and enzymes, diluting the sperms and possibly stimulating them into action, when lashing movements of their tails propel them along.

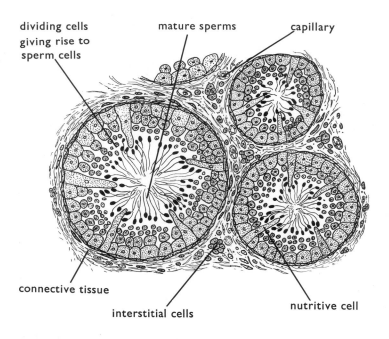

dividing cells giving rise to sperm cells

mature sperms

capillary

connective tissue

interstitial cells

nutritive cell

Fig. 23.8　Section through seminiferous tubules of mammalian testis (greatly enlarged)

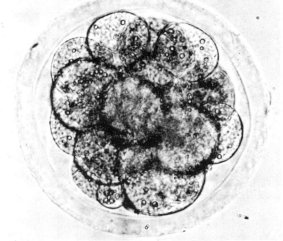

(Prof. W. J. Hamilton)

Plate 26.   EARLY STAGES OF CELL DIVISION
IN ZYGOTE OF SHEEP (× 400)

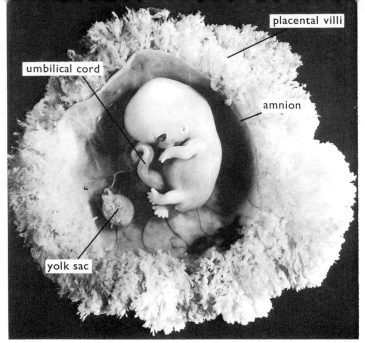

(Prof. W. J. Hamilton)

Plate 27.   HUMAN FOETUS, 7 WEEKS (× 1·5)

Fertilization. Fertilization occurs internally when the sperms meet the ovum as it passes down the oviduct. They are introduced into the female through the penis which is placed in the vagina. To facilitate this action the penis becomes erect, largely as a result of blood flowing into the blood spaces more rapidly than it escapes, so increasing the turgidity of the tissues round the urethra. The stimulation of the sensory organs in the penis sets off a reflex action which results in the accumulated sperms, together with the secretions of the prostate and Cowper's glands, being ejaculated into the vagina. The action is called copulation and may result in fertilization. The sperms deposited in the vagina swim through the cervix into the uterus and travel (it is not known exactly how) to the oviduct. If an ovum is present in the oviduct, one of the sperms will eventually collide with it and the head of the sperm sticks to the ovum. The sperm's nucleus passes into the cytoplasm and fuses with the female nucleus there (Fig. 23.9). (*See* also p. 189.)

Although a single ejaculation may contain two or three hundred million sperms, only one will actually fertilize the ovum, though the others may assist in the fertilization as a result of an enzyme they produce which helps to disperse the remaining follicle cells adhering to the surface of the ovum (not confirmed in man so far). In some mammals such as the rabbit, several ova are released from the ovary at the same time and will be fertilized by the corresponding number of sperms.

In man, the released ovum is thought to live for about 24 hours. The sperms may be able to fertilize an ovum for 2–3 days after their release. Thus there is a period of about 3–4 days each month when fertilization is likely (Fig. 23.12).

The cells of the follicle from which the ovum has been released continue to divide and grow, forming a solid body, the *corpus luteum*. If fertilization does not occur, the corpus luteum degenerates and gives way to ordinary ovary tissue. If fertilization does occur, the corpus luteum enlarges further and produces a hormone, *progesterone*, which stimulates the further thickening and increased blood supply of the uterine lining.

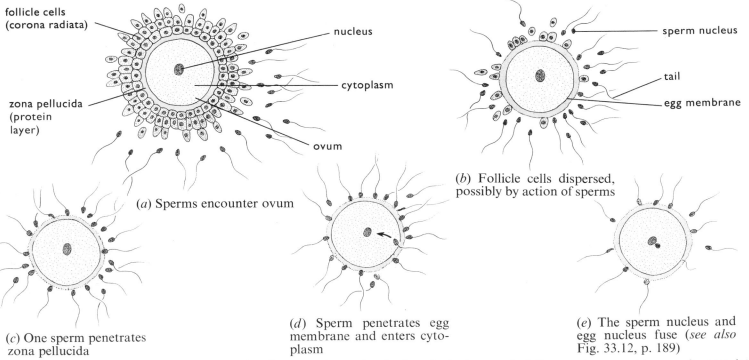

(a) Sperms encounter ovum

(b) Follicle cells dispersed, possibly by action of sperms

(c) One sperm penetrates zona pellucida

(d) Sperm penetrates egg membrane and enters cytoplasm

(e) The sperm nucleus and egg nucleus fuse (*see also* Fig. 33.12, p. 189)

Fig. 23.9   Fertilization of human ovum (the diagrams show what is thought to happen but the events are not known for certain)

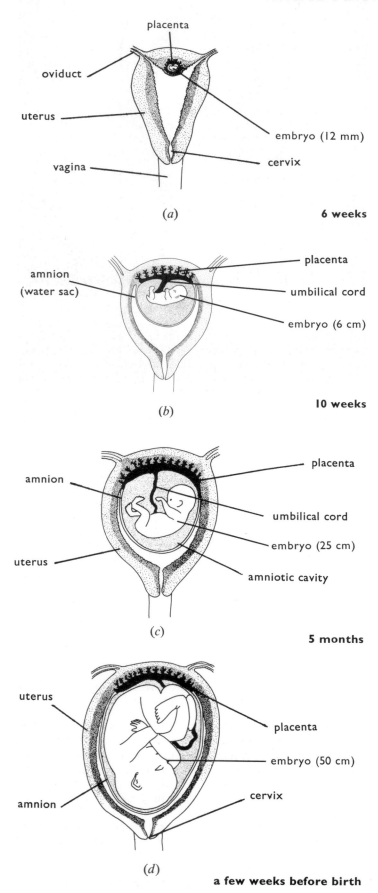

Pregnancy and development. The fertilized egg undergoes rapid cell division (Plate 26) as it passes down the oviduct and into the uterus where it adheres to and sinks into the uterine lining. Finger-like processes, *villi*, grow from the embryo into the uterine lining and absorb nourishment (Fig. 23.9a). The region bearing the villi does not form part of the embryo but develops into a special organ called the *placenta* which supplies the embryo with both food and oxygen.

The uterus, which at first has a volume of only 2 to 5 cm³, extends with the growth of the embryo to 5000 to 7000 cm³, enlarging the abdomen and displacing the organs in it to some extent. The uterine lining, under the influence of oestrone and progesterone, develops a rich supply of blood vessels and the walls become increasingly muscular.

The cells of the embryo divide repeatedly to form tissues. The tissues swell, roll, extend, etc., and so form organs of the body. The embryo's heart and circulatory system are formed quite early, after about one month.

Although the embryo depends on the mother's blood for its food and oxygen its circulatory system is never directly connected with the maternal blood vessels. If this did occur, the adult's blood pressure would burst the delicate capillaries forming in the embryo, and many substances in the mother's circulation would be poisonous to the embryo.

The placenta. The placenta becomes a large disc of tissue adhering closely to the uterine lining (Fig. 23.10 b and c). From the placenta villi protrude into the uterine lining which has thickened and developed a rich blood supply. The membranes separating the maternal and embryonic blood vessels are very thin; hence dissolved substances can pass across in both directions (Fig. 23.11). Dissolved oxygen, glucose, amino acids and salts in the mother's blood pass from the uterine vessels into those of the embryo, while carbon dioxide and nitrogenous waste from the embryo pass across in the opposite direction (Fig. 23.12). The membrane exerts some selective influence over the substances that pass into the placenta and so prevents harmful material from reaching the embryo. The capillaries in the placenta are connected to an artery and vein which run in the *umbilical cord* from the embryo's abdomen to the placenta.

The embryo is surrounded by a *water sac* or *amnion* which protects it from damage and prevents unequal pressures from acting on it. After about five month's growth the embryo moves its limbs quite vigorously inside the water sac and uterus. From fertilization to birth takes about nine months in humans. This length of time is called the *gestation* period.

Birth. A few weeks before birth the embryo has come to lie head downwards in the uterus with its head just above the cervix (Fig. 23.10d and Plate 28).

When the birth starts, the uterus begins to contract rhythmically. This is the onset of what is called "labour". These rhythmic contractions become stronger and more frequent. The opening of the cervix gradually dilates enough to let the child's head pass through, and the uterine contractions are reinforced by muscular contractions of the abdomen. The amnion ruptures at some stage in labour and the fluid escapes through the vagina. Finally, the muscular contractions of the uterus and abdomen expel the child head first through the dilated cervix and vagina.

The umbilical cord which still connects the child to the placenta is tied and cut. Later, the placenta breaks away from the uterus and is expelled separately as "after-birth".

The sudden fall in temperature experienced by the newly born baby stimulates it to take its first breath, usually accompanied by crying. In a few days the remains of the umbilical

Fig. 23.10 Growth and development in uterus
(not to scale)

cord attached to the baby's abdomen shrivel and fall away, leaving a scar in the abdominal wall, called the navel. The average birth weight of babies is 3 kg.

Shortly after its birth the baby starts to suckle. During pregnancy the mammary glands of the breast have developed and are stimulated to secrete milk by the first sucklings.

Parental care. All mammals suckle their young and protect them in various ways until they are old enough to move about efficiently and obtain their own food. Most mammals prepare a nest in which to bear their young, and in this way the babies are protected from animals of prey and from temperature changes. The nest reduces the chances of their wandering and getting lost and prevents them from injuring themselves. The young mammals are often born without fur but the presence of the mother's body prevents them from losing heat. The food at first is entirely milk, suckled from the mother. The milk contains nearly all the food, vitamins and salts that the young need for their energy requirements and tissue building but there is no iron present for the manufacture of haemoglobin. All the iron needed for the first weeks or months is stored in the body of the embryo during the period of gestation in the uterus. The parent's milk supply increases as the young animals grow larger and is supplemented by solid food. In carnivorous mammals the prey is brought back to the nest site and torn into pieces small enough for the young to swallow. Often the parents are more aggressive when they have young and react violently to intruders. When the young animals are old enough to obtain their own food and escape from predators, they leave the nest site and disperse. In humans, the period of dependence on parents is lengthy.

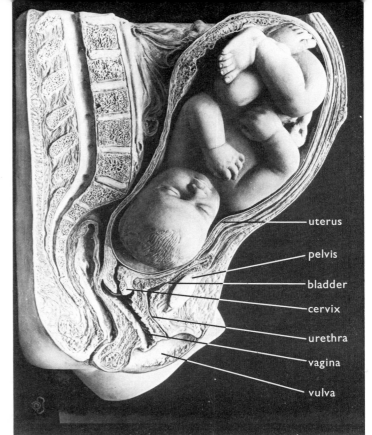

uterus
pelvis
bladder
cervix
urethra
vagina
vulva

(Reproduced with permission from the Birth Atlas published by Maternity Centre Association, New York)

Plate 28. MODEL OF HUMAN FOETUS JUST BEFORE BIRTH

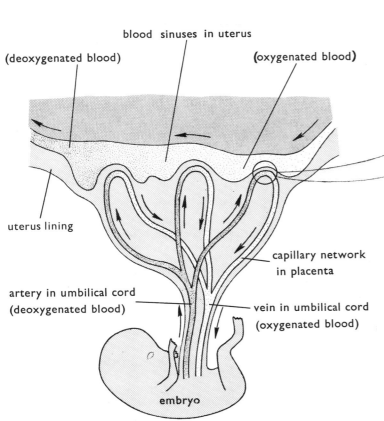

blood sinuses in uterus
(deoxygenated blood)
(oxygenated blood)
uterus lining
capillary network in placenta
artery in umbilical cord (deoxygenated blood)
vein in umbilical cord (oxygenated blood)
embryo

Fig. 23.11 Diagram to show relationship between blood supply of embryo, placenta and uterus

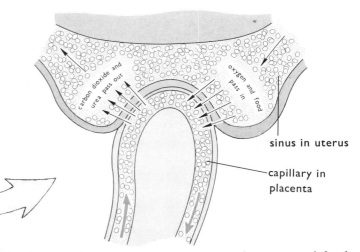

carbon dioxide and urea pass out
oxygen and food pass in
sinus in uterus
capillary in placenta

Fig. 23.12 Diagram to show exchange of oxygen and food from uterus to placenta

Twins. IDENTICAL TWINS. Sometimes a fertilized ovum divides into two parts at an early stage of cell division and each part develops separately into a normal embryo. Such "one egg" twins are the same sex and are identical in nearly every physical respect, although differences in position and blood supply while in the uterus may cause them to differ initially in weight and vigour.

FRATERNAL TWINS. If two ova are released from the ovary and fertilized simultaneously, twins will result. These twins may be different sexes and are not necessarily any more alike than other brothers and sisters of the same family.

Secondary sexual characters. In addition to producing gametes, the ovaries and testes make chemicals called hormones. At puberty these hormones are released into the blood stream, and as they circulate round the body they give rise to physical

118

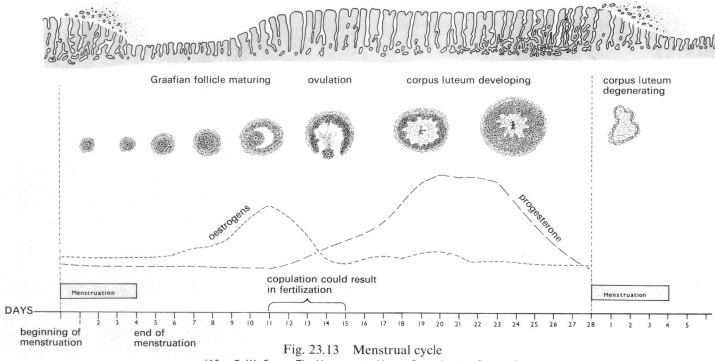

uterine lining thickening   becoming highly vascular   breaking down

Fig. 23.13   Menstrual cycle

(*After G. W. Corner*, The Hormones in Human Reproduction, *Princeton*)

and mental changes which we associate with masculinity or femininity.

In males, the voice becomes deeper, hair begins to grow on the face, in the armpits and in the region of the external genitalia, and the body becomes more muscular.

In females, the hormones cause the breasts to grow and the hip girdle to enlarge. These features are called secondary sexual characters.

Menstruation. Of the 500 or so ova produced in the life of a woman, not more than 12 are likely to be fertilized and form embryos. Nevertheless, at the time of release of each ovum the lining of the uterus becomes thicker with additional layers of cells into which the ovum will sink if fertilized. The blood supply is increased at the same time. If the ovum is not fertilized, however, the new uterine lining disintegrates and the unwanted cells, a certain amount of blood, and mucus are lost through the cervix and vagina. This menstruation, as it is called, occurs 12–14 days after the egg is released, once in about four weeks.

Birth control. When people wish to limit the size of their families they usually make use of one or other form of birth control. This may involve either a contraceptive practice or avoiding copulation during the period when fertilization is likely to occur, i.e. between the 10th and 16th day after the onset of menstruation (*see* Fig. 23.13). On its own, this is not a very reliable method because of variations in the time of ovulation, the interval between menstrual periods and the regularity of their occurrence.

The principal methods of contraception are as follows:

(a) *The sheath or diaphragm.* A thin rubber sheath worn on the penis, or a small rubber diaphragm inserted in the vagina prevents the sperms from reaching the cervix.

(b) *Intra-uterine loop.* A small plastic strip bent into a loop or coil is inserted and retained in the uterus. Whether it interferes with fertilization or implantation is not certain but it is very effective.

(c) *The contraceptive pill.* The pill contains chemicals which have the same effect on the body as the hormones oestrogen and progesterone. When mixed in suitable proportions, these hormones suppress ovulation and so prevent conception. The pills need to be taken each day for the 21 days between menstrual periods and are almost 100 per cent effective.

World population. With the increasing application of medical knowledge, fewer people are dying from infectious diseases. The birth rate, however, has not fallen off in proportion, with the result that the world population is doubling every 50 years or less. In the developing countries with limited natural resources, this leads to shortages of food and living space. In the industrialized countries, the population increase has contributed to the pollution of the environment as a result of waste disposal and intensive methods of food production.

There is clearly a physical limit to the number of people who can live on the Earth, though authorities may differ in their estimates of this number. Therefore it seems essential, at the very least, to educate people (a) into accepting the need to limit their families and (b) in methods of achieving this. The alternative to voluntary population control is control by famine and disaster.

QUESTIONS

1. In what ways does a zygote differ from any other cell in the body?
2. What is the advantage to the embryo of the early development of its heart and circulatory system?
3. What differences are there in the numbers, structure and activity of the male and female gametes in man?
4. What do you consider are the advantages of (a) internal fertilization over external fertilization and (b) development of the embryo in the uterus rather than in the egg?
5. In what ways is parental care in man similar to and different from parental care in other mammals?
6. List the changes in the composition of the maternal blood which are likely to occur when it passes through the placenta.
7. Explain why there are only a few days in each menstrual cycle when fertilization is likely to occur.

24 | The Skeleton, Muscles and Movement

SKELETAL tissues are hard substances formed by living cells. Frequently they contain non-living mineral matter such as calcium salts. The structures made of such non-living material can nevertheless grow and change as a result of the activities of living cells which dissolve away and replace the hard materials.

Exoskeletons. Where the hard material is formed mainly on the outside of the body it is often called an exoskeleton. Insects and crustaceans such as crabs have exoskeletons or cuticles, though there are projections from the exoskeleton into the body cavity for muscle attachment (p. 149). Animals with exoskeletons increase their size periodically by dissolving and absorbing most of the cuticle, splitting and shedding the outermost layers, and forming a new cuticle on the exposed surface. This is called *ecdysis* (p. 146).

Endoskeletons (Plate 29). Vertebrate animals have bony skeletons within their bodies. These animals can grow by a continuous increase in size and not by a series of ecdyses.

Functions of the skeleton

The functions can be grouped conveniently under the headings, support, protection, movement and locomotion, and muscle attachment.

Support. There are many invertebrate animals which have no skeleton. Those living in water may become fairly large because the water supports them and buoys them up to a certain extent. In others, e.g. the earthworm, they are supported by the pressure of fluid in their body cavities acting outwards against a muscular body wall. In larger, land-dwelling animals, a rigid skeletal support raises the body from the ground and allows rapid movement, it suspends some of the vital organs and prevents them from crushing each other, and maintains the shape of the body despite vigorous muscular activity. Examination of the skeleton of the rat (Fig. 24.1) will show the backbone as a bridge-like arch or span from which the organs of the body are suspended.

Protection. Certain delicate and important organs of the body are protected by a casing of bone. The brain is enclosed in the skull, the spinal cord in the "backbone", while the heart and lungs are surrounded by a cage of ribs between the *sternum* and spine. The organs are thus protected from distortion resulting from pressure, or injury resulting from impact. The rib cage plays a positive part in the breathing mechanism (p. 104) in addition to protecting the organs of the thorax. In animals with exoskeletons the entire body is protected by the cuticle.

Movement. Many bones of the skeleton act as levers. When muscles pull on these levers they produce movements such as the chewing action of the jaws, the breathing movements of the ribs and the flexing of the arms. Locomotion is the result of the co-ordinated action of muscles on the limb bones and is discussed more fully on p. 124. Movements of the skeleton require a system of joints and muscle attachments.

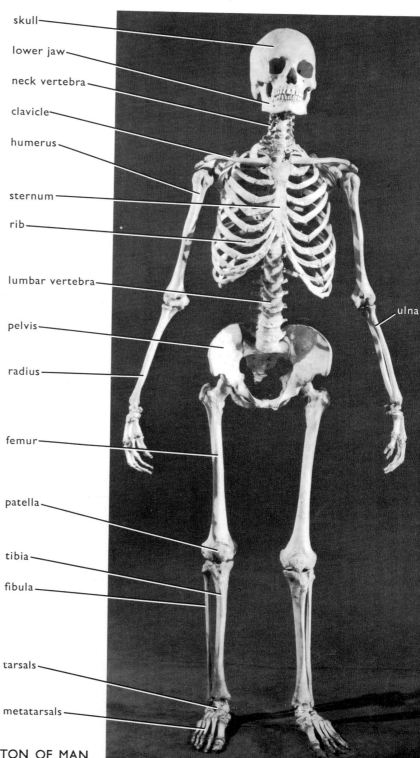

skull
lower jaw
neck vertebra
clavicle
humerus
sternum
rib
lumbar vertebra
pelvis
radius
femur
patella
tibia
fibula
tarsals
metatarsals
ulna

Plate 29.   **SKELETON OF MAN**
(*From* The Human Skeleton, Rank Audio Visual Ltd.)

119

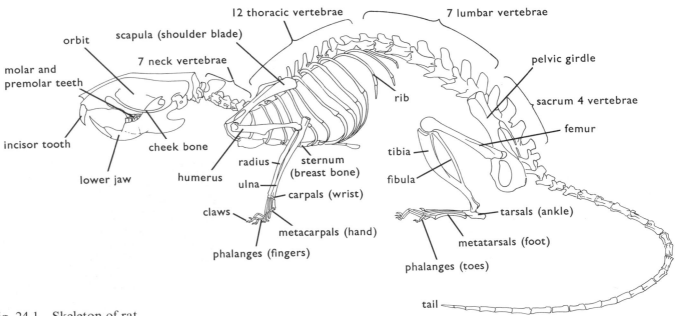

Fig. 24.1   Skeleton of rat

MUSCLE ATTACHMENT. The muscles must be attached to the limb bones at one end in order to produce movement but, in addition, they must have a rigid attachment at the other end so that only one part of the limb moves when the muscle contracts. (*See* Fig. 24.9.) Sometimes the "stationary" end is attached to the upper half of the limb. The extensor muscle which extends the foot is attached to the femur. The muscles which move the femur, however, are attached to the pelvic girdle. Bones frequently have projections or ridges where muscles are attached (Figs. 24.2 and 24.3).

JOINTS. Where two bones meet, a joint is formed. Sometimes, as in the sutures between the bones of the skull, no movement is permitted; in others, e.g. the vertebrae of the spine, only a very limited movement can occur, while the most familiar joints, *synovial joints*, allow a considerable degree of movement. The ball-and-socket joints of the *humerus* and *scapula* (Plate 30) or *femur* and *pelvis* (Plate 31) allow movement in three planes (Fig. 24.5 *a* and *b*). The hinge joints of the elbow and knee allow movement in only one plane (Fig. 24.4).

The surfaces at the heads of the bones which move over each other are covered with a tough cartilage which is slippery and smooth. This, together with a liquid called *synovial fluid* which is formed in the joint, allows friction-free movement (Fig. 24.5*a*). The relevant bones of the joint are held together by strong *ligaments* (Fig. 24.5 *a* and *b*) which prevent dislocation during normal movement. Surrounding the joint is a capsule of fibrous material whose inner lining, the *synovial membrane*, secretes the synovial fluid.

Plate 30.   THE SHOULDER JOINT
(*From* The Human Skeleton, Rank Audio Visual Ltd.)

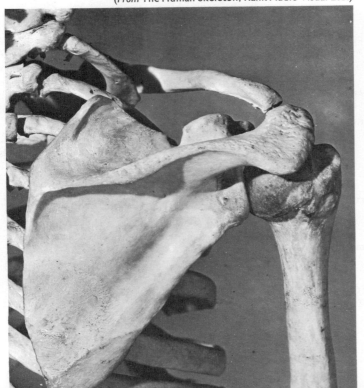

Plate 31.   THE HIP JOINT
(*From* The Human Skeleton, Rank Audio Visual Ltd.)

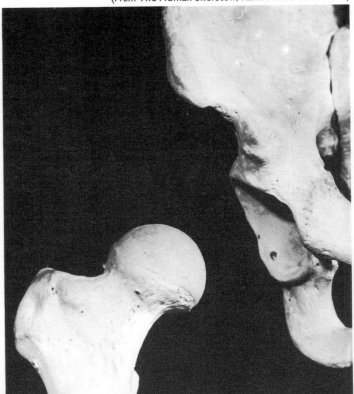

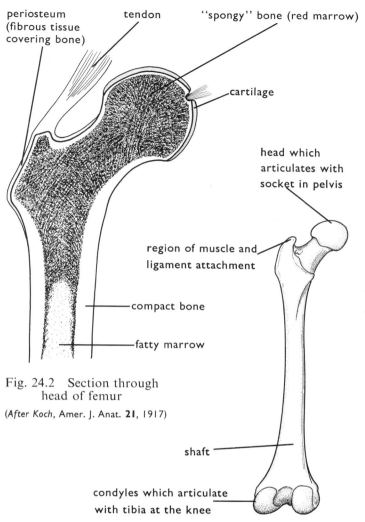

Fig. 24.2   Section through
          head of femur

(After Koch, Amer. J. Anat. 21, 1917)

Fig. 24.3   Femur

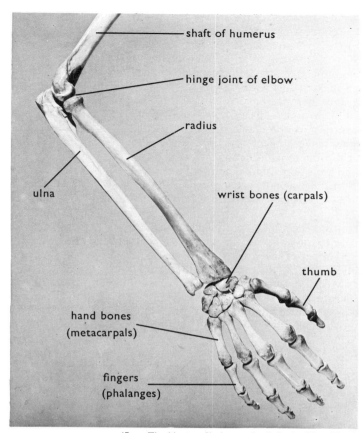

(From The Human Skeleton, Rank Audio Visual Ltd.)

Plate 32.   SKELETON OF THE FOREARM

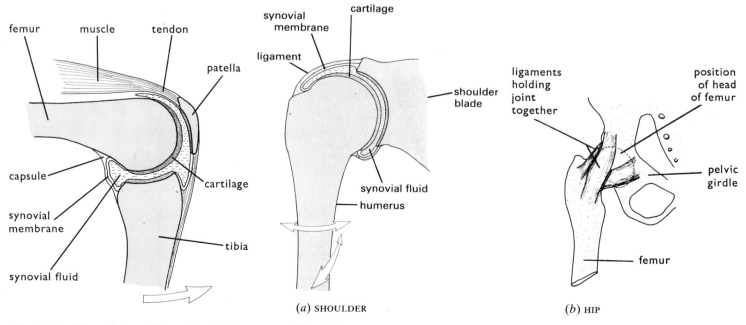

Fig. 24.4   Hinge joint of knee (section)

(a) SHOULDER

(b) HIP

Fig. 24.5   Ball and socket joints

The *vertebrae* of the spine can also move slightly so that the backbone as a whole is flexible. The vertebrae are separated by discs of cartilage (Figs. 24.6b and 24.7a).

MUSCLES are bundles of elongate cells enclosed in sheaths of connective tissue. Each end of a muscle is drawn out to form an inextensible *tendon*, which is attached to the tough membrane, *periosteum*, surrounding the bones of the skeleton (Fig. 24.2). Muscle cells, if stimulated by a nervous impulse, will contract to about two-thirds or one-half their resting length. This makes the muscle as a whole shorter and thicker and, according to its attachments at each end, it can pull on a bone and so produce movement.

Muscles usually act across joints in such a way that the bones are worked as levers with a low mechanical advantage. Figs. 24.8 and 24.9 may help to make this clear. The muscles can contract only a short distance, but because they are attached near to the joint the movement at the end of the limb is greatly magnified. The *biceps* muscle of the arm may contract only about 10 cm, but the hand will move about 60 cm.

Muscles can only contract and relax, they cannot lengthen of their own accord. They have to be pulled back to their original length. Consequently most muscles are in pairs: one produces movement in one direction, the other in the opposite direction. Where such *antagonistic* pairs act across a hinge joint they are called *extensor* and *flexor* muscles (Fig. 24.9). The extensor tends to extend or straighten the limb while the flexor bends or flexes it (Fig. 24.11). Of such pairs of muscles one is usually much stronger than the other. The biceps for flexing the arm is better developed than is the triceps for extending it. The frog's hind-leg extensor muscles which make it leap are stronger than the flexors which return the limb to rest. Locomotion is brought about by the co-ordinated movement of limbs by sets of antagonistic muscles contracting and relaxing alternately (p. 124). When the body is at rest, both antagonistic muscles remain in a state of tension or *tone* and so hold the body in position. The skeletal muscles and others such as those in the tongue are called "voluntary" muscles because they can be contracted at will. The muscle of the alimentary canal and arterioles is "involuntary" because it cannot be consciously controlled.

GIRDLES. To produce movement of the body as a whole the backward thrust of the limbs against the ground or the water must be imparted to the body. The force is usually transmitted through a skeletal structure called a girdle, which is attached to the spinal column. The pelvic girdle (Plate 34) is rigidly joined to the base of the spine (Fig. 24.11), so that in walking or jumping the force of the leg-thrust is transmitted to the spine, which is the central support of the whole body. By

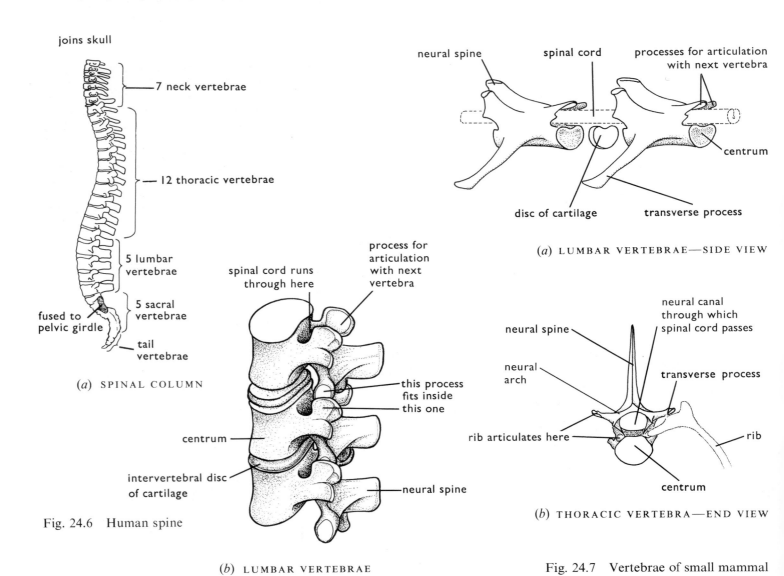

joins skull

7 neck vertebrae

12 thoracic vertebrae

5 lumbar vertebrae

fused to pelvic girdle

5 sacral vertebrae

tail vertebrae

(a) SPINAL COLUMN

Fig. 24.6   Human spine

spinal cord runs through here

process for articulation with next vertebra

centrum

intervertebral disc of cartilage

this process fits inside this one

neural spine

(b) LUMBAR VERTEBRAE

neural spine

spinal cord

processes for articulation with next vertebra

centrum

disc of cartilage

transverse process

(a) LUMBAR VERTEBRAE—SIDE VIEW

neural spine

neural arch

rib articulates here

neural canal through which spinal cord passes

transverse process

rib

centrum

(b) THORACIC VERTEBRA—END VIEW

Fig. 24.7   Vertebrae of small mammal

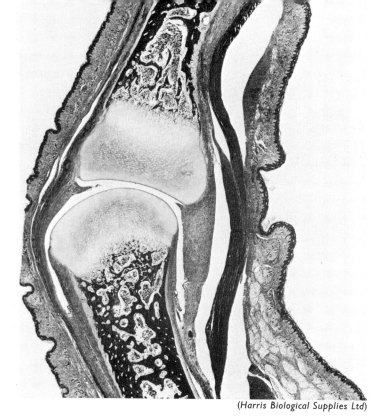

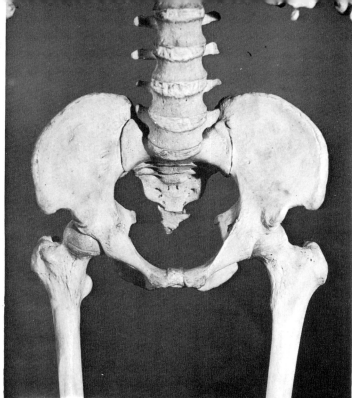

Plate 33.   FINGER JOINT OF HUMAN FOETUS

Plate 34.   THE PELVIC GIRDLE

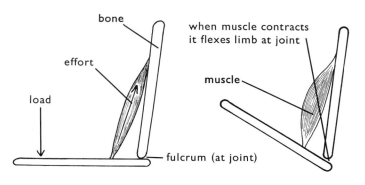

Fig. 24.8   The limb as a lever

this means also, the weight of the body is supported when at rest. The shoulder blades, which form part of the pectoral girdle (Plate 30) are not fused to the spine in mammals, but bound by muscles to the back of the thorax. The fusion of the pelvic girdle to the spine is very effective in transmitting force from the legs to the body. The muscular attachment of the shoulder blades to the spine is less effective in transmitting force from the arms to the body, but this function is not so necessary in the fore- as in the hind-limbs; and the free movement of the shoulders allows greater mobility of the arms. The shoulder in man is more mobile than in most mammals, and the *clavicle* (Plate 29) acts as a radius, limiting the movement of the scapula.

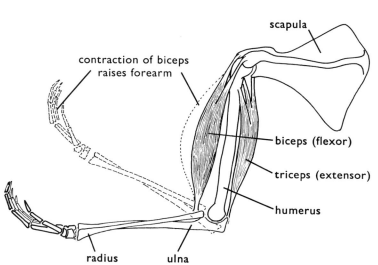

Fig. 24.9   Antagonistic muscles of the forearm

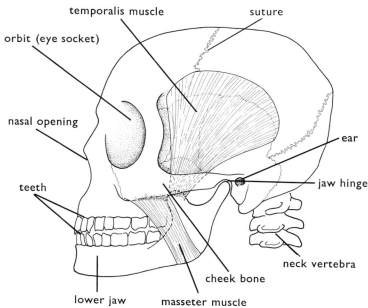

Fig. 24.10   Human skull and chewing muscles

Locomotion

The limbs are moved in a co-ordinated sequence, each one thrusting backwards on the ground and so propelling the animal forwards. While the limb is recovering its forward position it must be removed from contact with the ground.

In Fig. 24.11 some of the muscles of the hind-limb of the rabbit are shown in diagram form. If muscle A contracts it will pull the femur backwards. Friction between the ground and the toes prevents the foot sliding back so that a forward thrust is transmitted through the pelvic girdle to the spine and thence to the whole animal. Such a contraction would contribute to

To produce effective movement it is essential that the contraction of the many sets of muscles is co-ordinated so that, for example, the legs are moved in a logical sequence and antagonistic muscles do not contract simultaneously. Contributing to this co-ordination there is a system of stretch-receptors (p. 129) in the muscles. These fire nervous impulses to the spinal cord when the muscle is being stretched. Such internal sensory organs or proprioceptors, linked to the nervous system, feed back information to the brain about the position of the limbs and enable a pattern of muscular activity to be computed by the brain, so producing effective movement.

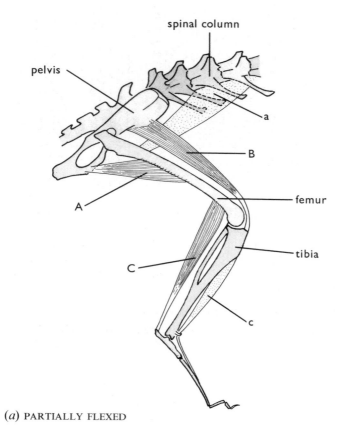

(*a*) PARTIALLY FLEXED

Fig. 24.11   Hind-leg of small mammal in "leaping"

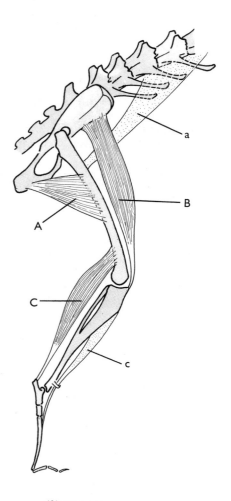

(*b*) EXTENDED

walking or crawling if the tone of muscles B and C was maintained or slightly adjusted. Relaxation of A followed by contraction of a and c would bring the hind-limb forward with the foot raised clear of the ground.

Contraction of B will straighten the leg at the knee. Contraction of C will extend the foot. Thus if muscles A, B and C contract simultaneously, the leg will extend and straighten at the same time as it is swinging backwards. The downwards and backwards thrust of both hind-limbs, with corresponding movements of the fore-limbs and spine will produce a leaping action. Muscles antagonistic to A, B and C, of which only a and c are shown, will contract when their opposite numbers relax, thus flexing the limb and returning it to its original position, before it touches the ground again.

There are, of course, many more muscles involved than are shown in Fig. 24.11 and their co-ordinated action is more subtle and complex than can be described here.

QUESTIONS

1. Construct a diagram similar to Fig. 24.4, to show a section through the elbow joint using Plate 32 for guidance. Show the attachment of the biceps and triceps tendons and state where you would expect to find the principal ligaments.

2. From Fig. 24.1 make an enlarged drawing of the scapula and fore-limb of the rat. Draw in muscles which you think would help to push the animal forward. Show the point of attachment very clearly and state what each muscle would do when it contracted.

3. What is the principal action of (*a*) your calf muscle, (*b*) the muscle in the front of your thigh and (*c*) the muscles in your forearm? If you don't already know the answer, try making the muscles contract and feel where the tendons are pulling.

4. Unlike most mammals, man stands upright on his hind-legs. What differences do you think this has made to his skeleton and musculature?

25 | Teeth

TEETH are produced by the skin where it covers the jaws. Their roots become enclosed in the developing jaw bone, and their crowns break through the skin into the mouth cavity (Plate 35). They are thought to have arisen in the course of evolution from the scales of fish such as the dogfish. Where the skin bearing the scales stretched over the jaws, the scales became enlarged, pointed and specialized for holding prey or breaking up food.

Tooth structure (Fig. 25.1)

Enamel is the hardest substance made by animals. It is deposited on the outside of the crown of the tooth by cells in the gum before the tooth reaches the surface. The enamel is a non-living substance containing calcium salts; it forms an efficient, hard, biting surface.

Dentine is more like bone in its structure. It is hard but not so brittle as enamel and running through it are strands of cytoplasm from cells in the pulp. These cells are able to add more dentine to the inside of the tooth.

Pulp. In the centre of the tooth is soft connective tissue called pulp. From this the living strands of cytoplasm in the dentine derive their food and oxygen. The pulp contains sensory nerve-endings and blood capillaries. Oxygen and food brought by the blood enable the tooth to live and grow. The nerve-endings are particularly sensitive to heat and cold but produce only the sensation of pain.

The **root** is not set rigidly in the jaw bone, but is held by tough fibres so that it moves slightly in its socket as a result of chewing and biting movements.

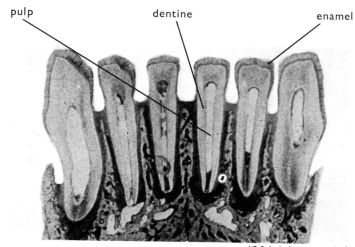

(G.B.I. Laboratories Ltd)

Plate 35. SECTION THROUGH TEETH AND JAW OF CAT

Cement is a thin layer of bone-like material covering the dentine at the root of the tooth. The fibres which hold the tooth in the jaw are embedded in the cement at one end and in the jaw bone at the other.

Specialization of teeth: carnivores

Where all the teeth serve the same purpose, such as merely holding the prey to prevent its escaping, they are all very

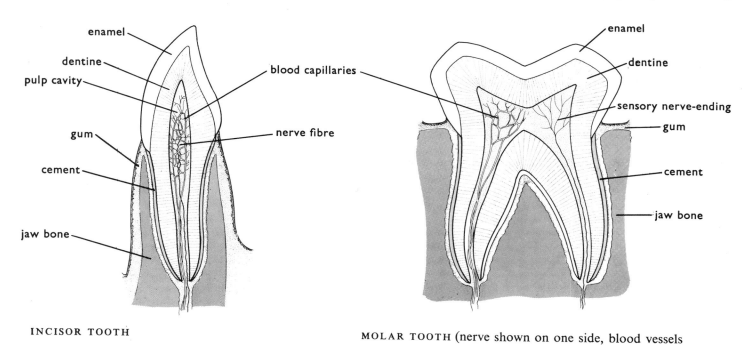

INCISOR TOOTH

MOLAR TOOTH (nerve shown on one side, blood vessels on the other)

Fig. 25.1 Sections through incisor and molar teeth

125

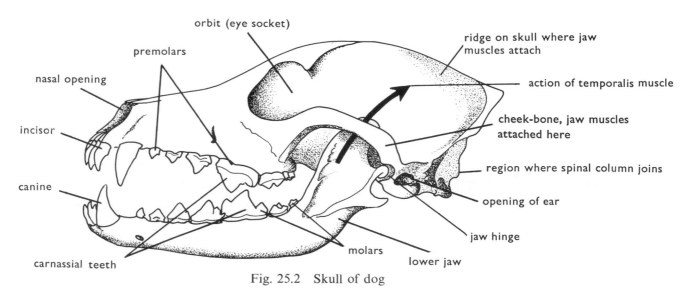

Fig. 25.2   Skull of dog

similar in structure. In most carnivorous fish the teeth are simply sharp pegs projecting backwards. In such animals the prey is often swallowed whole without chewing.

Where the food is captured, broken up and chewed, the teeth in different regions of the mouth may become specialized to a particular function. For example, a dog's *incisors* (Fig. 25.2) in the front of its mouth meet and can grip and strip off small pieces of flesh close to the bone. The long pointed *canines* are near the front and penetrate the prey, preventing its escape and often killing it. The massive *carnassial* teeth have sharp cutting edges. They pass each other and act like shears or snips, slicing off flesh and cracking bones (*see* Fig. 25.3). The *molars* have more flattened surfaces and meet each other, so crushing the bones and flesh to smaller particles before swallowing. The molars and premolars develop near the back of the jaw where the mechanical advantage is greater.

The dog's dentition is characteristic of carnivorous mammals, i.e. those which feed on other animals. Animals which feed exclusively on vegetation are called herbivores. The differences in shape, size and distribution of the teeth in these types of animal show adaptations to the differences in diet. Their alimentary canals also differ, herbivores having very long intestines and well developed caecum and appendix, features probably associated with the slowness of cellulose digestion. Flesh is digested relatively more rapidly and the intestine of carnivores is short with small caecum and appendix.

Growth of teeth

The teeth of herbivores have wide openings at the roots and grow throughout the life of the animal. In carnivorous and omnivorous mammals, including man, the teeth cease to grow beyond a certain size. This may be due to the gradual closing of the hole in the root, which constricts the blood vessels and reduces the blood supply, so preventing further growth.

Most mammals have two sets of teeth during their lives. The first set, or milk teeth, fall out as a result of their roots being dissolved away in the jaw, and they are replaced by the permanent teeth. A human two-year-old baby has 20 milk teeth which are replaced after the age of 5 years by 32 permanent teeth. These may not all appear until the age of 17 years or more.

Herbivores

The permanent teeth of herbivorous mammals continue to grow throughout the animal's life, being constantly worn down. The lower jaw moves sideways or backwards and forwards grinding the teeth across each other and wearing away first the cement, then the enamel, and finally the dentine. The molar and premolar teeth of the upper and lower jaw ground together in this way come to fit each other exactly (Fig. 25.4). The enamel, being the hardest of the three layers, is slower in wearing down and stands up in ridges with very sharp edges (Fig. 25.5). The grass and vegetation is ground and crushed between

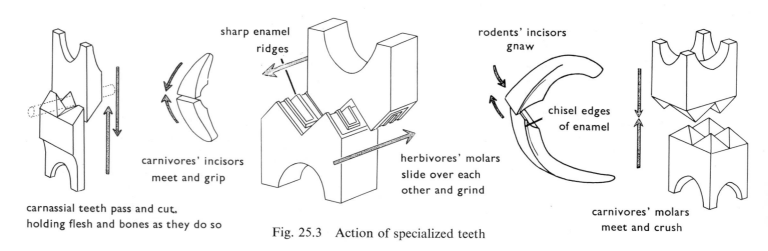

Fig. 25.3   Action of specialized teeth

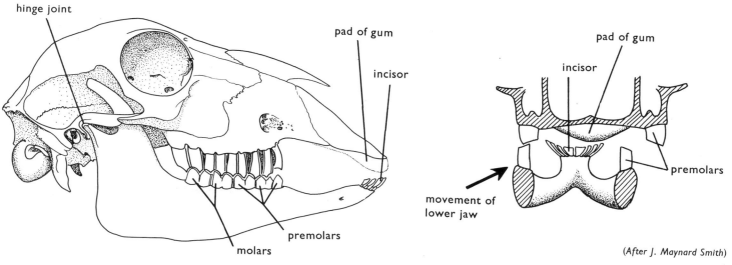

Fig. 25.4 Sheep's skull

Fig. 25.6 Section through herbivore's skull to show action of teeth

(After J. Maynard Smith)

these exactly fitting edges, a high proportion of the cellulose cell walls are broken down so providing a greatly increased surface. Vertebrates, having no enzyme for digesting cellulose, depend on bacterial action for its digestion. An increased surface accelerates this process and the easily digestible protoplasm and cell sap are released from the crushed cells.

Herbivores' canine teeth, if present at all, are usually indistinguishable from incisors and the toothless gap between the incisors and premolars allows the tongue to manipulate the food (*see* Fig. 25.4). The premolars and molars are almost identical in shape and size, as might be expected from the fact that they have the same functions. Many herbivores have no incisors or canines in the top jaw. The grass or other vegetation is gripped between the bottom incisors and the gum of the upper jaw (Fig. 25.6).

Jaw articulation. In the herbivores, the joints between the lower jaw and skull are fairly loose, allowing the sideways or back and forth movement of the lower jaw (Fig. 25.6). In carnivores the jaw muscles, particularly the temporales (Fig. 25.2), are very powerful and the hinge joint allows only up

and down movement of the lower jaw, an adaptation which probably prevents dislocation of the jaw by (a) the strong chewing muscles and (b) the struggles of the prey.

Dentition in man

In man, the top and bottom incisors can pass each other when the jaws close and so cut off manageable portions of food. The molar and premolar surfaces meet and serve to crush the food. The canines are little different in shape or size from the incisors. Human dentition does not show the same degree of specialization as seen in the carnivorous and herbivorous mammals (Fig. 25.7).

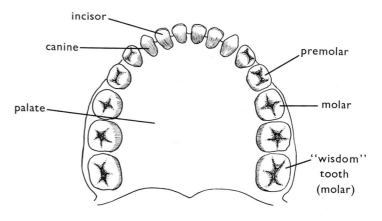

Fig. 25.7 Arrangement of teeth in man's upper jaw

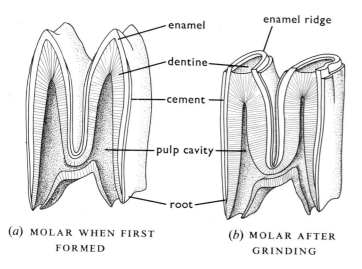

(a) MOLAR WHEN FIRST FORMED

(b) MOLAR AFTER GRINDING

Fig. 25.5 Sections of herbivore's molar to show how it is worn down

QUESTIONS

1. Make a list of the differences in structure and position between the incisor, canine, premolar and molar teeth of a dog and a sheep. Relate each difference to the normal diet of each animal.
2. Study Fig. 25.1 and suggest why the correct method of brushing the teeth is to start with the brush on the gum and sweep it upwards over the crown rather than brushing across or up and down equally.
3. What general aspects of the diet of civilized man differ from the diets of other mammals? What effects might these differences have on the way man uses his teeth?

26 | The Sensory Organs

THE sensory system makes the animal aware, though not necessarily in the sense of "conscious", of conditions and changes both outside and inside its body. In the simpler animals only very general stimuli such as light or darkness, heat or cold can be perceived by the sensory system. In the higher animals detailed information about surroundings such as distance, size and colours of objects can be gained as a result of the specialization of the sensory organs and the elaboration of the nervous system.

The general sensory system

Included in the general sensory system are the organs which are fairly evenly distributed through the dermis of the skin; hence any part of the skin is sensitive to touch, heat, pain and pressure. Examples of such sense organs are given in Fig. 26.1 and Plate 36.

It must be emphasized that, in general, a particular sense organ or sense cell can respond to only one kind of stimulus. Thus, a sense organ sensitive to touch will not be affected by the stimulus of heat; a cell which is sensitive to chemicals will not respond to pressure.

It is not yet certain just how specific some of the sense organs are in their responses, for the sensory-endings which produce the sensation of pain can be activated by a variety of stimuli such as pressure, heat and cold, and the ear lobe which contains only hair plexuses and free nerve endings can detect touch, heat, cold and pressure.

Certain regions of the skin have a greater concentration of sense organs than others. The finger tips, for example, have a large number of touch organs, making them particularly sensitive to touch. The front of the upper arm is sensitive to heat and cold. Some areas of the skin have relatively few sense organs and can be pricked or burned in certain places without any sensation being felt.

Stimulation and conduction of impulses. The sense organ or sense cell is connected to the brain or spinal cord by nerve fibres. When the sense organ receives an appropriate stimulus it sets off an electrical impulse which travels along the nerve fibre to the brain or spinal cord. When the impulse reaches one of these centres it may produce an automatic or reflex action, or record an impression by which the animal feels the nature of the stimulus and where it was applied.

The sense organs of one kind and in a definite area are connected with one particular region of the brain. It is the region of the brain to which the impulse comes that gives rise to the knowledge about the nature of the stimulus and where it was received. For example, if the regions of the brain receiving impulses from the right leg were eliminated or suppressed by drugs, no amount of stimulation of the sensory-endings would produce any sensation at all, although the sense organs would still be functioning normally. On the other hand, if a region of the brain dealing with impulses from sense organs in the leg is stimulated by any means, the sensations produced seem to be from the leg.

Another important consideration is the fact that the impulses transmitted along the nerve fibres are fundamentally all exactly alike. It is not the sensations themselves that are carried but

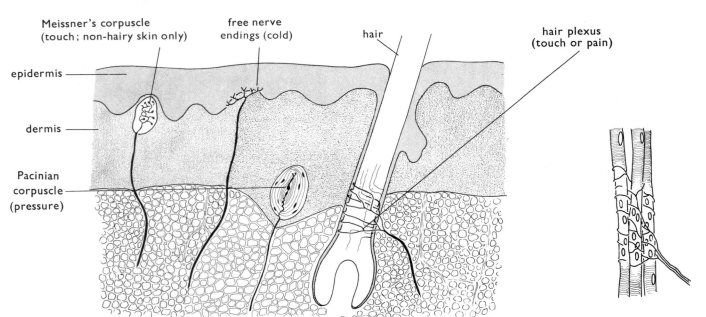

Fig. 26.1(*a*) Sense organs of the skin (generalized diagram)

Fig. 26.1 (*b*) Stretch receptor sensitive to tension in muscle fibre

simply a surge of electricity, and this is so whether it is a heat organ or a touch organ that sets off the impulse. It is only in the brain that the stimulus is identified, according to the region of the brain which the impulse enters. For example, if the nerves from the arm and leg were changed over just before they entered the brain, stubbing one's toe would produce a sensation of pain in the arm or hand.

Intensity of sensation. A strong stimulus usually produces a more pronounced sensation than a weak stimulus. This is probably due to (a) the greater number of sense organs stimulated in the area, and (b) the stimulation of a number of sensory cells which do not respond at all unless the stimulus is intense. Many sensory organs are groups of cells, some of which are triggered off by the slightest stimulus while others need a powerful stimulus to affect them. When these latter are activated, the stimulus is recognized as being stronger than usual.

Vigorous stimulation does not affect the quality or intensity of the electrical impulse travelling in the nerve fibres but increases the total number of these impulses reaching the brain.

Pain. Although we tend to regard sensations of pain as inconvenient and alarming, they have important biological advantages. By making animals respond quickly or automatically by reflex action they tend to remove the animal or the affected part from danger. Our response when touching something unexpectedly hot affords a good example. If there were no sensations of pain, untold damage to tissues could result before one was aware of it. A sensation of pain is not essential for an effective reflex but it probably helps the animal to learn to avoid the same situation. Where pain occurs without producing a reflex action, as in tooth-ache, it serves as a warning that all is not well in that region and gives an opportunity to seek advice or treatment.

Internal sense organs (*proprioceptors*). The tissues of the body also have sense organs. One kind, occurring within the muscles, responds to the degree of stretching (Fig. 26.1b). These sense organs enable an animal to learn to place its limbs accurately in movement and to know their exact position without having to watch them. Sensory pain-endings occur in many internal organs, but not in the brain.

Special senses

Sight, hearing and balance, smell and taste are called the special senses. The relevant sense organs each consist of a great concentration of cells which are sensitive to one kind of stimulus. These sensory cells may be associated with structures that direct the stimulus on to the sensitive region.

Taste. In the lining of the nasal cavity and on the tongue are groups of sensory cells that can be stimulated by chemicals

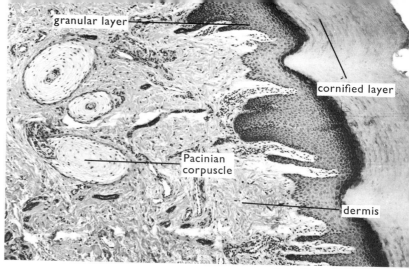

(Brian Bracegirdle)

Plate 36.   PACINIAN CORPUSCLE IN HUMAN SKIN (× 60)

which dissolve in the moisture overlying them. On the tongue these groups are called *taste buds*; they lie mostly in the grooves round the bases of the little projections on the upper surface of the tongue (Fig. 26.2).

Taste buds vary in their sensitivity to groups of chemicals that we describe as sweet, sour, salt or bitter. The chemicals producing similar taste sensations often have little in common, although a sour taste usually indicates an acid. It can be seen that the sense of taste is very limited and probably serves to distinguish only between food suitable and unsuitable for eating. The sensation of flavour has a much greater range and comes from the sense of smell. If the nose is blocked it is difficult to distinguish between many kinds of food which normally have quite distinctive flavours.

Smell. In the epithelium lining the top of the nasal cavity there are spindle-shaped cells with processes extending out into the mucus film that spreads over the epithelium. From these cells nerve fibres pass into the brain. The cells are stimulated by substances which dissolve in the moist lining of this region of the nasal cavity and so produce the sensation of smell. No satisfactory classification of smells, or explanation of how they are distinguished, has yet been made.

The sense of smell is easily fatigued, that is, a smell experienced for a long period ceases to give any sensation and we become unaware of it, though a newcomer may detect it at once.

Sight. The eyes are the organs of sight. They are spherical organs housed in deep depressions of the skull, called *orbits*, and are attached to the wall of the orbit by six muscles which can also move the eye-ball (Fig. 26.3). The structure is best seen in a horizontal section as shown in Fig. 26.4.

Hearing and balance. *See* page 134.

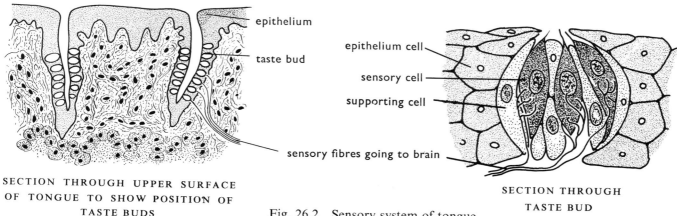

SECTION THROUGH UPPER SURFACE OF TONGUE TO SHOW POSITION OF TASTE BUDS

Fig. 26.2   Sensory system of tongue

SECTION THROUGH TASTE BUD

Structure and functions of the parts of the eye

The EYELIDS can cover and so protect the eye. Closing the eyelids can be a voluntary or reflex action. Regular blinking serves to distribute fluid over the surface of the eye and prevents its drying up.

The CONJUNCTIVA is a thin epithelium which lines the inside of the eyelids, the front of the sclera and is continuous with the epithelium of the cornea.

The TEAR GLANDS open under the top eyelids. They secrete a solution of sodium hydrogencarbonate and sodium chloride and keep the exposed surface of the conjunctiva and cornea moist. They also wash away dust and other particles. An enzyme which is present in tear fluid has a destructive action on bacteria. Excess fluid is drained into the nasal cavity through the *lachrymal duct* which opens at the inside corner of the eyes.

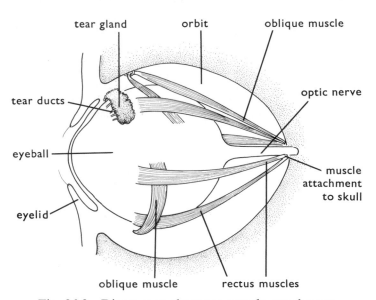

Fig. 26.3   Diagram to show eye muscle attachment
(left eye seen from side)

The EYE MUSCLES are attached to the *sclera* at one end and to the wall of the orbit at the other. Their contractions can make the eye move from side to side and up and down (Fig. 26.3).

The SCLERA is a tough, non-elastic, fibrous coat round the eye-ball.

The CORNEA is the transparent disc in the front part of the sclera. Light passes through the cornea into the eye. Since the cornea is a curved surface the light is refracted and the rays begin to converge.

The CHOROID is a layer of tissue lining the inside of the sclera. It contains a network of blood vessels supplying food and oxygen to the eye. It is also deeply pigmented, the black pigment reducing the reflection of light within the eye.

The AQUEOUS AND VITREOUS HUMOURS are solutions of salts, sugars and proteins in water. The aqueous humour is quite fluid, the vitreous jelly-like. These liquids help to refract the light and produce an image on the retina. Their pressure outwards on the sclera maintains the shape of the eye.

The crystalline lens, the cornea and the conjunctiva are made of living cells which are quite transparent. They contain no blood vessels and must absorb their food and oxygen from the aqueous humour.

The LENS. The cornea begins and the crystalline lens continues the refraction of light so producing an image on the retina. The lens is held in position by the fibres of the *suspensory ligament* which radiate from its edge and attach it to the *ciliary body*. The shape of the lens can be altered by contraction or relaxation of muscles of the ciliary body.

The CILIARY BODY is the thickened edge of the choroid in the region round the lens. It contains blood vessels and muscle fibres some of which run in a circular direction, that is, parallel to the outer edge of the lens.

The IRIS consists of an opaque disc of tissue. At its outer edges it is continuous with the choroid. In the centre is a hole, the pupil, through which passes the light that will produce an image on the retina. The contraction or relaxation of opposing sets of circular and radial muscle fibres in the iris increases or decreases the size of the pupil, so controlling the intensity of

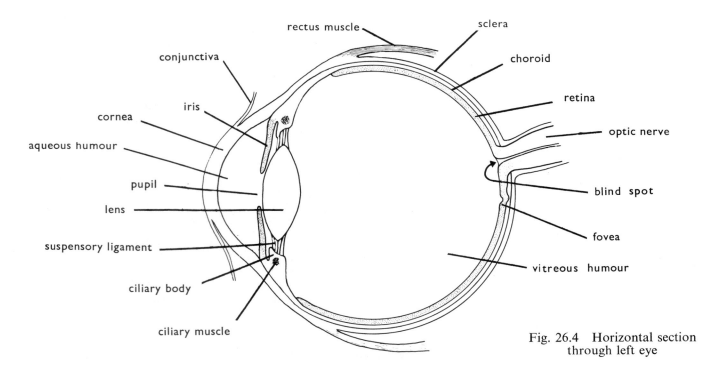

Fig. 26.4   Horizontal section
through left eye

light entering the eye. The iris contains blood vessels and sometimes a pigment layer that determines what is usually called the "colour" of the eyes. Blue eyes have no pigment, the colour being produced by a combination of the black backing, the blood capillaries and the white outer layers on the iris.

The RETINA. This is a layer of cells sensitive to light. There are two kinds of light-sensitive cell, called, according to their shape, *rods* and *cones*. Only the cones are sensitive to coloured light but the rods are more responsive to light of low intensity.

The nerve fibres from these cells pass across the front of the retina and all leave at one point to form the optic nerve which passes through the skull into the brain.

The BLIND SPOT. In the region where the nerve fibres leave the eye to enter the optic nerve there are no light-sensitive cells. If part of an image falls on that region no impression is recorded in the brain. We are not normally aware of this "blank" in our field of vision, partly because it is compensated by the use of two eyes scanning the same field and partly because it never coincides with the image of an object on which we are concentrating. (*See* Experiment 6, p. 136.)

The FOVEA is a small depression in the centre of the retina. It contains only cones, and it is the region of the retina with the greatest concentration of sensory cells and, therefore, gives the most accurate interpretation of an image. When an observer concentrates on an object, or part of an object, its image is thrown on to the fovea. Only in this region is there detailed appreciation of form and colour.

Image formation and vision. Light from an external object enters the eye. The curved surface of the cornea, the lens and the humours, refract the light and focus it so that "points" of light from the object produce points of light on the retina. The image thrown on to the retina is real, upside-down, and smaller than the object (Figs. 26.5 and 26.6). The light-sensitive cells are stimulated by the light falling on them, and impulses are fired off in the nerve fibres. These impulses pass along the optic nerve to the brain where, as a result, an impression is formed of the nature, size, colour and distance of the object. The inversion of the image on the retina is corrected in the optical centre of the brain to form the impression of an upright object.

The accuracy of the impression that the brain gains of the image depends on how numerous and how closely packed are the light-receiving cells of the retina, since each one can only record the presence or absence of a point of light and, in the cones, its colour. If there were only ten such cells, the image of a house falling on five of them would record an impression of its size, the fact that it was differently coloured at the top and bottom, and a vague representation of its shape. In a hawk's fovea there are about a million cones per square millimetre.

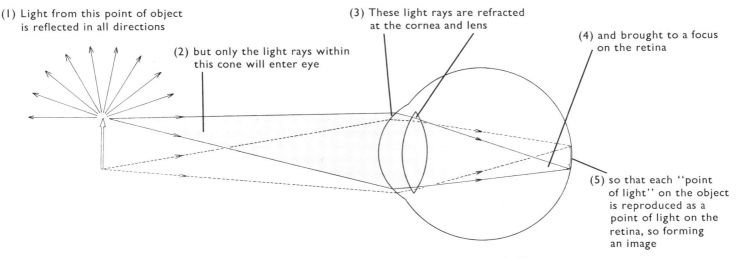

(1) Light from this point of object is reflected in all directions

(2) but only the light rays within this cone will enter eye

(3) These light rays are refracted at the cornea and lens

(4) and brought to a focus on the retina

(5) so that each "point of light" on the object is reproduced as a point of light on the retina, so forming an image

Fig. 26.5   Image formation on the retina shown graphically

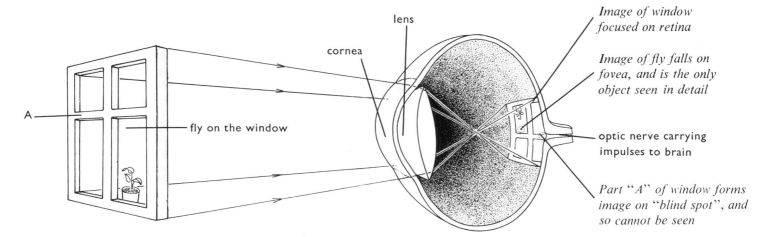

lens

cornea

fly on the window

A

Image of window focused on retina

Image of fly falls on fovea, and is the only object seen in detail

optic nerve carrying impulses to brain

Part "A" of window forms image on "blind spot", and so cannot be seen

Fig. 26.6   Image formation in the eye

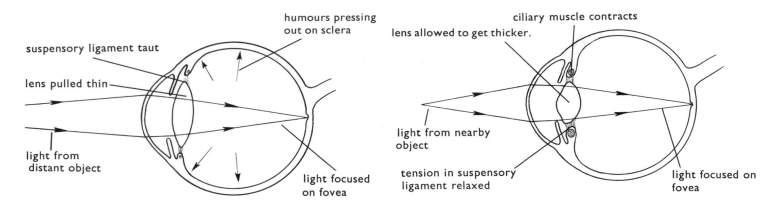

(a) EYE RELAXED (*distant accommodation*)   (b) EYE FOCUSED ON NEAR OBJECT

Fig. 26.7   Diagrams to explain accommodation

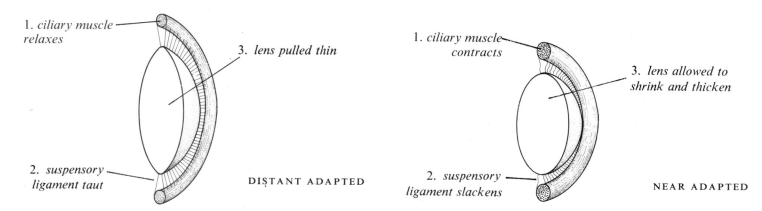

Fig. 26.8   Diagram to show how accommodation is brought about

Accommodation. With a rigid lens of definite focal length placed at a fixed distance from a screen it is possible to obtain a sharply focused image of an object only if the object is at a certain distance from the lens. The focal length of the lens in the eye can be altered by making it thicker or thinner. In this way light from objects from about 25 cm to the limits of visibility can be brought to a focus. This ability of the eye to alter its focal length is called accommodation.

The lens is surrounded by an elastic capsule and tends to contract, becoming thicker in the centre, but the eye fluids pushing out on the sclera maintain a tension in the suspensory ligament that stretches the lens into a thinner shape. Thus, when the eye is at rest, the lens is thin and has a long focal length and is adapted for seeing distant objects (Fig. 26.7a). When a nearby object is to be observed, the ciliary muscles running round the ciliary body contract and so reduce the diameter of the latter. The ciliary body holds the suspensory ligament which pulls on the lens, so any reduction in its diameter reduces the tension in the suspensory ligament, and allows the lens to contract and become thicker (Fig. 26.8). A thicker lens has a shorter focal length, and light from a close object can be brought to a focus (Fig. 26.7b). Relaxation of the ciliary muscles allows the fluid pressure acting on the sclera to pull the lens back to its thin shape.

Control of light intensity. When the circular muscles of the iris contract, the size of the pupil is reduced and less light is admitted. Contraction of radial fibres widens the pupil, so admitting more light. This is a reflex action set off by changes in the intensity of light. In poor light the pupils are wide open; in bright light the pupils are contracted. In this way the retina is protected from damage by light of high intensity, and in poor light the wider aperture of the pupil helps to increase the brightness of the image.

Colour vision. There are three kinds of cone in the human retina. All three respond to more than one colour but each is particularly sensitive to either blue, green or yellow light. Blue light falling on the retina stimulates the blue-sensitive cones most strongly. Green light stimulates the green-sensitive cones more than the other two. Yellow light stimulates the green- and yellow-sensitive cones but red light affects the yellow-sensitive cones far more than the green-sensitive ones and gives us the sensation of redness. When all three types of cone are equally stimulated, we get the sensation of white light.

Stereoscopic vision. Each eye forms its own image of an object under observation, so that two sets of impulses are sent to the brain. Normally the brain correlates these so that we gain a single impression of the object. Since each eye "sees" a slightly different aspect of the same object (Fig. 26.9) the combination of these two images produces the sensation of solidity and the three-dimensional properties of the object.

If the eyes are not aligned normally, or if the centres of the brain dealing with sight impressions are dulled by alcohol, for example, the two sensory impressions from the eyes are not properly correlated and we "see double".

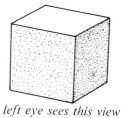 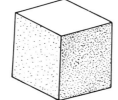

left eye sees this view *right eye sees this view*

Fig. 26.9   Different views of a cube seen by left and right eyes

No blind zones

ANGLE OF VISION OF A HARE

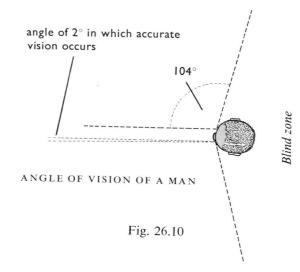

angle of 2° in which accurate vision occurs

104°

Blind zone

ANGLE OF VISION OF A MAN

Fig. 26.10

Judgment of distance. Our ability to judge distance probably depends on a number of factors; the apparent size of the object, overlapping of objects, parallax effects (see below). When we concentrate on close objects, our eye muscles must contract to rotate the eyeballs slightly inwards, and stretch receptors in these muscles may send impulses to the brain so providing information about distance. The stereoscopic vision described above probably helps us to judge distance. It is more difficult to estimate distance accurately using only one eye.

Animals with their eyes set in the front of their heads and directed forwards have stereoscopic vision. This occurs chiefly in animals of prey and is an advantage in judging the distance of their prey before they leap or dive. Examples are lions and tigers among the mammals, hawks, owls and gannets among the birds, and pike among the fish. The judgment of distance in the apes is probably associated with their tree-dwelling habits.

Most of the animals with eyes at the sides of their heads can judge distance only by the apparent size of objects and by parallax. Parallax is the name given to the apparent movement of nearby objects against a background of distant objects when the head is turned from side to side. In most birds the overlapping fields of vision of the two eyes could give stereoscopic vision within an angle of 6–10° from the head.

Animals with their eyes in the sides of their heads can usually see nearly all round (Fig. 26.10), including objects directly behind them. The eyes of most mammals seem particularly sensitive to movement. These last two factors favour the rapid escape of animals such as deer which are likely to be preyed upon by others.

Animals with eyes facing forward have a more limited field of vision, but even a man is aware of objects within an angle of about 200°, although only those included in an angle of 2° from the eye will form an image on the fovea and so be observed accurately. This is considerably less than most people imagine and means, for example, that only about two letters in any word on this page can be studied in detail.

Long and short sight. Its causes and corrections are explained diagrammatically in Fig. 26.11.

LONG SIGHT

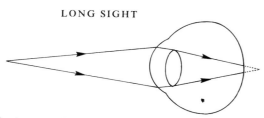

Long sight is caused by small or "short" eyeballs. Light from a close object would be brought to a focus behind the retina, so the image on the retina is blurred

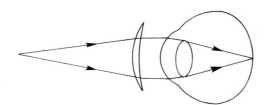

Long sight can be corrected by wearing converging lenses

SHORT SIGHT

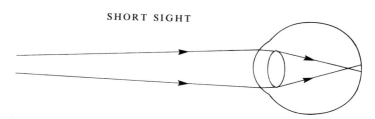

Short sight is usually caused by large or elongated eyeballs. Light from a distant object is focused in front of the retina, so the image on the retina is blurred

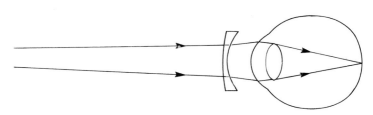

Short sight can be corrected by wearing diverging lenses

Fig. 26.11   Long and short sight

The ear

The ear contains receptors which are sensitive to sound vibrations in the air between the frequencies of 30 per second and 20,000 per second.

Structure (Fig. 26.12). The OUTER EAR is a tube opening on the side of the head and leading inwards to the ear-drum. At the outside end there may be an extension of skin and cartilage, the *pinna*, which in some mammals helps to concentrate and direct the vibrations into the ear and assists in judging the direction from which the sound came. A membrane of skin and fine fibres is stretched across the innermost end of the outer ear, closing it off completely. This is called the *ear-drum*.

worked out it is thought that the short fibres in the first part of the cochlea respond to high-frequency vibrations and the long fibres in the last part to low-frequency vibrations, with a continuous range of intermediate fibres which respond to other frequencies. When the transverse fibres vibrate they stimulate the sensory cells resting upon them. According to this theory the pitch of a note could be determined by the brain, owing to the fact that only a particular group of fibres is stimulated by a certain frequency and will send impulses through the auditory nerve to the brain, while the others will be unaffected.

Eustachian tubes. Air pressure in the middle ear is usually

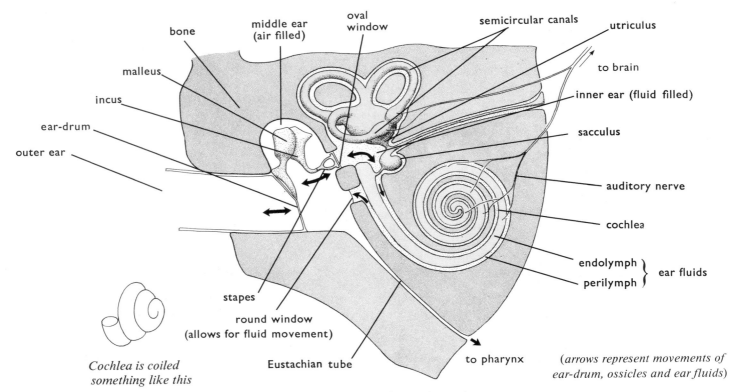

Cochlea is coiled something like this

Fig. 26.12   Diagram of the ear in section

(*arrows represent movements of ear-drum, ossicles and ear fluids*)

The MIDDLE EAR is an air-filled cavity in the skull. It communicates with the naso-pharynx (p. 87) through a narrow tube, the *Eustachian tube*. Three small bones, or *ossicles*, in the middle ear link the ear-drum to a small opening in the skull, the *oval window*, which leads to the *inner ear*.

The INNER EAR is filled with a fluid and consists mainly of a coiled tube, the *cochlea*, with sensory endings in it. It is here that the sound vibrations are converted to nervous impulses.

Hearing. Vibrations in the air that constitute sound waves enter the outer ear and set the ear-drum vibrating. This vibration is transmitted through the three ossicles which act as levers and cause the innermost of them, the *stapes*, to vibrate against the oval window. The fact that the ear-drum is greater than the oval window, together with the action of the levers of the ossicles, result in an increase of about 22 times in the force of the vibrations that reach the inner ear.

The oscillations of the stapes set the fluids of the inner ear vibrating, particularly in the cochlea. A membrane consisting of transverse fibres runs the length of the cochlea; in the first part of this membrane the fibres are short, and in the last part longer. Although details of the mechanism are not yet fully

the same as atmospheric pressure. If changes take place in the pressure outside the ear-drum, for example when gaining height rapidly in an aircraft or even in a lift, the pressure is equalized by the Eustachian tube opening and admitting more air to, or releasing excess air from, the middle ear. Normally the Eustachian tubes are closed, and are opened only when one is swallowing or yawning, when a "popping" sound may be heard in the ears.

Sense of direction of sound. With two ears the sound from a single source will be heard more loudly in one ear than the other, and very slightly earlier. The fact that the two ears are stimulated to different extents enables animals to estimate the direction from which the sound comes. Most mammals can also move their ear pinnae to a favourable position for receiving the sound and so obtain a more accurate bearing.

A source of sound which is equidistant from both ears is difficult to locate because it can be below eye-level, directly in front, directly above or behind the head and still stimulate both ears equally. In such a situation dogs will cock their heads on one side, resulting in one ear being stimulated more than the other.

A dog can locate the position of a sound in one out of thirty-two positions all round it, while humans are accurate in the perception of one out of only eight possible sources. Cats have been shown capable of distinguishing the position of two sounds only half a metre apart and eighteen metres away.

Semicircular canals and sense of balance (Fig. 26.13)

The *utriculus, sacculus* and *semicircular* canals are organs of balance and posture. In the fluid-filled cavities of the utriculus and sacculus are gelatinous plates containing chalky granules, called *otoliths*, which lie above sensitive patches of the lining. Sensory fibres from these patches are embedded in the otoliths

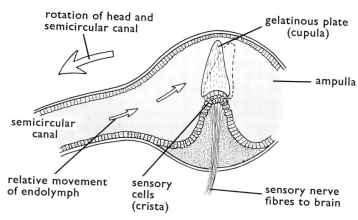

Fig. 26.14(a)   Diagrammatic section through ampulla

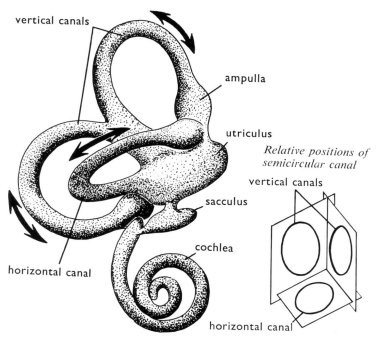

Fig. 26.13   Semicircular canals
Arrows show the direction of rotation which stimulates each canal.

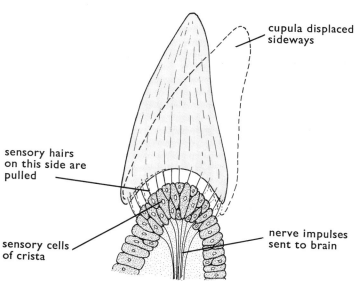

Fig. 26.14(b)   Detail of crista and cupula

and when the head is tilted, the otoliths pull on the fibres. The nervous impulses fired off from these organs as a result of such stimulation reach the brain and set off a reflex tending to return the body to its normal posture.

The semicircular canals contain a fluid and in the *ampullae* are sense organs which respond to movements of the fluid. When the head rotates, the fluid tends to remain stationary for a time and is thought to displace the *cupula* in the ampulla (Fig. 26.14). The three canals are in planes at right angles to each other and are stimulated by rotation in their respective planes.

The utricles are regarded as responding to the tilting movements of the head or body while the semicircular canals are stimulated by accelerations of a rotary kind in their particular plane. If the utricles and semicircular canals did not function properly, animals would keep falling over unless they relied on their eyes. Without the semicircular canals one could probably stand upright if quite stationary, but it would be very difficult to maintain balance while moving or changing direction.

Experiences of vertigo during night flying show that we normally rely on information from the eyes and other sense organs, as well as from the utriculus and semicircular canals, for accurate sensations of position and balance.

PRACTICAL WORK

SKIN SENSE. 1. **To find the sensitivity of the skin to touch.** A simple apparatus such as is shown in Fig. 26.15 can be used. The distance apart of the points is measured, and starting at about 5 cm apart, the experimenter touches the two points simultaneously on parts of the skin of a "volunteer" whose eyes are closed. In the more sensitive regions of the skin, the two points are felt as separate stimuli. Elsewhere, e.g. the back of the hand or the neck, only a single stimulus is felt, perhaps because there are fewer touch endings. By reducing the distance between the points from time to time, the degree of sensitivity of different regions of the skin can be mapped out.

It is best to vary the stimulus, using sometimes one point and sometimes two so that the subject does not know in advance which is to be used.

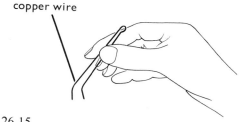

Fig. 26.15

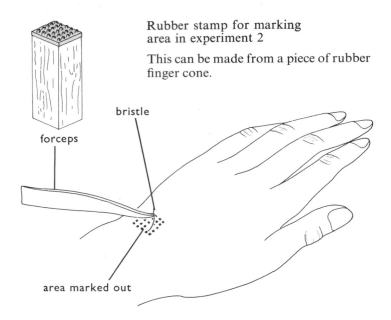

Rubber stamp for marking area in experiment 2

This can be made from a piece of rubber finger cone.

Fig. 26.16   Testing sensitivity to touch

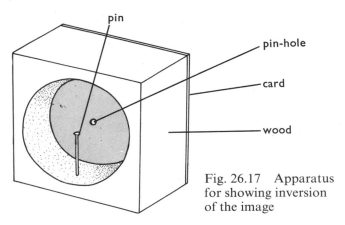

Fig. 26.17   Apparatus for showing inversion of the image

2. Sensitivity to touch. A patch of skin on the back of the wrist is marked with regular dots, using a rubber stamp such as is illustrated in Fig. 26.16. A similar pattern is stamped on a piece of paper so that the results can be recorded. Held by a pair of forceps or stuck to a wooden handle, a bristle such as a horse hair (Fig. 26.16) is pressed on the skin at each point marked by a dot, with enough force just to bend the bristle. The subject, who must not watch the experiment, states when he can feel the stimulus. A third person, with a duplicate set of marks on paper, indicates the positive or negative result of each stimulus, which can finally be expressed as a percentage. Using the same technique on different parts of the skin the relative concentration of touch organs can be estimated though the sensitive "spots" do not correspond to single nerve-endings.

3. Location of the source of stimulation. If a dried pea or marble is rolled about on a table between the crossed tips of the first and second fingers, an impression of two solid objects is received in the brain. The eyes should be closed while doing this so that only sensations of touch are received. Normally these regions of the fingers are stimulated simultaneously only by two separate objects, and it is this impression that has been learned by the brain.

EYES **4. Inversion of the image.** If the apparatus shown in Fig. 26.17 is held close to the eye and the pin observed by looking through the pin-hole, an upright silhouette of the pin's head is seen. The apparatus is now reversed so that the pin is nearer to the eye, and moved until the pin-head can be seen against the outline of the pin-hole. In this case, an upright and enlarged shadow is cast on to the retina, and the brain makes the usual correction so that the impression gained is of the pin-head upside down.

5. The double image. If a nearby object is observed, and a finger pressed against the lower lid of one eye so as to displace the eye-ball slightly, an impression of two separate images will result, one formed in each eye.

6. The blind spot. Hold the book about 60 cm away. Close the left eye and concentrate on the cross with the right eye. Slowly bring the book closer to the face. When the image of the dot falls on the blind spot it will seem to disappear.

7. To find which eye is used more. A pencil is held at arm's length in line with a distant object. First one eye is closed and opened and then the other. With one the pencil will seem to jump sideways. This shows which eye was used to line up the pencil in the first place.

EARS. **8. Location of sound.** Two large funnels, held in clamps, are connected to lengths of rubber tubing which can be inserted into the ears of the subject. The subject holds the tubes in his ears so that only sounds entering the funnels will reach the ear-drums. The subject is blindfolded and the two funnels crossed over so that the one leading to the left ear is pointing to the right and vice versa. When sounds are made on the right of the subject, he thinks they are coming from the left. By altering the position of the funnels, without the subject's knowledge, interesting results can be obtained.

9. Location of sound. A ticking clock is held, in turn, above, behind, and in front of a blindfolded subject, so that it is always equidistant from both ears. The subject is asked to indicate its position. These results are then compared with the number of successes scored when the clock is held in similar positions but to the sides of the subject.

TASTE. **10. Sensitivity of the tongue.** Solutions of sucrose (sweet), sodium chloride (salt), citric acid (sour), and quinine (bitter) are prepared. The subject puts out his tongue and the experimenter places a drop of one of the solutions at one point of the tongue using a pipette. Without withdrawing the tongue, the subject tries to identify the taste. The solutions are applied in turn to all parts of the tongue, washing the pipette between each application. In this way it may be possible to determine which regions of the tongue are most sensitive to particular groups of chemicals.

QUESTIONS

1. Most animals have a distinct head end and tail end. Why do you think the main sensory organs are confined to the head end?
2. Chemicals such as sugar and saccharine both taste sweet and yet they are chemically quite different. Middle C on the piano has a frequency of 264 vibrations per second whereas D has 297 vibrations per second. The difference is small and yet the two notes are easily distinguished.
    What are the properties of the sense organs concerned which make for poor discrimination of chemicals and precise discrimination of sounds?
3. In what functional way does a sensory cell in the retina differ from a sensory cell in the cochlea?
4. An eye defect known as "cataract" results in the lens becoming opaque. To relieve the condition, the lens can be removed completely. Make a diagram to show how an eye without a lens could, with the aid of spectacles, form an image on the retina. What disadvantages would result from such an operation?
5. In poor light, an object can be seen more clearly in silhouette by looking to one side of it than by looking at it directly. Explain this phenomenon.
6. A person whose ear ossicles are ineffective can often hear a ticking watch pressed against his head better than he can if it is held close to his ear. Explain this effect.

27 | Co-ordination

THE various physiological processes in living animals have been described so far as if they were quite separate functions of the body, the total result of which constitutes a living organism. Although these processes can be usefully considered individually, they are in fact all very closely linked and dependent on each other. The digestion of food, for example, would be of little value without a blood stream to absorb and distribute the products.

The working together of these systems is no haphazard process. The timing and location of one set of activities is closely related to the others. For example, in walking, the legs are moved alternately, not both at the same time, without the walker's having to think consciously about it. During exercise, when the body needs more food and oxygen, the breathing rate is automatically increased and the heart beats faster, so sending a greater volume of oxygenated blood to the muscles. When one is eating a meal the position of the food is recorded by the eyes, and as a result of this information the arms are moved to the

right place to take it up, not by trial and error, but with precision and accuracy. As the food is raised to the mouth the latter opens to receive it at just the right moment, chewing movements begin, and saliva is secreted. At the moment of swallowing, many things happen simultaneously as described on p. 86. In the stomach, the gastric glands begin to secrete enzymes which will digest the food when it arrives.

In the sequences described above, many bodily functions come into action at just the right moment, with the result that no unnecessary movements are made and no enzymes are wasted by their being secreted when no food is present.

The linking together in time and space of these and other activities is called co-ordination. Without co-ordination the bodily activities would be thrown into chaos and disorder: food might pass undigested through the alimentary canal for lack of enzyme secretion, even assuming it negotiated the hazard of the windpipe; both legs might be bent simultaneously in an attempt at walking; a runner would collapse after a few metres from lack of an increased oxygen supply, and so on.

Co-ordination is effected by the nervous system and the *endocrine system*. The nervous system is a series of conducting tissues running to all parts of the body (Fig. 27.1), while the endocrine system is a number of glands in the body which produce chemicals that circulate in the blood stream and stimulate certain organs (p. 144).

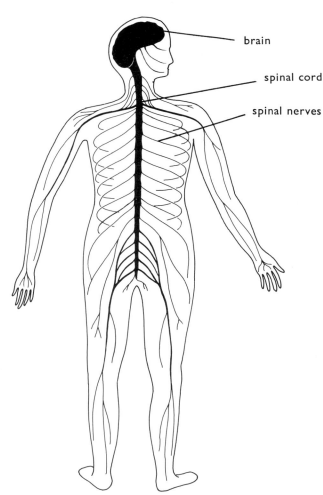

Fig. 27.1   Nervous system of man ($\times \frac{1}{14}$)

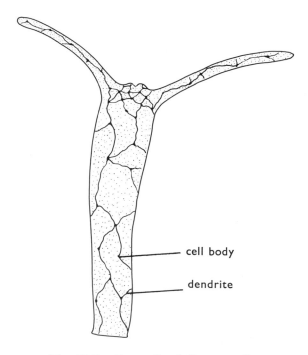

Fig. 27.2   Generalized diagram of nerve network of a Hydra ($\times 10$)

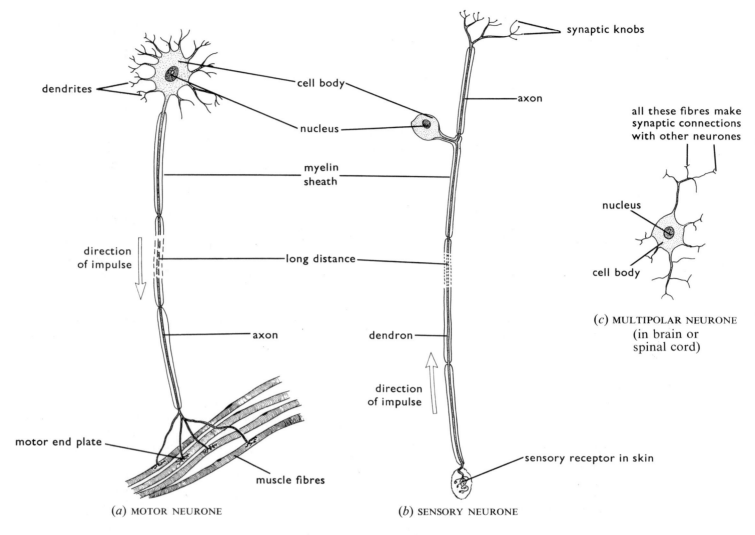

Fig. 27.3   Nerve cells (neurones)

The nervous system

Nerve cells (*neurones*). The units which make up the nervous system are nerve cells (Fig. 27.3). These are small masses of cytoplasm with a central nucleus. One or more branching, cytoplasmic filaments called *dendrites* conduct impulses towards the cell body, while a single, long fibre called an *axon* conducts impulses away. In sensory neurones the single, elongated dendrite is called a *dendron*. Dendrons and axons, collectively called nerve fibres in this account, consist of fluid-filled, cytoplasmic tubes, in certain cases surrounded by an insulating sheath of fatty materials called myelin. In mammals, the cell body is usually in the brain (Plate 37) or spinal cord, while the axon or dendron extends the whole distance to the organ concerned, often for considerable lengths, for example, from the base of the spine down to the big toe.

The nerve fibre has the special property of being able to transmit electrical impulses very rapidly down its entire length and pass them on to the next nerve cell in line. This transmission is not the same as electrical conduction in a metal, where the current flow depends on the voltage applied. The axon builds up within itself an electrical charge which is released when the nerve is stimulated and has to be built up again before the next impulse can pass. Nerve cells usually transmit impulses in one direction only. If the impulse travels

in a dendron from a sensory organ or receptor to the nerve centres, it is called a *sensory fibre*. If the impulse passes from a nerve centre to a muscle or gland (an *effector*), the axon is called a *motor fibre*.

The synapse. A nervous impulse is passed from one neurone to another by means of a synapse. Branching fibres from one neurone are applied to the dendrites or cell body of another (Fig. 27.4). The impulse is transmitted by the secretion of a chemical into a microscopic space which exists between

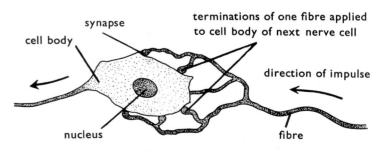

Fig. 27.4   Diagram of synapses

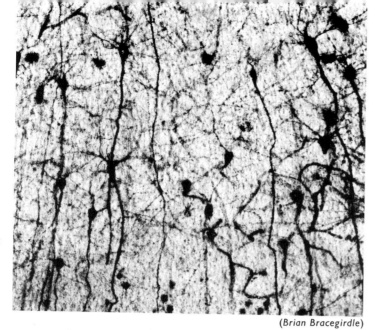

Plate 37. MULTIPOLAR NEURONES IN
BRAIN CORTEX (× 350)

(Brian Bracegirdle)

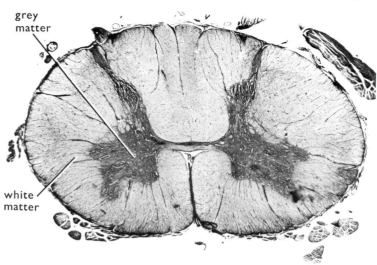

(Brian Bracegirdle)

Plate 38. SECTION THROUGH SPINAL CORD (×7)

the termination of the fibre and the membrane of the cell body. A single impulse does not necessarily get across the synapse. It may take two or three impulses arriving in rapid succession or perhaps arriving simultaneously from two or more fibres, to start an impulse in the next neurone.

An individual cell body may have synapses with many incoming fibres and it is via the synapses that the different parts of the body and brain are kept in communication. Because of the enormous possibilities of inter-connexion and since the simultaneous arrival of impulses at a cell body may stimulate or inhibit the relaying of a subsequent impulse, the synapse is probably the basic "computer" unit of the central nervous system, making possible effective co-ordination and learning.

The grey matter of the brain and spinal cord consists of cell bodies and their synapses. The white matter consists of large tracts of fibres.

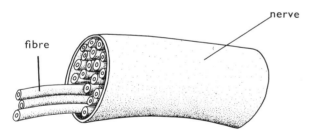

Fig. 27.5   Diagram to show nerve fibres grouped into a nerve

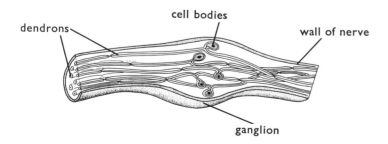

Fig. 27.6   Diagram of cell bodies forming a ganglion

Nervous systems. In relatively simple animals like the sea-anemone and Hydra, the nerve cells spread fairly evenly in all directions (Fig. 27.2), so that an impulse started at one point spreads out slowly in all directions encountering many synapses. In higher animals the nerve cells are bundled together into nerves which run in distinct paths from the nerve centres to important organs. Nerves are bundles of fibres (Fig. 27.5), the cell bodies of sensory fibres sometimes forming a bulge, or *ganglion*, in their length (Fig. 27.6). Most nerves contain both motor and sensory fibres, though one or other type may predominate.

Central nervous system. In vertebrate animals the central nervous system consists of the brain and spinal cord (Fig. 27.1). Most of the cell bodies lie in the central nervous system. Since all impulses from or to the body pass through it, it is possible to have a vast number of cross-connexions and linkages that could not arise if the nerves simply ran from one organ to another. The following analogy of the telephone exchange illustrates the advantages of a centralized nervous system—though in their actual mechanism the nervous system and the telephones are completely different.

If you were to connect your telephone directly to all the people you were likely to want to call up, hundred of wires would be needed, and if everybody did this the numbers and confusion of wires would be overwhelming. Even so, you would be limited to only those few hundred possible calls. A telephone exchange makes it possible for you to be placed in communication with anyone in the country, rapidly and efficiently. This gives some idea of the increased efficiency of co-ordination as a result of having a central nervous system.

Reflex action is a rapid, automatic response to a stimulus, by an organ or system of organs, which does not involve the brain for its initiation. For example, the iris of the eye can contract or dilate the pupil in response to changing light intensity without our being aware that it is happening. More commonly we are aware of a reflex occurring but are unable to control it. Blinking when a foreign particle touches the cornea is a reflex action which protects the eyes. We know it is happening but can do nothing to prevent it or modify it. Sneezing is a reflex response to a stimulus in the nose. The knee-jerk is another example. If the right leg is crossed over the left and struck sharply just above or below the knee cap, the lower leg jerks outwards by reflex action.

Reflex arc. It is possible to trace, in a simplified form, the path taken by the impulses involved in a spinal reflex action (*see* Fig. 27.7). If one unexpectedly touches a hot object, the hand is rapidly removed from the source of heat. Heat or pain receptors in the skin are stimulated and fire off impulses which travel along the sensory fibres in a nerve of the arm. The sensory fibres enter the spinal cord via the *dorsal root*, their cell bodies producing the swelling known as the *dorsal root ganglion*. In the grey matter of the spinal cord, the impulses pass from the sensory neurone to a relay or association neurone across a synapse. The relay neurone, in turn, makes a synapse with one or more motor neurones. The impulses are thus transmitted to the motor fibres which leave the spinal cord through the *ventral root* and pass in a nerve, probably the same one in which the sensory impulse travelled, to a muscle. In Figs. 27.7 and 27.9, the muscle is the biceps. The impulse causes the muscle to contract, so removing the hand from the painful stimulus and preventing damage to the tissues.

A similar reflex arc produces the knee jerk, but in this case the sensory fibres make a synapse directly with the motor neurone and there is no relay neurone. Striking the tendon below the knee cap stimulates stretch receptors in the leg extensor muscle. The impulse travels round the reflex arc and causes the same muscle to contract. Reflex actions are not usually so simple as described here. Several receptors of different kinds may be stimulated at once and many sets of muscles or glands may be brought into action, involving many more than the three nerve cells mentioned in the reflex arc described above. The relay nerve cell usually allows connexions to many other motor neurones. In addition, since we are usually aware that a reflex is taking place, nerve fibres must conduct the impulses passing in the reflex arc up the spinal cord to the brain.

The term spinal reflex refers to reflex actions in regions below the head, and in an animal such as the frog spinal reflex actions will occur even if the brain is destroyed. Reflex actions, such as blinking, concerning organs of the head take place in the brain (cranial reflex).

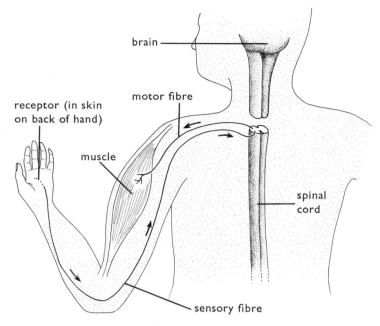

Fig. 27.7   A reflex pathway

Conditioned reflexes. In most simple reflexes, the stimulus and response are related. For example, the chemical stimulus of food in the mouth produces the reflex of salivation. After a period of learning or training, however, it is possible for a different and often irrelevant stimulus to produce the same response. In such a case, a "conditioned reflex" has been established, and the animal is said to be conditioned to this stimulus. Pavlov, a Russian biologist, carried out with dogs a great many experiments on conditioned reflexes, one of which is now something of a classic.

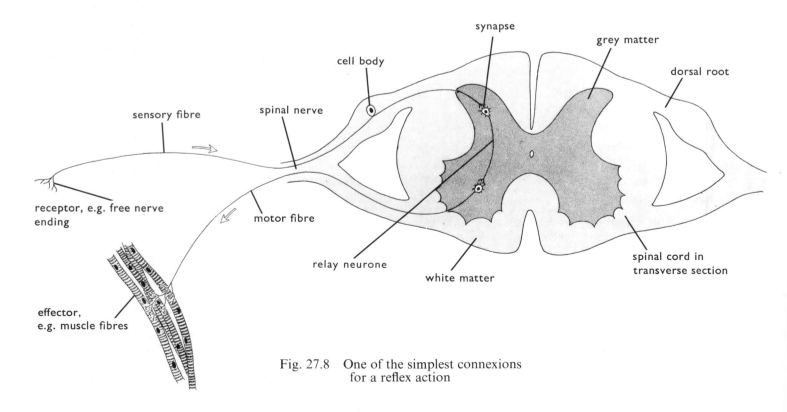

Fig. 27.8   One of the simplest connexions
for a reflex action

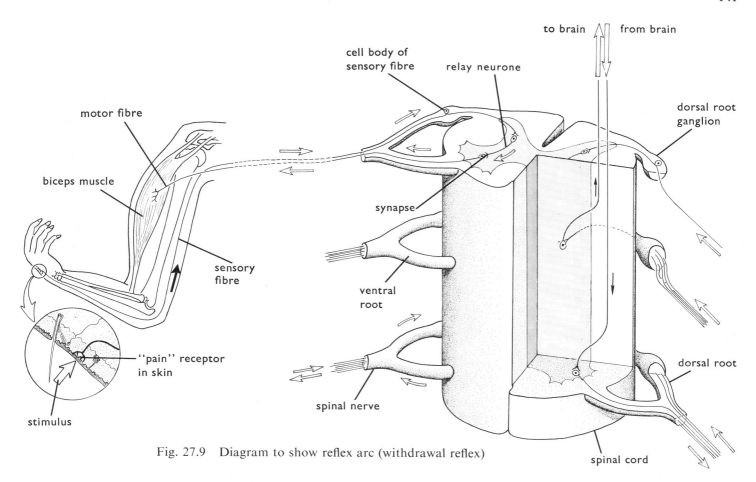

Fig. 27.9   Diagram to show reflex arc (withdrawal reflex)

The smell and taste of food is a stimulus that activates a dog's salivary glands, making its mouth water. For several days, Pavlov rang a bell at the time the food was given to the dogs. Later, the sound of the bell alone was a sufficient stimulus to cause a dog's mouth to water, without sight or smell of the food. The original chemical stimulus of the food had been replaced by an unrelated stimulus through the ears (Fig. 27.10).

The training of animals is done largely by conditioning them to respond to new stimuli. Many of our own actions, such as walking and riding a bicycle, are complicated sets of conditioned reflexes which we acquired in the first place by concentration and practice.

The **spinal cord** consists of a great number of nerve cells, both fibres and cell bodies, grouped into a cylindrical mass, running from the brain to the tail and protected by the bone of the spinal column. From between the vertebrae, spinal nerves

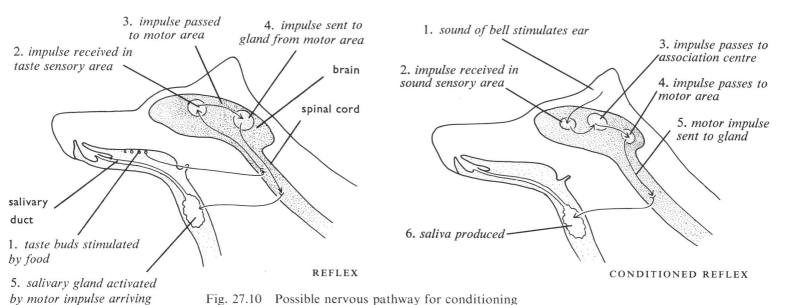

Fig. 27.10   Possible nervous pathway for conditioning

emerge and run to all parts of the body. The fibres of these nerves may be concerned with spinal reflexes or may be carrying sensory impulses to the brain or motor impulses from the brain to the muscles and other organs of the body (Fig. 27.9).

The nerve cell bodies are grouped in the centre of the cord, making a roughly H-shaped region of *grey matter*. Outside this is the *white matter* consisting of nerve fibres running up and down the cord or passing out to the spinal nerves (Plate 38). The spinal cord is concerned with spinal reflex actions and the conduction of nervous impulses to and from the brain.

The brain. During evolution, the increasing specialization of the organs of the head, particularly the eyes, ears and nose, has led to more and more sensory fibres entering the front part of the spinal cord. Consequently, this region has grown and developed to form the brain of the vertebrate animal. Like the spinal cord, it consists of nerve cells with a great concentration of cell bodies.

The brain is thus an enlarged, specialized front region of the spinal cord (Plate 39). In the simpler vertebrates, and in the course of development of the more advanced ones, three regions are distinguishable in the brain: the fore-, mid- and hind-brain (Fig. 27.11). The fore-brain receives impulses from the nasal organs. The mid-brain receives impulses from the eyes. Impulses from the ears, and semicircular canals enter the hind-brain, as do also the sensory impulses from the skin.

From the roof of the hind-brain a thickening develops which forms the *cerebellum*. This region controls and co-ordinates the balancing organs and the muscles, thus making precise and accurate movements possible.

The floor of the hind-brain thickens to form the *medulla oblongata*, and situated here are the involuntary centres which control the heart-beat, blood vessels and breathing movements.

The size of these principal regions of the brain usually bears a relation to the most important senses of the animal. In the dogfish, which hunts its prey by smell, the front lobes of the

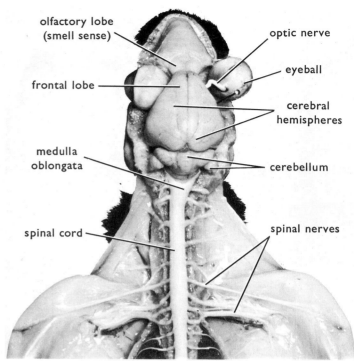

(Dissection by Griffin & George Ltd, Gerrard Biological Centre)

Plate 39.   DISSECTION OF THE BRAIN AND SPINAL CORD OF A SMALL MAMMAL (seen from above)

fore-brain are very large and well developed. In the salmon, which depends more on its sight for capturing food, the optic lobes of the mid-brain are much larger than the fore-brain.

MOTOR AREAS. As well as receiving impulses from the sense organs, the brain can send off from certain motor areas impulses which initiate activity in the body. Sometimes these

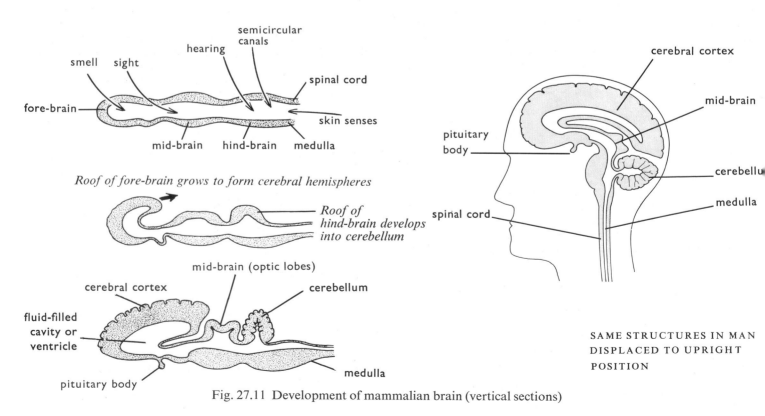

Fig. 27.11 Development of mammalian brain (vertical sections)

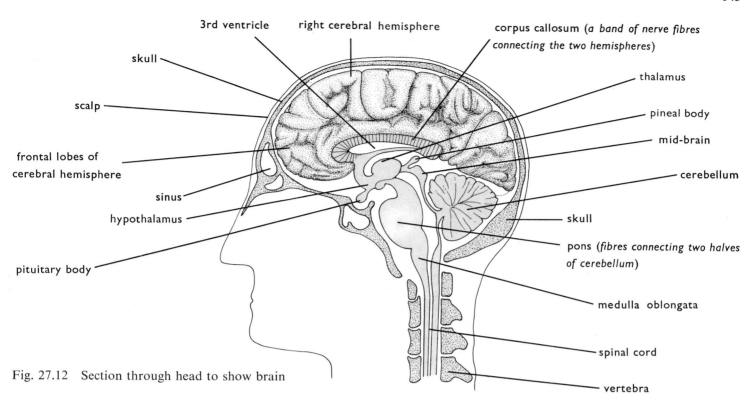

Fig. 27.12   Section through head to show brain

are simple reflexes in response to external stimuli or responses to internal stimuli such as sensations of hunger from the stomach.

ASSOCIATION CENTRES. Certain areas of the brain are supplied with fibres from the principal sense centres of the fore-, mid- and hind-brain, so that several impulses from different sense organs may be correlated. For example, the smell of meat may stimulate the nose of a dog and cause sensory impulses to be sent to the fore-brain. These would normally be relayed to the motor areas and produce co-ordinated movement towards the food, but the sight of another dog in possession and the sound of its ferocious growling will stimulate other sense organs and other brain centres. All these impulses will be relayed to the association centres and, according to the strength of the stimulation and the past experience "stored" in the brain, the motor areas will receive impulses from the association centre resulting in fight or flight.

Without association centres, conditioned reflexes and learning would not be possible. In Pavlov's experiment, sensations of hearing a bell would be most unlikely to produce salivation if only taste and smell centres were connected to the salivary glands.

CEREBRAL HEMISPHERES (*cerebrum*). In mammals, large outgrowths from the fore-brain spread backwards over the rest of the brain and form two lobes called the cerebral hemispheres (Figs. 27.11 and 27.12). These are important association centres where linkages between thousands of nerve cells allow intelligent behaviour, memory and, in ourselves at least, consciousness of our own activities. In animals without cerebral hemispheres the behaviour is a matter of simple and conditioned reflexes and inborn behaviour patterns called instinct.

Certain regions of the cerebral hemispheres have been shown to affect particular regions of the body or to be concerned with impulses from a particular sense organ (Fig. 27.13).

Functions of the brain. To sum up:

1. The brain receives impulses from all the sensory organs of the body.

2. As a result of these sensory impulses, it sends off motor impulses to the glands and muscles, causing them to function accordingly.

3. In its association centres it correlates the various stimuli from the different sense organs.

4. The association centres and motor areas co-ordinate bodily activities so that the mechanisms and chemical reactions of the body work efficiently together.

5. It "stores" information so that behaviour can be modified according to past experience.

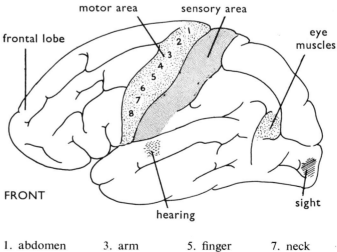

| 1. abdomen | 3. arm | 5. finger | 7. neck |
| 2. thorax | 4. hand | 6. thumb | 8. tongue |

Fig. 27.13   Localization of areas in the left cerebral hemisphere

The endocrine system (Fig. 27.14)

Co-ordination is also effected by chemicals called hormones, secreted from the endocrine glands. These glands have no ducts or openings. The chemicals they produce enter the blood stream as it passes through the glands and they are circulated all over the body. When the hormones reach particular parts of the body they cause certain changes to take place. Their effects are much slower and more general than nerve action and they control rather long-term changes such as rate of growth, rate of activity and sexual maturity. When they pass through the liver, the hormones are converted to relatively inactive compounds which are excreted, in due course, by the kidneys (hence the tests on urine for the hormonal products of pregnancy). The liver in this way limits the duration of a hormonal response which might otherwise persist indefinitely.

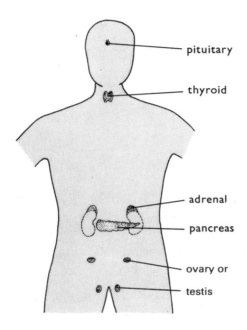

Fig. 27.14   Position of endocrine glands in the body

Thyroid. The thyroid gland is in the neck, in front of the wind-pipe. It produces a hormone, *thyroxine*, which in young animals controls the rate of growth and development. In tadpoles, for example, thyroxine brings about metamorphosis. Feeding tadpoles on thyroxine induces early metamorphosis. In adult humans thyroxine controls the rate of chemical activity, particularly respiration: too little tends to lead to overweight and sluggish activity; too much can cause thinness and over-activity. Deficiency of the thyroid in infancy causes a certain type of mental deficiency called *cretinism*, which can be cured in the early stages by administering thyroxine.

Adrenal. The adrenal glands are situated just above the kidneys. The outer layer of the adrenal body, the cortex, produces several hormones, including *cortisone*, one of whose functions is to accelerate the conversion of proteins to glucose (p. 90). Secretion by the adrenal cortex is stimulated by certain pituitary hormones.

The inner zone, medulla, of the adrenal gland is stimulated by the nervous system and produces *adrenaline*. When the sense organs of the animal transmit to the brain, impulses which are associated with danger or other situations needing vigorous action, motor impulses are relayed to the adrenal medulla which releases adrenaline into the blood. When this reaches the heart it quickens the heart-beat. In other regions it diverts blood from the alimentary canal and the skin to the muscles; it makes the pupils dilate and speeds up the rate of breathing and oxidation of carbohydrates. All these changes would increase the animal's efficiency in a situation that might demand vigorous activity in running away or putting up a fight. In ourselves, they do the same but, together with the nervous system, they produce also the sensation of fear: thumping heart, hollow feeling in the stomach, pale face, etc. In humans, adrenaline may be secreted in many situations which promote anxiety or excitement, and not only in the face of danger.

Pancreas. As well as containing cells which secrete digestive juices, the pancreas contains endocrine cells which control the use of sugar in the body. The hormone is called *insulin*; it determines how much sugar is converted to glycogen and how much is oxidized for energy.

Insulin (*a*) accelerates the rate at which blood sugar is converted to glycogen in the liver (p. 91), (*b*) promotes the uptake of glucose from the blood by muscle cells and (*c*) increases protein synthesis in some cells. The failure of the pancreas to produce sufficient insulin leads to *diabetes*. The diabetic cannot effectively regulate the blood sugar level. It may rise to above 160 mg/100 cm^3 and so be excreted in the urine, or fall to below 40 mg/100 cm^3 leading eventually to convulsions and coma. The diabetic condition can be corrected by regular injections of insulin.

Reproductive organs. The ovary produces several hormones called *oestrogens* of which oestradiol and oestrone are the most potent. These oestrogens (i) control the development of the secondary sexual characters at puberty (*see* p. 117), (ii) cause the lining of the uterus to thicken just before an ovum is released, and (iii), in some mammals at least, oestradiol brings the animal "on heat", i.e. prepares it to accept the male. Progesterone, the hormone produced from the corpus luteum (p. 115) after ovulation, promotes the further thickening and vascularization of the uterus. Progesterone also prevents the uterus from contracting until the baby is due to be born.

Testosterone is the male sex hormone, produced by the testis. It promotes the development of the masculine secondary sexual characters.

Duodenum. The presence of food stimulates the lining of the duodenum to produce a hormone, *secretin*, which on reaching the pancreas in the blood stream, initiates the production of pancreatic enzymes. In this way, the enzymes are secreted only when food is present.

Pituitary. The pituitary gland is an outgrowth from the base of the fore-brain (Figs. 27.11 and 27.12). It releases into the blood several different hormones. Some of them appear to have a direct effect on the organ systems of the body. For example, *anti-diuretic hormone* (ADH) controls the amount of water reabsorbed into the blood by the kidneys (*see* p. 108). *Growth hormone* influences the growth of bone and other tissues. Injection of growth hormone in experimental animals causes them to grow larger and to continue growing for longer than usual. Growth, however, is affected by other endocrine glands as well, in particular the thyroid and pancreas, and the growth hormone may exert its influence through these glands rather than directly on the tissues.

In fact, the majority of the pituitary hormones do act upon and regulate the activity of the other endocrine glands to such an extent that the pituitary is sometimes called the "master gland". It is the pituitary hormone (FSH) which acts on the ovary, and causes the Graafian follicle to develop and secrete its

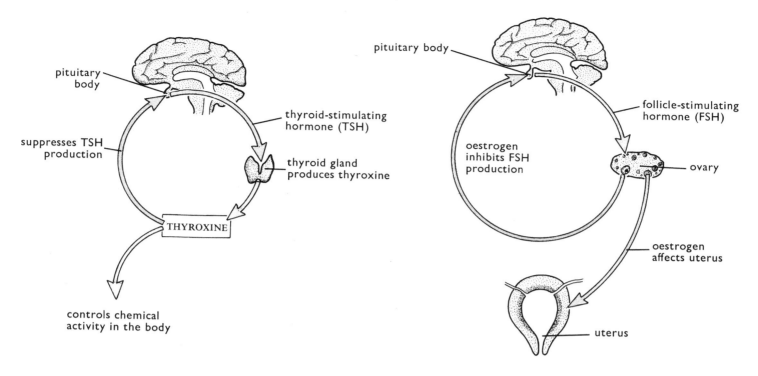

Fig. 27.15   "Feedback"

own hormone, oestrogen. Another pituitary hormone (TSH) stimulates the thyroid gland to grow and to produce thyroxine and a third acts on the cortex of the adrenal gland and promotes the production of cortisone.

Homeostasis

The foregoing account shows how the hormones (e.g. adrenaline) co-ordinate the organs of the body to meet various contingencies, to produce rhythmic patterns of activity (e.g. the sex hormones), and to maintain control over long-term processes such as the rate of growth (thyroid and pituitary). It can also be seen that they fulfil a homeostatic function in regulating the composition of the internal environment (*see* p. 108). If the blood sugar level rises, the pancreas is stimulated to secrete insulin which increases the amount of glucose removed from the blood and stored as glycogen in the muscles and liver. A fall in the blood sugar level suppresses the production of insulin from the pancreas. A fall in the water potential of the blood results in the release of ADH from the pituitary gland and the consequent reabsorption of water from the kidney tubules.

Interaction and "feed-back"

For effective control, two opposing systems are needed. The car needs an accelerator and brakes, a muscle must have its antagonistic partner (p. 122). The hormones too have antagonistic effects. Adrenaline promotes the release of sugar into the blood while insulin has the opposite effect. A fine adjustment of the balance of these antagonistic hormones helps to maintain the controlled growth, development and activity of the organisms in constantly changing conditions.

Such a balance is maintained partly by the "feed-back" effect of hormones, i.e. a system whereby "information" is "fed back" to a source "telling it" about events in the body and so enabling it to adjust its output accordingly. The pituitary hormone TSH (Fig. 27.15) stimulates the thyroid to produce thyroxine but thyroxine production is kept in check by the fact that when thyroxine reaches the pituitary via the circulation, production of thyroid-stimulating hormone is suppressed. The "feed-back" of thyroxine to the pituitary regulates the output of the latter. The ovarian follicles are stimulated to produce oestrogen by the pituitary hormone FSH (Fig. 27.15) but when the oestrogen in the blood reaches a certain level it suppresses the secretion of follicle-stimulating hormone by the pituitary. A delay in the feed-back effect leads to rhythmic changes. For example, it may take two weeks for the level of oestrogen in the blood to affect the pituitary, by which time the uterus lining has thickened and the ovum has been released from the follicle. The output of follicle-stimulating hormone is diminished as a result of increasing oestrogen and this in turn reduces the output of oestrogen from the ovary which, in the absence of fertilization and the development of the corpus luteum, leads to the breakdown of the uterine lining, characteristic of menstruation.

QUESTIONS

1. List the differences between control by hormones and control by the nervous system.
2. Trace by diagram or description, the possible reflex arc involved in (*a*) sneezing, (*b*) blinking. Do not attempt to describe the effector systems in detail and treat the brain as simply an enlarged region of the spinal cord.
3. All nervous impulses, whether from the eyes, ears, tongue or skin are basically the same. This implies that the information reaching the brain is little more than a rapid series of electrical pulses of identical strength. How then is it possible for us to distinguish between light and sound, heat and touch?
4. It is possible to train a dog to seek food concealed behind one of several identical doors by flashing a light over the appropriate door. Suggest a nervous pathway by which this behaviour is established.

28 Insects

THE arthropods are a large group of invertebrate animals which includes insects, spiders, millipedes, centipedes and crustacea (p. 6) such as lobsters and crabs. All arthropods have a hard exoskeleton or cuticle, segmented bodies and jointed legs. The crustacea and insects also have antennae, compound eyes (Plate 48) and, often, three distinct regions to their bodies: *head, thorax* and *abdomen*.

GENERAL CHARACTERISTICS OF INSECTS

The insects differ from the rest of the arthropods in having only three pairs of jointed legs on the thorax and, typically, two pairs of wings. There are a great many different species of insects and some, during evolution, have lost one pair of wings, as in the houseflies, crane-flies and mosquitoes. Other parasitic species like the fleas have lost both pairs of wings. In beetles, grasshoppers and cockroaches, the first pair of wings has become modified to form a hard outer covering over the second pair.

Cuticle and ecdysis. The value of the external cuticle is thought to lie mainly in reducing the loss from the body of water vapour through evaporation, but it also protects the animal from damage and bacterial invasion, maintains its shape and allows rapid locomotion. The cuticle imposes certain limitations in size, however, for if arthropods were to exceed the size of some of the larger crabs, the cuticle would become too heavy for the muscles to move the limbs. Between the segments of the body and at the joints of the limbs and other appendages, the cuticle is flexible and allows movement. For the most part, however, the cuticle is rigid and prevents any increase in the size of the insect except during certain periods of its development when the insect sheds its cuticle (ecdysis) and increases its volume before the new cuticle has time to harden. Only the outermost layer of the cuticle is shed, the inner layers are digested by enzymes secreted from the epidermis and the fluid so produced is absorbed back into the body. Muscular contractions force the blood into the thorax, causing it to swell and so split the old cuticle along a predetermined line of weakness. The swallowing of air often accompanies ecdysis, assisting the splitting of the cuticle and keeping the body expanded while the new cuticle hardens. In insects, this moulting, or ecdysis, is initiated by a hormone secreted by glands in the thorax and takes place only in the larval and pupal form and not in adults. In other words, mature insects do not grow.

Breathing. Running through the bodies of all insects is a branching system of tubes, *tracheae*, which contain air. They open to the outside by pores called *spiracles* (Figs. 28.1 and 28.20d) and they conduct air from the atmosphere to all living regions of the body (Fig. 28.1). The tracheae are lined with cuticle which is thickened in spiral bands (Fig. 28.2). This thickening keeps the tracheae open against the internal pressure of body fluids. The spiracles, typically, open on the flanks of each segment of the body, but in some insects there are only one or two openings. The entrance to the spiracle is usually supplied with muscles which control its opening or closure.

Since the spiracles are one of the few areas of the body from which evaporation of water can occur, the closure of the spiracles when the insect is not active and therefore needs less oxygen, helps to conserve moisture.

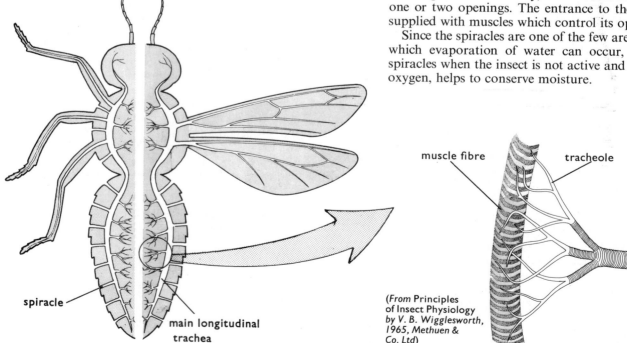

spiracle

main longitudinal trachea

muscle fibre   tracheole   trachea

(From Principles of Insect Physiology *by V. B. Wigglesworth, 1965, Methuen & Co. Ltd)*

Fig. 28.1   Tracheal system of insect
(Wings or legs shown on one side only)

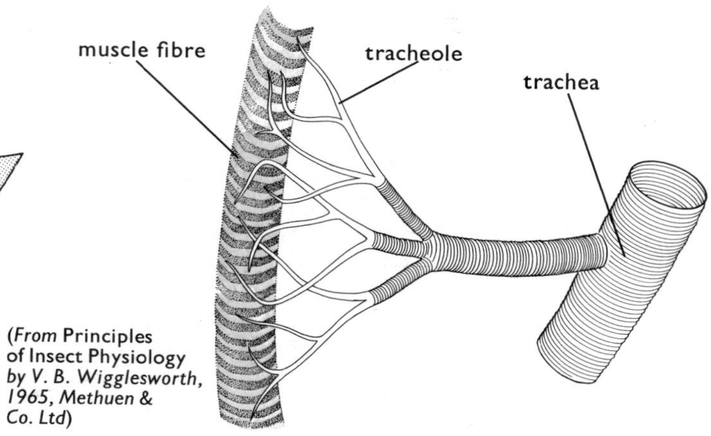

Fig. 28.2   To show how the tracheae supply oxygen to the muscles

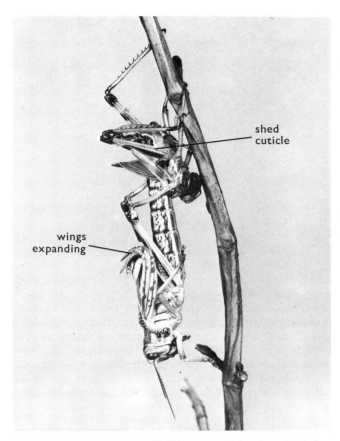

shed
cuticle

wings
expanding

(Shell International Petroleum Co. Ltd)

Plate 41. THE FINAL ECDYSIS OF THE LOCUST

tracheoles is most dense in the region of very active muscle, e.g. the flight muscles in the thorax.

The movement of oxygen from the atmosphere, through the spiracles, up the tracheae and tracheoles to the tissues, and the passage of carbon dioxide in the opposite direction, can be accounted for by simple diffusion but in active adult insects there is often a ventilation process which exchanges up to 60 per cent of the air in the tracheal system. In many beetles, locusts, grasshoppers and cockroaches, the abdomen is slightly compressed vertically (dorso-ventrally) by contraction of internal muscles. In bees and wasps the abdomen is compressed rhythmically along its length, slightly telescoping the segments. In both cases, the consequent rise of blood pressure in the body cavity compresses the tracheae along their length (like a con-certina) and expels air from them. When the muscles relax, the abdomen springs back into shape, the tracheae expand and draw in air. Thus, unlike mammals, the positive muscular action in breathing is that which results in expiration.

This tracheal respiratory system is very different from the respiratory systems of the vertebrates, in which oxygen is absorbed by gills or lungs and conveyed in the blood stream to the tissues. In the insects, the oxygen diffuses through the trachea and tracheoles directly to the organ concerned. The carbon dioxide escapes through the same path although a proportion may diffuse from the body surface.

Blood system. The tracheal supply carrying oxygen to the organs gives the circulatory system a rather different role in insects from that in vertebrates. Except where the tracheoles terminate at some distance from a cell, the blood has little need to carry dissolved oxygen and, with a few exceptions, it contains no haemoglobin or cells corresponding to erythrocytes. There is a single dorsal vessel (Fig. 28.3) which propels blood forward and releases it into the body cavity, thus maintaining a sluggish circulation. Apart from this vessel, the blood is not confined in blood vessels but occupies the free space between the cuticle and the organs in the body cavity. The blood there-fore serves mainly to distribute digested food, collect excretory products and, in addition, has important hydraulic functions in expanding certain regions of the body to split the old cuticle and in pumping up the crumpled wings of the newly emerged adult insect (Plate 41).

The tracheae branch repeatedly until they terminate in very fine *tracheoles* which invest or penetrate the tissues and organs inside the body. The walls of the tracheae and tracheoles are permeable to gases and oxygen is able to diffuse through them to reach the living cells. As might be expected, the supply of

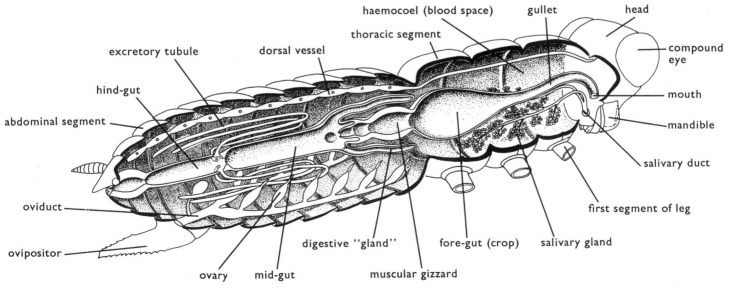

Fig. 28.3   Insect anatomy   *(After Nicholas Jago)*

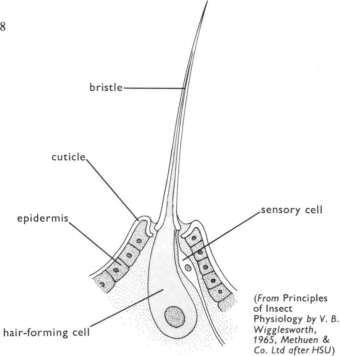

Fig. 28.4 Touch-sensitive bristle

(From Principles of Insect Physiology by V. B. Wigglesworth, 1965, Methuen & Co. Ltd after HSU)

(Rothamsted Experimental Station)

Plate 42. A MALE MOTH
showing feathery antennae

Sensory system

Touch. From the body surface of the insect there arises a profusion of fine bristles most of which have a sensory function, responding principally to touch, vibration, or chemicals. The tactile (touch-sensitive) bristles are jointed at their bases (Fig. 28.4) and when a bristle is displaced to one side, it stimulates a sensory cell which fires impulses to the central nervous system. The tactile bristles are numerous on the tarsal segments (Fig. 28.5), the head, wing margins, or antennae according to the species and as well as informing the insect about contact stimuli, they probably respond to air currents and vibrations in the ground or in the air.

Proprioceptors. Small oval or circular areas of cuticle are differentially thickened and supplied with sensory fibres. They probably respond to distortions in the cuticle resulting from pressure, and so feed back information to the central nervous system about the position of the limbs. Organs of this kind respond to deflections of the antennae during flight and are

thought to "measure" the air speed and help to adjust the wing movements accordingly. In some insects there are stretch receptors associated with muscle fibres, apparently similar to those in vertebrates (p. 128).

Sound. The tactile bristles on the cuticle and on the antennae respond to low-frequency vibrations but many insects have more specialized sound detectors in the form of a thin area of cuticle overlying a distended trachea or air sac and invested with sensory fibres. Such *tympanal organs* appear on the thorax or abdomen or tibia according to species and are sensitive to sounds of high frequency. They can be used to locate the source of sounds as in the case of the male cricket "homing" on the sound of the female's "chirp", and in some cases can distinguish between sounds of different frequency.

Smell and taste. Experiments show that different insects can distinguish between chemicals which we describe as sweet, sour, salt and bitter, and in some cases more specific substances. The organs of taste are most abundant on the mouth parts, in the mouth, and on the tarsal segments but the nature of the sense organs concerned is not always clear.

Smell is principally the function of the antennae. Here there are bristles, pegs or plates with a very thin cuticle and fine perforations through which project nerve endings sensitive to chemicals. Sometimes these sense organs are grouped together and sunk into *olfactory pits*. In certain moths the sense of

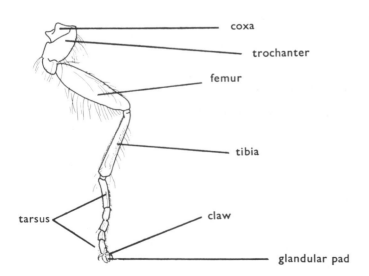

Fig. 28.5 Leg of house-fly

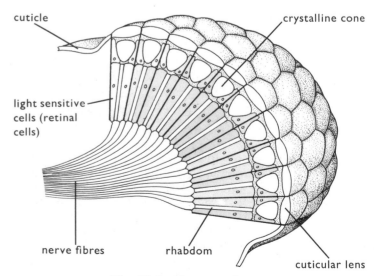

Fig. 28.6 Compound eye

(Shell International Petroleum Co. Ltd)

Plate 43.   HEAD OF HOUSE-FLY TO SHOW
COMPOUND EYES (× 25)

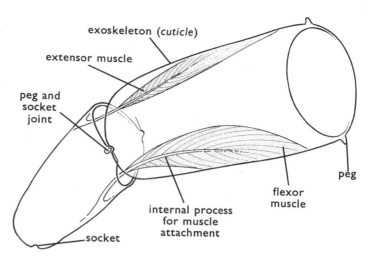

Fig. 28.7   Muscle attachment in arthropod limb

smell is very highly developed. Some male moths will fly to an unmated female from a distance of a mile, attracted by the "scent" which she exudes. Plate 42 shows a male moth's antennae which may carry many thousand chemo-receptors.

Sight. The compound eyes of insects consist of thousands of identical units called *ommatidia* (Fig. 28.6), packed closely together on each side of the head (Plate 43). Each ommatidium consists of a lens system formed partly from a thickening of the transparent cuticle and partly from a special *crystalline cone.* This lens system concentrates light from within a cone of 20°, on to a transparent rod, the *rhabdom.* The light, passing down this rhabdom, stimulates the eight or so *retinal cells* grouped round it to fire nervous impulses to the brain. Each ommatidium can therefore record the presence or absence of light, its intensity, in some cases its colour and, according to the position of the ommatidium in the compound eye, its direction. Although there may be from 2000 to 10,000 or more ommatidia in the compound eye of an actively flying insect, this number cannot reconstruct a very accurate picture of the outside world. Nevertheless, the *"mosaic image"* so formed probably produces a crude impression of the form of well-defined objects enabling bees, for example, to seek out flowers and to use landmarks for finding their way to and from the hive. It is likely that the construction of compound eyes makes them particularly sensitive to moving objects, e.g. bees are more readily attracted to flowers which are being blown by the wind.

Flower-visiting insects, at least, can distinguish certain colours from shades of grey of equal brightness. Bees are particularly sensitive to blue, violet and ultra-violet but cannot distinguish red and green from black and grey unless the flower petals are reflecting ultra-violet light as well. Some butterflies can distinguish yellow, green and red.

The simple eyes of, for example, caterpillars, consist of a cuticular lens with a group of light-sensitive cells beneath, rather like a single ommatidium. They show some colour sensitivity and, when grouped together, some ability to discriminate form. The *ocelli* which occur in the heads of many flying insects probably respond only to changes in light intensity.

Locomotion. Movement in insects depends; as it does in vertebrates, on muscles contracting and pulling on jointed limbs or other appendages. The muscles are within the body and limbs, however, and are attached to the inside of the cuticle. Fig. 28.7 shows diagrammatically how a pair of antagonistic muscles are attached across a joint in a way which could bend and straighten the limb. Many of the joints in the insect are of the *"peg and socket"* type shown. They permit movement in one plane only, like a hinge joint, but since there are several such joints in a limb, each operating in a different direction, the limb as a whole can describe fairly free directional movement.

Walking. The characteristic walking pattern of an insect is shown in Fig. 28.8. The body is supported by a "tripod" of three legs while the other three are swinging forward to a new position. On the tarsi are claws and, depending on the species,

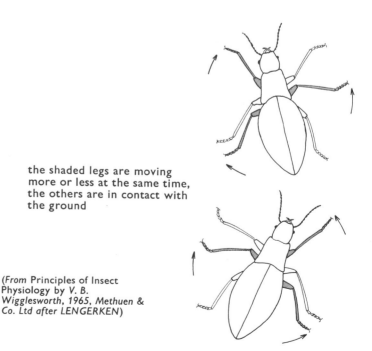

the shaded legs are moving more or less at the same time, the others are in contact with the ground

(From Principles of Insect Physiology by V. B. Wigglesworth, 1965, Methuen & Co. Ltd after LENGERKEN)

Fig. 28.8   Walking pattern in a beetle

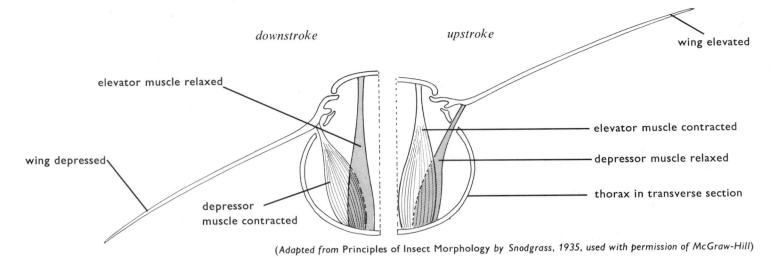

downstroke   upstroke

elevator muscle relaxed

wing elevated

wing depressed

elevator muscle contracted

depressor muscle relaxed

thorax in transverse section

depressor muscle contracted

(*Adapted from* Principles of Insect Morphology *by Snodgrass, 1935, used with permission of McGraw-Hill*)

Fig. 28.9   Action of direct flight muscles (e.g. dragonflies)

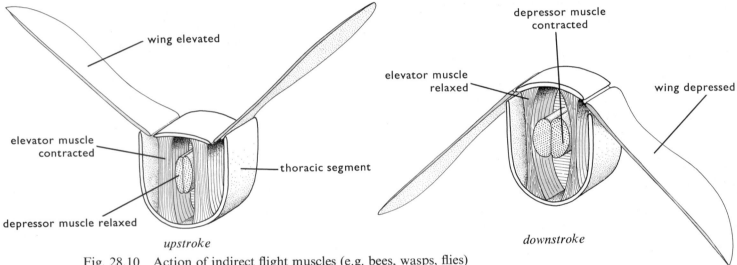

wing elevated

elevator muscle contracted

thoracic segment

depressor muscle relaxed

upstroke

depressor muscle contracted

elevator muscle relaxed

wing depressed

downstroke

Fig. 28.10   Action of indirect flight muscles (e.g. bees, wasps, flies)

adhesive pads which enable the insect to climb very smooth surfaces. The precise mechanism of adhesion in each case is in some doubt.

Modification of the limbs and their musculature enables insects to leap, as in the grasshopper, or swim, as in the water beetles.

Flying. Figs. 28.9 and 10 represent sections through the thorax of an insect. In insects such as dragonflies, the muscles which pull the wings down are attached directly to the wing base. The elevator muscles, which raise the wings, are attached to the roof of the thorax. When they contract, they pull the thorax roof down and pivot the wings upwards. The depressor muscles of insects such as bees, wasps and flies are attached to the walls of the thorax and not to the wing base. This is characteristic of compact insects with small wings and a rapid wing beat. In both cases there are direct flight muscles which, by acting on the wing insertion, can alter its angle in the air. Fig. 28.11 shows that during the downstroke (1 and 2) the wing is held horizontally, so thrusting downwards on the air and producing a lifting force. During the upstroke the wing is rotated vertically and offers little resistance during its upward movement through the air.

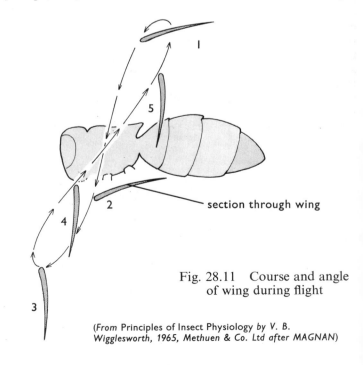

section through wing

Fig. 28.11   Course and angle of wing during flight

(*From* Principles of Insect Physiology *by V. B. Wigglesworth, 1965, Methuen & Co. Ltd after MAGNAN*)

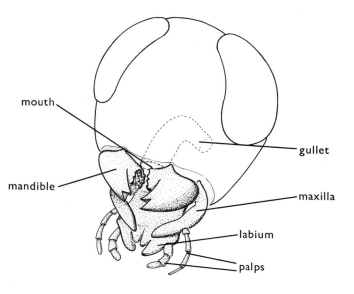

Fig. 28.12   Mouth parts of insect (e.g. cockroach)

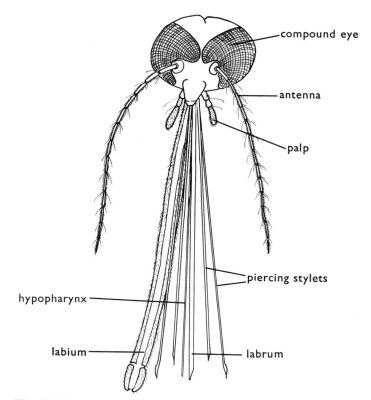

Fig. 28.13   Head of mosquito showing mouth parts

Feeding methods. It is not possible to make very useful generalizations about the feeding methods of insects because they are so varied. However, insects do have in common three pairs of appendages called *mouth parts*, hinged to the head below the mouth and these extract or manipulate food in one way or another. The basic pattern of these mouth parts is the same in most insects but in the course of evolution they have become modified and adapted to exploit different kinds of food source. The least modified are probably those of insects such as caterpillars, grasshoppers, locusts and cockroaches in which the first pair of appendages, *mandibles*, form sturdy jaws, working sideways across the mouth and cutting off pieces of vegetation which are manipulated into the mouth by the other mouth parts, the *maxillae* and *labium* (Fig. 28.12).

The mosquito has mandibles and maxillae in the form of slender, sharp stylets which can cut through the skin of a mammal as well as penetrating plant tissues. To obtain a blood meal the mosquito inserts its mouth parts through the skin to reach a capillary and then sucks blood through a tube formed from the *labrum* or "front lip" which precedes the mouth parts. Another tubular structure, the *hypopharynx*, serves to inject into the wound a substance which prevents the blood from clotting and so blocking the tubular labrum. The labium is rolled round the other mouth parts, enclosing them in a sheath when they are not being used (Figs. 28.13 and 28.14).

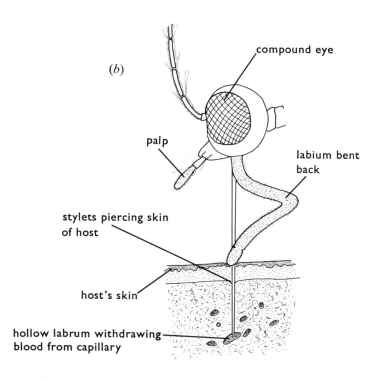

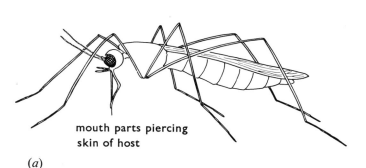

Fig. 28.14   Mosquito feeding

In the butterfly, only the maxillae contribute to the feeding apparatus. The maxillae are greatly elongated and in the form of half tubes, i.e. like a drinking straw split down its length. They can be fitted together to form a tube through which nectar is sucked from the flowers (Fig. 28.15).

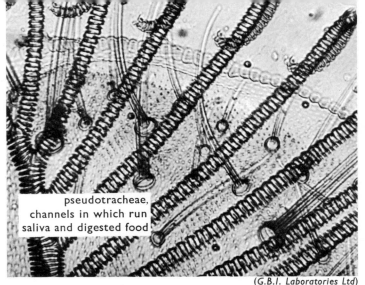

Plate 44. PART OF PROBOSCIS OF HOUSE-FLY (× 200)

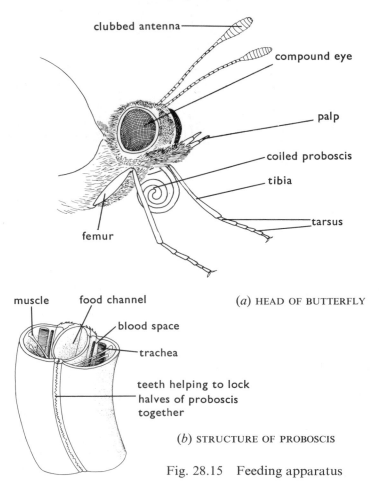

(a) HEAD OF BUTTERFLY

(b) STRUCTURE OF PROBOSCIS

Fig. 28.15   Feeding apparatus

The house-fly also sucks liquid but its mouth parts cannot penetrate tissue. Instead, the labium is enlarged to form a *proboscis* which terminates in two pads whose surface is channelled by grooves called *pseudotracheae* (Fig. 28.17 and Plate 44). The fly applies its proboscis to the food (Plate 47) and pumps saliva along the channels and over the food. The saliva dissolves soluble parts of the food and may contain enzymes which digest some of the insoluble matter. The nutrient liquid is then drawn back along the pseudotracheae and pumped into the alimentary canal (Fig. 28.16).

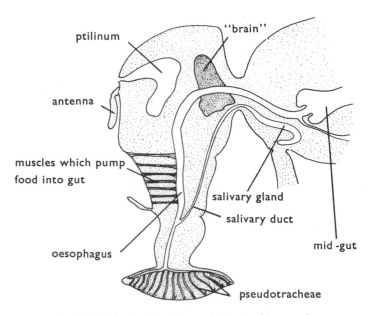

Fig. 28.16   Section through head of house-fly

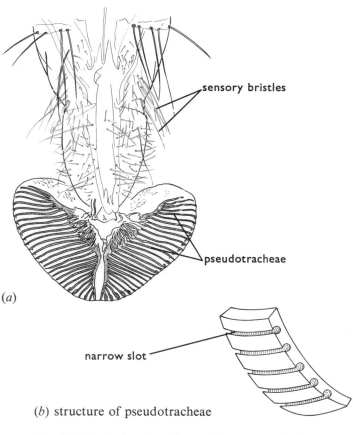

(a)

(b) structure of pseudotracheae

Fig. 28.17   Proboscis of house-fly, seen under the microscope

Insects as disease carriers. Many insects are known to play an essential part in transmitting diseases. Mosquitoes transmit malaria and yellow fever, tsetse flies carry sleeping sickness, and fleas harbour bubonic plague. Animals which carry organisms which can cause disease in other animals or plants are called *vectors*.

Malaria and the mosquito. Malaria is caused by a microscopic, single-celled parasite which enters and eventually destroys a large number of red blood cells. The parasites are transmitted from man to man by female mosquitoes of the genus *Anopheles*, which pierce the skin with their sharp mouth parts and feed on the blood which they suck from the superficial skin capillaries (*see* Fig. 28.14). If the blood so taken contains the malarial parasites, these undergo a complicated series of changes within the mosquito, including extensive reproduction, and eventually accumulate in large numbers in the salivary glands. If this mosquito now bites a healthy person, saliva containing hundreds of parasites is injected into his blood stream and he may develop malaria (*see* p. 209).

If mosquitoes could be prevented from biting humans, the disease could not be transmitted. Thus methods of controlling the disease, apart from drugs which kill the malarial parasite in the blood, concentrate largely on eliminating the mosquito. The species of mosquito which normally rest in dwellings can be attacked by sprays containing DDT or BHC. The spray remains effective on the walls of dwellings for several months and will kill any insects which settle on the sprayed surface. It is known that, although the adult mosquito spends its life on land, the larvae and pupae live in water. The female mosquito lays her eggs in the static water of lakes, ponds, ditches or even water collected in puddles, drinking troughs or tin cans. The eggs soon hatch to larvae which breathe air at the surface through a tracheal tube (Plate 45) and feed on microscopic algae in the water. The larva eventually pupates and although the pupa does not feed, it still breathes air (Plate 46). Finally, the pupal skin splits open, the imago emerges and flies away. Knowledge of this life cycle leads to methods of mosquito eradication directed at the larval and pupal stages. By draining swamps and

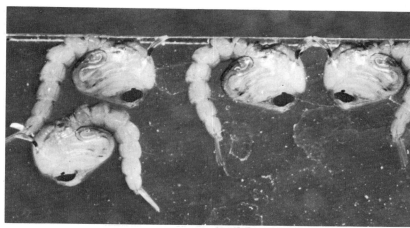

Plate 46.   PUPAE OF MOSQUITO (*Culex molestus*) (× 8)

turning sluggish rivers into swifter streams, the breeding grounds of the mosquito are destroyed. In towns and villages, water must not be allowed to collect in any container, e.g. tanks, pots or tins, accessible to the mosquito. Spraying stagnant water with oil and insecticides suffocates or poisons the larvae and pupae. Such spraying must include not only lakes and ponds but any accumulation of fresh water which mosquitoes can reach, e.g. drains, gutters and the receptacles mentioned above.

A technique, at present undergoing field trials is the use of a bacterium, *Bacillus thuringiensis*, which kills mosquito larvae but appears to be harmless to fish, man and other animals.

The plans of the World Health Organization to eradicate malaria are discussed on p. 223.

Some species of mosquito transmit the virus of yellow fever, and others carry the tiny nematode worms that enter the lymphatic system of man causing *filariasis*, a chronic inflammation and, ultimately, gross enlargement (elephantiasis) of the affected organ.

House-flies and disease. Although there is little direct evidence, the house-fly is thought to help in the spread of sixty or more diseases. A great many harmful bacteria and viruses are found in or on house-flies but, unlike the mosquito and malaria, flies are incidental rather than essential to the spread of disease. The indiscriminate feeding habits of flies constitute some of the circumstantial evidence against them. They will settle on decaying organic matter in refuse tips where bacteria are abundant, or alight on human faeces containing, possibly, the germs of typhoid, cholera, poliomyelitis or dysentery. The germs adhere to their legs or their proboscis; they lodge in the pseudotracheae or pass through the alimentary canal to be released with the faeces. If a contaminated fly alights and feeds on food intended for human consumption, it seems very likely that the germs from the feet, proboscis or faeces will arrive on the food and eventually be ingested by people.

House-flies also carry the organisms that cause *trachoma*, a disease affecting the eyes and, if untreated, leading to blindness. The flies alight on the face and eyelids to feed on the liquid covering the conjunctiva and margins of the lids. In so doing, they carry the disease germs from one person to another.

The principal methods of preventing transmission of disease by house-flies are described on p. 155.

Plate 45.   LARVAE OF MOSQUITO (*Culex molestus*) (× 10)

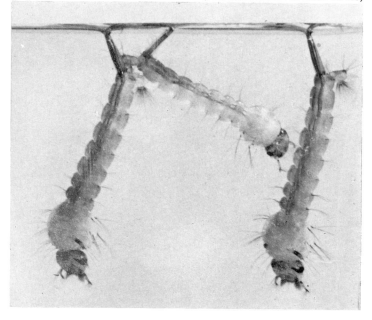

Life history and metamorphosis

(a) *Complete metamorphosis.* Insects lay eggs which hatch into *larvae*. These larvae are usually quite unlike the adult and are called grubs, maggots or caterpillars according to the species of insect. Generally the larva is the feeding and growing stage, eating voraciously, shedding its cuticle several times and growing rapidly. When it has reached full size, the larva becomes inactive, neither moving nor feeding, and extensive breakdown and reorganization takes place within its body, giving rise eventually to the adult or imago form. The stage in the insect's life when these changes take place is called the *pupa* and the changes are called *metamorphosis*. The adults then mate and lay eggs. Butterflies, moths, bees, wasps and flies are examples of insects that undergo complete metamorphosis.

(b) *Incomplete metamorphosis.* With insects such as the cockroach or locust the egg does not hatch into a larva but a *nymph* which, though still very different from the imago, more closely resembles it than does a larva. The nymph has three pairs of jointed legs, compound eyes and rudimentary wings. At each moult, changes occur which bring it nearer to the adult form. There is no prolonged "resting" stage as there is in a pupa, though the final ecdysis usually reveals drastic changes that have occurred in the final weeks of the nymph's development. In both types of metamorphosis the habitat, behaviour, locomotion and feeding habits of the adult are often quite different from the larvae or nymphs.

HOUSE-FLIES (Complete metamorphosis)

The house-fly is an example of an insect which undergoes complete metamorphosis during its development from egg to adult. The larva is a legless maggot and the pupa does not move or feed.

Eggs. The mature female house-fly lays many batches of eggs with 100 to 150 eggs in each batch. Decaying organic matter such as manure heaps, faeces, or almost any exposed food material, is selected as a suitable breeding ground. The last four segments of the abdomen of the female house-fly, normally retracted and withdrawn into the body, are extended to make an *ovipositor*, by which means the eggs are placed a few millimetres below the surface, and danger of drying out is avoided.

The eggs are white, elongate ovals, about one millimetre long and with two rib-like thickenings down each side (Fig. 28.19a). They hatch after eight to twenty-four hours according to the temperature. The bacteriological fermentation that goes on within a manure heap usually keeps the temperature high and fairly independent of external changes so that development proceeds rapidly.

Larva (Fig. 28.19b). Emerging from the split egg-case, the larva is a semi-transparent maggot, later becoming white. Twelve segments are visible, becoming larger at the posterior end. The tiny head is usually pulled back into the anterior segments and is not visible. Two black, hook-like teeth projecting from above the mouth are used for movement through the breeding place and for tearing up potential food. The larva has no legs, but on the lower sides of segments six to twelve are crescent-shaped pads bearing short spines which assist its movement. Spiracles open on the second and last segments only.

The larva feeds on the organic matter in which it finds itself, taking in only fluids and tiny particles. It has no simple or compound eyes but must be able to distinguish light and darkness since it moves away from light. This negative response to light tends to keep it in the warmer, moister regions of its breeding ground. It grows to about one cm long in five days, shedding its cuticle twice. Before its final ecdysis its reactions to light and moisture change, and it migrates to a drier position just below the surface of its breeding ground where it pupates.

Pupa. The last larval skin is not cast but retained as a pupal case or *puparium* (Fig. 28.19c). The latter darkens and hardens, becoming a brown, cigar-shaped object. In the next three days the pupa metamorphoses (Fig. 28.19d) to the perfect insect in a similar way to that described for the butterfly. A sac-like structure, the *ptilinum*, in the head, can be blown out by blood pressure and by this means the top of the puparium is burst open, after which the ptilinum is withdrawn into the head.

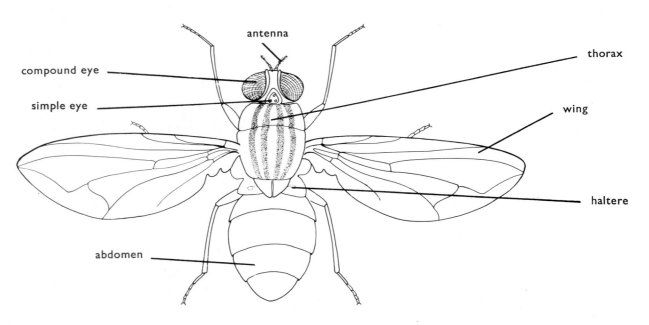

Fig. 28.18   House-fly

(a) EGG OF HOUSE-FLY

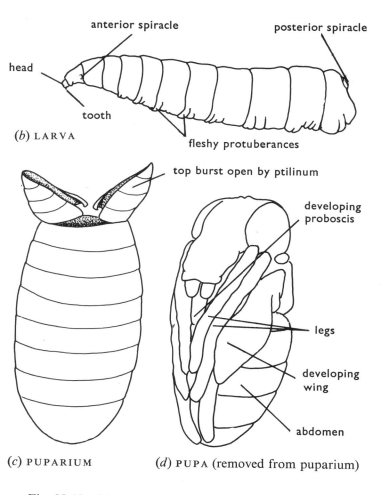

(b) LARVA

(c) PUPARIUM (d) PUPA (removed from puparium)

Fig. 28.19 Metamorphosis of house-fly (after Hewitt)

Imago (Plate 47). The imago crawls out of the puparium on to the surface of the breeding ground where its wings expand and harden in the next few hours, and then it flies away. In ten to fourteen days it may become sexually mature and lay eggs four days after mating. In suitable conditions of temperature, humidity and food, the entire life cycle may be complete in three or four weeks.

Adult structures (Fig. 28.18). There are distinct divisions into head, thorax and abdomen. The house-flies, like the mosquitoes, are *Diptera* and have only one pair of wings, the second pair being reduced to halteres. The leading edges of the wings are thickened, and unlike the aphids which depend on chance air currents, house-flies are powerful fliers. Spiracles open on the first and third thoracic segments and on each of the abdominal segments.

The three pairs of legs, like most of the rest of the body, are covered with sensory setae, and the last tarsus on each leg bears a pair of claws and two glandular pads which secrete a sticky substance enabling the fly to walk on smooth vertical surfaces (Fig. 28.5).

The pair of compound eyes on the head each have about 4000 facets (Plate 43), and there are three simple eyes or *ocelli* on the top of the head. Only the last segments of the short antennae are visible between the eyes.

Control. Since house-flies are thought to be responsible for distributing many human diseases as a result of their indiscriminate feeding habits (*see* p. 153) it is important to know how best to destroy them or prevent them transmitting disease germs. The principal methods of control are obvious once the ways in which flies can spread disease are known. Human faeces, particularly if known to be infected, must be disposed of in such a way that flies cannot possibly reach them. Other sources of infection such as manure heaps must not be allowed to accumulate for long periods near houses. Where this cannot be avoided the material should be stored in fly-proof containers. Food for human consumption must not be stored or displayed in such a way as to allow house-flies to settle on it. The numbers of house-flies should be kept as low as possible by removing decaying organic detritus in which they breed, or by spraying it regularly with insecticides to kill the eggs and pupae just below the surface. Flies in the house should be killed by spraying with insecticides such as DDT or BHC (benzene hexachloride).

Plate 47. BLOWFLY FEEDING
(Heather Angel)

Plate 48. BACTERIA COLONIES GROWN ON AGAR CULTURE PLATE OVER WHICH A HOUSE-FLY HAS BEEN ALLOWED TO WALK
(G.B.I. Laboratories)

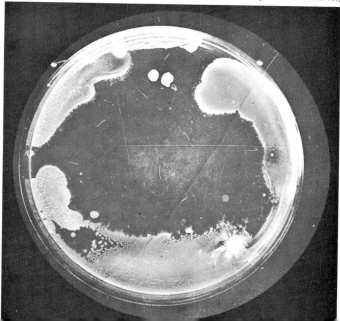

THE DESERT LOCUST (Incomplete metamorphosis)

Mating. The male locust mounts the back of the female, applies the tip of his abdomen to hers and passes sperms into her reproductive tract. The sperms are stored in a sperm sac in the female's abdomen, and as the eggs pass down the oviduct during laying the sperms are released and so fertilize the eggs.

Eggs. After mating, the female lays her eggs in warm moist sand following a rainy spell. She pushes her abdomen down into the sand, extending the membranes between the segments, and burrowing to a depth of 70 or 80 mm (Plate 49). In this burrow, 50 to 100 eggs are laid and mixed with a frothy fluid, which hardens slightly and may help to maintain an air supply round the eggs. In 10 to 20 days depending on temperature and moisture, the eggs hatch and the nymphs make their way to the surface.

(Shell International Petroleum Co. Ltd)

Plate 49. FEMALE LOCUST LAYING EGGS

(a) FIRST INSTAR 8 mm

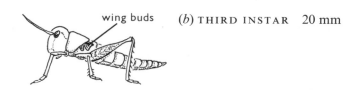

(b) THIRD INSTAR 20 mm

wing buds

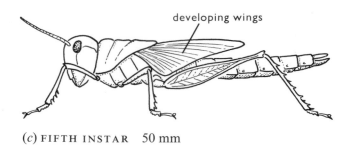

developing wings

(c) FIFTH INSTAR 50 mm

Nymphs. As the nymphs grow they shed their skin five times. The stage between each moult is called an *instar* and each instar lasts 4 to 5 days, except for the fifth which occupies about 8 days. The first instar nymphs are about 8 mm long, with three pairs of legs but no wings. At each successive moult the wings grow larger until by the fifth instar they are quite prominent (Fig. 28.20).

There is no resting stage or pupa, but the changes in form which take place after the fifth moult are more pronounced than any previous changes (Plate 41). During the 26 days from hatching until the final moult, the nymphs or "hoppers" move by crawling or leaping with their long and powerful hind legs. They feed on vegetation, biting off pieces of leaf and stem with their jaws (*see* Fig. 28.12).

Adult. The adult may live for up to six months. It can crawl or leap, but also has two pairs of wings which enable it to fly. Like the nymphs, it feeds on vegetation using its biting jaws. The adults are sexually mature within a few weeks of the final ecdysis and the female may lay three or four batches of eggs during her lifetime.

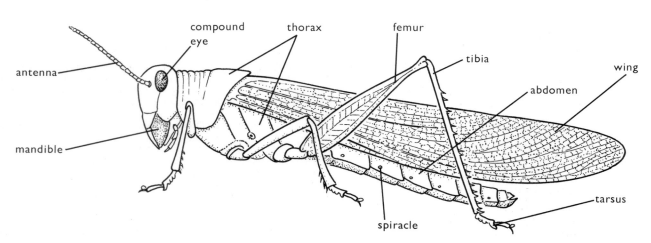

(d) ADULT 80 mm

Fig. 28.20 Incomplete metamorphosis of the locust

(Shell International Petroleum Co. Ltd)

Plate 50.   SWARM OF LOCUSTS

Swarming. If food is in adequate supply and the hoppers are not forced to crowd together when they emerge from the eggs, the locusts live their lives separately as do other grasshoppers. If, however, the hoppers are crowded together for one reason or another, they enter a gregarious phase of activity. The hoppers tend to keep together in a band and move forward together. The crowding effect also results in a change of colour from the normal green, buff or brown to a striking black and yellow (or orange) coloration. There are also structural differences from the solitary form. The bands of hoppers vary in size from hundreds to millions, covering a few square metres or several square kilometres, depending partly on the age of the hoppers and how many bands have combined. As hoppers, they migrate only a few kilometres each day, basking in the early morning sun until their body temperature rises to a level which allows them to move off and eat all the vegetation in their path. When the temperature drops at night they climb bushes and plant stems and remain immobile.

After the final ecdysis, the adult locusts take to the wing (Plate 50), and after a few days of short flights set off on extensive migrations, settling at night and in the middle of the day when it is hottest. A medium-sized swarm may contain a thousand million locusts and cover an area of 20 square kilometres. Such a swarm will consume some 3000 tonnes of vegetation per day; and so if a swarm lands on agricultural crops, the locusts will strip them of every vestige of leaf and edible stem. The swarms may travel many hundreds of kilometres from their place of origin, e.g. from Africa to India, and the females will lay eggs during their journey, so leaving the nucleus of successive swarms within a few weeks.

Methods of control. The range of the adult locusts is so great that international cooperation is essential for effective control. A swarm may originate in India but cause devastating damage to crops in Africa. Sixty countries in Asia and Africa are threatened by swarms of the desert locust (Fig. 28.21).

The main method of control is by spreading poisoned bait, for example bran containing BHC insecticide, in the path of the migrating bands of hoppers. The BHC kills them by being eaten and by its contact with their bodies. Poisoned bait can only be used when the locality of the hoppers is known, and a careful watch must be kept over wide areas so that swarms are discovered as soon as possible after they emerge. The information is then sent to anti-locust centres, e.g. in Nairobi or London, and trucks and personnel are mobilized to take the bait to the appropriate location.

Other methods employed are to spray insecticides over swarms of hoppers or settled adults using aircraft or motor vehicles, or to spray the vegetation in the path of the hoppers. If the region of egg-laying is known, the vegetation in the area can be sprayed with an insecticide which kills the hoppers at their first meal. The danger with all spraying techniques is that the chemicals used may be poisonous to man and other animals, particularly if used on food crops (p. 60).

Two other species, the red locust and the migratory locust, have been held in check for many years by effective control measures, but the desert locust still constitutes a major threat. Constant vigilance and international cooperation are needed if crops are to be protected against this insect.

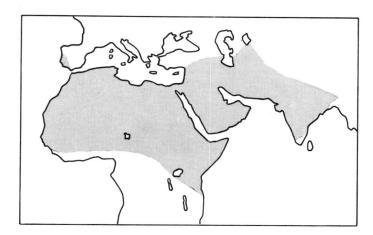

Fig. 28.21   Parts of the world subject to locust invasion

QUESTIONS

1. What structural features do nearly all insects have in common?
2. The mandibles, maxillae and labium represent the basic external feeding apparatus of most insects. Say how these head appendages are modified to cope with the feeding methods of the butterfly, the mosquito and the house-fly.
3. Outline the stages in metamorphosis of (*a*) a house-fly, (*b*) a mosquito and (*c*) a locust.
4. State briefly how the larva and imago of a house-fly are adapted in their feeding and locomotion to exploit differing aspects of their environment.
5. What features of a vertebrate eye enable it to convey a more detailed impression of the environment to the brain than does an insect's compound eye?
6. Mention the sense organs involved and the part they play in the event of a butterfly approaching a flower, alighting and seeking nectar with its proboscis.
7. In what ways does a knowledge of the life history and habits of a harmful insect (e.g. a vector of disease organisms) enable man to work out methods designed to control it?

29 | Fish

FISH are vertebrate animals living in fresh- or sea-water. They are *poikilothermic* and reproduce by laying eggs. Fish are streamlined in their shape, their bodies are covered with scales, they possess fins and breathe by means of gills.

Poikilothermic. An animal whose body temperature varies with that of its surroundings is said to be poikilothermic. The temperature of such an animal is usually a few degrees above that of its environment, but a rise or fall in the temperature of the air or water in which it lives will produce a corresponding change in the animal's body temperature.

Since the speed of most chemical changes that take place in living organisms is increased by a rise in temperature, it follows that the rate of activity of a poikilothermic animal will depend to a large extent on the surrounding temperature. Some animals may, at a low temperature, be reduced to a state of torpor, while high temperatures may lead to vigorous activity.

The popular term "cold-blooded" is unsatisfactory since it conveys the impression of a constant temperature; for example, fish living in "warm" tropical seas would, according to popular definition, be correspondingly "warm-blooded"!

External features (Fig. 29.1)

Nostrils. The nostrils of fish do not open into the back of the mouth as do those of mammals, and are not, therefore, used for breathing. They lead into organs of smell which are, as a rule, very sensitive, so that a fish can detect the presence of food in the water at considerable distances. The nostrils are double, so allowing water to pass through the organ of smell.

Eyes. The eyes of a fish have large round pupils which do not vary in size.

Hearing. Although fish have no ears visible externally they can hear by transmission of vibrations through the body to sensitive regions of the sacculus or utriculus in the inner ear. There are no ossicles or cochlea.

Mouth. The mouth serves for taking in food; also for the breathing current of water.

Scales are bony plates made in the skin. In sharks, rays and dogfish the scales grow out through the skin but in other fish they are covered by skin. They overlap each other and give a protective covering. Under the microscope, rings can be seen in the scales, and from these rings the age of the fish can be estimated. One ring does not correspond to one year, but the groups of rings appear spaced close together or far apart according to the rate of feeding of the fish, since its growth rate affects the increase in size of the scales.

The **operculum** is a bony structure covering and protecting the gills; it plays an important part in the breathing mechanism.

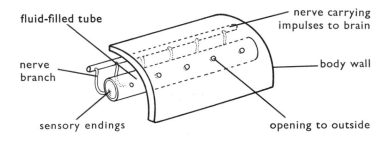

Fig. 29.2   Diagram of lateral line

The **lateral line** (Fig. 29.2) is a fluid-filled tube or canal just below the skin. It opens to the water outside by a series of tiny pores. Its function is to detect movements in the water. A disturbance set up, for example, by a person's hand moving in the water, will cause the fluid in the tube to vibrate. The canal is lined with nerve endings which are stimulated by vibrations and send impulses to the brain. The fish can thus detect the direction and intensity of water movements and this sense helps it to navigate round obstacles or to avoid enemies even if its vision is impaired, e.g. in muddy water.

Fins give stability, and control direction of movement during swimming, as explained later.

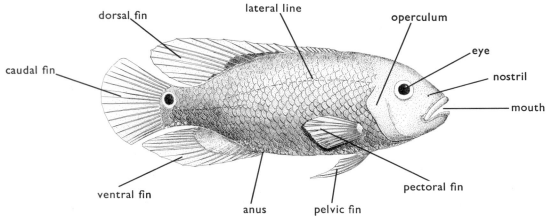

Fig. 29.1   *Tilapia*

Swimming

The vertebral column consists of a series of *vertebrae* held together by *ligaments*, but not so tightly as to prevent slight sideways movement between each pair of vertebrae. The whole spine is, therefore, flexible.

The muscles on each side of the spine contract in a series from head to tail and down each side alternately, causing a wave-like movement to pass down the body (Fig. 29.3). Such a movement may be very pronounced in fish such as eels, and hardly perceptible in others. The frequency of the waves varies from about 50/min in the dogfish to 170/min in other fish. The greater weight and limited flexibility of the head leads to a far greater movement at the tail as a result of these waves of contraction.

The sideways and backwards thrust of the tail and body against the water results in the resistance of the water pushing the fish sideways and forwards in a direction opposed to the thrust. When the corresponding set of muscles on the other side contracts, the fish experiences a similar force from the water on that side. The two sideways forces are equal and opposite, unless the fish is making a turn, so they cancel out, leaving the sum of the two forward forces. The tail, in its final lash, may contribute as much as 40 per cent of the forward thrust.

The swimming speed of fish is not so fast as one would expect from watching their rapid movements in aquaria or ponds. A 10 kg salmon may be able to reach 16 km/h, while the majority of small fish probably do not exceed 4 km/h.

Function of the fins in swimming. It must be emphasized that the swimming movements are produced by the whole of the muscular body, and in only a few fish do the fins contribute any propulsive force. Their main function is to control the stability and direction of the fish.

The *median fins*, that is, the *dorsal, anal* and *ventral* fins, control the rolling and yawing movements of the fish by increasing the vertical surface area presented to the water (Fig. 29.4).

The *paired fins*, pectoral and pelvic, act as hydroplanes and control the pitch of the fish, causing it to swim downwards or upwards according to the angle to the water at which they are held by the muscles. The pectoral fins lie in front of the centre of gravity and, being readily mobile, are chiefly responsible for sending the fish up or down. The paired fins are also the means by which the fish slows down and stops.

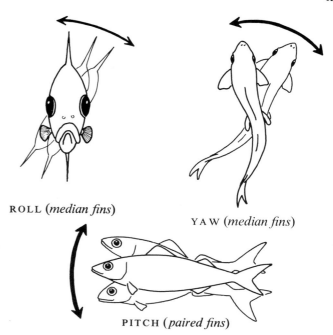

Fig. 29.4   Movements controlled by fins

Swim bladder. Fish other than those of the shark family have in their body-cavity a long air-filled bladder running just beneath the spinal column.

In some fish the bladder opens into the gut and the air pressure in it may be increased or decreased by gulping or releasing air through the mouth. In others, the bladder has no such opening, and the blood vessels surrounding it secrete or absorb air and so control the pressure in it.

The swim bladder makes fish buoyant so that, unlike the shark or dogfish, they do not sink when they stop swimming. When the fish swims to a different depth the pressure needs to be regulated. Some lung-fish which live in poorly oxygenated water in swamps use their swim bladders for breathing air.

Fig. 29.3 Diagrams to show how swimming movements produce motion

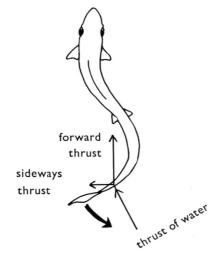
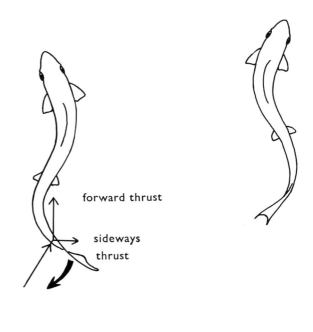

Breathing

Oxygen dissolved in the water is absorbed by the gills. The movements of the mouth and operculum are co-ordinated to produce a stream of water, in through the mouth, over the gills and out of the operculum.

There are usually four gills on each side consisting of a curved bony gill bar bearing many fine filaments (Fig. 29.5a). Through the gill bar run blood vessels which send branches into the gill filaments. The filaments bear smaller filaments down their length which, in turn, divide into smaller branches (Fig. 29.5b). So great a number of minute branches provides a very large surface area when the gills are immersed in water. The walls of the gill filaments are very thin, enabling the oxygen to diffuse rapidly into the blood. A convenient way of visualizing the gills is as an orderly system of blood capillaries exposed to the water in such a way as to absorb oxygen.

Although there is more oxygen in air than in water, a fish will suffocate in air. This is probably because the muscular system of mouth and operculum which can work in water will not function in air. In other words, the valve system which is water-tight is not air-tight. Another important reason is that when a fish is out of water, the surface tension of the water-film covering the gill filaments sticks them together so that the total surface exposed is very much reduced.

The mechanism for pumping water over the gills varies in detail with the type of fish, but in general the pressure in the mouth cavity is reduced by the floor of the mouth being lowered so that water enters through the mouth. The free edge of the operculum is pressed against the body wall by the higher pressure outside, so preventing the entry of water by this route. Next, the volume of the mouth cavity is decreased by raising the floor of the mouth. The escape of water from the mouth is prevented by the closure of two inturned folds of skin along the upper and lower jaws.

The pressure thus forces water between the gill filaments, assisted by an outward movement of the operculum which "sucks" the water from the front to the back of the mouth cavity and over the gills. Finally, as the mouth and operculum close, the fold of skin along the free edge of the operculum is forced outwards and water escapes between the operculum and body wall (Fig. 29.6).

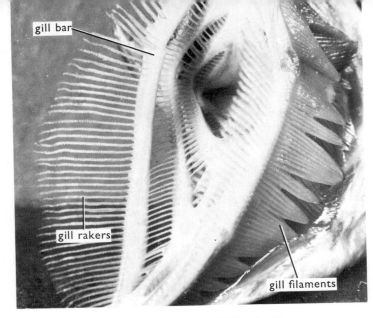

Plate 51.   GILL RAKERS ($\times 3$)

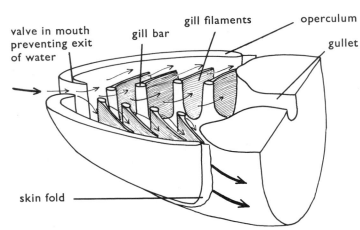

Fig. 29.6   Diagram to show respiratory currents

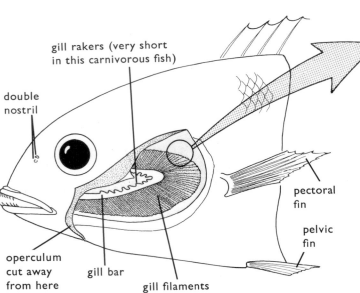

Fig. 29.5   Fish's gills (a); operculum cut away to show gills

(b)   Tips of filaments seen under the microscope

Filter feeding

The current of water passing into the mouth and out of the operculum also serves as a feeding mechanism in certain fish. These filter feeders have long gill rakers (Plate 51) projecting forwards from the gill bars and when the fish swims through surface waters in which zooplankton (Plate 11, p. 55) is abundant, the microscopic animals are trapped in the basket-like array of gill rakers and eventually swallowed.

[Note: for Questions see p. 171.]

30 | Amphibia

FROGS and toads are some of the few remaining members of the amphibia, a group which flourished 250 million years ago. Other present-day members of the group are the newts and salamanders. The amphibia are so adapted that they can, in general, move, feed and breathe as well on land as they do in fresh water. At certain times of their life history or at particular seasons, however, they show a dependence on or preference for one or the other.

External features (Fig. 30.1)

The toad is *poikilothermic* (*see* p. 158) with a loose-fitting, warty skin. It is about 9 cm long and there is no neck between the head and trunk, though the head can be turned to a limited extent. The head bears a wide mouth, a pair of nostrils and protruding eyes. Only the lower eyelid is mobile but it has a folded, transparent margin, the *nictitating membrane*, which can slide rapidly over the eye, cleaning and moistening it, probably without greatly reducing vision. The whole eyeball can be withdrawn farther into the head by muscles. This can sometimes be seen to happen when the toad is swallowing.

The nostrils open into the mouth cavity and they have valves by which they can be opened or closed. Behind the eyes are circular ear-drums. Sounds travelling through the air set these membranes vibrating and the vibration is transmitted by a small bone to a sensory region which sends nervous impulses to the brain.

Behind the ear-drums are raised glandular patches of skin from which can be secreted an unpleasant-tasting substance that may offer some protection against enemies.

The hind-limbs are longer than the fore-limbs and are normally kept flexed close to the body when the toad is not moving. The front legs support the anterior part of the body clear of the ground. The five toes on the hind legs have a slight web between the bases of the toes; the front legs have four toes and no web.

At the hind end of the body is a single opening, the *cloaca*, which serves for the discharge of urine, faeces and gametes.

Frogs are similar to toads in most respects but their skins are smooth and, having more mucous glands, more slimy. The frog's hind legs are relatively longer than the toad's and in many species the web between the toes is more extensive and thus more effective in swimming.

Breathing

(*a*) By raising and lowering the floor of the mouth, air is taken in and expelled from the mouth cavity. Oxygen dissolves in the moist lining, diffuses into capillary blood vessels and is carried away in the blood. Similarly, carbon dioxide diffuses out of the blood into the mouth cavity. The breathing movements are rhythmical but not necessarily continuous as they are in a mammal; the movements may stop altogether from time to time during periods of inactivity.

(*b*) During and after activity the toad may use the lungs. As before, movements of the mouth floor drive air in and out, but by closing the nostrils, the air can be forced into the lungs. The lungs lie in the body cavity of the toad and neither diaphragm nor ribs are present. The air is forced into the lungs by the pumping action of the floor of the mouth, in contrast to the breathing action of mammals where movements of the ribs and diaphragm expand the lungs and draw air in.

(*c*) Frogs breathe in the same way as toads but, in addition, the skin is a respiratory surface. It is kept moist with secretions from the mucous glands, and oxygen from the air or water diffuses in solution through the thin skin into the network of capillaries beneath. Breathing through the skin enables the frog to extract dissolved oxygen from the water when it is swimming, but at the surface it can still breathe through nostrils (Fig. 30.2).

The drier skin of the toad is probably less effective as a respiratory surface than the skin of the frog.

Fig. 30.2   Head of frog partly submerged

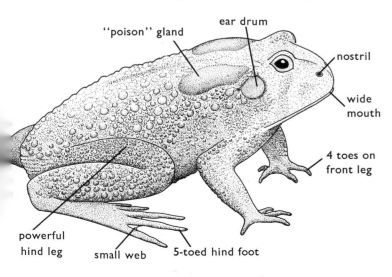

Fig. 30.1   (*a*) COMMON TOAD

(*b*) TREE FROG

1. At rest: hind legs flexed

2. Hind legs extended pushing frog forward and upwards

3. Front legs being extended: beginning to draw up the hind legs

4. Front legs extended to take first shock of landing: hind legs drawn up

(a) FROG LEAPING

(b) TOAD CRAWLING

(*From* James Gray, *How Animals Move*, Cambridge University Press)

Fig. 30.3

Locomotion

The toad's hind legs are used for crawling and leaping. In leaping, the strong extensor muscles of the thigh contract, extending the limb and thrusting the foot against the ground. The thrust is transmitted through the body by the pelvic girdle and spine so that the whole animal is pushed forward (Fig. 30.3a). The front limbs help to absorb the shock of landing.

Unlike many species of frog, toads spend little time in the water, though the clawed toad (*Xenopus*) is an exception, spending most of its life there. When a frog swims, its webbed hind feet provide a greater surface area for pushing backwards on the water and the smaller front legs help to steer. Tree frogs can leap very effectively and they can also cling to leaves and branches by means of suckers on their toes.

Feeding

Adult frogs and toads are carnivorous, feeding on worms, beetles, cockroaches and other insects. Worms and beetles may simply be picked up by the mouth but flying insects can be caught in flight. On occasions the frog or toad will leap towards the insect and trap it in its wide, gaping mouth; at other times its tongue is used. The tongue is attached to the front of the mouth and can be rapidly extended by muscles. It is shot out in a half circle, and the insect is trapped by the sticky saliva covering its surfaces (Fig. 30.4). In a similar way insects can be picked off the ground or from vegetation. The prey is swallowed whole but there are rows of tiny, closely set teeth in the upper jaw and in the roof of the mouth (which prevent the prey from escaping). In swallowing, the eyes are often pulled farther into the head and press down on the prey.

Skin and colour

The common toad is brown, lighter underneath and with irregular, dark patches on its back and limbs. The female differs from the male in having light-coloured skin under the floor of the mouth. The toad's colour can change to some extent; a redistribution of pigment in certain cells of the skin makes the toad darker or lighter. Such tones may correspond more closely to the toad's background in different circumstances and may help to conceal it, but in many amphibia, temperature and humidity play a part in causing colour changes. The colour change operates through the sense organs and brain; a chemical secreted by the pituitary gland circulates in the blood stream and has an effect on the pigment in certain cells.

In the frog's skin are mucous glands which make the slimy fluid that covers the body. The sliminess makes the frog difficult to catch and keeps the skin moist. Only with a constant film of moisture on the surface can oxygen go into solution and so reach the blood beneath the skin.

In the toad also, there are mucous glands, though less mucus is produced.

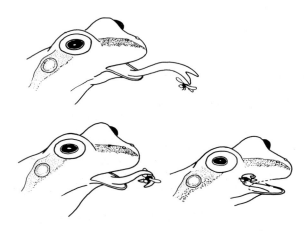

Fig. 30.4 Diagrams to show frog catching a fly with its tongue

Life cycle

(*a*) **Fertilization.** Nearly all amphibians must return to water to breed although some species of tree frog make a "pond" in a rolled-up leaf or hollow tree, the "pond" being derived from liquefaction of the jelly round the eggs. In one South American species the female places the fertilized eggs in little pouches on her back where they develop through all the tadpole stages into tiny but fully formed frogs.

Pairing in the toad may take place at any time during the wet season when conditions are sufficiently moist. The female is larger than the male, her body being swollen with eggs. The male mounts on her back, clasping her with his front legs. In this condition they make their way to the nearest pond or other suitable water. When the female lays the eggs, the male produces a *seminal fluid* containing *sperms*. This pours on to the eggs as they leave the female's body, and the sperms swim through the jelly and fertilize the eggs. Fertilization occurs when the nuclei of the sperm and egg meet and join together or fuse.

The eggs or sperms leave the body through an opening, the cloaca, just above the region where the hind legs join the body.

Since the jelly, or albumen, round the eggs swells on contact with the water, fertilization would be impossible unless carried out at the moment the eggs leave the female's body. Thus, although fertilization is external, the pairing of frogs ensures that it happens.

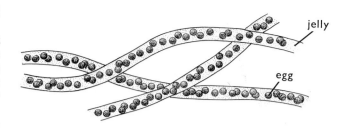

Fig. 30.5   Toad spawn

(b) Development

1. The jelly round the eggs (Fig. 30.5) has several advantages. It keeps the eggs together and prevents their being swept away or eaten. It also protects them from mechanical injury, from drying up and, probably, from fungi and bacteria.

2. The egg itself is a small sphere of semi-liquid protoplasm in a tough, black membrane. There is a nucleus, and the lower cytoplasm contains yolky granules that are the only food supply for the first days of development. Sufficient oxygen must be able to diffuse through the jelly and the egg to allow the vital processes to go on (Fig. 30.6a).

3. Shortly after fertilization, the time depending partly on the temperature, the nucleus of the egg divides into two smaller nuclei which separate. The cytoplasm then divides to include each nucleus in a separate unit of cytoplasm, so that there now appear two smaller cells, each with a nucleus (Fig. 30.6 b and c).

4. A similar division takes place again in each cell, but at right angles to the first division, making four smaller, roughly equal cells (Fig. 30.6d).

5. A third division takes place in the four cells, this time at right angles to the other two, round the "equator", forming eight cells of which the lower four are slightly larger than the upper four (Fig. 30.6e).

6. The cells continue to divide again and again until the "egg" becomes a hollow ball of tiny cells. The cells are very numerous and too small to be seen even with a hand lens. There is little increase in size during this division or *cleavage* but a great increase in the number of cells and nuclei. The egg has become an embryo, but to a casual observer it is still a spherical black ball and there is little evidence of the vigorous activity that has been going on (Fig. 30.6 f and g).

7. (Fig. 30.7.) All this happens in the first few hours. Later, the sphere begins to elongate and develop a distinct head and tail. Meanwhile the cells are being organized internally to form the structures and organs of the tadpole. The energy and raw materials for this process of development come from the yolk.

8. After about thirty hours the tadpole escapes from the jelly. At this stage its mouth has not yet opened and it is still digesting and using the remains of the yolk in its intestine. It clings to water-weed or to the surface of its jelly by its *mucous glands* which produce a sticky secretion. It is quite black, and the external gills are visible (Fig. 30.7d).

Although the tadpoles are merely attached to and not feeding on the water-weed, a good deal of spasmodic wriggling takes place in the clusters of tadpoles.

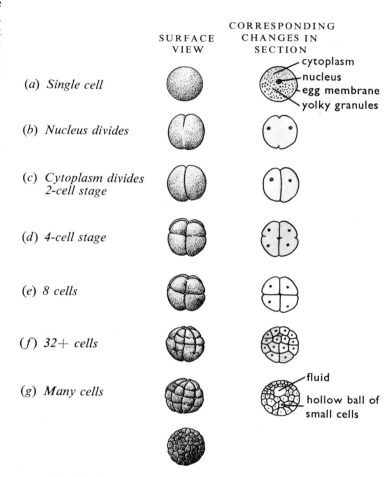

SURFACE VIEW | CORRESPONDING CHANGES IN SECTION

(a) *Single cell*

(b) *Nucleus divides*

(c) *Cytoplasm divides 2-cell stage*

(d) *4-cell stage*

(e) *8 cells*

(f) *32+ cells*

(g) *Many cells*

Fig. 30.6   Changes in the ovum after fertilization

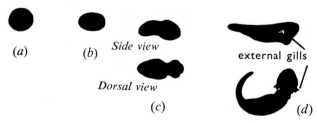

(a)   (b)   *Side view*

Dorsal view

(c)   external gills   (d)

(a) Small sphere consisting of two or three layers of cells
(b) Elongates
(c) Tail and head distinguishable
(d) Wriggling in jelly. Ready to emerge (2·5 mm long)

Fig. 30.7   Changes taking place before hatching (×7)

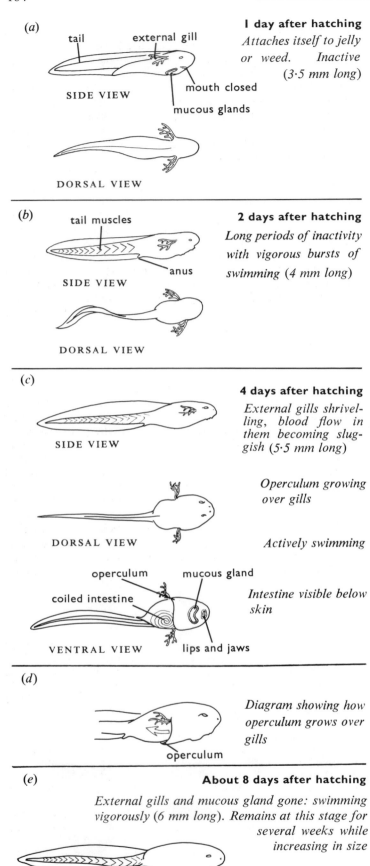

Fig. 30.9   Diagram of external gill showing blood circulation

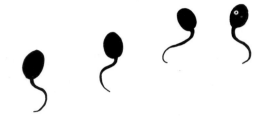

Fig. 30.10   Swimming movements

9. In two or three days the mouth has opened and the tadpoles can scrape the coatings of microscopic plants and other deposits from the surface of pond-weeds by using a pair of horny, toothed jaws. The two pairs of external branched gills have developed (Fig. 30.8a) and with the aid of a low power microscope the blood can be seen circulating in them (Fig. 30.9). These gill filaments are thin-walled and present a fairly large surface area to the water so that oxygen dissolved in the water passes through the filament walls and into the blood close to the surface.

10. After about four days the mucous glands begin to "disappear" and a distinct division into body and tail occurs, together with a rapid increase in size. Internal gills are formed, opening by slits from the mouth cavity (the pharynx) to the outside. A fold of skin from the front of the head grows back (Fig. 30.8 c and d) and covers the slits on both sides, fuses with the skin behind the slits and so forms a continuous chamber, the *atrium*, round the slits. On the left side the atrium opens to the outside by a single hole, the *spiracle*. The fold of skin enclosing the space outside the gills is called the *operculum*.

By six to eight days the external gills have shrivelled and been reabsorbed into the body. In breathing, water is taken in through the mouth, passed over the gills, through the gill slits into the gill chamber formed by the operculum and, finally, out through the spiracle (Fig. 30.11a). As the water passes over the gill filaments, dissolved oxygen diffuses into the blood.

11. The tail elongates and develops a broad, transparent web along its dorsal and ventral surfaces. Vigorous wriggling movements of the body and tail propel the tadpole through the water in a similar way to a fish but with less speed and precision (Fig. 30.10).

A long, coiled intestine has developed (Fig. 30.8c) and can be seen through the skin of the abdomen. The long intestine is adapted to the digestion of an exclusively vegetable diet. Eyes and nostrils are easily seen at this time. In this stage the tadpole grows considerably in size with little pronounced change in form for six or seven weeks.

12. At two months from hatching, the tadpole frequently comes to the surface to gulp air into its lungs, which have begun to form. The hind-limb buds near the junction of the body and tail begin to grow and in two to three days develop

Fig. 30·8   Changes in the first days after hatching

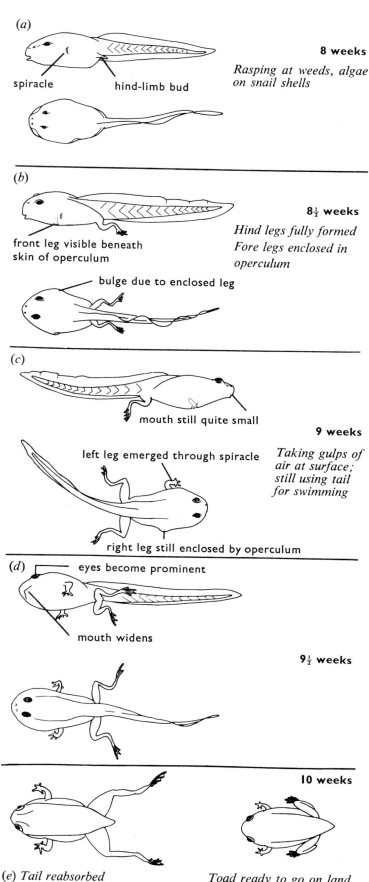

(a)

spiracle   hind-limb bud

8 weeks

Rasping at weeds, algae on snail shells

(b)

front leg visible beneath skin of operculum

bulge due to enclosed leg

8½ weeks

*Hind legs fully formed
Fore legs enclosed in operculum*

(c)

mouth still quite small

9 weeks

Taking gulps of air at surface; still using tail for swimming

left leg emerged through spiracle

right leg still enclosed by operculum

(d) eyes become prominent

mouth widens

9½ weeks

10 weeks

(e) Tail reabsorbed   *Toad ready to go on land*

Fig. 30.11   Changes leading up to metamorphosis

into perfect legs (Fig. 30.11 *a* and *b*). The front legs also grow but do not yet appear because they are covered by the operculum; nevertheless they can be seen bulging beneath the skin in this region. The hind-limbs are not yet used for locomotion but hang limply by the side of the body while the fish-like wriggling movements take place. The diet changes from vegetation, the tadpoles nibbling preferentially at dead animals or raw meat, at least in the aquarium, and associated with this is the shortening of the intestine and, later, the narrowing of the abdominal region.

13. **Metamorphosis.** At about ten weeks, the front legs break through the operculum, the left leg appearing first by pushing through the spiracle (Fig. 30.11*c*) while the right has to rupture the operculum (Fig. 30.11*d*). The tail shortens (Fig. 30.11*e*), being internally digested and absorbed, so providing a source of nutriment for the tadpole which has by this time stopped feeding. The skin is shed, taking with it the larval lips and horny jaws, and leaving a much wider mouth and a lighter coloured skin. Finally, the young toad climbs out of the pond on to the land, still with a tail stump, but able to use its legs for jumping and crawling. The lungs, skin and mouth are now being used for breathing and the young toad starts to catch and eat insects.

Habitat

In the wet season, the common toad, *Bufo regularis*, spends most of its time on land and is commonly found in gardens and compounds. It is nocturnal, i.e. is active and does most of its feeding by night, sometimes entering dwellings in search of insects. During the day, the toad retreats to the shade and shelter of a hole in the ground, or conceals itself beneath a stone or in dense vegetation where conditions are humid and where it is unlikely to dry out. In the dry season, the toad spends all its time concealed in this way, inactive and without feeding. This is called *aestivation*.

The habitat of frogs depends very much on the species. Some species of tree frog, for example, spend most of their time in the vegetation near to water, while others spend all their time in trees and do not revert to water even for breeding.

PRACTICAL WORK

1. *Circulation in a tadpole's tail.* If a tadpole with a well-developed tail web but no legs is placed on a slide with as little water as possible, and the tail web observed under the low power of the microscope, the capillary circulation and the pigment cells can be seen. The tadpole may be anaesthetized beforehand by placing a drop of 1% chlorobutanol in its water. One or two minutes out of water in this way does not seem to harm the tadpole. This circulation (Fig. 30.9) can also be seen in the gills of a younger tadpole.

2. *Control of metamorphosis by thyroxine.* A group of tadpoles is separated from others of the same age, and placed in a solution of 1 part thyroxine to 20×10^6 parts tap water. These tadpoles will metamorphose more rapidly and give rise to miniature frogs, while the controls are still immature tadpoles increasing in size.

3. *Feeding tadpoles.* Tadpoles can be fed by leaving raw meat in their water. If the meat is tied to a thread it can be removed easily before it begins to decompose, but the water should always be changed every few days unless the tadpoles are in a balanced aquarium.

QUESTIONS

For questions relating to this Chapter, see end of Chapter 31, p. 171.

31 | Birds

Characteristics

Birds are warm-blooded (*homoiothermic**) vertebrates, with fore-limbs modified to wings, and with their skins covered with feathers. Typically they have the power of flight, and all reproduce by laying eggs. The skull is extended forward into *mandibles* which make a beak. (*See* Fig. 31.1 for external features.)

The feathers are the single external feature that distinguish birds from other vertebrates. The feathers are produced from the skin which is loose and dry, without sweat glands, and they form an insulating layer round the bird's body, helping to keep its temperature constant, and repelling water. The wings are specially developed for flight, having a large surface area and very little weight.

The *barbules* of the feathers interlock in such a way (Fig. 31.2)

The down feathers are fluffy (Fig. 31.2*a*), trapping a layer of air close to the body. The *flight feathers* and *coverts* are broad and flat and offer resistance to the passage of air.

The shape of the bird and the lay of its feathers make it streamlined in flight.

The bird's legs and toes are covered with overlapping scales.

Birds possess a third, transparent eyelid, the *nictitating membrane*, which can move across the eye.

Features which adapt the bird for flying (Fig. 31.4)

1. The fore-limbs are wings with a large surface area (Fig. 31.3) provided by feathers.

2. Large *pectoral muscles* for depressing the wings. They may account for as much as one-fifth of the body weight in some birds.

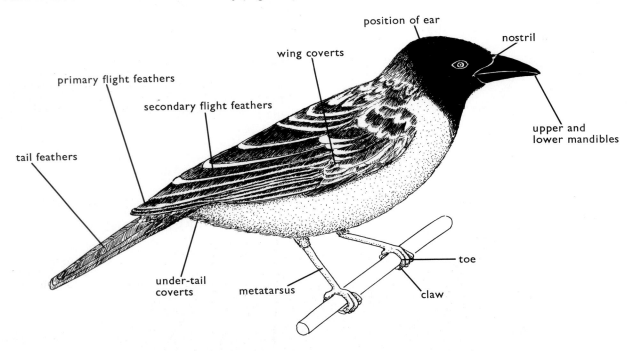

Fig. 31.1　External features of the village weaver bird
(*Ploceus cucullatus*): male

that should a feather be damaged in flight, for example, preening with the beak will re-form it perfectly.

Attached to the quills are muscles which when they contract can alter the angles of the feathers; for example, when a bird fluffs its feathers out in cold weather. They also have a nerve supply which, when the feathers are touched, is stimulated in a similar way to a cat's whiskers.

* Contrasted with poikilothermic. The animal's body temperature normally remains constant, despite changes in the temperature of its surroundings. This temperature is higher than the surroundings.

3. A deep, keel-like extension from the *sternum* (breast bone) for the attachment of the pectoral muscles. Well-developed *coracoid* bones which transmit the lift of the wings to the body.

4. A rigid skeleton (Fig. 31.8) giving a firm framework for attachment of muscles concerned with flying movements. Many of the bones which can move in mammals are fused together in birds; for example, the vertebrae of the spinal column in the body region.

5. Hollow bones, which reduce the bird's weight.

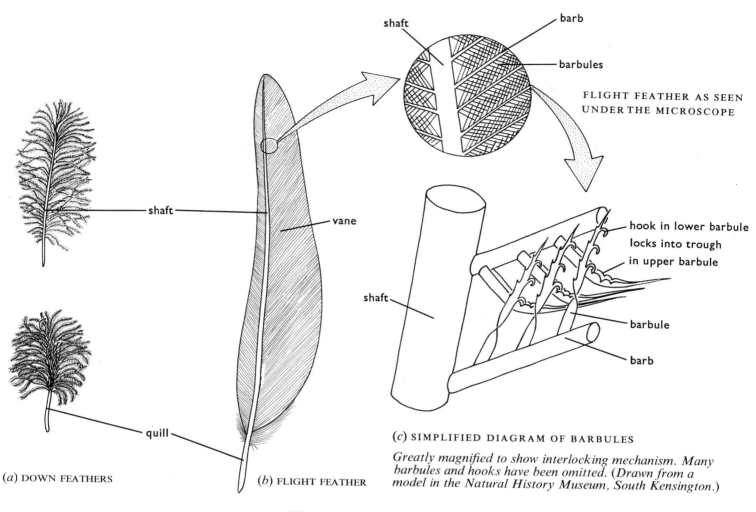

FLIGHT FEATHER AS SEEN
UNDER THE MICROSCOPE

(c) SIMPLIFIED DIAGRAM OF BARBULES

Greatly magnified to show interlocking mechanism. Many barbules and hooks have been omitted. (Drawn from a model in the Natural History Museum, South Kensington.)

(a) DOWN FEATHERS

(b) FLIGHT FEATHER

Fig. 31.2   Feather structure

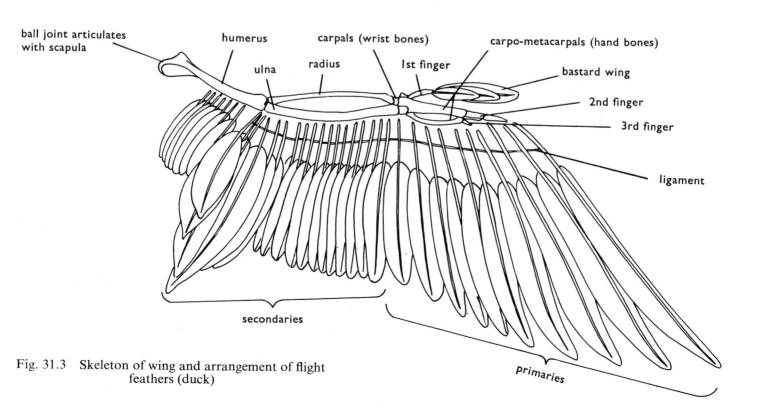

Fig. 31.3   Skeleton of wing and arrangement of flight
feathers (duck)

Locomotion

The flight of a bird can be divided into flapping, and gliding or soaring, different species of birds using the two types to varying extents. In flapping flight the *pectoralis major* muscle contracts, pulling the fore-limb down (Fig. 31.4). The resistance of the air to the wing produces an upward reaction on the wing. This force is transmitted through the coracoid bones to the sternum and so acts through the bird's centre of gravity, lifting it as a whole.

In addition to the lift, forward momentum is provided by the slicing action of the wing, particularly near the tip. In the down-stroke the leading edge is below the trailing edge so that the air is thrust backwards and the bird moves forward. Roughly, the *secondary feathers* provide the lifting force and the *primaries* most of the forward component.

The *bastard wing* may be important during take-off for giving a forward thrust. During flight it may function as a slot maintaining a smooth flow of air over the wing surface.

The up-stroke of the wing is much more rapid than the down-stroke. The *pectoralis minor* contracts and raises the wing, since its tendon passes over a groove in the coracoid to the upper side of the humerus. Often the arm is simply rotated slightly so that the leading edge is higher than the trailing edge and the rush of air lifts the wing. The wing is bent at the wrist during the up-stroke, thus reducing the resistance. In addition, the way in which the primary and secondary feathers overlap (Fig. 31.6) produces maximum resistance during the down-stroke and minimum on the up-stroke. (*See* Fig. 31.7 *b–e*.)

In gliding (Fig. 31.7*a*) the wings are outspread and used as aerofoils, the bird sliding down a "cushion" of air, losing height and gaining forward momentum. Sometimes upward thermal currents or intermittent gusts of wind may be used to gain height without wing movements; in sea-gulls and buzzards for example.

Generally, the fast-flying birds have a small wing area and a large span, with specially well-developed primaries, while the slower birds have shorter, wider wings with well-developed secondaries.

Estimates of speed vary from 160 km/h in swifts to 60 km/h in racing pigeons. The tail feathers help to stabilize the bird in flight and are particularly important in braking and landing.

In walking, the posture of the bird brings the centre of gravity of the bird below the joint of the *femur* and *pelvis*.

Reproduction

The detailed pattern of reproduction and parental care varies widely in different species but, in general, it follows the course outlined below.

Pairing. A sequence of behavioural activities, e.g. courtship display, leads to pair formation, a male and female bird pairing at least for the duration of the breeding season.

Nest building. One of the pair or both birds construct a nest which may be an elaborate structure woven from grass, leaves, feathers, etc. (Fig. 31.5) or little more than a hollow scraped in the ground.

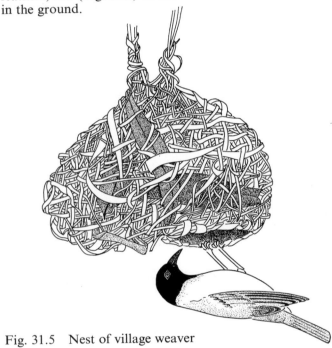

Fig. 31.5   Nest of village weaver

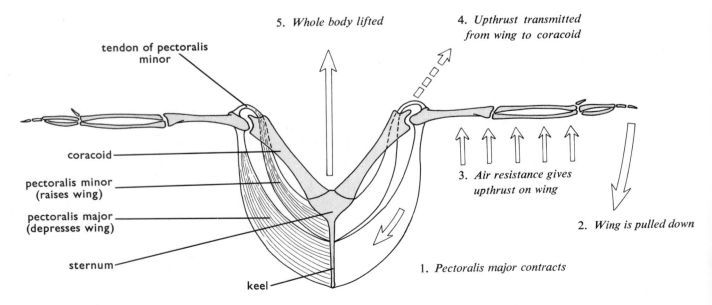

Fig. 31.4   Front view of skeleton concerned with flight showing how muscles and bones work together

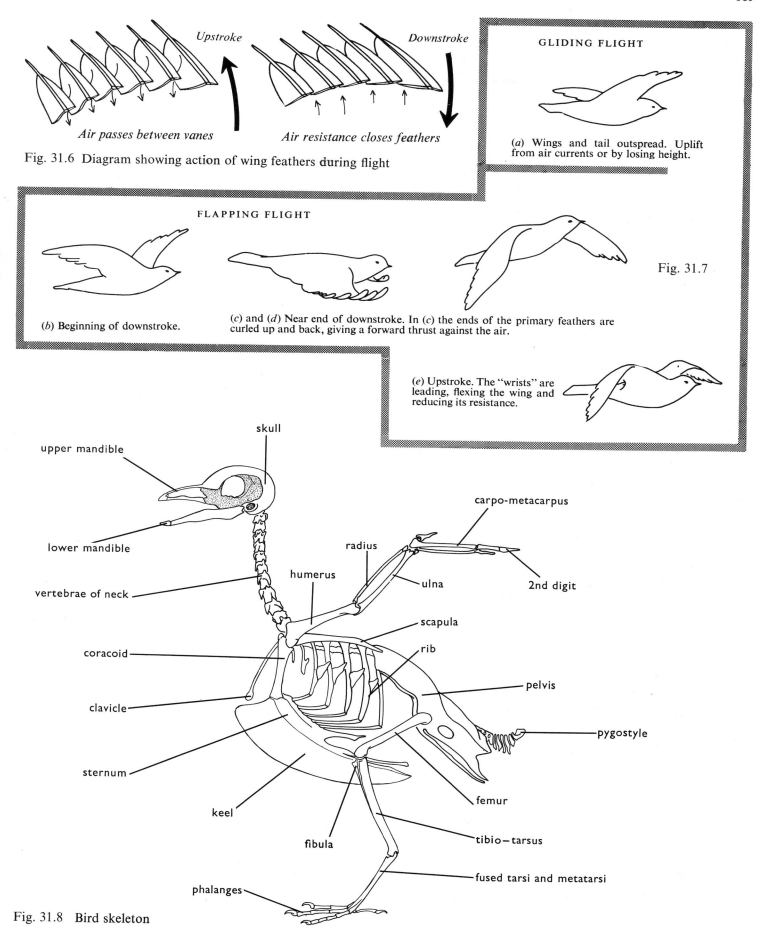

Upstroke

Air passes between vanes

Downstroke

Air resistance closes feathers

Fig. 31.6 Diagram showing action of wing feathers during flight

GLIDING FLIGHT

(*a*) Wings and tail outspread. Uplift from air currents or by losing height.

FLAPPING FLIGHT

Fig. 31.7

(*b*) Beginning of downstroke.

(*c*) and (*d*) Near end of downstroke. In (*c*) the ends of the primary feathers are curled up and back, giving a forward thrust against the air.

(*e*) Upstroke. The "wrists" are leading, flexing the wing and reducing its resistance.

skull

upper mandible

lower mandible

vertebrae of neck

humerus

radius

carpo-metacarpus

ulna

2nd digit

scapula

rib

coracoid

pelvis

clavicle

pygostyle

sternum

femur

keel

fibula

tibio−tarsus

phalanges

fused tarsi and metatarsi

Fig. 31.8 Bird skeleton

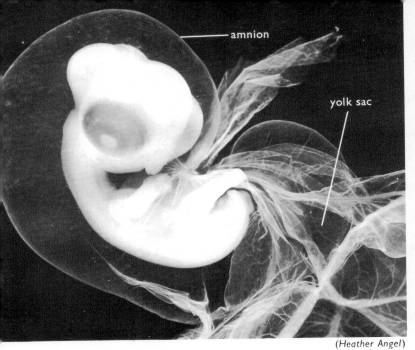

(Heather Angel)

Plate 52.   7-DAY CHICK EMBRYO (×4)

(Heather Angel)

Plate 53.   CHICKS GAPING FOR FOOD

Mating. Further display leads to mating. The male mounts the female, applies his reproductive openings to hers and passes sperm into her oviduct, thus enabling the eggs to be fertilized internally.

Egg laying. The fertilized egg is enclosed in a layer of albumen and a shell during its passage down the oviduct and is finally laid in the nest. Usually, one egg is laid each day and incubation does not begin until the full clutch has been laid.

Incubation. The female bird is usually responsible for incubation, keeping the eggs at a temperature approximating to her own by covering them with her body and pressing them against her brooding patches, i.e. areas devoid of feathers which allow direct contact between the skin and the egg shell. Incubation also reduces evaporation of water from the shell. At this temperature, the eggs develop and hatch in a week or two.

Development. The living cells in the egg divide to make the tissues and organs of the young birds. The yolk (Fig. 31.9) provides the food for this and the albumen is a source of both food and water. The egg shell and shell membranes are permeable, and oxygen diffuses into the air space, being absorbed by part of the network of capillaries which spread out over the yolk and over a special sac, the *allantois*, which has become attached to the air space (Fig. 31.10). The blood carries the oxygen to the embryo. Carbon dioxide is eliminated by the reverse process through the egg shell. When the chicks are fully developed, they break out of the shell by using their beaks.

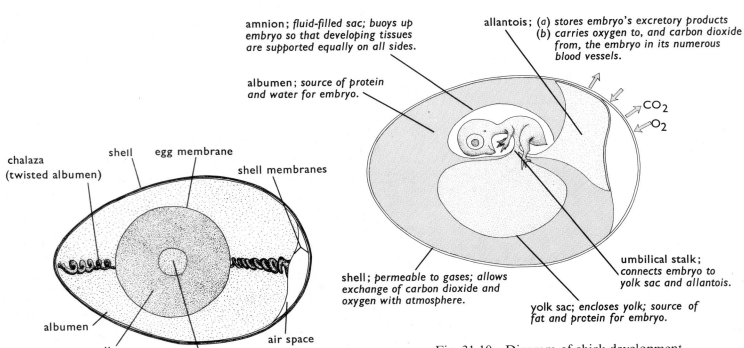

Fig. 31.9   Bird's egg with top half of shell removed

Fig. 31.10   Diagram of chick development
(Note. Before hatching, the amnion bursts; yolk sac is absorbed into body; allantois is left behind in shell.)

COMMON VULTURE*
Hooked upper mandible for tearing pieces
of flesh from carcasses; absence of feathers
probably an adaptation to plunging head
into entrails.

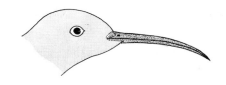

SUNBIRD
Long slender beak; probes into flowers and
obtains nectar.

AFRICAN GREY PARROT
Hook-like upper mandible assists in climbing; sturdy, short beak enables seeds to be
gripped and cracked open.

Fig. 31.11   Beaks and feet

The shape and size of a bird's beak and feet are usually
adapted to its methods of feeding and locomotion. The
drawings are not to scale.

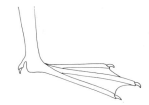

OSPREY*
Sharp, curved talons which grip and kill prey

* From D. A. Bannerman, *Birds of Tropical West Africa*,
Oliver & Boyd, 1930

DUCK
Hind toe very small; web between three
forward toes gives increased surface for
swimming and walking on mud

Parental care. The chicks of large, ground-nesting birds are
covered with downy feathers and can run about soon after
hatching. They peck at objects on the ground and soon learn
to discriminate material suitable for food. They stay close to
the hen, responding to her calls by taking cover or seeking
her out according to the circumstances.

In most other species, the chicks hatch with few or no
feathers, helpless and with closed eyelids. Having no feathers,
they are very susceptible to heat loss and desiccation, and the
parents brood them, covering the nest with the body and wings,
so reducing evaporation and temperature fluctuations. Both
parents will collect suitable food, often worms, caterpillars,
insects and other materials equally rich in protein. The sound
or sight of the parents approaching the nest causes the nest-
lings to stretch their necks and gape their beaks. The bright
orange colour inside the beaks induces the parent to thrust the
food it is carrying into the open beaks (Plate 53).

After a week or two, the young birds begin to climb out of
the nest and sit in the bush or tree but the parents still find and
feed them. When the primary and secondary feathers have
developed, the fledglings begin short practice flights. This is
one of the most dangerous periods of their lives since they can
feed themselves to only a limited extent and cannot escape from
predators such as cats and hawks. Some estimates suggest that
only 25 per cent of the eggs laid in open nests of this kind
reach the stage of fully independent birds.

Adaptations of beaks and feet

Many birds show interesting variations in the structure of
their beaks and feet. These differences are thought to be adaptations to the mode of life and methods of feeding. Some are
illustrated in Fig. 31.11.

PRACTICAL WORK

Flight feathers and down feathers should be examined, drawn and
observed under the microscope. Collections of wings, feet and heads
from dead birds are very useful. Wings should be pinned out and
allowed to dry, otherwise the tendons, etc., will set in the contracted
form. All feathers, wings, etc., should be kept in a moth-proof box
containing a moth repellant such as para-di-chlor-benzene.

If possible a bird should be dissected to show the pectoral muscles
and air sacs. *Practical Vertebrate Morphology*, by Saunders and
Manton (O.U.P.), gives detailed dissection methods.

QUESTIONS (Chapters 29–31)

Apart from simple recall of facts, the most likely types of essay question
in public examinations are those demanding a comparison of these organisms from the point of view of their methods of locomotion, breathing or
reproduction, e.g. the contrast between the lack of parental care in the
frog and the highly evolved parental behaviour of birds; the use of trachea
in insects, and gills in fish for gaseous exchange. The best practice for
answering questions of this type is to select pairs of animals and draw up
lists of features common to both in connexion with breathing, locomotion
or reproduction and then tabulate the differences relevant to those activities. The similarities will usually be concerned with fundamental principles,
e.g. oxygen and carbon dioxide are exchanged in both lungs and gills but
the methods of ventilation are quite different.

To make the answers relevant, only points of similarity or difference
should be mentioned. Try to start all sentences with either "Both . . ." or
"Whereas . . .", at least in practice answers, e.g. "Both fish and frog can
exchange oxygen and carbon dioxide with the water surrounding them",
"Whereas the frog uses only its skin for this process, the fish has specialized
structures, gills, with a greatly increased surface area for gaseous exchange."

Bear in mind that a "compare" question requires both similarities and
differences while a "contrast" question demands only differences. For
either type of question, two separate accounts will not do.

32 | Some simple organisms

Most of the organisms described so far in this book are extremely complicated in their structure and physiology. They all consist of thousands of cells which are specialized in certain ways and have specific functions. Some cells are specialized for conduction of fluids, some for contraction and some for the manufacture of chemicals.

However, there are in existence many organisms in which all these processes are carried on, not by specialized groups of cells but in the single cell which makes up the entire organisms. These creatures are microscopic and could be considered as organisms with bodies undivided into cells. Some examples of such organisms will be described and their biological significance discussed later.

Spirogyra

Spirogyra is a simple green alga seen as a filmy, rather slimy, growth in ponds. It consists of long rows of cylindrical cells joined end to end, producing long filaments easily visible to the naked eye.

Each cell consists of a cellulose wall surrounding a large central vacuole lined with cytoplasm. The nucleus is supported by strands of cytoplasm. One or two ribbon-like chloroplasts form a helix (a cylindrical spiral) in the cytoplasm (*see* Figs. 32.1 and 32.2).

The sub-kingdom *Algae* to which *Spirogyra* belongs, includes many similar filamentous forms, and the much larger, multi-cellular seaweeds.

Nutrition. Spirogyra makes its food in the same way as other green plants, but without the elaborate system of roots, stem and leaves of the higher plants. It is surrounded by water containing dissolved carbon dioxide and salts so that in the light, with the aid of its chloroplast, it can build up starch by photosynthesis. From this carbohydrate, with additional elements, it can synthesize all the other materials necessary for its existence.

Growth. Any of the cells can divide transversely, the daughter cells remaining together, so forming the filament and increasing its length. The retention of daughter cells after division represents the way in which many-celled organisms could have arisen from single-celled creatures.

Reproduction. Asexual reproduction is an outcome of the cell division and growth described above. Pieces of the growing filament simply break away and continue to grow independently of the "parent" filament. Sexual reproduction takes place in Spirogyra under certain conditions when two filaments lie side by side (Fig. 32.3). In the cells of each filament the cytoplasm shrinks away from the cell wall, the detailed structure of chloroplast, nucleus and cytoplasm seems to disappear, and a rounded protoplasmic mass is formed. Meanwhile outgrowths from the walls of opposite cells in the two filaments have met and joined to form a continuous tube through which the cell contents of one filament pass into the other, leaving one filament quite empty. In the cells of the other filament the protoplasmic masses fuse and a thick wall is secreted round the resulting zygote, forming a zygospore which, when released by the breakdown of the cell wall of the filament, falls to the bottom of the pond. The zygospore can remain dormant and withstand adverse conditions. In this form it may also be transported to fresh ponds in the dried dust or mud from its original habitat.

When the zygospore germinates, its cytoplasm extends from the split wall of the spore and grows into a new filament (Fig. 32.4).

(*a*) FILAMENT

chloroplast

Fig. 32.1 Spirogyra

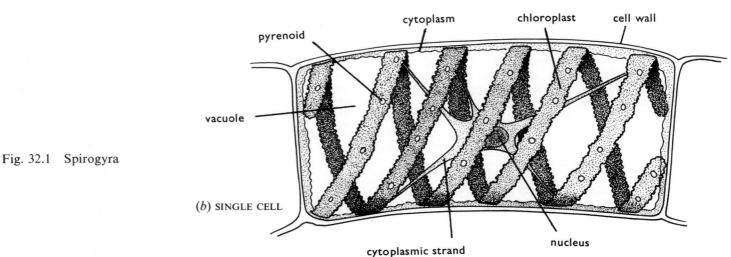

(*b*) SINGLE CELL

172

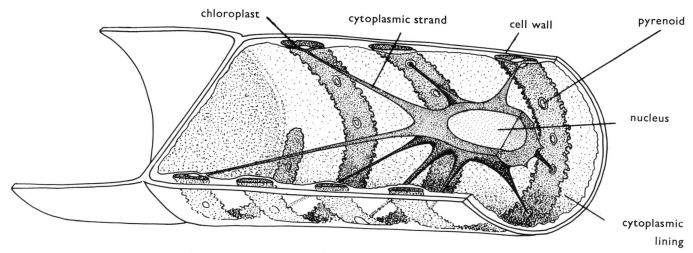

Fig. 32.2   Stereogram of Spirogyra cell in section

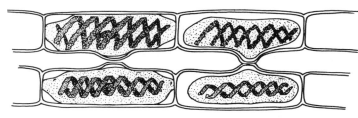

(a) Adjacent cells develop protuberances. Cell contents shrink and round off.

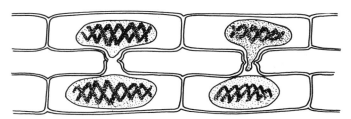

(b) Protuberances meet and form tube. Cell contents from one filament pass into the other.

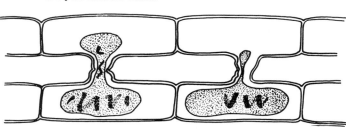

(c) Cell contents fuse.

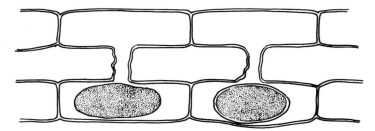

(d) Zygote secretes thick wall.

Fig. 32.3   Sexual reproduction in Spirogyra

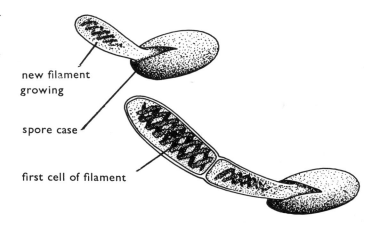

Fig. 32.4   Zygospore of Spirogyra germinating

The process of reproduction described above is called *conjugation*. The entire cell-contents form the gametes and, since the cells of a particular filament all discharge their gametes or receive the gametes of the other filament, the filaments can be said to exhibit a difference of sex, although no structural differences are visible before conjugation.

Other simple algae

There are many other algae which consist of only one or a few cells, e.g. the *Desmids* (Fig 32.5) and the *Diatoms* (Fig. 32.6 and Plate 10, p. 54).

These live in fresh water or the sea, but some can be collected

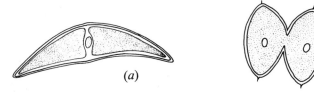

Fig. 32.5   Examples of common desmids

and studied by washing out mosses and liverworts with a little water. Diatoms constitute the greater part of the phytoplankton, and are therefore very important as the basis of the food chain on which fish depend.

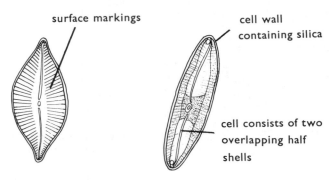

surface markings

cell wall containing silica

cell consists of two overlapping half shells

Fig. 32.6   Two kinds of diatom (greatly magnified)

Euglena

The many species of Euglena and some of the related organisms, all called flagellates, form an interesting group of unicellular creatures. Although many flagellates have chloroplasts and feed *holophytically* (p. 59), there are some which take in and digest solid particles (i.e. holozoic feeders) and some which feed *saprophytically*, i.e. they absorb dissolved substances from their surroundings.

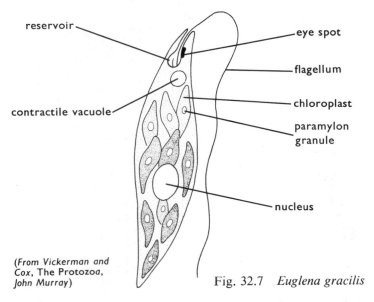

reservoir

eye spot

flagellum

chloroplast

paramylon granule

contractile vacuole

nucleus

(From Vickerman and Cox, The Protozoa, John Murray)

Fig. 32.7   *Euglena gracilis*

The illustration of *Euglena gracilis* (Fig. 32.7) shows most of the structural features of the family. Unlike Spirogyra, and plants in general, it has not a rigid cell wall. The Euglena can change its shape as it swims along, though movement is effected by the lashing of the flagellum. Food is synthesized, as in green plants, with the aid of chloroplasts, the shapes of which vary in the different species. If *Euglena gracilis* is kept in the dark it will lose its green colour and become unable to photosynthesize, but it will continue to live if suitable organic matter is present in the water. In this respect it is very similar (some biologists think it is identical) to some of its relatives in the genus *Astasia*. These colourless flagellates live only in water rich in organic materials such as the fluid in the

puddles round cowsheds. They absorb the organic substances from their environment and use them as food, although they may still be able to synthesize complex materials from relatively simple inorganic chemicals. They cannot, however, build up starch from carbon dioxide.

Other colourless flagellates are able to take in solid particles of food material and digest them in a way described in the section dealing with Amoeba (*see* below). This holozoic feeding is essentially an animal characteristic. The distinction between holozoic and holophytic feeding is the fundamental difference between animals and plants, and this leads some biologists to suggest that the remote ancestors of present-day flagellates such as Euglena and Astasia could have given rise to the plant and animal kingdoms in the early stages of evolution; for it is only in this group of unicellular creatures that closely related individuals, or even single creatures, exhibit both plant and animal characteristics.

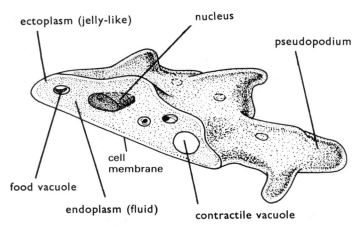

ectoplasm (jelly-like)

nucleus

pseudopodium

food vacuole

cell membrane

endoplasm (fluid)

contractile vacuole

Fig. 32.8   Structure of Amoeba (in section)

Amoeba (Fig. 32.8)

The species of Amoeba are single-celled organisms. They have no chlorophyll or cell walls and they take in and digest solid food. Such single-celled organisms are called *Protozoa*. Amoebae live in ponds, ditches and other moist places, and in the soil.

Locomotion. There are no special locomotory organs like flagella or cilia. Amoebae move by the flowing of their cytoplasm over the surface of the mud or soil (Fig. 32.9). At the surface of the Amoeba the fluid cytoplasm begins to flow out into a protuberance called a *pseudopodium*. In time, all the protoplasm will have flowed into this so that the Amoeba is brought to a new position. Changes of direction are effected when a new pseudopodium begins to form at another point of

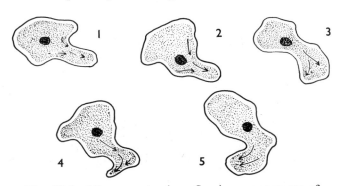

Fig. 32.9   Diagrams to show flowing movements of Amoeba

the Amoeba's surface. The direction of movement is probably determined by local differences in the water. Slight acidity or alkalinity may cause the protoplasm to start flowing or prevent its doing so altogether. The chemicals diffusing from suitable food material may cause the protoplasm to flow in that direction.

Feeding. When an Amoeba encounters a microscopic organism such as a flagellate, pseudopodia flow out rapidly and surround it (Fig. 32.10) so that the organism is ingested with a

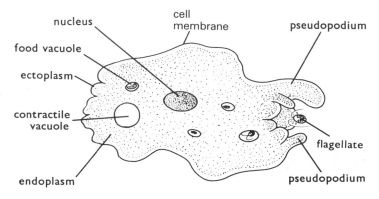

Fig. 32.10   Amoeba ingesting a microscopic organism

drop of water into the cytoplasm of the Amoeba. This forms a *food vacuole*. The surrounding cytoplasm secretes into the food vacuole, enzymes which digest parts of the organism. The soluble, digested materials are then absorbed into the surrounding cytoplasm, and the undigested residue is left behind or egested, as Amoeba flows on its way.

Food vacuoles with material in various stages of digestion can be seen in the cytoplasm of the Amoeba. Ingestion and egestion can take place at any point on the surface; there is no "mouth" or "anus".

Osmo-regulation. The cell boundary of Amoeba is selectively permeable, with the result that the low water potential of the solutions in the *endoplasm* causes water to enter. This excess water is collected up in a spherical *contractile vacuole* which gradually swells, and then seems to contract or burst, liberating the accumulated water to the exterior.

Reproduction. Amoeba stops moving and its nucleus divides. The cytoplasm then divides to make two daughter individuals (Fig. 32.11). This is *binary fission*.

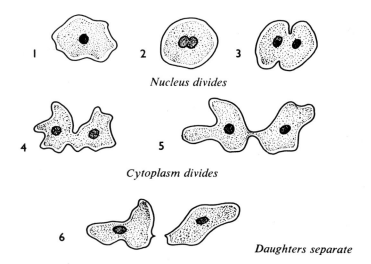

Nucleus divides

Cytoplasm divides

Daughters separate

Fig. 32.11   Amoeba reproducing by binary fission

In some species a *cyst* is formed: that is, a resistant wall is secreted round the more-or-less spherical Amoeba. In this cyst the Amoeba is able to resist unfavourable conditions and may be carried to other situations. The protoplasm within the cyst divides repeatedly so that when it bursts open a fairly large number of daughter Amoebae are released.

There is no evidence of any form of sexual reproduction.

Related protozoa

Ciliates. The protozoans most frequently encountered, belong to the ciliates. These move by means of rows of cytoplasmic filaments, *cilia*, extending from their surface. These cilia flick in rhythmic waves and propel the microscopic animals smoothly forwards or backwards.

There is a more complicated organization in the body than appears in Amoeba. For example, in the *Paramecium* illustrated in Fig. 32.12, a row of special cilia waft food particles into a shallow gullet, and ingestion can take place only at the end of this gullet. The food vacuoles move in a very definite path through the body of Paramecium, and egestion takes place at only one point near the region of ingestion.

Enterozoic protozoa. There are many protozoa which live only in the gut or other regions within the bodies of higher

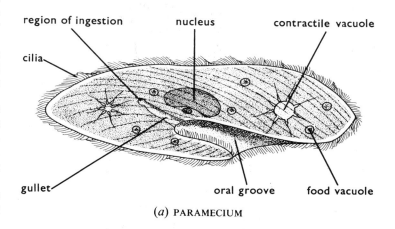

(a) PARAMECIUM

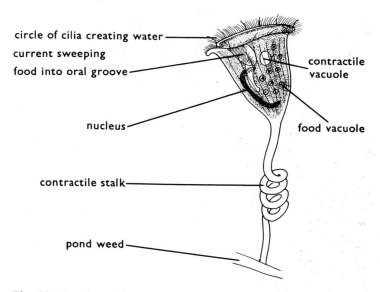

Fig. 32.12   Two ciliates   *(b)* VORTICELLA

animals. They are often quite harmless or even beneficial, and some play an important part in the digestion of cellulose in the paunch of the cow and the caecum of the rabbit, to mention only two examples. If those present in the alimentary canals of certain termites are killed, the termite can no longer digest the woody material on which it feeds and it will die of starvation.

There are some protozoa, however, like the malarial parasite, which lives in red blood cells, and others like the dysentery amoeba in the intestine, which cause severe symptoms of disease (p. 222).

Biological significance of the Protoctista

The single-celled organisms are included in the Kingdom *Protoctista* (*see* p. 206). Those which feed holozoically are usually called *Protozoa*; those which feed holophytically may be called *Protophyta*. The unicellular protoctista are of particular interest because similar creatures were probably some of the earliest living organisms to inhabit the earth, and many of the present-day animals and plants may have evolved from such a stock.

The other point of interest is the way in which these minute creatures carry out all the vital processes associated with living, without the complicated cellular organization seen in the higher organisms. In many instances the greater size of the higher organisms would not be possible without an organization into cells and the development of special organs. It is worthwhile to consider some of the vital processes and to see how the single-celled organisms carry them out.

Respiration. The fundamental chemical changes involved in releasing energy by oxidation are similar in nearly all living creatures but their methods of obtaining oxygen differ.

The small size of the unicells makes special respiratory organs unnecessary since diffusion over small distances, from the outside of the organisms to their innermost protoplasm, is rapid enough to meet their needs. Moreover, the smaller an organism is, the greater is the ratio of its surface area to its volume, and so the more rapid is the intake and release of substances from its surface. Carbon dioxide is eliminated by diffusion in the reverse direction to the uptake of oxygen.

The small distances involved also make a specialized transport system unnecessary. The digested materials from a food vacuole in an Amoeba are distributed by the flowing of the cytoplasm during movement. The cytoplasm in many other unicellar organisms shows similar "streaming" movements.

Excretion. Excretory products almost certainly diffuse out from the general surface as soon as their concentration rises above that in the environment. The contractile vacuoles represent a specialized area of cytoplasm in which the excess water collects and is expelled, and in this sense is an "organ" within a cell. There is no evidence to suggest that anything other than water is eliminated: the contractile vacuole is considered to be an organ of osmo-regulation rather than excretion.

Sensitivity. Often the entire surface of the cytoplasm is sensitive to touch and chemical stimulation. An Amoeba prodded with a needle will flow away from it no matter where the needle is placed. Many of the holophytic unicells respond to variations in light intensity as a result of their having a region of cytoplasm particularly sensitive to light.

Co-ordination. Conduction of an electrochemical nature probably takes place over the entire surface of the freely moving unicells. There must also be some path of conduction between a light-sensitive region and a flagellum which responds to the stimulus.

Reproduction. In binary and multiple division of the single-celled creatures the entire protoplasm becomes incorporated in the offspring and nothing is left behind to die of old age. In the higher animals only the small fraction of their protoplasm, represented by the sperm and ovum of a fertilized egg continues the existence of the adult. The greater proportion of the protoplasm and other materials in the body is bound to die sooner or later. The single-celled organisms may die as a result of desiccation, extreme temperature changes, lack of food or oxygen, but not from old age or senile decay.

Nutrition. The holophytic unicells feed in a similar way to the higher green plants, but because they are surrounded by the water, carbon dioxide and salts that they use, no specialized conducting systems are needed.

The protozoa break down complex substances to simple substances just as do the higher animals, but have no need of elaborate digestive tracts or glands since almost any part of the cytoplasm is capable of secreting enzymes in food vacuoles once the food has been ingested.

Movement. Movement in the higher animals is brought about by a complex relationship of muscles and skeleton. Movement in unicells is due to the flowing of the cytoplasm or the lashing of cilia or flagella. Although the flagellum has no organization comparable to that of a limb, it is not structureless. The organization depends on the arrangements of the tiny cytoplasmic filaments, just as in other cell "organs" the chemical nature of the local cytoplasm or the arrangement of its molecules may confer special properties upon it.

In conclusion, the organization, specialization and division of labour which occur in unicells result from the different nature of the cytoplasm in certain regions and are not due (as in higher organisms) to the existence of various groups of special cells.

PRACTICAL WORK

1. **Sources.** (*a*) Stagnant, green-looking water in puddles, ditches, drinking troughs and roof gutters usually has abundant microscopic organisms containing many unicells. Amoeba may be collected in the skimmings of mud and humus from sluggish streams. (*b*) Hay infusions. Chopped hay is boiled with rain-water, filtered and the filtrate left to stand in an open jar. Bacterial spores germinate in the fluid. If fresh hay or soil is added, any micro-organisms present may feed on the bacteria or protophyta which appear, and so flourish and reproduce.

2. **Culture methods.** The procedure described above gives rise to very mixed colonies of unicells. If a colony of only one group is required, a few individuals must be taken up in a sterilized pipette and transferred to a clean dish with filtered rain-water and given suitable food material. To keep the creatures in a state of active reproduction a few individuals must be transferred to a fresh culture each week as the old cultures tend to degenerate.

3. **Suitable food.** A few wheat grains, boiled to prevent germination and placed in the water, provide a suitable basis for the kind of food chain in which Amoeba can take its place. Rain-water is better than tap-water since it is not likely to be too acid or alkaline or to contain harmful chemicals.

The hay infusion, with added fresh hay, will usually give rise to bacteria on which Paramecium will feed.

Water boiled with guano provides a suitable medium for Euglena and other flagellates.

33 | Chromosomes and Heredity

MOST living organisms start their existence as a single cell, a *zygote* (fertilized egg, p. 112). This single cell divides into two cells, four, eight and so on to produce eventually the thousands of cells which make up the new organism.

In the cell divisions that turn a zygote into an organism, there must be forces directing the process which determine that some cells become muscle, some skin, some bone or blood, and these cells must be directed into groups in the right order and in the right place to produce tissues, organs and ultimately the complete, integrated, co-ordinated organism.

Moreover, a zygote does not produce just any organism. It will produce one which resembles the parents from whom the zygote was derived. The zygotes of a human and a cat may look identical, a nucleus surrounded by a little cytoplasm, but they will develop in quite different ways. The cat zygote will produce a cat and not a man. A mouse zygote will produce a mouse and not a rat. The study of the mechanism by which the characteristics of the parent are handed on to the offspring is known as *genetics*.

The zygote of a bird develops into a chick inside the egg without any outside interference other than incubation. It follows, therefore, that the "instructions" for building a bird from a single-celled zygote must reside somewhere inside the zygote. What is more, the "instructions" must be present in the two gametes which fuse to form the zygote. They could be in the cytoplasm, the nucleus or both.

When one examines the gametes of most animals, the egg usually has a large volume of cytoplasm associated with its nucleus. The male gamete, on the other hand, consists of little more than a nucleus with a very thin layer of cytoplasm round it, and a tail. However, there is nothing to suggest that the male's contribution to the "instructions" or *genotype* of the zygote is any less than the female's, so it looks as if the bulk of the genotype, the "instructions" for building a horse or a man, resides in the nucleus.

The next question is, can the "instructions" be seen or studied in some way? One would not expect to see printed directions, but there might be structures to be seen which would give some idea about the nature of the "instructions". Thus, a study of the nucleus would seem to be the most profitable course, particularly at a time when the nucleus is dividing because the genetic information, the genotype, must be handed on intact and undiminished to each cell. For example, if the two cells resulting from the first division of a toad's zygote (p. 163) are separated, each cell can develop into a complete toad. This is true of cells even at the 4- and 8-celled stage. Thus the "toad-building instructions" are intact and complete in each of these cells after cell division.

Thus, if one could observe a structure or structures, reproduced exactly in the nucleus and shared equally between the two nuclei at cell division, this might give a clue to the site of the genetic information. The next section, consequently, examines the events in the nucleus at cell division in some detail.

Cell division

In the early stages of growth and development of an organism, all the cells are actively dividing to produce new tissues and organs. Later, particularly when the cells become specialized, this power of division is lost and only a limited number of unspecialized cells retain the power of division, e.g. cambium cells in plants and cells of the Malpighian layer in the skin which produce new epidermis. In those cells that continue to divide, the sequence of events leading to cell division is basically the same. Firstly, the nucleus divides into two and then the whole cell divides, separating each nucleus in a unit of cytoplasm, so that two cells now exist where previously there was only one. Both cells may then enlarge to the size of the parent cell. Such cell division and enlargement gives rise to growth.

The detailed sequence of events which takes place when the nucleus of a cell divides has been worked out over the last eighty years and is called *mitosis*.

Mitosis (Fig. 33.2 and Plate 54)

Prior to division, the nucleus of the cell enlarges and in the nucleus there appear a definite number of fine, coiled, thread-like structures called *chromosomes* (Fig. 33.1). The behaviour of these chromosomes during cell division is usually described as a series of stages, prophase, metaphase, etc., though, in fact, the events occur in a smoothly continuous pattern and do not occupy equal periods of time (*see* p. 178).

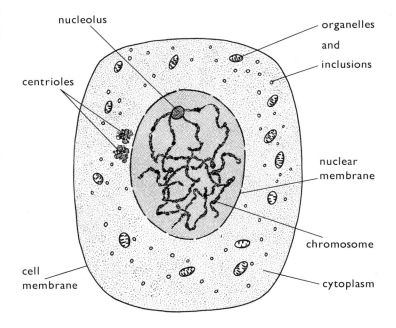

Fig. 33.1   Animal cell at early prophase

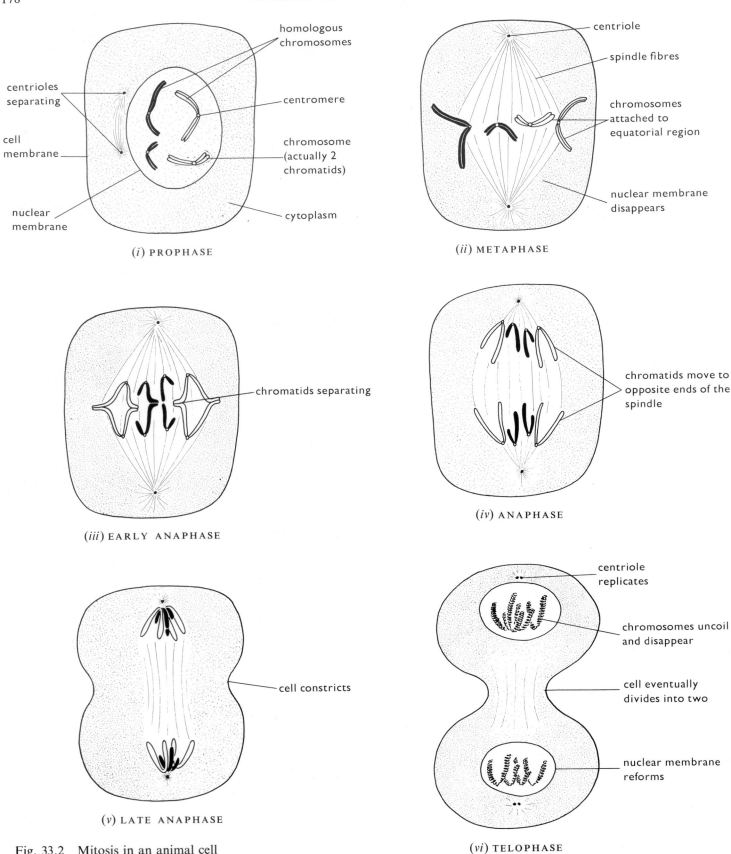

Fig. 33.2   Mitosis in an animal cell

Although the stages of mitosis are necessarily shown as static events, it must be emphasized that the process is a continuous one and the names "anaphase", "metaphase", etc., do not imply that the process of mitosis comes to a halt at this juncture. Moreover, the stages shown are not selected at regular intervals of time, e.g. in the embryonic cells of a particular grasshopper the timing at 38°C is as follows: **prophase** 100 min, **metaphase** 15 min, **anaphase** 10 min, **telophase** 60 min.

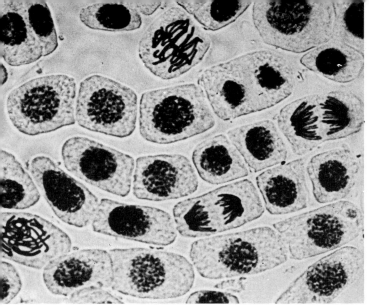

Plate 54. CELLS FROM A ROOT TIP SHOWING MITOSIS
(× 500)

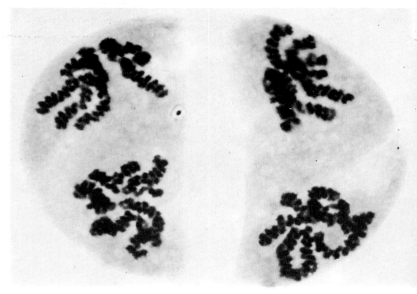

Plate 55. CHROMOSOMES OF *TRILLIUM ERECTUM* AT TELOPHASE OF MEIOSIS (p. 186), SHOWING COILING
(× 2000)

1. **Prophase.** The chromosomes become more pronounced (that is, they react more readily to stains and chemical fixatives). They shorten and thicken (Plate 56a), probably by coiling like a helical spring, but with the coils so close to each other that they are not visible at low magnifications (Fig. 33.3 and Plate 55). The nuclear membrane dissolves, leaving the chromosomes suspended in the cytoplasm, and at the same time the one or more *nucleoli* disappear.

2. **Metaphase.** In the cells of animals and some of the simpler plants there is a pair of minute bodies called the *centrioles* which lie just outside the nucleus. At this stage they move away from each other and migrate to opposite ends of the cell. From each centriole there radiate what appear to be cytoplasmic fibres which meet and join near the centre of the cell. This system of "fibres" makes a web-like structure called the *spindle* (Fig. 33.2ii) and the chromosomes become attached by their centromeres (Fig. 33.3) to the equatorial region of the spindle. (Most plant cells do not have centrioles but a spindle is formed nevertheless.) By this time it is apparent that each chromosome consists of two parallel strands, called *chromatids* (Plate 56b), joined in one particular region, the *centromere*. In forming two chromatids, the chromosome *replicates;* that is, it produces an exact copy of itself, but the two identical chromosomes remain in contact along their length. This

replication has occurred before prophase but is more evident during metaphase.

3. **Anaphase.** The two chromatids now separate at the centromere and begin to migrate in opposite directions towards either end of the spindle (Plate 56c). Experiments show that the spindle fibres play some part in separating the chromatids. The appearance is that of the chromatids first repelling each other at the centromere and then being pulled entirely apart by the shortening spindle fibres, although such a mechanism has not yet been verified.

4. **Telophase.** The chromatids, now chromosomes, collect together at the opposite ends of the spindle (Plate 56d) and become less distinct, probably by becoming uncoiled and therefore thinner. The one or more nucleoli reappear, and a nuclear membrane forms round each group of daughter chromosomes so that there are now two nuclei present in the cell. At this point in animal cells, the cytoplasm between the two nuclei constricts, and two cells are formed. Both may retain the ability to divide, or one or both may become specialized and lose their reproductive capacity. In plant cells, the cytoplasm does not constrict to form two new cells; instead, a new cell wall is formed across the cell in the region originally occupied by the equatorial plane of the spindle (Fig. 33.4 and Plate 56e).

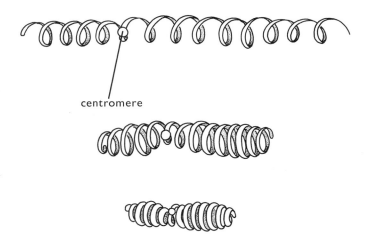

centromere

Fig. 33.3 Diagram illustrating how chromosomes appear to become thicker and shorter during prophase

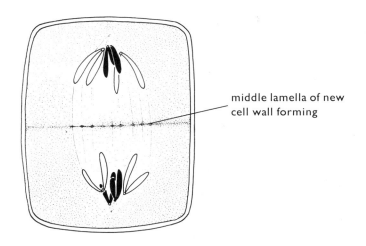

middle lamella of new cell wall forming

Fig. 33.4 Late anaphase in a plant cell showing how separation of daughter cells differs from animal cells

179

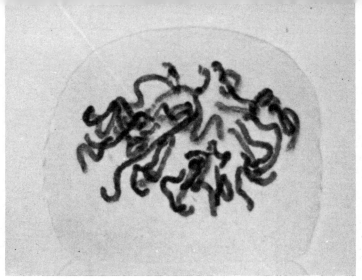

(a) PROPHASE
The chromosomes have become short and thick

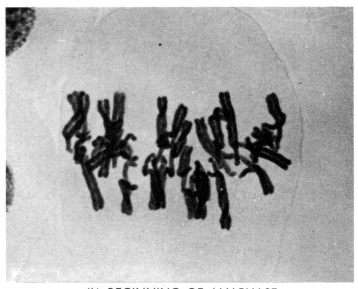

(b) BEGINNING OF ANAPHASE
Each chromosome is seen to consist of two chromatids which are attached to the equator of the spindle and are beginning to separate

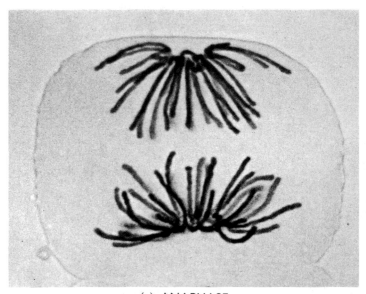

(c) ANAPHASE
The chromatids have completely separated. The spindle is not visible in this photograph

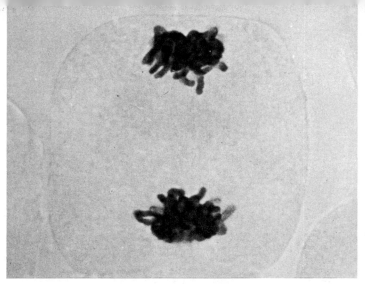

(d) TELOPHASE
The chromosomes are becoming less distinct

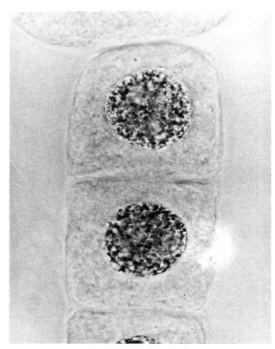

(e) THE END OF CELL DIVISION
The daughter nuclei are separated by a new cell wall

Plate 56.   STAGES IN MITOSIS (× 1800)

(Photomicrographs of cells from the root tip of Lilium regale *from McLeish and Snoad,* Looking at Chromosomes, *Macmillan, 1958)*

From a study of mitosis it seems very likely that the chromosomes are the site of the genetic instructions since they reproduce themselves when they form chromatids and the chromatids are shared equally between the cells by the events of mitosis. A further study of chromosomes provides more evidence that they carry genetic information.

Chromosomes

Chromosomes are so called because they take up certain basic stains very readily (*chromos* = colour, *soma* = body), but they can also be observed by phase contrast microscopy in the unstained nuclei of dividing, living cells. When the cell is not dividing, the chromosomes cannot be seen in the nucleus, even after staining. Nevertheless, it is thought that they persist as fine, invisible threads, isolated patches of which still respond to dyes and show up as flakes or granules of deeply staining material. The chromosomes consist of protein and a substance called *deoxyribonucleic acid* (DNA: *see* p. 184), but the exact relationship between these two components in forming the chromosomes is not known.

Counts of chromosomes show that there is a definite number in each cell of any one species of plant or animal, e.g. mouse 40, crayfish 200, rye 14, fruit fly (*Drosophila*) 8, and man 46 (*see* also Fig. 33.5). This confirms our expectation that the chromosomes determine the difference between one species and another. It can also be seen (Plate 58) that the chromosomes exist in pairs, although not actually joined together, each pair having a characteristic length and, during anaphase, a characteristic shape (Plate 56c) governed by the position of the centromere at which the chromatids are pulled apart; e.g. a V shape if the centromere is central, or a √ shape if it is close to one end. In other words, human cell nuclei contain 23 pairs of chromosomes, mouse cells 20 pairs and so on, one member of each pair having been derived from the male and one from the female parent. The members of each pair are called *homologous chromosomes*, and the number of chromosomes in the cell is the *diploid number*.

Although the constituent chemicals of the cytoplasm of a cell are constantly being broken down and rebuilt from fresh material, the chemicals of the chromosomes remain remarkably stable. Other investigations show that during cell division, no protoplasmic material is shared so exactly as that of the chromosomes in the nucleus. Such evidence points again to the chromosomes as the main source of the chemical information which determines that a cell should become like its parent cell, and that in their development, the cells of the organism will endow the animal or plant with all the characteristics of its species. Although the supporting evidence is very sketchily outlined here, the hereditary material must almost certainly lie on the chromosomes of the nucleus and be passed on to each daughter cell by the process of mitosis. In a similar way the nuclei of the gametes carry a set of chromosomes from the male and female parent, and these chromosomes determine that the zygote grows and develops to an animal or plant of the same species as the parents, reproducing to quite a minute degree individual characteristics of both parents.

(*World Health*)

Plate 57. STUDYING HUMAN CHROMOSOMES
A member of a team of scientists under Professor Jerôme Lejeune at the Institut de Progénèse, Paris, identifies and prepares pictures of human chromosomes

(*a*) *Man* [46]

(*b*) *Kangaroo* [12]

(*c*) *Domestic fowl* [36]

(*d*) *Drosophila* [8]

Fig. 33.5 Chromosomes of different species

(*From C. C. Hurst*, The Mechanism of Creative Evolution, *Cambridge University Press, 1933*)

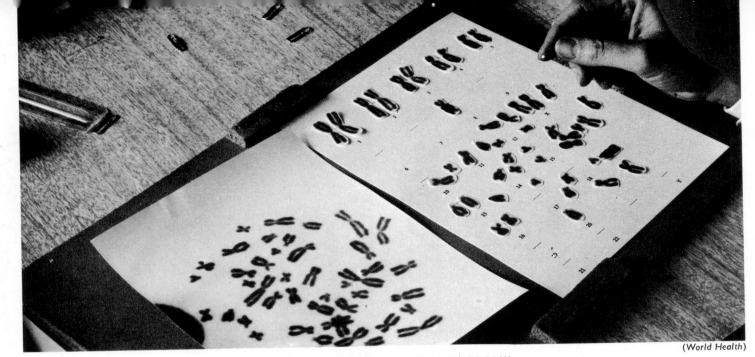

Plate 58.   PREPARING A "KARYOGRAM"
The chromosome silhouettes from the photomicrograph on the left are cut out and arranged in order on the right-hand chart

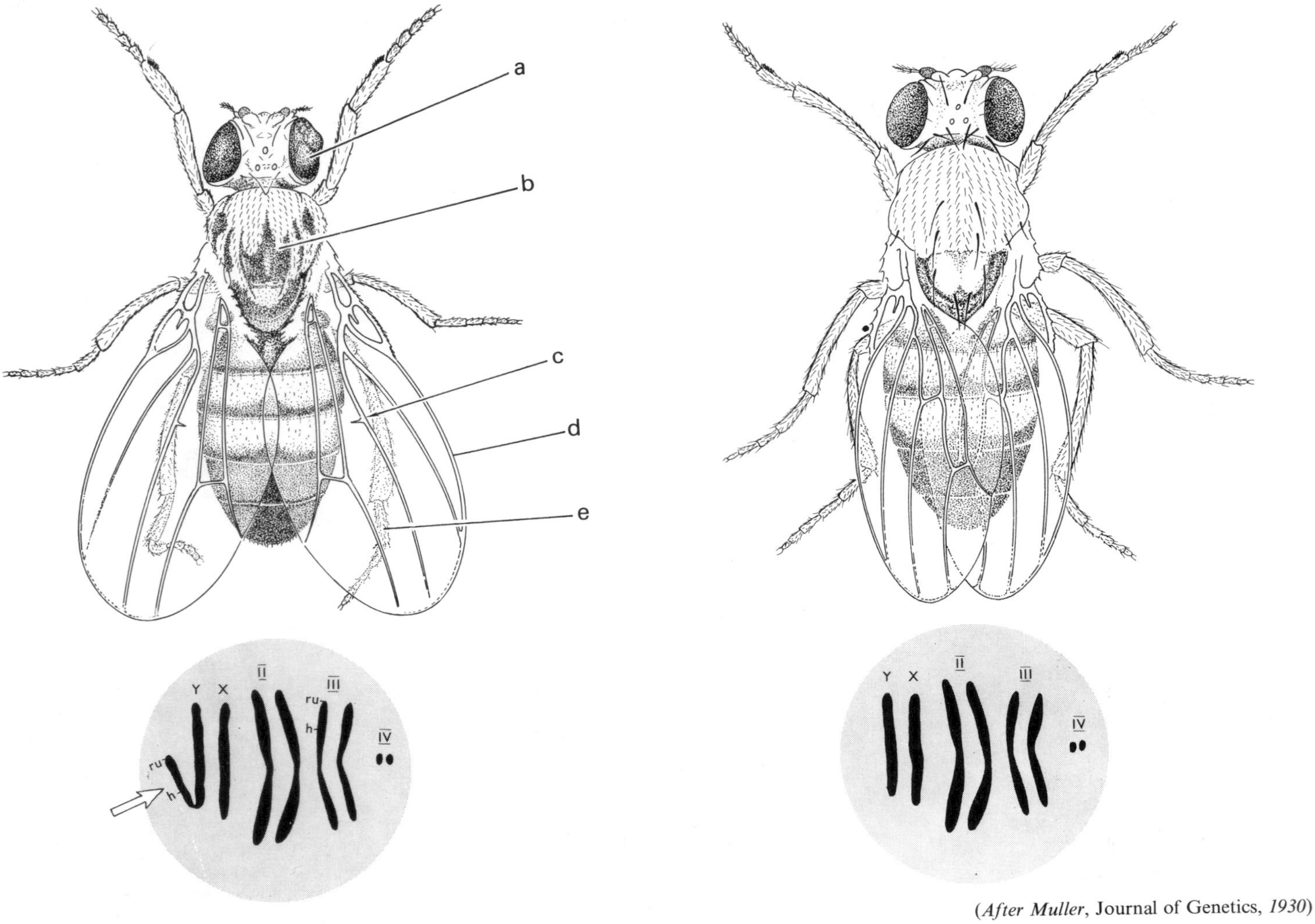

(World Health)

a

b

c

d

e

(After Muller, Journal of Genetics, 1930)

The cells of the fruit fly on the left have an extra segment of chromosome no. 3 which has become attached to the Y chromosome. As a result, this fly has (a) mis-shapen eyes, (b) dark patterned thorax, (c) imperfect cross veins, (d) broad wings, (e) incurved hind legs. The normal fly is shown on the right.

Fig. 33.6   Effects of a chromosome mutation in Drosophila

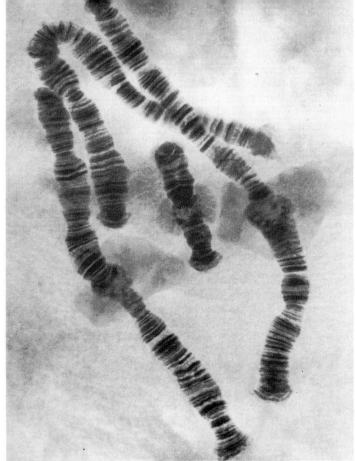

(*Courtesy of Professor Wolfgang Beermann, Max Planck Institute, Tübingen, from Sci. Amer., April 1964*)

Plate 59.   GIANT CHROMOSOMES
Four giant chromosomes from a cell in the salivary gland of the midge larva, *Chironomus tentans*, showing transverse banding. (× 600)

The fruit fly, *Drosophila melanogaster*, which has four pairs of chromosomes in its nuclei is, for various reasons, a suitable subject for study. By breeding many hundreds of flies through many generations, geneticists have become very familiar with the detailed anatomy of the fly and the appearance of its chromosomes. It has been observed on many occasions that some unexpected change in the external appearance of a fly is associated with a change in the chromosome pattern (*see* Fig. 33.6). This chromosome aberration must take place at an early stage in the development of the fly for it to affect so many parts of the body, or it may have occurred in one of the gametes from which the zygote was formed.

Cells from the salivary glands of Drosophila and other flies have very large chromosomes called giant chromosomes, on which bands can be seen (Plate 59). The size, shape and position of these bands is quite consistent and characteristic for any pair of chromosomes. If, due to some accident in replication, one or other of the bands is lost, there is a corresponding malformation in the adult fly (Fig. 33.7). Although the bands can be seen on only these rather unusual, giant chromosomes, it is thought that they represent the site of genes, or gene activity on all the chromosomes in the body.

Genes. A gene is a theoretical unit of inheritance, theoretical in the sense that the word was coined long before chromosome structure was investigated in detail or the DNA theory of

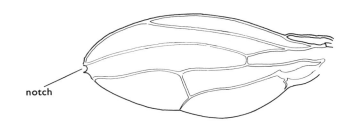

notch

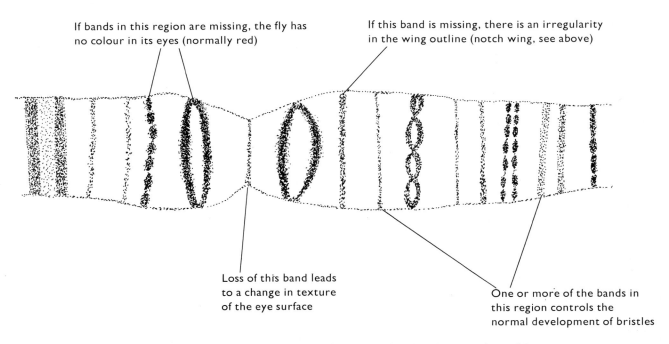

If bands in this region are missing, the fly has no colour in its eyes (normally red)

If this band is missing, there is an irregularity in the wing outline (notch wing, see above)

Loss of this band leads to a change in texture of the eye surface

One or more of the bands in this region controls the normal development of bristles

Fig. 33.7   Part of salivary gland chromosome of Drosophila showing location of four genes

(*From Curt Stern*, Principles of Human Genetics, *3rd edn., W. H. Freeman & Company, 1973. After Slizynska*, Genetics, *1938, 23*)

inheritance put forward. The gene is one of the "words" in the genetic "instructions" (see p. 177). For example one gene will specify whether the cat is to have black fur or white fur. Another gene will determine whether the fur is long or short. Today the gene is thought to consist of a sequence of bases in the DNA molecule of a chromosome.

Gene function

The picture that emerges from this and other evidence is that the genes which determine the characteristics of the organism are somehow arranged in line down the chromosome. These genes control the production of enzymes which in turn determine what functions go on in a cell, and eventually in the organs and entire organism. If anything happens to a gene it will affect the organism, e.g. in mice there is a gene which determines that the coat will be coloured. If this gene is missing, the mouse will be without pigment; it will be white with pink eyes. In this case, as in many others, more than one gene will in fact play a part in determining the characteristic.

The number of genes in man is not known but it could be about 1000 per chromosome. At mitosis, each chromosome, and therefore each of any of the genes it carries is exactly reproduced.

Two problems arise from this account. Since every cell in the body carries an identical set of chromosomes and since cell structure and function are determined by the genes on the chromosomes, why is not every cell of the body identical? Furthermore, what possible part can a gene for brown eyes play when it is in the nucleus of a cell lining the stomach wall? Briefly, when we follow the development of a particular cell, it seems that the way in which one of its genes will affect the cell depends not only on the gene itself but also on the physiology of the cell, which in turn is related to its particular position in the body. For example, the chemical environment in a certain cell in the scalp allows the gene for black hair to operate in a particular way. Just what the same gene does in another part of the body is not certain, its action may simply be suppressed, but it is known that most genes have more than one effect, and the characteristic by which they are recognized is not necessarily their most important function; e.g. the genes responsible for producing colour in the scales of one kind of onion also confer a resistance to fungus disease because they determine the presence of certain chemicals which act as a fungicide. The colour, however, is the more obvious characteristic. The gene in Drosophila which produces the effect of diminutive wings also reduces the expectation of life to half that of normal flies. The wing characteristic is the more immediately obvious effect but the effect on life span may be far more important and damaging to the species. The idea that the expression of a gene depends to some extent on the physiology of the cell and the situation in which it finds itself is illustrated by the experimental work with certain amphibian embryos. If a piece of tissue, which would normally become skin, is taken from the abdomen and grafted into a region overlying the developing eye, the graft will be incorporated into the eye as a lens. It has the same chromosomes and genes, but its new position has altered its fate. This effect is by no means true of all animals and is certainly not the case in insects in which the fate of individual cells seems to be determined at a very early stage in development and is not affected by moving the cells to a new situation.

How genes work

It was mentioned earlier (p. 181) that chromosomes consist of protein and a nucleic acid, deoxyribonucleic acid (DNA).

Although the precise relationship between the DNA and the protein is not known, the structure of DNA has been intensively studied. This chemical consists of long molecules coiled in a double helix. The strands of the helix are chains of sugars and phosphates, the sugar being a 5-carbon compound, deoxyribose. The two helices in a DNA strand are linked together by cross-bridges made by pairs of organic nitrogenous bases joined to the sugar molecules (Figs. 33.8 and 33.9). Although there are only four principal kinds of base in the DNA molecule, adenine, cytosine, thymine and guanine, it is thought that the sequence of these bases is the important factor in heredity, and that a gene may consist of a particular sequence of up to 1000 base pairs in a DNA molecule.

The different sequence of bases along the length of the DNA molecule seem to act like a code, instructing the cell to make certain proteins, the order of bases indicating the sequence of amino acids to be joined up in order to make the protein. For example, the sequence CAA (cytosine-adenine-adenine) specifies the amino acid valine; three thymines in a row, TTT, specify lysine, while AAT specifies leucine. So the sequence of bases CAA-TTT-AAT would direct the cell to link up the amino acids valine-lysine-leucine to make the appropriate peptide, and in a similar way proteins are formed.

Most of the proteins made are enzymes which direct the pattern of chemical activity in the cell. Thus DNA, by determining the kinds of enzyme formed in the cell, will control the cell's activities. This in turn will affect the nature of the cell, the organ of which it is a part and eventually the organism as a whole. A change in the sequence of bases in the DNA molecule will produce a different order of amino acids in the resulting protein, and hence a different and probably ineffective enzyme. This will usually act adversely on the metabolism of the cell.

A rat with coloured fur has a gene which controls the production of the enzyme tyrosinase. This enzyme converts tyrosine, a colourless amino acid, to melanin, a black pigment. An albino rat has no gene for tyrosinase production, and consequently no pigment is formed from the tyrosine in its body.

Normal humans have a gene which controls the production in the blood of an enzyme which accelerates the breakdown of a chemical, alcapton. Persons having no gene for the enzyme excrete in the urine unchanged alcapton which darkens on exposure to the air. This relatively harmless effect is associated with pigmentation in other parts of the body and, later, with arthritis. The condition is inherited as a recessive factor (p. 192). This is a rather peculiar example of the mechanism of inheritance, but if a gene controlled the production of an enzyme essential in a much earlier stage of a series of vital reactions, the absence of the gene could have devastating effects even to the extent of causing premature death. Conversely, since normal physiology is the result of hundreds of chemical changes catalysed by hundreds of enzymes, it is not surprising that characteristics such as intelligence, stature and activity come under the influence of many genes.

Mutations

A mutation is a spontaneous change in a gene or a chromosome which may produce an alteration in the characteristic under its control. Fig. 33.6 shows a chromosome mutation. A mutation in a single cell may not be very important in heredity but if the cell is a gamete mother cell, a gamete or a zygote, the entire organism arising from this cell may be affected. Since the mutant form of the gene is inherited in the usual way, the mutation may persist in subsequent generations.

On the whole, genes are stable structures because DNA is a stable chemical, but once in a hundred thousand replications or more a gene may mutate. The frequency with which certain genes mutate has been estimated for many abnormalities in man and in experimental animals. Most mutations that produce an observable effect seem to be harmful if not actually lethal. This is not surprising, since any change in a well- but delicately-balanced organism is likely to upset its physiology. Most mutations, however, are recessive* and so may not find expression in the heterozygous* form.

In humans, a form of dwarfism arises as a result of a dominant mutation having a frequency of about 1 in 20,000. A fairly frequent form of mental deficiency known as Down's syndrome results from a chromosome mutation in which the ovum carries an extra chromosome so that the child has 47 chromosomes in his cells instead of 46.

Radiation and mutations. The cause of mutation is not known, but exposure to X-radiation, gamma-radiation, ultra-violet light, etc., is known to cause an increase in the mutation rate in experimental animals such as fruit flies and mice. The artificially-induced mutations are the same as those which occur naturally, but the frequency with which they occur is greatly increased.

There is a fairly constant background of radiation on the Earth's surface as a result of cosmic rays. Individuals also receive radiation from X-rays used in medicine, television tubes and luminous watch dials. Workers in atomic power stations and other people handling radioactive materials in industry or research may receive additional radiation. The radioactive fall-out from atomic explosions has increased the background radiation.

It is of obvious importance to assess the effect of any increase in radiation on the health of individuals and, as a result of mutations in their reproductive cells, the health of their children.

There is, so far, insufficient information to determine the correlation between the radiation dose and the mutation rate in man. The maximum safe dose in respect of direct effects on the individual, e.g. leukaemia, is still a matter of controversy. Nevertheless it is probably safe to say that any increase in the mutation rate is likely to have harmful effects on the population. Consequently, the exposure of individuals to the hazards of radiation is limited, though somewhat arbitrarily, by law.

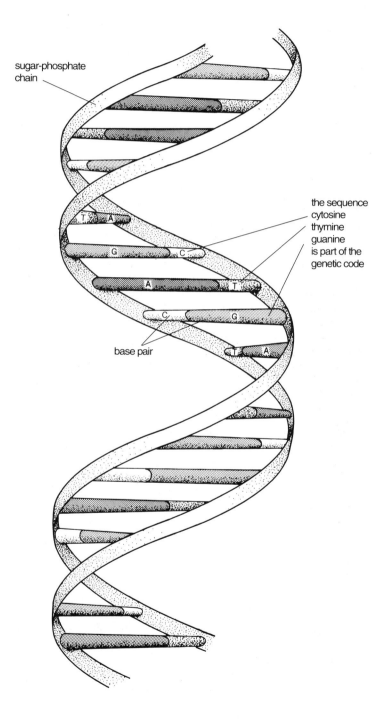

Fig. 33.9   Model of part of a DNA molecule

Fig. 33.8   Part of a DNA molecule

($\bigcirc$ = *deoxyribose*)

* See p. 192.

Variation

The exact replication of chromosomes and genes and their equal distribution between cells at mitosis produces conformity; the organism breeds true to type, e.g. a sheep reproduces sheep and not goats or antelopes. Nevertheless, the offspring will differ in many respects from its brothers and sisters and from its parents. It is possible for two black mice to have some white babies as well as black ones. Sometimes variations arise from gene or chromosome mutation but these are infrequent and usually harmful. The variations of, for example, blood groups result from rearrangement of parental genes and chromosomes in the zygote. The rearrangement is the direct result of the way in which the chromosomes separate at the cell division which leads to gamete formation. This sequence of chromosome separation is called meiosis.

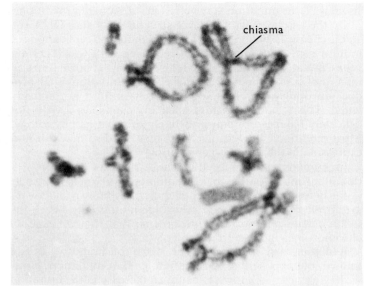

(From colour slide set, Meiosis in Chorthippus brunneus *published by Harris Biological Supplies Ltd)*

Plate 60.   MEIOSIS IN GRASSHOPPER TESTIS
(late prophase) (× 2000)

Meiosis (Fig. 33.10)

Cells in the reproductive organs, which are going to form gametes, e.g. sperms and ova, undergo a series of mitotic divisions resulting, in the case of male gametes, in a vast increase of numbers. The final divisions, however, which give rise to mature gametes are not mitotic. Instead of producing cells with 46 chromosomes in man. they form gametes with only 23 chromosomes. When, at fertilization, there is a fusion of the two gametes, the resulting zygote contains the diploid number of 46 chromosomes, and this number is present in all the cells of the offspring which develop from the zygote. The halving of the chromosome number which occurs at gamete formation ultimately maintains the diploid number of chromosomes characteristic of the species. If gametes were produced by mitosis, a human egg and sperm would each contain 46 chromosomes and when they fused at fertilization would give rise to a zygote with 92 chromosomes. The gametes from the resulting organism would in turn give rise to offspring with 184 chromosomes and so on.

1. **Prophase.** In meiosis, the chromosomes appear in the nucleus in much the same way as described for mitosis, but although it is reasonably certain that two chromatids are present in each chromosome, the chromosomes still appear to be single threads. Another difference from mitosis seen at this stage is the failure of the chromosomes to shorten by coiling.

In complete contrast to mitosis the homologous chromosomes now appear to *attract* each other and come to lie alongside so that all parts of the two chromosomes correspond exactly. The pairs of chromosomes so formed are called *bivalents*, e.g. a cell with a normal complement of six chromosomes would have, at this stage, three bivalents.

In this paired state the chromosomes shorten and thicken by coiling, and now each chromosome is seen to consist of two chromatids. As soon as this occurs, however, the pairs of chromatids seem to repel each other and move apart, except at certain regions called *chiasmata* (Plate 60). In these regions, the chromatids appear to have broken and joined again but to a different chromatid. The significance of this exchange of sections of chromatids, or "crossing over", is discussed on p. 188. All these changes occur during prophase while the nuclear membrane is still intact.

2. **Metaphase.** The nuclear membrane disappears, a spindle is formed and the bivalents approach the equatorial region.

3. **Anaphase.** The paired chromatids of each bivalent now continue the separation that began in prophase and move to

opposite ends of the spindle in a manner superficially similar to that of the chromatids in mitosis. The outcome is that only half the total number of paired chromatids reaches either end of the spindle. Thus, although there may originally have been six chromosomes in the nucleus, there are now only three paired chromatids at each end of the spindle.

4. **Second meiotic division.** A nuclear membrane does not usually form round the paired chromatids at this stage. Instead two new spindles form at right angles to the first one and the chromatids of each pair separate and become chromosomes.

5. **Telophase.** The four groups of chromosomes are now enclosed in nuclear membranes so forming four nuclei, each containing half the original number of chromosomes (the *monoploid* or *haploid* number). Finally, the cytoplasm divides to separate the nuclei, giving rise, in the case of males at least, to four gametes. In sperm formation (*spermatogenesis*) in most animals, the four cells will develop "tails" to become sperms.

Since it gives rise to cells containing half the diploid number of chromosomes, meiosis is sometimes called the *reduction division*.

Formation of ova: oogenesis. During the formation of ova the cytoplasm is not shared equally. After the first division of meiosis, one of the daughter nuclei receives the bulk of the cytoplasm and the other nucleus is separated off with only a vestige of cytoplasm to form the first *polar body*, which, although it may undergo the next stage of its meiotic division, cannot function as an ovum and subsequently degenerates.

In a similar way, the next meiotic division of the remaining egg nucleus produces a second polar body and a mature ovum. In many vertebrates, the first polar body is not formed until after the potential ovum is released from the ovary, and the second polar body, until after the penetration of the sperm in fertilization. In man, when a sperm bearing 23 chromosomes fuses with a 23-chromosome ovum, a 46-chromosome zygote is formed.

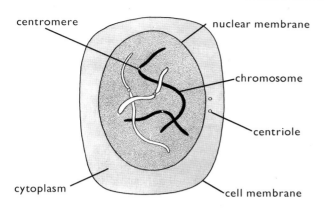

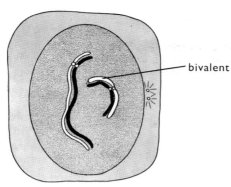

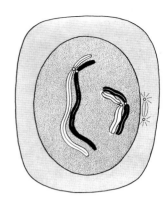

Prophase

(*a*) The diploid number of chromosomes appear

(*b*) Homologous chromosomes pair with each other, shorten and thicken

(*c*) Replication has occurred and the chromatids become visible

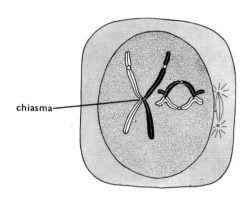

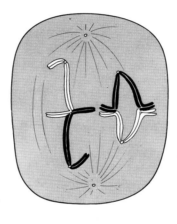

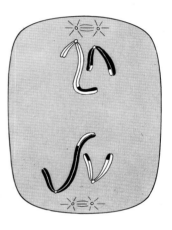

(*d*) Homologous chromosomes move apart except at the chiasmata where the chromatids have exchanged portions

Anaphase

(*e*) A spindle forms and homologous chromosomes move to opposite ends taking the exchanged portions with them

(*f*) Homologous chromosomes separated but not enclosed in nuclear membranes

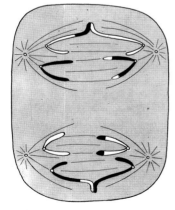

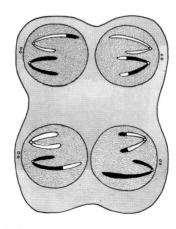

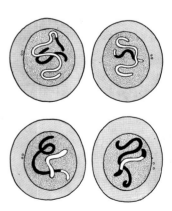

Second meiotic division

(*g*) Spindles form at right angles to the first one and the chromatids separate

Telophase

(*h*) Four nuclei appear, each enclosing the haploid number of chromosomes

(*i*) Cytoplasm divides to form four gametes

Fig. 33.10   Meiosis in a gamete-forming cell

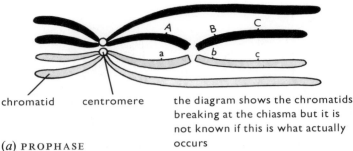

chromatid   centromere   the diagram shows the chromatids
                            breaking at the chiasma but it is
                            not known if this is what actually
                            occurs

(a) PROPHASE
Homologous chromosomes have paired up

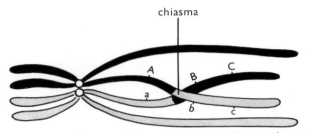

(b) PROPHASE   the terminal portions of the adjacent chromatids
                  have become attached to the opposite chromatid

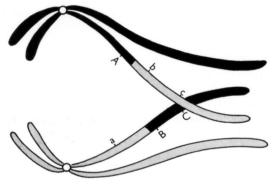

(c) METAPHASE
*The pairs of chromatids seem to repel each other except
at the chiasma*

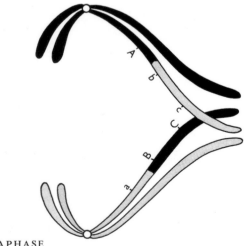

(d) ANAPHASE
*The chromosomes separate, but as a result of crossing over,
the genes A, B, C and a, b, c on the 'inner' chromatids are
rearranged*

Fig. 33.11   Crossing over

Linkage and crossing over. During that early stage of meiosis when homologous chromosomes pair up, the maternal and paternal chromosomes exchange portions as mentioned on p. 186 and shown in Fig. 33.11. This leads to variability in the gene combinations in the gametes. In the absence of crossing over, the maternal genes A-B-C on the same chromosome would always appear together no matter how the chromosomes were assorted in meiosis. Similarly the paternal genes a-b-c would always remain together. For example, in Drosophila, since the genes for black body, purple eyes and vestigial wings occur on the same chromosome, one might expect that a black-bodied Drosophila would always have purple eyes and vestigial wings. Crossing over between chromatids, however, gives the possibility of breaking these *linkage groups* as they are called, so that new combinations, ABc, Abc, aBC, abC, aBc, AbC, could arise in the gametes, for example black body with red eyes and normal wings, or black body with purple eyes and normal wings.

Fertilization (Fig. 33.12)

The cytoplasm of the sperm fuses with that of the ovum and the male nucleus passes into the ovum, coming to lie alongside the egg nucleus: the zygote is formed, but in many cases there is no fusion of nuclear material at this stage. Each nucleus simultaneously undergoes a mitosis with the axes of the spindles parallel to each other, but at the telophase stage the adjacent chromatids, originally from different parents, become enclosed in the same nuclear membrane, thus restoring the diploid number of chromosomes. These events are followed by the first cleavage, the zygote dividing into two cells. Subsequent mitotic division produces a multicellular organism with the diploid number of chromosomes in all its cells.

Recombination of genes in the zygote. In man there are about 200 million sperms in a single ejaculation and about 300 to 400 eggs produced in a reproductive lifetime. The eggs will have a genetic content differing from the sperms (e.g. a white European wife with curly red hair; husband with straight black hair). When the chromosomes of the sperm and egg combine, the zygote may contain genes for red, black, curly and straight hair. The genes for curly and black are dominant (p. 192) to those for straight and red, so that although the child may carry all 4 genes, his hair will be curly and black—a new combination of characters not represented in either parent. When this child grows up and his own gametes are formed, he could produce sperms with 4 alternative combinations of these genes; namely, red and straight, black and straight, red and curly, black and curly.

Determination of sex. In humans, one pair of the smallest chromosomes is known to determine sex. In the female, these two chromosomes are entirely homologous and are called the *X chromosomes*, while in the male, one is smaller and is called the *Y chromosome* (Fig. 33.5b). Femaleness normally results from the possession of two X chromosomes and maleness from possession of an X and a Y chromosome. At meiosis, the sex chromosomes are separated in the same way as the others (Fig. 33.13), so that all the female gametes will contain an X chromosome, but half the male gametes will contain an X and half will contain a Y chromosome. If a Y-bearing sperm fertilizes an ovum, the zygote will be XY and give rise to a boy. Fertilization of an ovum by an X-bearing sperm gives an XX zygote which develops to a girl. There should be an equal chance of X or Y sperm meeting an ovum, and therefore equal numbers of boy and girl babies should be born. In fact,

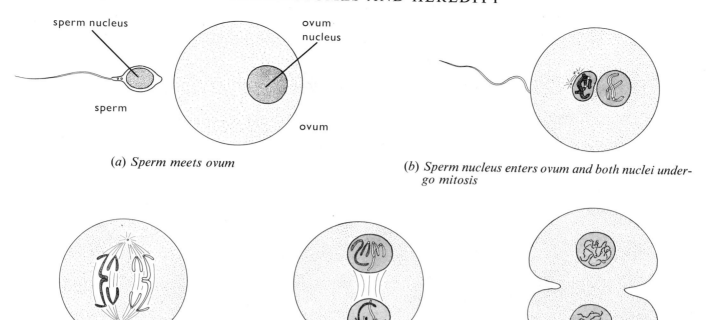

(a) *Sperm meets ovum*

(b) *Sperm nucleus enters ovum and both nuclei undergo mitosis*

(c) *The spindles are parallel but separate*

(d) *The chromatids at each end of the spindle are enclosed in a common nuclear membrane*

(e) *The zygote divides to form two cells*

Fig. 33.12   Fertilization (*polar bodies not shown*)

slightly more boys than girls are born in most parts of the world. The reason for this is not clear, but it also happens that the mortality rate for boy babies and men is slightly higher than for girl babies and women, which tends to restore the balance.

Although the X and Y chromosomes determine sex, it does not necessarily follow that male and female characteristics are determined by genes found only on the sex chromosomes. In man, genes for male and female characters may be scattered fairly evenly throughout all the chromosomes, but the presence of the Y chromosome in an XY zygote may tip the balance in favour of maleness. Femaleness results from the absence of the Y chromosome but this is not the case in all the animals studied; e.g. it is true for the mouse but not for Drosophila.

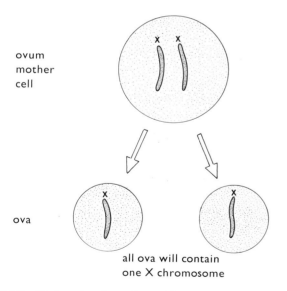

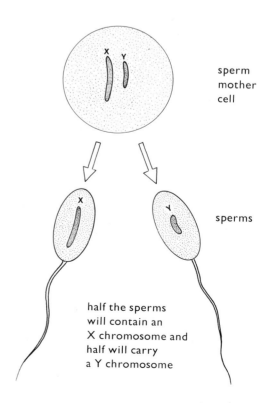

Fig. 33.13   Determination of sex (*diagrammatic only*)

Note (a) Only the X and Y chromosomes are shown.
   (b) The Y chromosome is not smaller than the X in all animals.
   (c) Details of meiosis have been omitted.
   (d) Theoretically, four gametes would be produced, but two are sufficient here to show the distribution of X and Y chromosomes.

Sex linkage. Certain genes which occur on the X chromosome are more likely to affect a male than a female. The gene or genes for a certain form of colour blindness in man are carried on the X chromosome. Normal vision is dominant (p. 192) to colour blindness so that if a colour-blind woman, who must be homozygous (p. 192) for the character, marries a normal man, all their sons but none of their daughters will be colour blind. This can be explained by the fact that the Y chromosome is homologous with only a small section of the X chromosome and the non-homologous part of the X chromosome carries genes which are not represented on Y. It is assumed that the Y chromosome plays no part in the determination of colour vision. Fig. 33.14 shows how this type of sex linkage produces its effect.

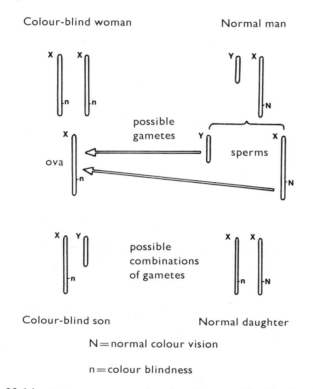

Fig. 33.14 SEX LINKAGE, showing the possible distribution of X and Y chromosomes between the gametes and the chances of combination in the zygotes

The normal daughter is heterozygous (*see* p. 192) for colour blindness and is therefore a "carrier" for the recessive gene. If she marries a normal man the possible combinations of genes in the children are shown by:

Parents:	XN Xn carrier woman		XN Y normal man	
Gametes:	XN	Xn	XN	Y
Possible combinations of gametes:	XN XN normal girl	Xn XN girl carrier	XN Y normal boy	Xn Y colour-blind boy

The theoretical expectations are that all the girls will be normal but half of them will be carriers, half the boys will be normal and half of them colour blind. The types of children expected from the marriage between a woman carrier and a colour-blind man, or a normal woman and a colour-blind man can be worked out in a similar way.

Other X-linked factors are *haemophilia* and brown enamel on the teeth. Haemophilia causes a delay in the clotting time of the blood. Although there are two kinds of sex-linked haemophilia, at least three other clotting disorders are known which are controlled by genes not on the sex chromosomes.

Sexual characteristics such as bass voice, beard and muscular physique in males, mammary glands and wide pelvis in females, are not the result of sex-linked genes but the different expressions of the same genes present in both sexes. Both sexes carry genes controlling the growth of hair, mammary glands and penis but in the physiological environment of maleness or femaleness they have different effects, with the result that e.g. the mammary glands in males are small and functionless; the penis in females is represented by only a small organ, the *clitoris*.

Only a few rare abnormalities are thought to be linked to the Y-chromosome and even these are now open to doubt.

PRACTICAL WORK

1. *Squash preparation of chromosomes using acetic orcein.*
   Material. *Allium cepa* (onion) root tips. Support onions over beakers or jars of water using tooth-picks as shown in Fig. 33.15. Keep the onions in darkness for several days until the roots growing into the water are 2–3 cm long. Cut off about 5 mm of the root tips, place them in a watch glass and

   (*a*) cover them with 9 drops acetic orcein and 1 drop molar hydrochloric acid;

   (*b*) heat the watch glass gently over a very small Bunsen flame till steam rises from the stain, but do not boil;

   (*c*) leave the watch glass covered for at least five minutes;

   (*d*) place one of the root tips on a clean slide, cover with 45 per cent acetic (ethanoic) acid and cut away all but the terminal 1 mm;

   (*e*) cover this root tip with a clean cover-slip and make a squash preparation as described below.

   Making the squash preparation. Squash the softened, stained root tips by lightly tapping on the cover-slip with a pencil: hold the pencil vertically and let it slip through the fingers to strike the cover-slip. The root tip will spread out as a pink mass on the slide; the cells will separate and the nuclei, many of them with chromosomes in various stages of mitosis (because the root tip is a region of rapid cell division) can be seen under the high power of the microscope ($\times 400$).

   Preparation of reagents
   (i) **Acetic orcein.** 2 g orcein; 100 cm³ glacial acetic (ethanoic) acid. Dilute a small portion with an equal volume distilled water just before use.
   (ii) **Molar hydrochloric acid** (i.e. one mole of HCl per litre). Make up 87·3 cm³ of concentrated acid to 1 litre by adding distilled water.
   (iii) **Glycerol albumen.** Shake 50 cm³ egg white with a few drops of dilute acetic acid; add 50 cm³ glycerol and 1 g sodium salicylate. Filter.

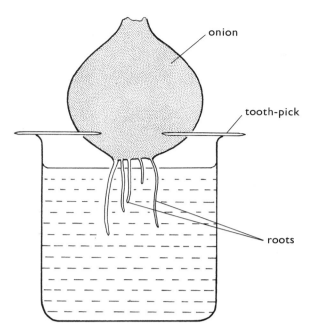

Fig. 33.15   Method of supporting an onion to promote growth of roots

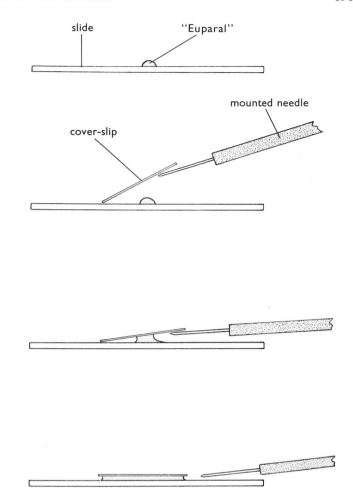

Fig. 33.17   Method of applying cover-slip in a permanent preparation

To make a permanent preparation. The slide prepared as above will last for weeks if the cover-slip is "ringed" with a suitable material, e.g. melted wax or nail varnish, to prevent evaporation of the liquid, but a more permanent slide can be made by using, at stage (*d*) above, a slide smeared with egg albumen. Place a small drop of glycerol albumen (*see* (iii) above) on the slide and then smear it over with the finger, as if trying to wipe it all off, thus leaving a very thin film. Pass the slide through a Bunsen flame until it begins to "smoke" but not to the point of charring. Make the squash preparation as before and then invert the slide in a shallow dish of 10 per cent ethanoic acid (Fig. 33.16) until the cover-slip falls off, leaving the squashed root tip adhering to the slide. Dip the slide in 80 per cent alcohol and then into "Ethex" (ethylene glycol monoethyl ether) to dehydrate it for 10–30 minutes.

Finally, mount the preparation by lowering a cover-slip over a drop of Euparal covering the root cells (Fig. 33.17).

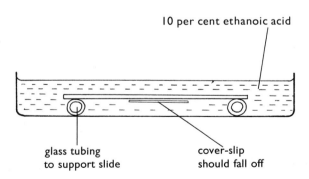

Fig. 33.16   Floating-off the cover-slip

QUESTIONS

1. Sometimes, at meiosis, the bivalent chromosomes fail to separate properly with the result that the gamete so formed contains the diploid number of chromosomes. If such a diploid sperm were to fertilize a normal monoploid ovum, (*a*) what effect would you expect this to have on the zygote and offspring and (*b*) supposing the zygote grew into a normal individual, what might happen when the individual produced gametes by meiosis?

2. A horse and a donkey are related closely enough to be able to reproduce when mated together. The offspring from this mating is a mule and though healthy in all other respects is sterile. Suggest an explanation, to do with chromosomes and meiosis, for this phenomenon.

3. It is possible for a cross between a short-winged, grey-bodied Drosophila and a normal-winged, black-bodied Drosophila, to produce some short-winged, black-bodied offspring. Explain how this could happen (*a*) if the genes for body colour and wing size are on different chromosomes and (*b*) if these genes are on the same chromosome.

34 | Heredity and Genetics

FROM its parents an individual inherits the characteristics of the species, e.g. man inherits highly developed cerebral hemispheres, vocal cords and the nervous co-ordination necessary for speech, a characteristic arrangement of the teeth and the ability to stand upright with all its attendant skeletal features. In addition, he inherits certain characteristics peculiar to his parents and not common to the species as a whole, e.g. hair and eye colour, blood group and facial appearance. The study of the method of inheritance of these "characters" is called genetics.

In sexual reproduction a new individual is derived only from the gametes of its parents. The hereditary information must therefore be contained in the gametes. For many reasons, this information is thought to be present in the nucleus of the gamete and located on the chromosomes (*see* pp. 177, 181 and 183).

Genes and inheritance

The term gene was originally applied to purely theoretical units or particles in the nucleus. These particles, in conjunction with the environment, were thought to determine the presence or absence of a particular characteristic. On p. 184 it was suggested that the genes may correspond to regions on the chromosomes and may consist of a large group of organic bases linked in a particular sequence in the chromosome.

In some cases, the presence of a single gene may determine the appearance of one characteristic, as in the eye colour of Drosophila (p. 183), but most human characteristics are controlled by more than one gene. This *multifactorial* inheritance and the impossibility with humans of breeding experiments, make it difficult to collect and present simple, clear-cut genetical information about man. In order to provide some clear ideas about heredity, simple cases amongst other animals will first be considered.

Single-factor inheritance. If a pure-breeding i.e. homozygous (*see* below) black mouse is mated with a pure-breeding brown mouse, the offspring will not be intermediate in colour i.e. dark brown or some combination of brown and black, but will all be black. The gene for black fur is said to be *dominant* to that for brown fur because, although each of the baby mice, being the product of fusion of sperm and egg, must carry genes for both blackness and brownness, only that for blackness is expressed in the visible characteristics of the animal. The gene for brown fur is said to be *recessive*. The black babies are called the first filial or F_1 *generation*. If, when they are mature, these F_1 black mice are mated amongst themselves, their offspring, the F_2 *generation* will include both black and brown mice and if the total number for all the F_2 families are added up, the ratio of black to brown babies will be approximately 3 to 1. It must not be assumed, however, that if two black F_1 mice have 4 babies, 3 will be black and one brown. In a mating which produced, say, 8 babies, it would not be at all unusual to find all black, or 5

black to 3 brown etc. The ratio 3:1 appears only when large numbers of individuals are considered.

The appearance of brown fur in the second generation is proof of the fact that the F_1 black mice carried the recessive gene for brown fur even though it did not find expression in their observable features.

In explanation, it will be assumed that a pure-breeding black mouse carries, on homologous chromosomes (*see* p. 181), a pair of genes controlling the production of black pigment. The genes are represented in subsequent diagrams (Fig. 34.1 *a* and *b*) by the letters **BB**, the capital letters signifying dominance.

In the same position on the corresponding chromosomes in brown mice are carried the genes bb for brownness. The genes B and b are called *allelomorphic genes* or *alleles*. During the formation of gametes the process of meiosis (p. 186) will separate the homologous chromosomes, so that the gametes will contain only one allele from each pair. All the sperms from the pure-breeding black parent will carry the **B** allele and all the eggs from the brown parent will carry the **b** allele. When the gametes fuse, the zygotes will contain both alleles B and b but since B is dominant to b, only the former allele is expressed, i.e. the offspring will all be black.

When, later on, these black F_1 mice produce gametes, the process of meiosis will separate the chromosomes carrying the B and b alleles (*see* Fig.34.1*b*) so that half the sperms of the male parent will carry B and half will carry b. Similarly, half the ova from the female will contain B and half b. At fertilization there are equal chances that a B-carrying sperm will fuse with either an egg carrying the B allele or an egg with the b allele so producing either a BB or a Bb zygote. Similarly there are equal chances of a b-carrying sperm fusing with either a B- or a b-carrying ovum to give bB or bb zygotes.

This results in the theoretical expectation of finding, in every four F_2 offspring, one pure-breeding black mouse BB, one pure-breeding brown mouse bb, and two "impure" black mice Bb.

The separation at meiosis of the alleles **B** and b into different gametes is called *segregation*. The pure-breeding black (BB) and brown (bb) mice are called *homozygous* for coat colour and the "impure" black mice (Bb) are called *heterozygous*. The heterozygous mice will not breed true i.e. if mated with each other their litters are likely to include some brown mice. The homozygous BB mice mated together can produce only black offspring and the bb homozygotes only brown offspring.

Genotype and phenotype. The BB mice and Bb mice will be indistinguishable in their appearance i.e. they will both have black fur and they are thus said to be the same *phenotypes*, in other words they are identical in appearance for a particular characteristic, in this case blackness. Their genetic constitutions, or *genotypes*, however, are different, namely BB and Bb. In short, the black phenotypes have different genotypes.

To distinguish between the black phenotypes, the usual practice is to do a further breeding experiment called a *back-cross*.

SINGLE-FACTOR INHERITANCE

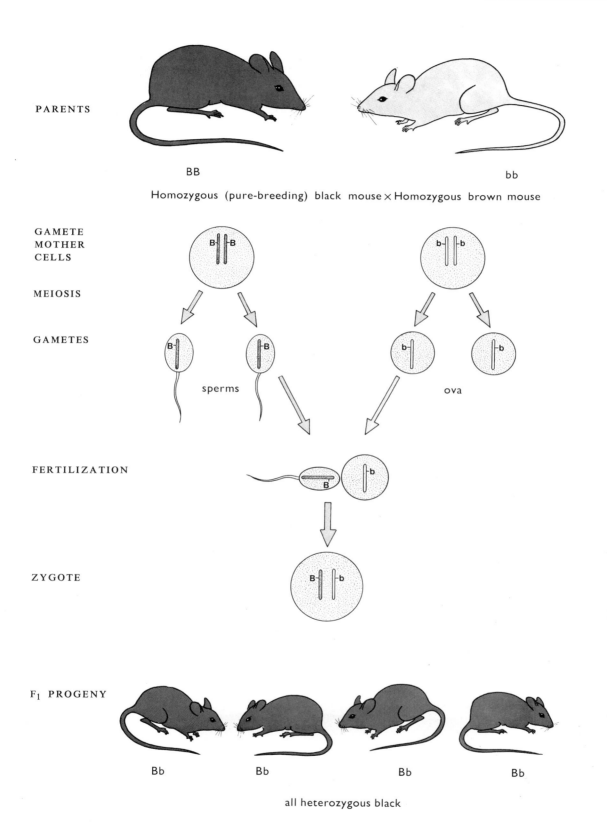

PARENTS

BB   bb

Homozygous (pure-breeding) black mouse × Homozygous brown mouse

GAMETE
MOTHER
CELLS

MEIOSIS

GAMETES

sperms   ova

FERTILIZATION

ZYGOTE

F_1 PROGENY

Bb   Bb   Bb   Bb

all heterozygous black

Fig. 34.1(a) Inheritance of a single factor for coat colour in mice

194

SINGLE-FACTOR INHERITANCE

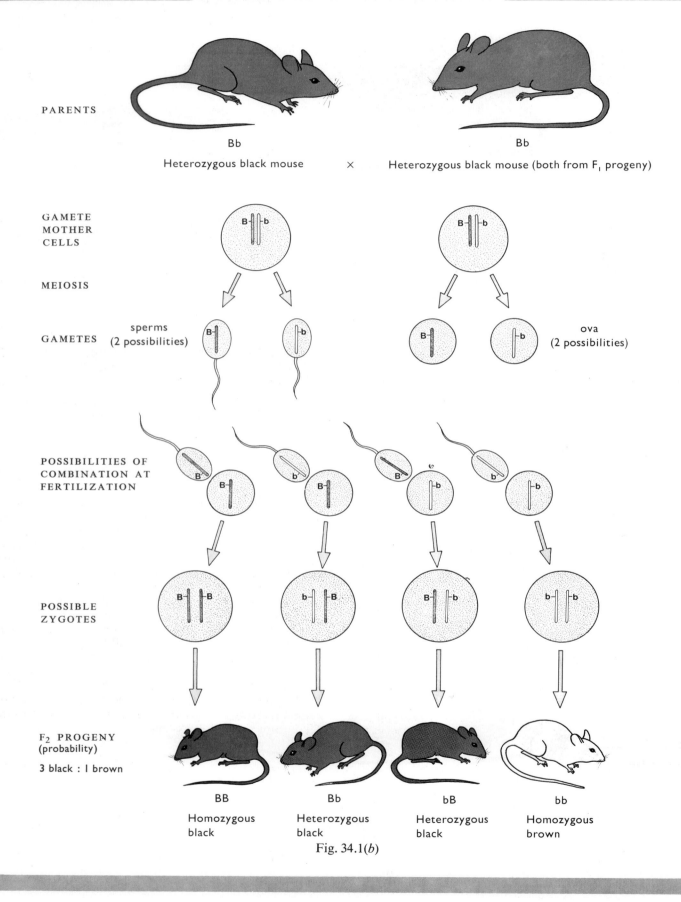

PARENTS

Bb — Heterozygous black mouse × Bb — Heterozygous black mouse (both from F₁ progeny)

GAMETE MOTHER CELLS

MEIOSIS

GAMETES — sperms (2 possibilities) / ova (2 possibilities)

POSSIBILITIES OF COMBINATION AT FERTILIZATION

POSSIBLE ZYGOTES

F₂ PROGENY (probability)
3 black : 1 brown

BB — Homozygous black

Bb — Heterozygous black

bB — Heterozygous black

bb — Homozygous brown

Fig. 34.1(b)

The back-cross. To discover their genotypes, the black F$_2$ phenotypes are each mated with mice of the same genotype as their brown grandparent i.e. the homozygous recessive, bb. Half the gametes from the heterozygous black mice Bb will carry the B gene and half will carry the b gene. The gametes from the homozygous black mouse, BB, will all carry the B gene. Similarly, the gametes of the homozygous recessive brown mouse will all carry the b gene. Thus, when the black parent is heterozygous, one would expect the back-cross to yield approximately equal numbers of black and brown babies in the litters but if the black parent was homozygous, the babies must all be black since they receive the dominant gene for blackness, B, from this parent (Fig. 34.2).

Codominance. If a certain breed of red cows are mated with white bulls the coats of the calves carry both red and white hairs, giving a colour called *red roan*. Neither the red nor the white allele is dominant.

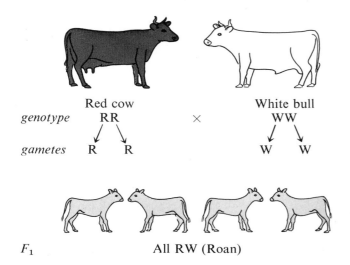

genotype   Red cow   White bull
                RR   ×   WW

gametes   R   R   W   W

F$_1$ All RW (Roan)

Red cows and bulls when mated together will breed true, i.e. all their offspring will have red coats. White cows and bulls, similarly, are homozygous and will breed true. The F$_1$ roan cattle, however, are heterozygous and will not breed true; their progeny will include red calves and white calves as well as roans.

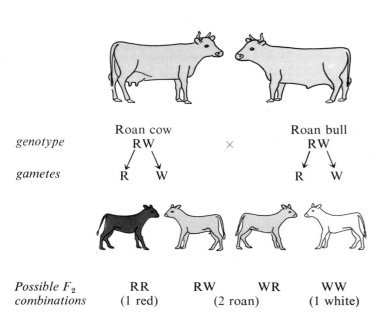

genotype   Roan cow   Roan bull
                RW   ×   RW

gametes   R   W   R   W

Possible F$_2$ combinations	RR (1 red)	RW	WR (2 roan)	WW (1 white)

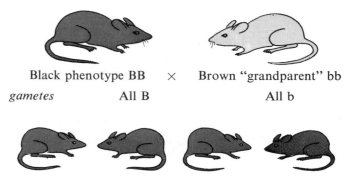

Black phenotype BB   ×   Brown "grandparent" bb
gametes   All B   All b

Offspring will all be Bb (black phenotypes)

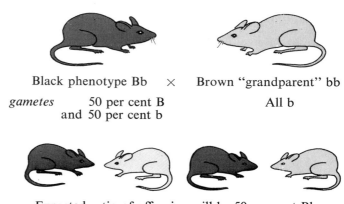

Black phenotype Bb   ×   Brown "grandparent" bb
gametes   50 per cent B   All b
     and 50 per cent b

Expected ratio of offspring will be 50 per cent Bb (black) and 50 per cent bb (brown)

Fig. 34.2   The back-cross

The inheritance of the AB blood group in humans is an example of codominance. According to whether their blood will mix without clotting during a transfusion, people are classified into four major blood groups, **A**, **B**, **AB**, and **O**. The blood group is controlled by any two of three alleles, **I^A**, **I^B** and **i**, acting at the corresponding site on homologous chromosomes.

A person will inherit two of these alleles, one from each parent. Allele **i** is recessive to both **I^A** and **I^B**, but **I^A** and **I^B** are codominant, i.e. if a person inherits **I^A** from one parent and **I^B** from the other, he or she will be group **AB** because neither allele is dominant to the other. It follows that group **O** people must have the genotype **ii**, while group **A** persons could be **I^{A}I^A** or **I^{A}i**. Group **B** individuals could be **I^{B}I^B** or **I^{B}i**. The following example shows the possible blood groups of children born to a group **A** man and a group **B** woman, both of whom are heterozygous.

Phenotype	group **A**		group **B**	
Genotype	**I^{A}i**		**I^{B}i**	
Gametes	**I^A** and **i**		**I^B** and **i**	
F$_1$ Genotype	**I^{A}I^B**	**I^{A}i**	**iI^B**	**ii**
Phenotype	group **AB**	group **A**	group **B**	group **O**

The work of Mendel and Morgan

In the 1850s an Austrian monk called Gregor Mendel tried cross-pollinating different varieties of pea plants. The pea flower is self-pollinating (p. 31) and to prevent this self-pollination, Mendel opened some of the flower buds and removed·the stamens before they were ripe. He then collected pollen from one variety of plant and dusted it on to the stigmas of another variety from which the anthers had been removed. In this way he could be sure of cross-pollinating any two varieties. Because the pea plant has a closed flower which normally self-pollinates, bees and other insects could not get into the flowers and bring "foreign" pollen to his experimental plants.

Mendel crossed several varieties of pea plants which differed in the colour of their seeds, the shape of their pods, the colour of pods, position of flowers and length of stem. The first cross-pollination produced an F_1 generation. The seeds of the F_1 generation were planted and allowed to grow and self-pollinate to produce the F_2 generation. (This is the same thing as mating the Bb mice together in Fig. 34.1b.)

Table 34.1 shows some of Mendel's results:

Table 34.1 Mendel's results from crossing pea plants

		F_1	F_2	Ratio
yellow seeds	× green seeds	all yellow	6022 yellow 2001 green	3.01:1
green pods	× yellow pods	all green	428 green 152 yellow	2.82:1
tall stem	× short stem	all tall	787 tall 277 short	2.84:1

Notice that yellow seeds are dominant to green, green pods are dominant to yellow and tallness is dominant to shortness. Notice also that the results from the large number of offspring in the F_2 are nearly (but never exactly) 3:1.

From his results, Mendel deduced that each of the pea characteristics he studied was controlled by a pair of "factors" (now called genes) and that only one of each pair of "factors" could be present in a gamete. Since chromosomes were not discovered until 1882, these deductions were remarkable. Mendel published his results and conclusions in 1865, but their importance was not realized until much later.

It was in the early 1900's that three botanists, working independently of each other, made the same deductions as Mendel had done, fifty years earlier. When they came to search through the published literature on the subject, they rediscovered Mendel's original papers.

One of these botanists, Hugo de Vries, also observed the effect of mutations (p. 184). Although animal breeders had long been familiar with these sudden, unexplained changes in the characteristics of some of their stock, de Vries' experiments showed that the mutations could be inherited in a Mendelian way.

In 1907, an American professor, T. H. Morgan, began work with *Drosophila* (p. 182) whose cell nuclei, having only four pairs of chromosomes (p. 181) were relatively easy to study. The flies also bred rapidly and had large numbers of offspring. Although a German professor of anatomy, Flemming, had already described chromosomes, it was Morgan who proposed that the genes were located on the chromosomes and used his observations of meiosis and crossing over to explain the processes of Mendelian inheritance and linkage (p. 188).

Human genetics

The "one gene–one character" effects described above illustrate very clearly the Mendelian* principles of inheritance, but they are the exceptions rather than the rule. Rarely do single genes control one trait. Colour in sweet peas (*Lathyrus* spp.) is controlled by two pairs of alleles, CC and RR. Gene C controls the production of the colour base and gene R the enzyme which acts on it to make a colour. The recessive cc will produce no colour base and rr will have no enzyme, CCrr and ccRR combinations will thus be unable to produce coloured flowers. At least six factors operate to produce coat colour in mice. In man, eight of the chemical changes involved in blood clotting are known to be under genetic control so that several genes are responsible for coagulation; absence of any one of them may lead to blood-clotting disease such as haemophilia (p. 190).

When one gene only is responsible for an important physiological change, its absence or modification will have serious consequences. Therefore most known instances of single-factor inheritance in humans are associated with rather freakish abnormalities. These are usually rare conditions, e.g. occurring once in 10,000 to 100,000 individuals, but there are a great number of different kinds of genetic abnormality.

Examples of known single-factor inheritance involving a dominant gene in man are white forelock, woolly hair, one form of night-blindness, one form of *brachydactyly* in which the fingers are abnormally short owing to the fusion of two phalanges and achondroplastic dwarfism in which the limb bones fail to grow. Recessive single genes are known to control, for example, red hair, inability to taste phenylthiourea, red-greed colour visions, and one form of *albinism* which is the absence of pigment from the eyes, hair and skin.

In the white-skinned races, although skin and hair colour are not controlled by single gene pairs, the number of alleles involved is probably quite small. If one assumes that for hair pigmentation there are only three genes, B_1, B_2 and B_3, B_1 producing a light pigmentation and B_3 a heavy pigmentation, then it is possible to predict five possible phenotypes for hair colour as follows: blond (B_1B_1), light brown (B_1B_2), medium brown (B_2B_2 or B_1B_3), dark brown (B_2B_3) and black (B_3B_3).

In experimental animals or plants, the type of inheritance and the genetic constitution can often be established by breeding together the progeny of the F_1 generation, or by back-crossing one of the F_1 individuals with the mother or father and producing numbers of offspring large enough to give results that have statistical significance. These methods are obviously not applicable to man and our knowledge of human genetics comes mainly from detailed analyses of the pedigrees of families, particularly those showing abnormal traits such as albinism, from statistical analysis of large numbers of individuals from different families for characteristics such as sex ratio, intelligence, susceptibility to disease, etc., and from individual studies of identical twins.

Despite the scarcity of evidence for single-factor inheritance in humans, there is plenty of evidence to suggest genetic control of many physiological, physical and mental characteristics. Body height, eye colour, hair colour and texture, susceptibility to certain diseases, and facial characteristics are all genetically controlled but in a more complex way than that described for mice on p. 192.

Identical twins are the result of a zygote or very early embryo separating into two parts (p. 117). The two parts develop into fully formed individuals which, since they are derived from the same fertilized ovum, will inherit identical genotypes. It is assumed, therefore, that any differences between identical twins are due to environmental rather than genetic causes.

Discontinuous and continuous variation

The individuals within a species of plants or animals are alike in all major respects; indeed, it is these likenesses which determine that they belong to the same species. Nevertheless, even though an organism recognizably belongs to a particular species, it may differ in many minor respects from another individual of the same species. A mouse may be black, brown, white or other colours, the size of its ears and tail may vary but despite these variations, it is still recognizably a mouse.

Discontinuous variation. The variations in coat colour are examples of discontinuous variation because there are no intermediates. If black and brown mice are bred together they will produce black or brown offspring. There are no intermediate colours and no problems arise in deciding in which colour category to place the individuals. It is not possible to arrange the mice in a continuous series of colours ranging from brown to black with almost imperceptible differences of colour between adjacent members of the series. The way sex is inherited is another example of discontinuous variation. With the exception of a small number of abnormalities, one is either male or female and there are no intermediates.

Discontinuous variation in humans is rather more difficult to illustrate. There are, for example, four major blood groups designated A, B, AB and O. Blood from different groups cannot be mixed without causing a clumping of the red cells. A person must be one or other of these four groups; he cannot, for example, be intermediate between group O and group A, he must be one or the other. Eye colour in white races is inherited in a discontinuous manner; one has blue eyes or pigmented eyes, but there are some individuals who would be difficult to classify. Clear-cut examples of discontinuous variation occur among the more serious variants e.g. one is either an achondroplastic dwarf or one is not; intermediates do not occur.

The features of discontinuous variation are clearly genetically determined; they cannot be altered during the lifetime of the individual. You cannot alter your eye colour by changing your diet. An achondroplastic dwarf cannot grow to full height by eating more food. An albino cannot acquire a darker skin colour by sunbathing. Moreover, the variations are likely to be under the control of a small number of genes. One dominant gene makes you an achondroplastic dwarf; the absence of one gene for making pigment causes albinism.

Continuous variation. When one tries to classify individuals according to height or weight rather than eye colour, the decisions become more difficult and the classes more arbitrary. There are not merely two classes of people, tall and short, but a whole range of intermediate sizes differing from each other by barely measurable distances. Categories can be invented for convenience e.g. people from 1·4 to 1·6 m, 1·6 to 1·8 m, 1·8 to 2·0 m, but they do not represent discontinuous variations of 0·2 m between individuals.

There is no reason why continuous variations should not be genetically controlled but they are likely to be under the influence of several genes. For example, height might be influenced by 20 genes, each gene contributing a few centimetres to the stature. A person who inherited all 20 would be tall whereas a person with only 5 would be short. Although this example is purely hypothetical, it is known that height is at least partially genetically determined because tall parents have, on average, tall children and vice versa, but how many genes are involved is not known.

Continuous variations are also those most likely to be influenced by the environment. A person may inherit genes for tallness but if he is undernourished in his years of growth he will not grow as tall as he might if he had received adequate food. In fact, most continuous variations result from the interaction of the genotype with the environment. A person will grow fat if he eats too much food; he will lose weight if he goes on a diet. This seems to be an entirely environmental effect until one realizes that another person may eat just as much food and yet remain slim because of his different, inherited constitution. Whether one catches a disease or not would appear to be dependent on exposure to the disease germs, an exclusively environmental effect, and yet it is apparent that one may inherit susceptibility or resistance to a disease. If a person with inherited susceptibility to an infectious disease is never exposed to the infection, he will not develop the disease.

Heredity or environment?

It is possible to experiment with plants and animals to discover whether an observed variation is due primarily to the genetic constitution or to environmental differences. A species of plant growing in a valley may have larger leaves and taller stems than individuals of the same species growing on a mountain side. If the two varieties are collected, planted in the same situation and grown through one or two generations, interbreeding being prevented, and still show the differences of leaves and stem size, one may assume that the differences are genetically controlled. If, however, the two varieties, after growing in the same environment, produce offspring which are indistinguishable, the original variations must have been due solely to the environmental differences.

Similar experiments with man are not possible or desirable. Even when situations occur which resemble the experiment, such as the "uniformity" of an institutional environment for orphaned children, the observations are always susceptible to more than one interpretation. Thus, there is usually a great deal of argument about very little evidence when people discuss whether our intelligence, for example, is predominantly due to the genes we inherit or the conditions of home and school in which we were brought up. One source of evidence in the "nature v nurture" controversy is the study of identical twins.

Applications of genetics to human problems

(*a*) **Screening.** Tests can be carried out to predict, with varying degrees of certainty, whether a person is carrying the genes for a heritable disorder. These tests can be made on potential parents, on babies, or even on fetuses in the uterus.

A blood test can reveal a raised level of phenylalanine in a baby with two recessive alleles for phenylketonuria, PKU or a low level of thyroxine (p. 144) in a baby which has inherited congenital hypothyroidism. Both these conditions can lead to severe mental impairment if not treated early enough.

Samples of amniotic fluid taken from a pregnant woman (amniocentesis) will contain cells shed from the fetus. These cells can be examined microscopically to see if they contain the extra chromosome indicative of Down's syndrome (p. 185).

Potential parents can also be screened to see if either or both are carrying recessive genes for a hereditary defect. Abnormal levels of sodium chloride in sweat may indicate (though not with 100 per cent certainty) that the individual is a carrier (i.e. heterozygous) for the cystic fibrosis gene. Carriers of the blood diseases thalassaemia and sickle cell anaemia (p. 205) can be detected by abnormalities in the size or shape of some of their red cells.

In many instances, it is now possible to detect the presence of a harmful gene in a DNA sample from a person's cells. This test may be used as a first resort or to confirm a less reliable screening test, e.g. for cystic fibrosis.

Who should be screened? Potential parents with a family history of a genetic disease are obvious candidates for screening to see if they too carry the relevant genes.

In Britain, babies are routinely screened for PKU and congenital hypothyroidism. This has the obvious advantage that the conditions can be effectively treated by special diet or hormone supplements respectively, before irreversible damage is done.

In Cyprus, mass screening for thalassaemia reduced the incidence of the disease by 95 per cent in ten years.

However, the outcome is not always so positive. The heterozygotes for thalassaemia revealed by screening in Greece were regarded as unsuitable marriage partners. Similarly there are fears that widespread screening for more and more conditions might lead to undue anxiety and also discrimination by employers and insurance companies.

(*b*) **Counselling.** Screening should always be followed by genetic counselling. Counselling is possible, however, even without prior screening. If the family history is known to

of two cousins, John and Mary. Cousin John is assumed to be heterozygous for a comparatively rare recessive gene, Nn. (He would be known to be Nn for certain only if one of his parents was nn.) John could have inherited this gene from his grandparents A or B. There is a 1 in 2 chance that the gene came from grandparents B, and in this case there is also a 1 in 4 chance that Mary has inherited the gene. There is thus a chance of 1 in 8 ($\frac{1}{2} \times \frac{1}{4}$) that cousin Mary is also Nn, in which case the chance of an affected child from their marriage is 1 in 4. The overall chances of an affected child are thus $\frac{1}{8} \times \frac{1}{4} = \frac{1}{32}$, i.e. 1 in 32.

If the gene is fairly rare in the general population, e.g. occurs once in 100 individuals, the chances of John marrying an Nn person from the general population are 1 in 100. The overall chances of an affected child in this case are $1/100 \times 1/4$, i.e. 1 in 400.

Although these considerations would apply equally well to beneficial genes, cousin marriages are not usually encouraged and brother-sister marriages forbidden by law. This does not reduce the total number of homozygous recessives which occur in a population but does reduce the chances of their occurring in a particular family. Consanguinity is bound to occur sooner or later, otherwise we should need to have had an impossibly large number of ancestors.

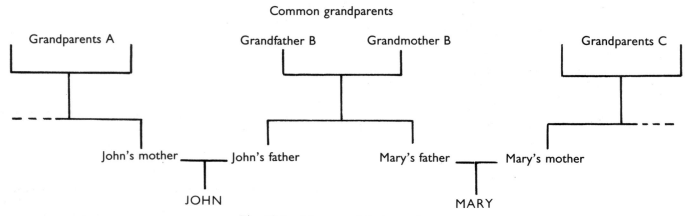

Fig. 34.3   Lineage of first cousins

include affected individuals, it is possible to assess the *chances* of an individual inheriting the gene (see below).

If screening reveals that both parents are carriers of a faulty gene, they can be told that the chance of having an affected child is one in four (p. 194). They can then decide whether to try for a baby, and what to do if it proves to be affected. If amniocentesis reveals that the fetus carries a serious genetic disorder, the parents can decide whether or not to terminate the pregnancy.

You will, by now, appreciate that genetic screening introduces many ethical problems. It would be very undesirable to use it, for example, in trying to control the sex, IQ, physique or other normal attributes of an offspring.

(*c*) **Consanguinity.** The study of human genetics enables predictions to be made on the chances of the recombination of two harmful genes in the children of marriages between first cousins.

Fig. 34.3 shows diagrammatically the theoretical pedigree

Intelligence

Intelligence is a product of a person's genetic constitution and the effect of his environment; i.e. he may inherit from his parents the mental equipment for intelligent thought, but this will not produce his full potential of intelligent behaviour unless he is educated.

The part of intelligence which is genetically controlled is almost certainly influenced by a large number of genes and is not susceptible to simple analysis. When a graph or histogram is plotted to show the different numbers of individuals possessing a particular IQ value, the type of picture obtained is that shown in Fig. 34.4, often called a "normality" curve or *curve of normal distribution*. Similar curves are also obtained for factors such as height and skin colour and can be explained on the basis of several genes influencing the characteristic. Instead of the straightforward presence or absence of a condition, such as albinism, there is a continuous variation with every grade of intermediate.

Genetics and agriculture

A knowledge of genetics can be used to improve crop plants and farm animals. For example, cross-pollinating a high-yielding, disease-prone variety of maize with a low yielding, disease-resistant variety will produce some offspring with both desirable characteristics, high-yield + disease-resistance. It will also produce some offspring with both undesirable characters, i.e. low-yield + disease-prone.

This crossing process is called *hybridization* and the offspring are called *hybrids*. If the hybrids with the desirable characteristics are selected, they may form the basis for improved strains of crop plants. By a series of hybridizations the genes for resistance to a fungus disease in a wild grass *Aegilops ventricosa* have been introduced into a variety of wheat so that the final hybrid is both high yielding and disease resistant. With cotton plants, programmes of hybridization have enabled plant breeders to introduce genes for resistance to bacterial and virus disease. Cotton grown in the Sudan is particularly prone to leaf curl virus and a bacterial infection called blackarm. From varieties already in the Sudan, it was possible to introduce genes for virus resistance but the genes for resistance to the bacterial disease had to be incorporated by crossing with a species of cotton from Central America.

Similar principles can be applied to farm animals. In most cases the hybrid offspring are intermediate between the two parental types for characteristics such as milk yield, fertility, growth rate and mortality rate. In some crosses of cattle, however, the F_1 hybrids have proved to have significantly higher fertility and reduced mortality rates; in other words, they produce more offspring and are less prone to diseases. Nevertheless, there is evidence that, in dairy cattle at least, the variation in, say, milk yield between herds of the same breed is 75 per cent due to management and environmental conditions and only 25 per cent is attributable to genetic differences.

The disadvantage of hybrids is that they do not breed true. The desirable characters combined in the hybrid organism tend to segregate out at meiosis (*see* p. 192). For a long-lived hybrid organism such as a cow this is not so important but for plants it means that fresh hybrid seed must be obtained for each planting. Alternatively the desirable characteristics of the hybrid must be preserved by vegetative propagation (*see* p. 27).

Beneficial genes may sometimes be 'fixed' by inbreeding. This means repeated self-pollination of a crop-plant, or brother-sister matings between farm animals. If the unwanted varieties from these crosses are eliminated, inbreeding results eventually in pure-breeding lines with predictable offspring. However, it also results in some falling off in yields or disease resistance, perhaps because of the accumulation of a number of undesirable genes in the homozygous condition.

PRACTICAL WORK

Breeding experiments with Drosophila

Drosophila is a small fly which is easy to breed in large numbers in the laboratory. By carrying out controlled cross-breeding experiments with mutant forms and wild types, it is possible to illustrate and investigate some of the principles of heredity.

Sources. Wild type and several mutant strains can be obtained from the usual biological supply firms.

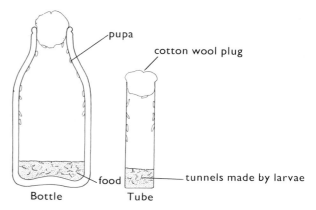

Fig. 34.5   Drosophila cultures

Culture medium. Mix together 50 g maize meal, 15 g agar, 13 g dried yeast, 25 g brown sugar, 800 cm³ water and boil gently for several minutes. Dissolve 2 g "Moldex" (a mould-inhibitor) in 40 cm³ boiling water and add it to the mixture. Pour the mixture into 100×25-mm specimen tubes to a depth of 20 mm, plug the tubes with cotton wool wrapped in butter muslin and sterilize in an autoclave at 10^5 N/m² (15 lb/in²) for 15 min. On the day before introducing the flies, add 3 drops of a suspension of fresh yeast to each tube.

The tubes will hold about one hundred flies for experiments but for maintaining stocks of Drosophila, wide-mouthed bottles, e.g. half-pint milk or cream bottles, should be used and new cultures started every five or six weeks (Fig. 34.5).

Setting up experiments. It is essential that the females used for the breeding experiments have not already mated with the males in the culture bottle. From a flourishing culture with many unhatched pupae, all the flies are shaken into a clean, dry bottle and the culture bottle re-plugged. The flies that emerge from the pupae in the culture bottle during the day will be virgins and can be easily recognized by the unexpanded wings. These flies are etherized, and males and females sorted into separate dry tubes where they can recover from the ether. About three virgin females of a given strain, e.g. wild type, are transferred to a fresh culture tube and six males of a different strain, e.g. vestigial wings, are introduced. The males need not be virgins and can be taken directly from stock cultures.

The flies will mate and lay eggs in the culture medium. Larvae hatch from the eggs, burrow through the food, grow, and in about 10–14 days from laying, pupate on the sides of the tube. The parent

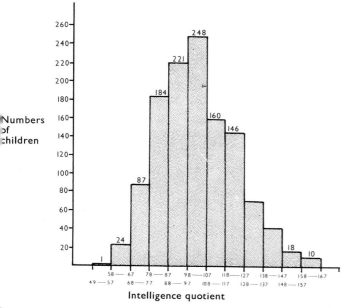

Fig. 34.4   Distribution of IQ rating in a random sample of 1207 Scottish eleven-year-old children

(*From C. O. Carter*, Human Heredity, *Penguin Books, 1962*)

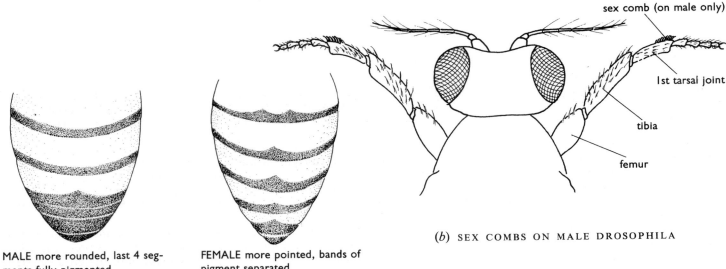

(b) SEX COMBS ON MALE DROSOPHILA

MALE more rounded, last 4 segments fully pigmented

FEMALE more pointed, bands of pigment separated

(a) DROSOPHILA ABDOMEN: DORSAL ASPECT
These differences are not easy to see on newly hatched flies or ebony-body mutants.

Fig. 34.7   Distinguishing the sexes

flies should be removed after one week. When the F_1 progeny have been emerging from the pupal cases for about 10 days they should be etherized, the different sexes and strains counted and recorded, and the flies killed in alcohol or retained for F_2 experiments. From the results, the ratios of the different strains can be calculated, and interpretations attempted on the lines of the principles of Mendelian inheritance.

(a) ETHERIZING (The same method, without ether, is used to transfer flies from one container to another)

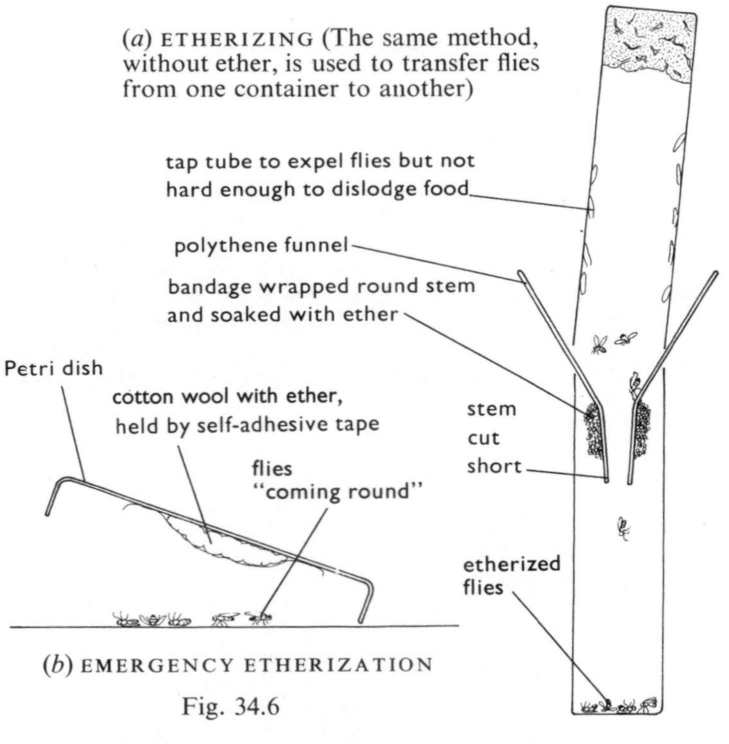

tap tube to expel flies but not hard enough to dislodge food

polythene funnel

bandage wrapped round stem and soaked with ether

Petri dish

cotton wool with ether, held by self-adhesive tape

flies "coming round"

stem cut short

etherized flies

(b) EMERGENCY ETHERIZATION

Fig. 34.6

Etherizing (ether is very inflammable; no naked flame should be allowed while it is in use). The technique is depicted in Fig. 34.6a. The flies should not be exposed to ether for more than one minute. If they begin to recover while being counted, etc. they can be covered for a few seconds by a Petri dish lid carrying a small pad of ether-soaked cotton wool (Fig. 34.6b). If etherized flies are placed directly into a culture tube, the latter should have dry sides and be placed horizontally, otherwise the anaesthetized flies will stick to the food or the glass.

Sexing (see Fig. 34.7 a and b). The presence or absence of sex combs on the fore-legs is the surest guide. A hand lens or dissecting microscope is essential.

Suitable crosses. Wild type × vestigial wing; wild type × ebony body; wild type × white eye: each cross should be made in two ways, reversing the sexes, e.g.

vestigial winged male × wild type female

and   wild type male × vestigial winged female.

QUESTIONS

1. Two black guinea pigs are mated together on several occasions and their offspring are invariably black. However, when their black offspring are mated with white guinea pigs, half of the matings result in all black litters and the other half produce litters containing equal numbers of black and white babies.

   From these results, deduce the genotypes of the parents and explain the results of the various matings, assuming that colour in this case is determined by a single pair of genes (alleles).

2. The blood groups, A, B, AB and O are determined by a pair of alleles, one inherited from each parent. The allele for group O is recessive to that for either A or B. Thus a group A person may have the genotype $I^A I^A$ or $I^A i$. Inheritance of I^A from one parent and I^B from the other produces the phenotype AB.

   (a) What are the possible blood groups likely to be inherited by children born to a group A mother and group B father? Explain your reasoning.

   (b) A woman of blood group A claims that a man of blood group AB is the father of her child. A blood test reveals that the child's blood group is O. Is it possible that the woman's claim is correct? Could the father have been a group B man? Explain your reasoning.

3. A geneticist wishes to find out the colour of F_1 flowers from a cross between red- and white-flowered insect-pollinated plants such as antirrhinum. Revise, if necessary, the section on pollination (p. 33) and describe how he should conduct his experiments, assuming that pollen can effectively be transferred by means of a dry paintbrush.

4. Individuals of a pure-breeding line of Drosophila are exposed to X-rays to induce mutations in their gametes. Most mutated genes are recessive to normal genes. How could one find out if mutations had occurred?

5. Two black rats thought to be homozygous for coat colour were mated and produced a litter which contained all black babies. The F_2, however, resulted in some white babies which meant that one of the grandparents was heterozygous for coat colour. How would you find out which parent was heterozygous?

35 | Evolution and the Theory of Natural Selection

THE theory of evolution offers an explanation of how the great variety of present-day animals and plants came into existence. It supposes that life on Earth began in relatively simple forms which over hundreds of millions of years gave rise, by a series of small changes, to a succession of living organisms which became more varied and more complex. Taken to its logical conclusion, the evolutionary theory must suppose that life itself evolved from non-living matter. It must be emphasized that evolution is a theory and not an established fact. In general terms, it is an acceptable hypothesis to account for the existence of the living organisms which we know today.

The arguments for evolution are drawn from the kind of evidence which follows, though much of the evidence is either very incomplete or circumstantial.

1. Reproduction and spontaneous generation

As far as we know, all living organisms are derived by reproduction from pre-existing organisms and do not arise spontaneously from non-living matter. This knowledge weakens any alternative theory to evolution, if it claims that each kind of organism known today arose spontaneously or was created suddenly at different points in time, e.g. that horses were created suddenly one million years ago and have remained the same ever since, reproducing their kind exactly over thousands of generations.

The evolutionary theory would thus assume that when new forms of life appear on the Earth, they have been derived by reproduction from organisms which already exist, e.g. that mammals were derived from reptiles, reptiles from amphibia and amphibia from fish. In general, for vertebrates at least, the fossil record supports this contention. The question which must arise, however, is "Where did the *first* living creatures come from?" To this the biologist is obliged to say that, although spontaneous generation of life from non-living substances is not known to occur today and is thought to be very improbable during the geological period of which we have some knowledge, there was a time, some 500 million years ago or more, when conditions were favourable for such an event or series of events. For example, the atmosphere might have been devoid of oxygen but rich in methane and ammonia which makes feasible the production of amino acids and proteins.

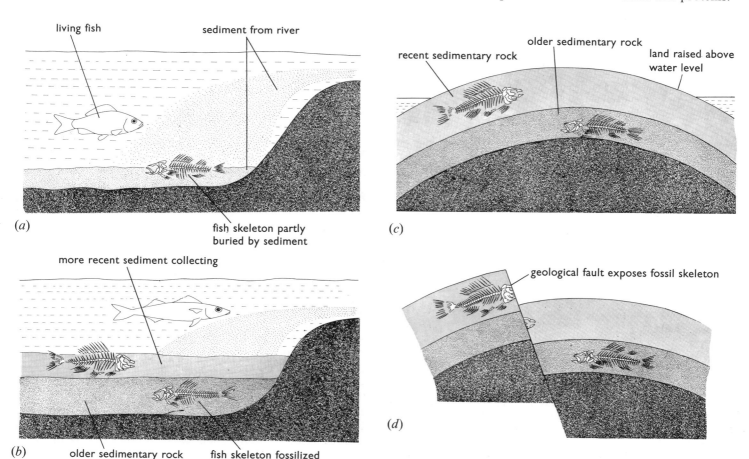

Fig. 35.1   Formation of fossils

2. The fossil record

Sedimentary rocks were formed by the settling down of mineral particles in lakes and oceans. These particles often became cemented together and the layers of sediment were compressed over millions of years to form rock. The dead remains of animals and plants, falling to the bottom of the lakes or seas became incorporated in the sediment and so preserved in a variety of ways as *fossils* (Fig. 35.1). As a result of slow earth movements, many sedimentary rocks were raised above the water and the fossils they contained became accessible for study.

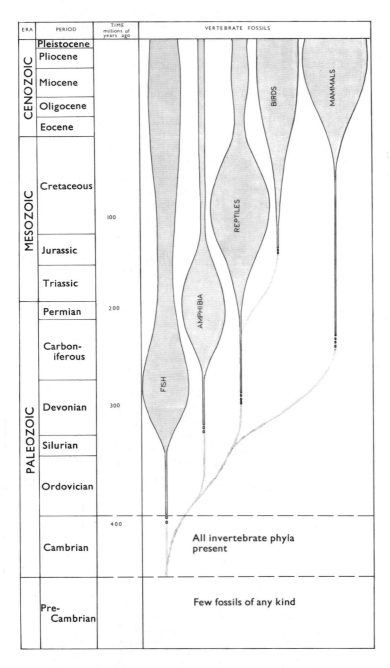

Fig. 35.2   Chart to show the earliest occurrence and relative abundance of fossil vertebrates (possible evolutionary relationships are shown by the faint lines)

(*After Grove and Newell*, Animal Biology, *University Tutorial Press*)

If not too contorted by the earth movements, in an exposed series the lowest sedimentary rocks will be the oldest, and from the fossils in successive layers, the scientist can form some idea of the animals and plants present millions of years ago. When the fossils in various layers are studied it appears (*a*) that many present-day animals and plants are not represented (Fig. 35.2), and (*b*) that a vast number of organisms represented by skeletal remains in the rocks no longer exist today. For example, 300 million years ago there were apparently no mammals, that is, no fossil remains have yet been found; but there were at that time some "armour-plated" fish (Fig. 35.3) which no longer seem to exist.

Such evidence seems to detract from any idea that all the organisms existing today have been reproduced exactly since life began. Even if spontaneous generation or *biogenesis* could have taken place 300 million years ago, it seems unlikely that it would "generate" anything so complex as a mammal in a single operation or even a number of operations in a very short time.

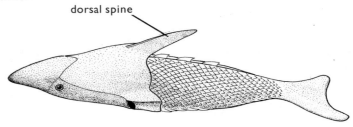

Fig. 35.3   Pteraspis—one of the extinct, "armour-plated" fish of the Silurian period (a reconstruction from fossil remains)

Alternatively it could be argued that mammals did exist 300 million years ago, but were so sparsely or locally distributed that we have not found any fossil remains. This does not help us to answer the question of how mammals arose, but simply pushes their hypothetical origin back to an earlier date.

More acceptable is the idea that mammals were derived from reptile-like ancestors by a long series of small changes, and the fact that scientists have found fossil remains of animals intermediate in many respects between reptiles and mammals lends support to this idea.

It must not be supposed, however, that mammals evolved from reptiles in the sense that present-day reptiles could produce a mammal, even over a very long period of time; or even that existing reptiles represent the form of the ancestral animals that gave rise to mammals. The evolutionary theory postulates that mammals and reptiles share one or a small number of common ancestors that were neither wholly reptilian nor wholly mammalian and which became extinct in due course. Similarly it supposes that reptiles had fish-like ancestors not represented amongst present-day fish and that each group has continued to evolve, but in different ways, since the first divergence.

There is little or no evidence in the fossil record to suggest that any of the large invertebrate groups of animals share a common ancestor. This may be because (*a*) our knowledge of the fossil record does not go back far enough, (*b*) the common ancestors, if they existed, have not been preserved, or (*c*) the events which produced living organisms from non-living matter occurred more than once, initiating a number of different, primitive forms of life that evolved into the invertebrates but share no common, living ancestor.

3. Circumstantial evidence

By studying the structure and distribution of modern animals it is possible to point out features which can be interpreted as supporting the theory of evolution. One such study is *comparative anatomy*, and perhaps the most familiar example is the skeleton of mammalian limbs (Fig. 35.4). The limbs of seals, moles, bats and antelope look very different from each other and are adapted to the functions of swimming, digging, flying and running. Despite this difference of appearance and function, they all have basically the same skeletal structure. If these mammals did not originate from a common ancestor but arose independently (and spontaneously?), there seems no convincing reason why the pattern of bones in limbs performing such different functions should be so similar. On the other hand, it does seem reasonable to visualize these limbs as modifications of the primitive, unspecialized limbs of a common ancestor, the differences coming about during evolution as the limbs became more closely adapted to each special method of progression, while retaining the fundamental pattern of bones and joints.

Many other examples of comparative anatomy could be cited in the vertebrates, including fundamental similarities of the skeletal, circulatory and nervous systems. Also, other lines of circumstantial evidence, such as the similarity between the embryonic forms of different vertebrates, could be discussed. Being circumstantial evidence, i.e. attempting to fit known facts into a pattern of events in the past which is suspected but impossible to reproduce, the evidence is often subject to alternative interpretations and further discussion is suited to more advanced study than this book can offer.

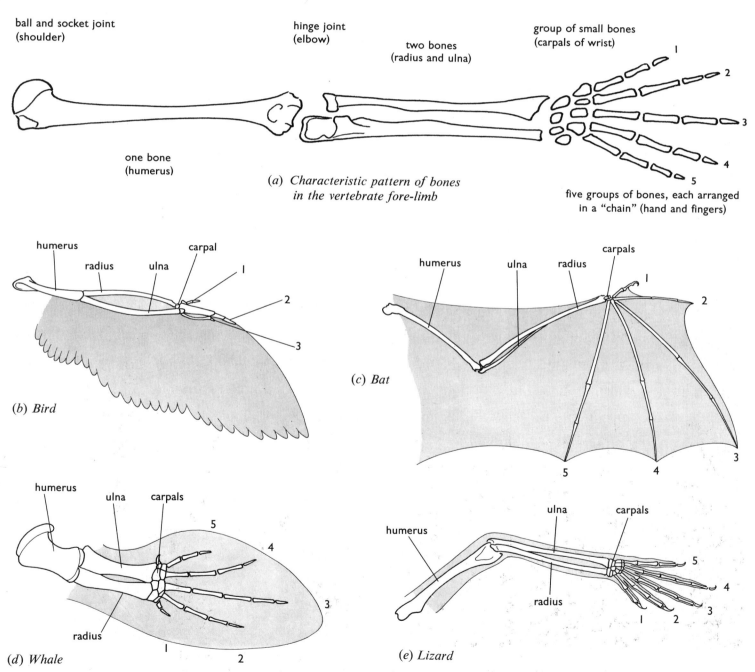

Fig. 35.4   Comparative anatomy of vertebrate limbs

NATURAL SELECTION

In 1858 Charles Darwin and Alfred Russel Wallace put forward a theoretical explanation of how evolution could have taken place and new species arisen. The theory of evolution by natural selection is the one which so far fits most, but not all, of the observed facts and has been strengthened by discoveries since 1858.

The arguments for the theory of natural selection can be summarized as follows:

(a) *Observation* 1. The offspring of animals and plants outnumber their parents.

(b) *Observation* 2. Despite this tendency to increase, the numbers of any particular species remain more or less constant.

(c) *Induction* 1. Since fewer organisms live to maturity than are produced, there must be a "struggle" for survival.

(d) *Observation* 3. The individual members within any plant or animal species vary from each other by small differences; some of these differences can be inherited.

(e) *Induction* 2. (i) Some of these varieties are better adapted to the environment or mode of life of the organism and will tend to survive longer and leave behind more offspring. If the variations are harmful, the organism possessing them may die before reaching reproductive age and so the variation will not be passed on.

(ii) If an advantageous variation is inherited by an organism, it will also live longer and leave more offspring, some of which may also inherit the variation.

Small but favourable variations may thus accumulate in a population over hundreds of years until the organisms differ so much from their predecessors that they no longer interbreed with them. The "variety" would now be called a new species. Certain points in the argument above need elaboration to make them clear.

(a) If a pair of rats had 8 offspring which grew up and formed 4 pairs, eventually having 8 offspring per pair, in four generations the number of rats stemming from the original pair would be 512, i.e. $2 \rightarrow 8 \rightarrow 32 \rightarrow 128 \rightarrow 512$.

(c) An induction is an argument in which a generalization is made as a result of observations of actual events. The potential number for the fourth generation of rats is 512. If, however, the population of rats is to remain constant, 510 must have died or not been born, leaving only two of this vast potential family still alive.

The "struggle" for survival, however, does not imply actual fighting; the participants may never meet but they could be in competition for food and shelter. Often the competition will not only be between adults, but between eggs or larvae or seeds, i.e. the most prolific stage of the life history of a species at which mortality rate is often high. The "struggle" is often quite passive and may depend on the relative resistance of eggs to adverse conditions, or concealment patterns on the body leading to effective camouflage.

(d) Man is a species and the variations between members of this species are obvious at a glance. Variations in other organisms are less obvious but very evident to an experienced observer. If a variation is to play an effective part in evolution it must be heritable. A variation acquired in the lifetime of an organism, e.g. the well-developed muscles of an athlete, is not usually heritable.

(e) A species of a normally light-coloured moth, *Biston betularia*, the peppered moth, produces from time to time a black variety. This black variety was first recorded in 1848 in an industrial area of England, and by 1895 it had increased to 98 per cent of the population in this district. Observations showed that the light-coloured form was well camouflaged against the lichen-covered tree trunks where it normally rested. The atmospheric pollution of industrial areas, however,

(From the experiments of Dr H. B. Kettlewell, University of Oxford)

Plate 61. LIGHT AND DARK FORMS OF THE PEPPERED MOTH AT REST ON TREE TRUNKS

(a) Soot-covered oak trunk near an industrial city   (b) Lichen-covered trunk in unpolluted countryside

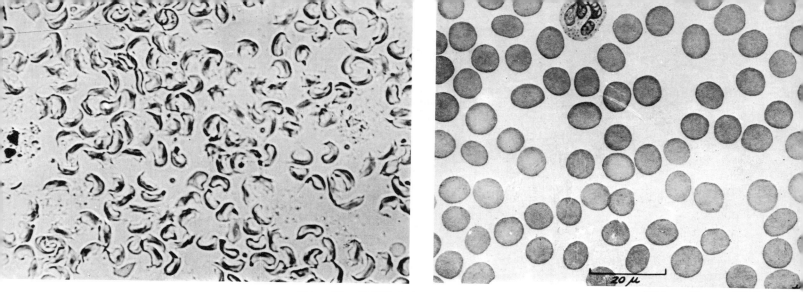

Plate 62. SICKLE CELL ANAEMIA (×1000)

(a) At low oxygen concentrations the cells become distorted

(b) Normal red cells for comparison

(Wellcome Museum of Medical Science)

reduced or eliminated the lichens on the tree trunks and also darkened them with deposits of soot, so that the dark forms were better concealed (Plate 61) than the light forms. Better concealment led to fewer moths being eaten by birds, e.g. a Redstart in England was observed to eat 43 pale forms and only 15 dark forms from equal numbers resting on trees. The "struggle" here is very indirect, being a "struggle" for concealment, but the outcome is that more of the dark forms would survive and lay eggs. The dark colour in many cases is due to a single, dominant gene (p. 192) and so would be inherited by some of the offspring. The dark variety, however, is not yet a new species since it will interbreed with the light form, but this account illustrates how a new species could arise by natural selection.

HERITABLE VARIATION

The sources of heritable variation were not known to Darwin but have since been shown to arise principally in two ways: by mutation and by recombination.

Recombination and natural selection

A mutant gene which is harmful in one genetic constitution (genotype) may be neutral or beneficial in another. Similarly, certain advantageous genes may exist in one population and different beneficial genes in another. If interbreeding takes place between the populations, individuals may arise in which the two beneficial genes recombine, so conferring a selective advantage on the new phenotype. For example, the genes in a wild grass which render it resistant to fungus disease have been combined by cross-breeding with the genes for large grain size in cultivated wheat thus producing a variety with a high yield and good resistance to disease. Although segregation (p. 192) tends to separate these beneficial genes their combined selective advantage could cause them to maintain a constant frequency in a population as happens with sickle cell trait (Plate 62).

Sickle cell anaemia occurs when two recessive mutant genes controlling haemoglobin production, combine in an individual. Such individuals have severe anaemia and generally die before reaching the reproductive age, i.e. natural selection removes the "h" genes from the population. The recessive genes remain in the population, however, in the heterozygous individuals, e.g. HH = normal; hh = sickle cell anaemia; Hh = heterozygous for sickle cell anaemia. Although from one quarter to one half of

the haemoglobin of the heterozygotes is affected, usually less than 1 per cent of their red cells show sickling in low oxygen concentrations. Such heterozygotes are said to have the sickle cell *trait*. When two heterozygotes marry, one would expect on average a quarter of their children to have sickle cell anaemia

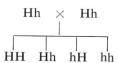

and would die before reaching reproductive age. In this way the h genes would be eliminated by selection from the population since for every four offspring from the HH genotypes there will be only three from the Hh genotypes. In certain African populations, however, as many as 34 per cent of the people carry the recessive gene and there is evidence to suggest that this is because the heterozygotes are more resistant to malaria, i.e. persons with the genotype Hh enjoy a selective advantage in malarious districts while the HH genotypes are reduced by the selective pressure of malaria. Investigations of Negro populations in America show an incidence of only 4 to 5 per cent of the trait compared with the 15 to 20 per cent characteristic of the African population from which the migrants were originally derived. In some non-malarial regions therefore, it looks as if the heterozygotes lose their selective advantage.

Mutation and natural selection

Mutation (p. 184). A mutation is a change in a gene or a chromosome. Most mutations are harmful, e.g. vestigial wings in Drosophila, and so are unlikely to be handed on to the offspring. The mutations which result in advantageous characteristics, however, may be passed on to the offspring and preserved in a population. The dark variety of the peppered moth, mentioned above, results in most cases from the mutation of a single gene which is dominant to the normal gene. Usually gene mutations are recessive and the characters controlled by the gene may not be expressed, e.g. if gene A mutates to a the organism Aa may not noticeably differ from AA. If the mutation occurs frequently in the population, however, there is a chance of a and a coming together at fertilization, so producing a homozygous recessive aa in which the new character is fully expressed.

Mutation rate. One cannot predict when a gene is going to mutate but the frequency of its occurrence can be determined in some cases; for example in achondroplastic dwarfism it is possibly as high as one mutation in 20,000 compared with one in 100,000 for many genes. The rate of mutation is characteristic of particular genes in particular species but the frequencies are such that in a human ejaculate of, say, 200 million sperms, there are likely to be a considerable number of nuclei bearing gene and chromosome mutations.

Exposure to radio-activity, X-rays and ultraviolet radiation is known to increase the rate of gene and chromosome mutation (*see* p. 185).

Significance of mutation. Since so many mutations are harmful to the individual bearing them and are eliminated by natural selection it might seem that a well-adapted organism with no mutations would be at an advantage. This may be true so long as the environment does not alter and the organism does not move to a different situation where it is subjected to new selection pressures for which it is poorly adapted. If a species of bacteria were incapable of mutation, exposure to streptomycin might eliminate the species. The fact that streptomycin-resistant mutants occur, allows the bacteria to survive such an adverse change in the environment.

The dark mutant of the peppered moth had little selection advantage prior to the Industrial Revolution but with the advent of pollution and the consequent darkening of tree trunks, the mutation enjoyed favourable selection pressure. The elimination of mutants by natural selection in one environment is the price which populations have to pay if they are to retain the ability to adapt to a changing environment. Mutations should not therefore be regarded as "accidents" since they are events which occur normally in all populations and are essential for survival and evolution, though they may well be harmful to the many individuals in which they occur.

Balanced polymorphism

The existence of genetically controlled varieties within a population provides the raw material on which natural selection acts, with one or other variety being favoured or reduced by the selective process. However, in most populations over a short term, the different varieties persist in about the same numbers; for example, although in certain environments the light forms of some moths have a selective advantage, dark mutants still occur with a low but consistent frequency partly as a result of new mutations appearing in the population and partly because the dark forms enjoy some positive selective advantage. It seems that although the dark forms are more easily seen when resting on trees, they are better concealed from predators while in flight, thus selection operates in their favour on certain occasions.

The term "balanced polymorphism" refers to the persistence of such varieties in a population.

Variations in eye and hair colour and the existence of different blood groups are examples of genetically controlled variations in human populations. It is not always possible to discern the selective advantage of one or other variant but this does not mean that the variant is selectively neutral. Human blood group A would appear to have no selective advantage until statistical analysis reveals that such individuals are less affected by duodenal ulcers, a factor which may enhance their reproductive capacity. This is also an illustration of the fact that the characteristic which we recognize as being controlled by a gene or group of genes is not necessarily the one on which selection is acting.

Isolation and the formation of new species

A mutation or recombination may give rise to a variety with characteristics which enable it to colonize new areas not accessible to the parent stock. In this way the variety may form a breeding population which is isolated from the original population. Further mutations may occur in this isolated population and accumulate until individuals are incapable of interbreeding with the original stock. In this way a variety will have given rise to a new species.

There are many ways in which populations can become isolated. Geographical isolation is an obvious case where rivers, oceans or mountains separate populations. Another cause could be a difference in breeding season or incompatibility of mating behaviour. If variety *A* breeds only in April while variety *B* breeds in July, the breeding populations are effectively isolated even if they occupy the same area.

Evolution by natural selection can be visualized as proceeding as follows: mutations and genetic recombinations arise in a population; those which are not so harmful as to be lethal give rise to a balanced polymorphism; environmental change or migration of the population favours certain varieties which leave more offspring which inherit these same variations; isolation allows other favourable genes to accumulate in the population until it differs so much from the parental stock that interbreeding is impossible.

Classification

The process of classification has at least two purposes. One is to sort out living organisms into "manageable" groups in which the individuals have a great deal in common. Another purpose is to try and recognize how evolution may have given rise to diverse but related organisms.

It would be quite convenient to classify organisms into those which live in fresh water, sea water or on land but this would not give us any clue to their evolutionary relationships. So the biologist looks for points of anatomy or physiology which are shared by as large a group as possible, and then subdivides each group as it proves necessary.

Since we do not know for sure what took place during evolution, we have to study present-day organisms and fossils and try to make logical deductions about which of their features might have been inherited from a common ancestor and which have developed as a result of special adaptation. For example, dogfish and dolphins are both streamlined marine animals with fins or flippers to help in locomotion. The dolphin, however, is a mammal and is believed to have become "fish-like" as a result of adaptation to life in the sea. There are many anatomical and physiological reasons why dolphins and dogfish are not closely related.

The largest group of organisms recognised by biologists is the *kingdom*. But how many kingdoms should there be? Most biologists used to favour the adoption of two kingdoms, plants and animals. This however, caused problems in trying to classify fungi, bacteria and single-celled organisms which do not fit obviously into either kingdom. A scheme now favoured by many, but by no means all biologists, is the Whittaker 5-kingdom scheme, comprising the *Monera, Protoctista, Fungi, Plants* and *Animals*.

Monera. These are the bacteria (p. 70) and the blue-green algae. They differ from other single-celled organisms in having no nuclear membrane.

Protoctista; single-celled (unicellular) organisms which have a nuclear membrane. Some of them, e.g. *Euglena* (p. 174) possess chloroplasts and make their food by photosynthesis. They are often called unicellular 'plants' or *protophyta*. Organisms such as *Amoeba* and *Paramecium* take in and digest solid food and thus resemble animals in their feeding. They may be called unicellular 'animals' or *protozoa*.

Fungi. Most fungi are made up of hyphae (p. 75), rather than cells and there are many nuclei distributed throughout the cytoplasmic lining of the hyphae.

Plants; multicellular organisms. Their cells contain plastids with photosynthetic pigments, e.g. chlorophyll, and are bounded by cell walls containing cellulose. Plants make their food by photosynthesis.

Animals; multicellular organisms. Their cells have no cell walls or plastids. Most animals ingest solid food and digest it internally.

It is still not easy to fit all organisms into this scheme. For example, the kingdom *Protoctista* includes organisms as different as the microscopic, holozoic unicellular *Amoeba* and the large, holophytic multicellular seaweeds. This kind of problem will always occur when we try to devise rigid classificatory schemes with distinct boundaries between groups. The process of evolution was unlikely to have been concerned with producing a tidy scheme of classification for biologists to use.

Sub-divisions of the kingdoms

A kingdom can be sub-divided into *phyla* (singular, *phylum*). The phyla in the plant kingdom are; the *Bryophytes* (liverworts and mosses), the Ferns, the Conifers and the *Flowering Plants*.

However, many botanists do not accept that a "phylum" in the animal kingdom is eqivalent to a "phylum" in the plant kingdom and prefer to use the term, "*Division*". In this case, some of the algae are classified into Sub-Kingdoms and some into Divisions.

The Divisions of the botanist and the Phyla of the zoologist in each case encompass a number of *Classes*.

The division (or phylum), Bryophytes, contains the two classes *Liverworts* and *Mosses*. The two classes *Monocotyledons* and *Dicotyledons* constitute the *Flowering Plants*. The Monocots have only one cotyledon in their seeds (p. 37) and the class includes grasses, cereals, palms and those plants which have bulbs or corms (p. 24). The Dicots have two cotyledons in their seeds (p. 37) and the class contains all the other flowering plants, i.e. the herbs, shrubs and trees.

The animal kingdom is sub-divided into about 23 phyla, (the number depends on whose scheme of classification you adopt). Some of the familiar phyla are the *Molluscs*, (snails, slugs, clams, etc.), the *Annelids* (segmented worms) and the *Arthropods* (crustaceans, insects, spiders, millipedes).

The *Vertebrate* phylum includes all the animals with vertebral columns, i.e. the vertebrates. There are five classes in the Vertebrate phylum; *Fish, Amphibia, Reptiles, Birds* and *Mammals*. Each class is further sub-divided into *Orders*. For example, in the Mammal class there are about 25 Orders such as *Cetaceans* (whales), *Rodents* (rats and mice), *Carnivores* (lions, dogs, etc.) and *Primates* (lemurs, monkeys, apes and man). Within each Order are a number of *Families*. Lemurs, monkeys, apes and man are Families in the Primate order.

So if we are to classify man, we would say he was in

Kingdom	Animal
Phylum	Vertebrate
Class	Mammal
Order	Primate
Family	Hominidae (present-day and fossil man).

Use of observable features in classification

Using the criteria laid down for each kingdom, it should be possible to assign an unfamiliar organism to the most appropriate group by asking a series of questions. For example:

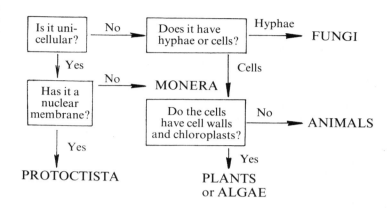

The same technique may be used for assigning an organism to its phylum, class, order, family or species. However, the important features may not always be "observable". You may want to distinguish a Monocot from a Dicot at a time when no seeds are available. In this case it is necessary to look for observable but less reliable features such as the narrow leaves and parallel veins characteristic of many (but not all) Monocots.

QUESTIONS

1. Explain briefly why the positions of fossils in a vertical series of rocks may be used to decide, relatively, how long ago the organisms were alive. Can you think of any possible snags to ths explanation?

2. In the account of polymorphism on p. 206, eye and hair colour were mentioned as polymorphic features. What other polymorphic features in human populations can you think of? What selective advantages might these have in different environments (e.g. tropical, arctic)?

3. Try to explain the difference between a variation which results from mutation and one which results from recombination. Which of these two sources of variation do you think is more likely to produce a selective advantage?

4. Suggest some of the anatomical and physiological reasons why dogfish and dolphins are not closely related.

5. In the 'flowchart' above, what further questions would you need to ask to distinguish between Plants and Algae?

6. Birds and bats are both classified as Chordates. Although both groups have wings, they are not put in the same class. Explain the reasons for this classification.

36 | Ecology

ECOLOGY is the study of living organisms in relation to their natural environment as distinct from in the laboratory. This does not mean that laboratory work is ruled out, but its object is always to try and explain how the organism survives and why it is successful in its particular environment.

Ecological terms

It is worth while at this stage to define some of the terms used in any discussion of ecology.

Environment. This means everything in the surroundings of an organism that could possibly influence it. The environment of a tadpole (p. 163) consists of water, the temperature of which will influence the tadpole's rate of growth and activity. The watery environment contains plants and animals on which the tadpole will feed, but it also contains fish and insects which may eat the tadpole. The water contains dissolved oxygen which the tadpole breathes by means of its gills. The water, the oxygen, the food and the predators are all part of the tadpole's environment.

Habitat. A habitat is where an organism lives. The habitat of the rhinoceros beetle is the crown of a palm tree. The environment includes air and sunlight but the habitat is the tree. The habitat of the tapeworm (p. 225) is the intestine of a mammal. Its environment, however, is the warm digested food and digestive juices of its host. The habitat of the weaver bird (p. 166) may be a palm tree, but its environment will include sun, wind, rain, insects and bacteria.

Community. A community is made up of all the plants and animals living in a habitat. In the soil (p. 78) there is a community of organisms which includes earthworms, termites and other insects, arachnids, crustacea, fungi and bacteria. In a lake, the animal community will include fish, insects, crustacea, molluscs and protozoa. The plant community will consist of rooted plants with submerged leaves, rooted plants with floating leaves, reed-like plants growing at the lake margin, plants floating freely on the surface, filamentous algae like *Spirogyra* (p. 172) and single-celled plants like the diatoms (p. 174) in the surface waters.

Ecosystem. The community of living organisms in a habitat, plus the non-living part of the environment, make up an ecosystem. A lake is an ecosystem which consists of the plant and animal communities mentioned above, and the water, minerals, dissolved oxygen, soil and sunlight on which they depend. An ecosystem is self-supporting. In a forest ecosystem, the plants absorb light and rain water for their photosynthesis, the animals feed on the plants and on each other. The dead remains of animals and plants return nutrients to the soil. Lakes and ponds are clear examples of ecosystems. Sunlight, water and minerals allow the plants to grow and support animal life. The recycling of materials from the dead organisms maintains the supply of nutrients.

It is quite reasonable to regard a single tree as an ecosystem. The tree grows as a result of photosynthesis. Epiphytic ferns may grow on its branches, and vines will climb up its trunk. Aphids and caterpillars feed on its leaves. Bees or sunbirds collect nectar from its flowers (pp. 32 and 171). Birds eat the caterpillars and may nest in the branches. The tree, the community of plants and animals which live on it, and the air, water and sunlight which nourish it, all form an ecosystem.

On the other hand, the whole of that part of the Earth's surface which contains living organisms (called the *biosphere*) may be regarded as one vast ecosystem.

The flow of energy in ecosystems is discussed on p. 57.

Population. In biology, this term always refers to a single species. A biologist might refer to the population of weaver birds (p. 166) in a village or the population of *Tilapia* in a lake. In each case he would mean the total numbers of weaver birds or the total numbers of *Tilapia* in the stated area.

So, a *population* of *Tilapia* forms part of the plant and animal *community* living in a *habitat* called a lake. The communities in this habitat, together with their watery *environment*, make up a self-supporting *ecosystem*.

Ecological studies

Ecological studies may be directed towards (*a*) a particular organism (autecology) or (*b*) a community (synecology) or (*c*) a whole ecosystem.

(*a*) **Autecology.** The study of the ecology of a species of *Tilapia* (p. 158) would investigate its preferences for running water or still water, the kind of temperatures it can tolerate, how it is affected by oxygen shortage, what it feeds on at different times of the year, what animals feed on it, special conditions needed for breeding and so on.

The ecological study of a population of *Tilapia* would consider the numbers of *Tilapia* present in a lake, the numbers of fish of different age, sex and size, seasonal fluctuations in these numbers, migratory movements, competition between individuals for territory, food and mates, number of eggs laid, survival rate of eggs and young, etc.

(*b*) **Synecology.** A study of the ecology of the plant and animal communities in a lake would involve trying to find out all the different types of plants and animals present, their numbers, and how they are distributed through the lake (e.g. in the surface waters or in the mud at the bottom). It would involve a study of how they affected each other. For example, the plants would provide food and shelter for the animals; the animals might compete for plant food or eat other animals (*see* Food Chains, p. 53). The dead bodies of plants and animals would be recycled (p. 54) and provide nutrients for the plant growth.

(*c*) **Ecosystem.** The study of a lake ecosystem would require an analysis of the water entering the lake (e.g. pH and minerals), seasonal or daily variations in level or temperature of the water, the amount of light reaching the bottom layer and the kind of material on the bottom. If there is little light, the plant growth will be poor because the plants cannot photosynthesize (p. 48). Consequently the animal community will consist of only those organisms which can feed on other creatures swimming into this environment, or on dead organic remains carried in by the current.

The types of plant growing will depend not only on the amount of light but also on the minerals present in the water (p. 51) or in the material which makes up the lake floor. The kinds of plant and animal present will also be determined by the extremes of temperature in the lake, whether the lake dries up during the year, or how much silt is carried into it during seasonal flooding.

ECOLOGICAL METHODS

Whether you embark on an autecological or synecological study, you will want to try to find out the numbers and different kinds of organisms present. You will also need to describe the physical conditions in the environment as fully as possible. It may then be possible to decide how these conditions influence the distribution and activity of the organisms. It would be useful to find out how much light reaches the ecosystem for photosynthesis, how much water is available for plant growth, what nutrients are present or in short supply, what fluctuations take place in temperature during a day or a longer period, and how dry or moist the air is (humidity). In most cases it is difficult to obtain accurate measurements of these conditions but it is usually possible to find a method which allows a comparison of the conditions either in two different habitats or in the same habitat at different times. For example, it is usually sufficient to be able to say that one habitat receives twice the light intensity or has a greater temperature range than another. In this case, the actual figures are often not important. There is no point in collecting a great many readings unless you can make use of them.

Physical factors

Light intensity. A light meter used for photography (Fig. 36.1a) will measure the light reaching various points in an ecosystem. The figures on the scale are meant for setting exposure times on cameras but can be used to compare light intensities in different areas. It is best to place a sheet of white paper over the region to be measured and to point the meter at the paper to measure the light reflected back from it (Fig. 36.1b). In this way, the reading is a measure of the light falling on the area and is not affected by the density or colour of the vegetation.

To compare the depths to which light penetrates in lakes and rivers, a white disc (Fig. 36.2) is lowered into the water until it just disappears from view. By noting the length of string let out, the depth of water which is needed to obscure the disc can be measured. The clearer the water, the greater will be the depth to which the disc is lowered before it disappears.

Water. The amount of water in samples of soil can be measured by the method described on p. 81. The amount of rain falling on a habitat can be measured with a simple rain gauge like that in Fig. 36.3. The bottle is partly sunk into the ground so that the funnel catches rain just above ground level, to avoid collecting any surface run-off. The water level in the bottle must be checked each day or more often in rainy conditions. The depth of rain falling on the soil is then calculated by $(d^2/D^2) \times h$. For example, if the diameter of the funnel (D) is 20 cm, the internal diameter of the bottle (d) is 8 cm and the height (h) of the rain water in the bottle is 6 cm, then the depth of rain reaching the soil is

$$\frac{8^2}{20^2} \times 6 = \frac{64}{400} \times 6 = 0.96 \text{ cm}$$

Temperature. The simplest way to find the temperature of a habitat is to place a mercury thermometer in a position where it does not receive direct sunlight and watch for the reading to become steady. In water, the temperature in the surface layers may be higher than that at the bottom. In this case, the thermometer bulb can be carefully coated with warm wax and lowered to the bottom for about 10 minutes. It can then be pulled up through the top layers and the temperature read. The layer of wax slows down the exchange of heat so that the bottom temperature can be read before the mercury starts to rise again.

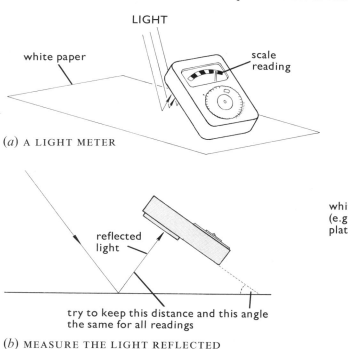

(a) A LIGHT METER

(b) MEASURE THE LIGHT REFLECTED FROM A SHEET OF PAPER

Fig. 36.1 Measuring light intensity

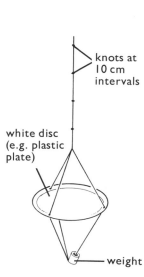

Fig. 36.2 Absorption of light by water

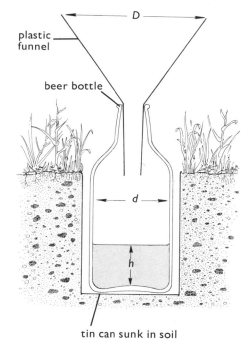

Fig. 36.3 A simple rain gauge

To find the daily temperature range in a habitat, a maximum and minimum thermometer is needed (Fig. 36.4). As the temperature rises, the alcohol in the bulb expands and pushes the mercury column to the left in the upper limb and to the right in the lower limb. The small metal "rider" in the lower limb is pushed to the right, while the upper one remains in the minimum temperature position. When the alcohol cools, the mercury column moves back, leaving the lower rider at the maximum position. The riders can be returned each day by tilting the thermometer.

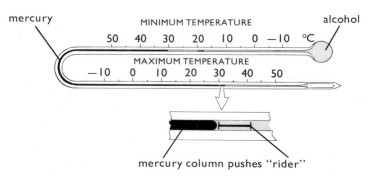

Fig. 36.4   A maximum and minimum thermometer

Humidity. The amount of water vapour in the atmosphere affects the rate of transpiration (p. 67). It also affects animals. For example, the cuticle of an insect makes it resistant to drying out but the skin of a frog or an earthworm rapidly loses water by evaporation. One would, therefore, expect frogs and earthworms to be restricted to humid situations, whereas many kinds of insect could survive in a dry environment.

Humidity is usually measured as a percentage saturation or *relative humidity*. A relative humidity of 100 per cent means that the air contains as much water vapour as possible (it is saturated) at that particular temperature. A relative humidity of 30 per cent means that the air is only 30 per cent saturated and is, therefore, fairly dry.

A simple device to measure relative humidity is a paper hygrometer (Fig. 36.5). The pointer is attached to a spiral made up of a metal and paper strip. When the air is damp (high humidity), the spiral coils up more tightly and moves the pointer over the scale to the right. When the air is dry (low humidity) the spiral opens up and carries the pointer to the left.

Comparisons of humidity may be made more simply by noting the time taken for blue cobalt chloride paper to turn pink as described on p. 69.

pH (acidity or alkalinity). To measure the pH of a soil sample, about 10 mm of the soil is placed in the bottom of a test-tube and about 10 mm barium sulphate powder is added. This is a neutral salt which will precipitate the clay particles so that, later on, the colour of the solution can be seen. A graduated pipette is used to add 10 cm³ distilled water and 2 cm³ soil indicator to the tube. The mouth of the tube is closed with a bung and the contents shaken vigorously. If the tube is allowed to stand for a minute, the soil particles will settle down leaving a clear, coloured solution above them. The colour is produced by the soil's acidity or alkalinity acting on the indicator dye.

The tube is held against a special colour chart (which may be part of the label on the indicator bottle) and the colour of the liquid matched as closely as possible with one of the colours on the chart. This colour will correspond to a particular pH range.

The pH of fresh water may be estimated in the same way, but there is no need to add barium sulphate unless the water contains fine suspended matter.

Other physical factors. There are many other factors one would like to measure in the environment, such as air movement, water flow, oxygen concentration in water and the minerals present in the soil. Some of these are easy and others are beyond the scope of elementary studies. Rate of water flow can be measured by timing a partly submerged object (e.g. a half-filled plastic bottle) between two fixed points on the bank. To find the mineral content of soil or water, however, is not so easy because the concentration of the salts is so low.

Sampling techniques

It might be possible to count all the palm trees in a school compound or extract and count all the insects in a piece of rotting wood, or all the earthworms in a soil sample. To identify

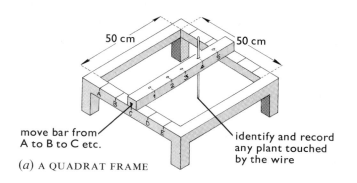

(a) A QUADRAT FRAME

Quadrat No. ....
Position ....
Date ....

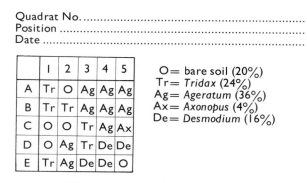

	1	2	3	4	5
A	Tr	O	Ag	Ag	Ag
B	Tr	Tr	Ag	Ag	Ag
C	O	O	Tr	Ag	Ax
D	O	Ag	Tr	De	De
E	Tr	Ag	De	De	O

O = bare soil (20%)
Tr = *Tridax* (24%)
Ag = *Ageratum* (36%)
Ax = *Axonopus* (4%)
De = *Desmodium* (16%)

(b) RECORDING THE RESULTS

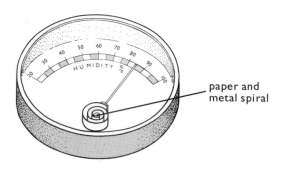

Fig. 36.5   A paper hygrometer for measuring humidity

Fig. 36.6   Using a quadrat frame

and count all the different kinds of fish in a lake or all the *Tridax* plants on a patch of waste ground would be difficult or impossible. Consequently, the ecologist has to sample a small part of an ecosystem, identify and count the organisms in this fraction of the habitat, and then estimate the total numbers in the habitat as a whole. Since the organisms may not be evenly distributed, he will have to take several samples from different parts of the habitat. There are likely to be seasonal fluctuations in the environment and so the samples will also need to be taken at regular intervals throughout the year.

Plant communities. QUADRATS. If you wanted to compare the plants growing on a roadside verge with those which colonized a recently abandoned farm, you would probably use the *quadrat frame* as a sampling method. The quadrat frame (Fig. 36.6) is placed at random on the ground. If the number of plants is small, it may be possible to identify, count and write down all the plants included in the frame. If there are too many plants for this, the bar is advanced across the frame 10 cm at a time and a straight piece of wire lowered through each hole in turn. The plant touched by the wire is identified and recorded each time. Since the wire will touch 25 different places in the quadrat, the number of times any one species of plant is recorded multiplied by 4 will give its percentage coverage of the ground. A single large plant may be touched by the wire, say, four times in different positions. In this case you have to decide whether to record four touches or one plant. In the first case you will be recording the percentage coverage of the ground (e.g. one or two large plants could cover 100 per cent of the ground). In the second case you will be recording the relative number of plants but not the percentage. In some investigations you may need to find the relative numbers of only one species of plant, e.g. the numbers of *Tridax* growing in sunny or shaded habitats.

LINE TRANSECT. This method is used to show how the vegetation changes from one part of a habitat to another. A length of string or clothes line is laid out across the area to be studied (Fig. 36.7). The string is knotted at intervals of 10 cm or

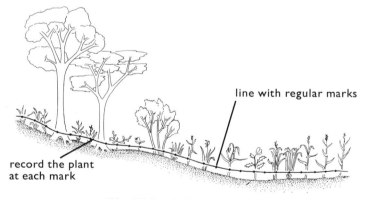

record the plant at each mark

line with regular marks

Fig. 36.7   A line transect

the plastic clothes line may have 10 cm marks inked on it. The plant which is underneath each 10 cm mark is identified and recorded. In this way any gradual change of vegetation can be shown. The change might be from a swampy area to a dry region, from fallow farmland to bush, from non-irrigated to irrigated land, or from a shaded to a sunny area. The transect record should always include the physical changes that are thought to influence the vegetation. For example, if the change is from light to shade, meter readings should be made at 10 cm intervals. If the transition is from a wet to a dry habitat, estimates of water content of the soil must be made at suitable intervals. The transect can also include soil depth or slope.

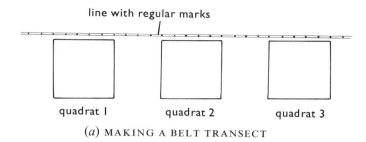

line with regular marks

quadrat 1   quadrat 2   quadrat 3

(*a*) MAKING A BELT TRANSECT

species found in this part of transect

} relative number of plants

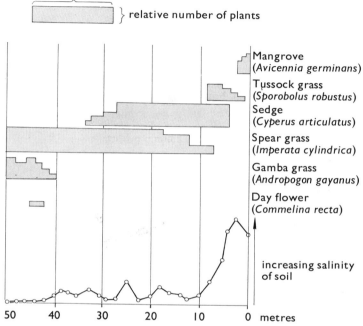

Mangrove (*Avicennia germinans*)

Tussock grass (*Sporobolus robustus*)

Sedge (*Cyperus articulatus*)

Spear grass (*Imperata cylindrica*)

Gamba grass (*Andropogon gayanus*)

Day flower (*Commelina recta*)

increasing salinity of soil

50   40   30   20   10   0   metres

(*b*) RESULT OF A 50 m BELT TRANSECT taken from a mangrove swamp to grassland. The change in salinity is shown but there was also a rise of 2·5 m from right to left and the soil composition and texture changed

(*After Swaine, Okali, Hall and Lock, Folio Geobot. Phytotax., Prague, 1979*)

Fig. 36.8   A belt transect

Fig. 36.9   A grapnel (When pulled through the water, the hooks collect pieces of plant)

BELT TRANSECT. A more complete and accurate picture of a transition from one part of a habitat to another is provided by a belt transect. This is done by taking a line of quadrat samples across the transition area (Fig. 36.8a). The quadrats can be taken continuously or at suitable intervals according to the length of the transect. Fig. 36.8b shows the result of a belt transect across 50 metres of grassland sloping downwards to a mangrove swamp.

AQUATIC PLANTS. The distribution of plants in shallow water can be plotted by the quadrat or transect method provided the water is free from *Schistosoma* (p. 225) and safe to wade in. If the water is too deep for wading, the plants can be collected by means of a grapnel (Fig. 36.9) on the end of a pole

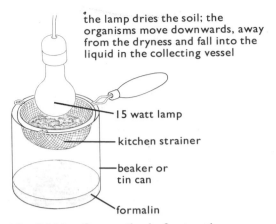

the lamp dries the soil; the organisms move downwards, away from the dryness and fall into the liquid in the collecting vessel

— 15 watt lamp

— kitchen strainer

— beaker or tin can

— formalin

Fig. 36.10   One method of extracting soil arthropods

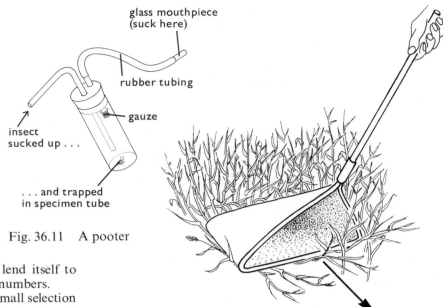

glass mouthpiece (suck here)

rubber tubing

gauze

insect sucked up . . .

. . . and trapped in specimen tube

Fig. 36.11   A pooter

sweep the net through the vegetation

Fig. 36.12   A sweep net

or on a line. This method, however, does not lend itself to accurate recording of the plants' distribution or numbers.

Animal communities. The following are just a small selection of methods for estimating the numbers and distribution of animals in a community.

QUADRATS AND TRANSECTS. These methods can be used for static or slowly moving animals in a community, such as barnacles or molluscs on a rocky shore or burrowing worms on a sandy beach. A quadrat would help to count the numbers of worm casts on a square metre of lawn or the snails in a patch of grassland.

DIRECT COUNTS. If the habitat is small or the animals are large, it may be possible to count them. For example, one could count the number of nests in a weaver bird colony or the number of aphids feeding on a leaf. A community of insects in a soil sample can be extracted, identified and counted as shown in Fig. 36.10.

SWEEP NETTING. A wide-mouthed net (Fig. 36.12) is swept through grass or similar vegetation (but not through thorny shrubs). Some of the insects will be knocked off the plants and fall into the net. At the end of the sweep, the net is twisted to trap the insects, which are then transferred to a collecting jar or picked up with a "pooter" (Fig. 36.11). By measuring the area of the net mouth and the length of the sweeps, it is possible to calculate the volume of the vegetation being sampled.

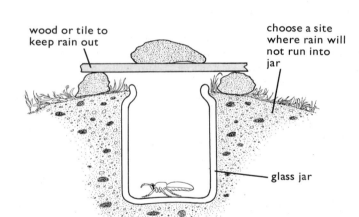

wood or tile to keep rain out

choose a site where rain will not run into jar

glass jar

Fig. 36.13   A pitfall trap

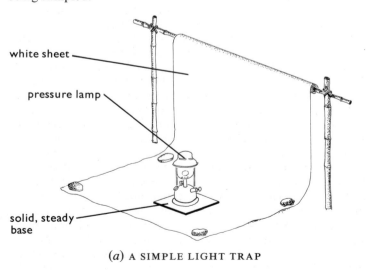

white sheet

pressure lamp

solid, steady base

(a) A SIMPLE LIGHT TRAP

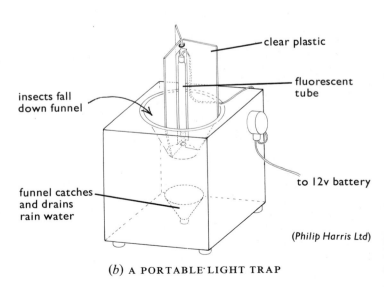

clear plastic

fluorescent tube

insects fall down funnel

funnel catches and drains rain water

to 12v battery

(Philip Harris Ltd)

(b) A PORTABLE LIGHT TRAP

Fig. 36.14   Light traps

TRAPPING. *Pitfall traps.* A jam jar is sunk into the ground as shown in Fig. 36.13. Insects such as beetles will fall into the trap, which should be inspected at regular intervals to see which insects are active at different times of the day. It can be left empty or baited with rotting meat, or with jam or syrup. The use of different baits will result in different insects being caught. If the traps are set up at regular intervals, e.g. 5 × 5 grid, it may be possible to build up a picture of the distribution of the organisms caught.

Sticky traps. A mixture of honey, sugar and stale beer, with a few drops of amyl acetate is spread on cardboard squares which are then hung in trees or on fences. Some weakly flying insects are passively blown on to the trap; others are attracted by the sugary mixture and get stuck when they land.

Light traps. A strong light source such as a 100 watt bulb or a paraffin pressure lamp is set up at night in front of a white sheet (Fig. 36.14a). The bulb must be protected from rain by covering it with a large beaker. Nocturnal insects are attracted to the light and can be picked off with a pooter or in a sweep net.

A manufactured light trap is shown in Fig. 36.14b.

SOIL ARTHROPODS. The arthropod population in the soil can be sampled by placing the soil in a kitchen strainer and heating it from above with a 15 watt lamp (Fig. 36.10). As the heat dries the soil from the top, some of the organisms will move down through the soil and fall into the liquid in the beaker.

MARKING AND RECAPTURE. The organisms caught by some of the methods described above can be marked, e.g. a drop of quick-drying paint on the thorax of a grasshopper. They are then released and on the same sampling method used again next day over the same area. Suppose that 10 grasshoppers (N_1) were captured, marked and released on the first day. Next day, 16 grasshoppers (N_2) were caught in the same area and 4 of these (N_3) were ones marked yesterday. The total population (T) of grasshoppers in that area can then be estimated from

$$\frac{N_1}{T} = \frac{N_3}{N_2} \quad \text{i.e.} \quad \frac{10}{T} = \frac{4}{16} \quad \text{so the population is 40 (approx)}$$

There are many sources of error in this method. The released organisms must be as numerous as possible and undamaged by either the capture or marking methods. The recapture must be carried out in identical conditions, using the same method, in the same area, for the same length of time as before.

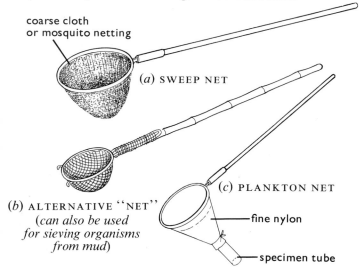

coarse cloth or mosquito netting

(a) SWEEP NET

(b) ALTERNATIVE "NET" *(can also be used for sieving organisms from mud)*

(c) PLANKTON NET

fine nylon

specimen tube

Fig. 36.15   Collecting nets for fresh-water organisms

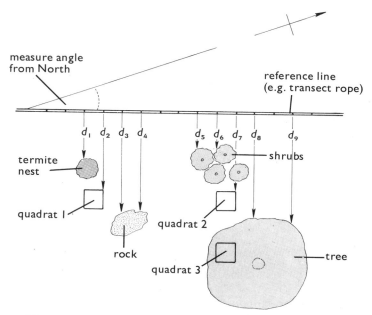

measure angle from North

reference line (e.g. transect rope)

d_1 d_2 d_3 d_4 d_5 d_6 d_7 d_8 d_9

termite nest

shrubs

quadrat 1

quadrat 2

rock

quadrat 3

tree

Fig. 36.16   Mapping an area for sampling (Measure the distances d_1, d_2, etc. and draw them to scale on your map)

Aquatic animals. No attempt should be made to collect samples from any fresh water that is likely to contain *Schistosoma* (p. 225). The area health authority will probably be able to offer advice on this.

SWEEP NET. A fixed number of sweeps are made with a strong net such as that in Fig. 36.15a, through an area of water. The net is then inverted into a tray of water and the organisms can be identified and recorded or transferred to a carrying jar. The same number of sweeps should be made in a different area if a comparison is to be made. A kitchen strainer can be used instead of a net. It can be tied to a bamboo pole to get a longer reach (Fig. 36.15b).

PLANKTON NET. This is similar to a sweep net but the very fine nylon mesh traps small crustacea and some algae and protista from the plankton. The net must be moved slowly through the surface water at about 50 cm per second, to allow the water to pass through the fine mesh. Small organisms are collected in the specimen tube at the end (Fig. 36.15c). From the diameter of the net opening and the length and number of sweeps, the volume of water sampled can be calculated.

All these methods have their disadvantages. In direct counting, animals may be overlooked or counted twice; sweep netting dislodges and catches only relatively inactive insects; a predator in a pitfall trap may eat all the other animals which fall in. The limitations of each method must be clearly thought out before trying to draw firm conclusions from the field studies.

Recording. In the accounts of sampling methods, mention has been made of the need to keep records. However, even before a habitat is sampled, it is necessary to make a map of the area so that the position of the samples can be marked on it. It may be sufficient to make a simple sketch map by just pacing out the distances and marking the positions of trees or buildings. A more accurate map can be made by the offset method. The string or line used for transects is laid along one side of the habitat. The distances from the line to particular features of the habitat are then measured at right angles to the line. The lines and these distances are then drawn to scale and the compass direction marked in (Fig. 36.16).

THE ECOLOGY OF FRESH WATER

Ponds, lakes and rivers form clearly defined examples of ecosystems. Some of the properties of a pond can be reproduced by setting up a balanced aquarium in the laboratory.

Physical aspects of a fresh-water environment

Density. Water is far more dense than air. It offers resistance to moving animals but it also physically supports the animals and plants. Plants and animals living in rivers and streams must be able to withstand or avoid the force of the flowing water.

Temperature. Water can absorb a good deal of heat from the sun without its temperature rising much. Similarly, when water loses heat, its temperature does not fall much. A very small or shallow pond might heat up during the day and cool down at night but in most fresh-water habitats, the temperature remains fairly constant (Fig. 36.17).

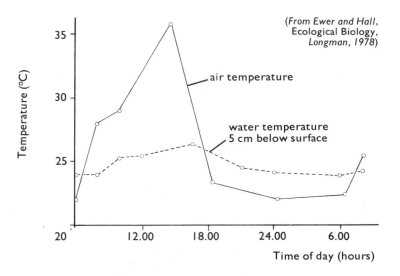

(From Ewer and Hall, Ecological Biology, Longman, 1978)

Fig. 36.17   Daily temperature change in air and water (small lake near Accra)

Small, shallow ponds may evaporate completely in the dry season and rivers may also dry up, leaving a series of static pools. This means that the organisms which live there will be killed unless they have some means of withstanding the drought. Plants may have resistant seeds; animals may burrow into the mud.

Light. Except for places where trees and shrubs grow on the banks, the surface water will receive a high light intensity. The small particles suspended in the water absorb the light so that at a depth of a metre or two, there may not be enough light to allow plants to photosynthesize and grow. The changes in light intensity and other conditions are shown in Fig. 36.18.

Oxygen. Although water is H_2O, the oxygen in its molecule is not available for respiration. The oxygen that plants and animals use for respiration is *dissolved* in the water. It comes from the plants' photosynthesis during the day and also diffuses continuously through the water surface from the air.

There is much less oxygen in water than there is in air. At 0°C, 100 cm³ water can hold only about 1 cm³ dissolved oxygen. (100 cm³ air contains about 20 cm³ oxygen.) This means that a stationary animal or plant in still water quickly uses up all the oxygen from the water immediately around it. Anything, such as eutrophication (p. 56), which reduces this small oxygen concentration in fresh water puts the animals at risk of

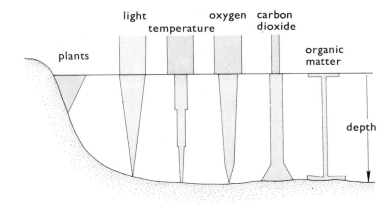

(From Bennett and Humphries, Introduction to Field Biology, *Arnold, 1974)*

Fig. 36.18   How conditions change with depth. The width of each column is proportional to the factors named

suffocation. Any event which breaks up the surface of the water, e.g. waterfalls or breaking waves, helps to introduce more oxygen from the air.

Minerals. The water flowing in a river or into a lake brings a supply of minerals. Water draining from heavily fertilized farm land may even bring too many minerals (*see* p. 58). In enclosed lakes and ponds, the supply of minerals will be maintained by normal recycling processes (p. 54).

Substrate. This is the mud or silt on the bottom. It allows plants to root and animals to burrow in it. If it contains a lot of decaying organic matter, it may be very short of oxygen. This is because the bacteria which break down the organic matter use up oxygen in their respiration. Streams which flow into a lake may bring down deposits of silt which collect on the bottom and gradually fill the lake.

The plant community

The surface waters of ponds, lakes and rivers contain the microscopic algae which form the phytoplankton (p. 53). There will be diatoms and blue-green algae, and in small ponds there may be filamentous algae like *Spirogyra* (p. 172). The high light intensity of these surface waters allows rapid photosynthesis.

Floating freely on the surface of still waters in lakes and ponds are plants such as the water lettuce (*Pistia*, Fig. 36.19) and duckweed (*Lemna*). Since these plants receive direct sunlight and can reproduce rapidly by vegetative propagation (p. 23) they may spread to cover a large surface of the water (Plate 64) and restrict the light reaching the submerged plants. The roots and lower parts of the leaves contain air spaces which enable the plants to float, and the waxy cuticle on the leaves repels water if the leaves are temporarily submerged by waves.

Submerged plants. Plants such as *Vallisneria* (Fig. 36.20) are rooted in the substrate and can only grow where the water is shallow enough or clear enough to allow plenty of light to penetrate. The thin, ribbon-like leaves of *Vallisneria* present a large surface area to the water and so are able to absorb the necessary amount of carbon dioxide for photosynthesis. The many, thin, branching leaves of hornwort (*Ceratophyllum*, Fig. 36.21) also present a large surface area to the water. In both plants the cuticle is very thin and the epidermal cells, unlike

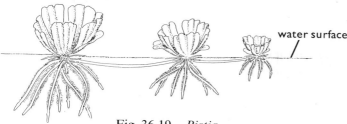

Fig. 36.19   *Pistia*

Submerged and aerial leaves. In plants such as *Heteranthera* (Fig. 36.22) and *Hygrophila*, the submerged leaves show the adaptations described for an aquatic environment, while the aerial leaves are characteristic of land plants.

Growing on the underwater parts of all these plants there is a community, called the *periphyton*, of small organisms such as *Hydra* (p. 137), *Vorticella* (p. 175), filamentous algae (p. 172) and blue-green algae. These are grazed by fish, tadpoles, pond snails and insect larvae.

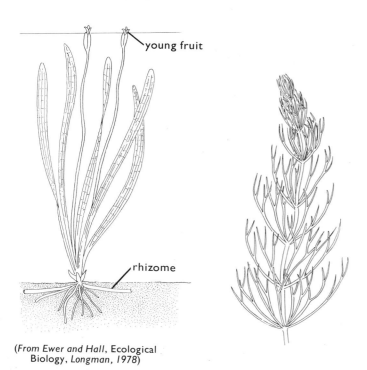

(*From Ewer and Hall*, Ecological Biology, Longman, 1978)

Fig. 36.20   *Vallisneria*   Fig. 36.21   *Ceratophyllum*

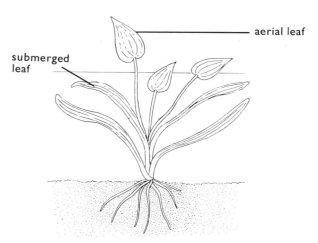

(*From Ewer and Hall*, Ecological Biology, Longman, 1978)

Fig. 36.22   *Heteranthera*

most land plants, contain chloroplasts. Inside the leaves there are air spaces which keep the plant shoots or leaves floating as near to the surface as possible. *Ceratophyllum* has no roots and so the whole plant floats near the surface.

The thin leaves of plants such as *Vallisneria* also offer very little resistance to water flow. They stream out with the current and are not likely to be pulled off. Because water is so much denser than air, it buoys up and supports the plants submerged in it. Consequently the plants do not need as much strengthening tissue in their stems and leaves as do land plants. For this reason aquatic plants removed from their environment are limp and floppy.

Plants with leaves floating at the surface. The leaves of plants such as the water lily (*Nymphaea*) receive direct sunlight. Their stomata are on the upper surface and so exchange gases directly with the atmosphere rather than with the water. The upper surface of the leaf has a waxy cuticle which allows wave splashes and rainwater to run off.

There is very little oxygen in the mud at the bottom of lakes and rivers and it is not always clear how plant roots can respire in these conditions. In some cases, such as in the water lily, there are air spaces running from leaves to roots, which would allow diffusion of oxygen (Plate 63).

The flowers of these plants and of those in the next group are brought above the surface and pollinated probably by insects or the wind.

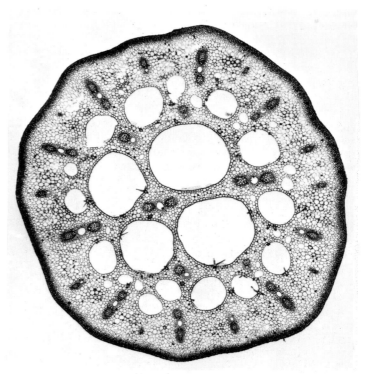

(*Brian Bracegirdle*)

Plate 63.   *NYMPHAEA* LEAF STALK, TRANSVERSE SECTION (× 12)

The large air spaces may allow diffusion of carbon dioxide and oxygen between the leaves and roots

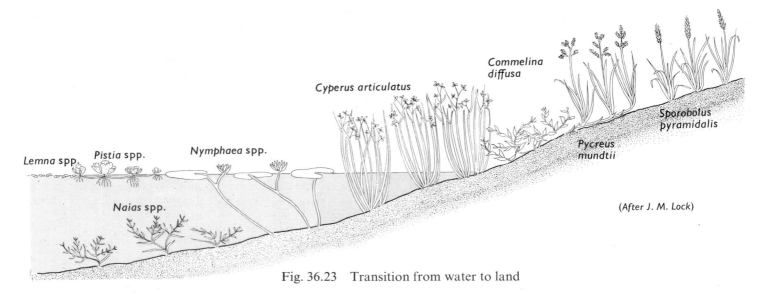

Fig. 36.23   Transition from water to land

Plants growing at the edge. If the banks are shelving, there is usually a gradual transition from water plants to land plants (Fig. 36.23). This is an informative area in which to make a transect (see p. 211).

The roots and lower stems of plants such as the sedge (*Cyperus*) are totally submerged in shallow water. The abundant air spaces in the lower stem permit oxygen to diffuse into the roots. The types of plants represented in the change from aquatic to terrestrial vegetation probably reflect the extent to which they can tolerate having their roots submerged and deprived of oxygen.

Succession. The stems and submerged leaves of aquatic plants interfere with the free flow of water and cause it to deposit part of the sediment it is carrying. This gradually makes the water shallower and so favours the growth of plants which thrive better in these new conditions. The wholly submerged plants are gradually replaced by partly submerged plants and then by the water-side plants. So the natural tendency for any lake, or area of slowly moving water, is to fill with sediment and change over to a land ecosystem. The process by which an aquatic community is gradually replaced by a land community is an example of *succession* (Plate 64). The gradual change of neglected agricultural land back into bush, over a period of 10 years or so, is also an example of succession.

The animal community

There are a great many different species of animals living in fresh-water habitats and it is possible to mention only a few representative examples here.

Surface film. Pond skaters (Fig. 36.24) are insects which move about on the surface film of static or sluggish water. The water-repelling bristles on the tips of their legs prevent them breaking through the surface film and so the pond skater can glide over the water surface by brisk movements of the middle pair of legs. Most species feed on the dead bodies of insects floating at the surface by sucking the fluids from their bodies through the piercing mouth parts. Tiny springtails (Fig. 36.25) also live on the surface film. They are simple, wingless insects and are thought to feed on microscopic plants in the surface film.

Plankton. In the top few centimetres of water, there is usually a dense population of zooplankton (p. 53). This includes protozoans such as *Paramecium* (p. 175) and small crustaceans such as water fleas and *Cyclops* (Figs. 36.26 and 36.27). *Paramecium* feeds on the microscopic plants and bacteria in the phytoplankton. The water fleas have a filter-feeding mechanism. They draw a current of water between the two halves of their body covering and filter out the edible plankton.

(Michael Lock)

Plate 64.   LAKESIDE ZONATION

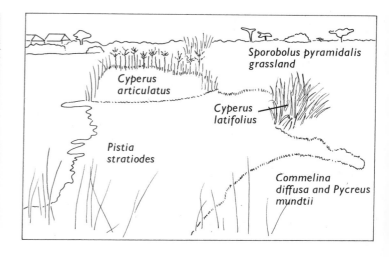

Key to Plate 64

The vegetation changes from floating plants, to plants rooted in the water, to dry grassland (See Fig. 38.24)

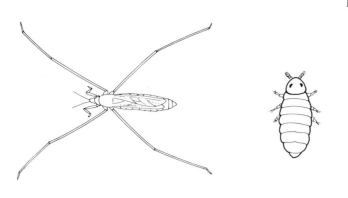

Fig. 36.24   Pond skater
(× 1)

Fig. 36.25   Springtail
(× 10)

in fast streams, or swimming about fairly freely in sluggish waters. Caddis fly larvae (Fig. 36.29) also live in the bottom waters of well-aerated streams and lakes. They make themselves a tubular casing of pebbles, sand or vegetation and some species spin a silk net for catching their food. Also living on the substrate or in the vegetation is the water louse, *Asellus* (Fig. 36.30). This appears to be a scavenger in its feeding. Another crustacean, the fresh-water shrimp, *Gammarus* (Fig. 36.31), prefers well-oxygenated water.

Fresh-water clams are molluscs which live in the mud at the bottom of lakes and rivers. Inside their two shells are net-like gills, covered with cilia. The beating of the cilia draws water into the shells and the gills filter out small organisms from the water. These organisms are then trapped in sticky mucus and swallowed by the clam.

Free-swimming animals. Water beetles (Fig. 36.32) and water boatmen move about freely in ponds and lakes though they do cling to water weed to stop themselves floating to the surface when they stop swimming. There are many different species of water beetle which may be either carnivorous or plant eaters. There are two common families of water boatmen, *Notonecta* (Fig. 36.33), which swims on its back, and *Corixa* (Fig. 36.34), which swims the right way up. They have short, tubular mouth parts which they use to suck up particles of plant and animal debris.

Fish such as the catfish (*Clarias*), guppy (*Lebistes*) and *Tilapia* may be found swimming in any part of ponds, lakes and rivers though they have preferred areas for obtaining their food.

Surface feeders. Mosquito larvae hang from the surface film and filter out plankton by the flicking movements of their "mouth brushes" (p. 153). Some species of flatworm may be found gliding along under the surface film by means of their cilia. They are probably feeding on insects and crustacea in the surface film. Flatworms and pond snails are also to be found on the underside of floating leaves. The snails feed by rasping off pieces of leaf, or the algae covering the leaf, with their tongues. Small fish, such as the guppy, feed at the surface on mosquito larvae and water fleas.

Bottom-living animals. Dragonflies and mayflies have larvae (Fig. 36.28) which live in fresh water. When the larvae reach full size, they emerge from the water and metamorphose into the imago. There are many different types of mayfly and their larvae may be adapted to burrowing in mud, clinging to stones

tube made from plant debris

Fig. 36.29   Caddis fly larva
(× 1·5)

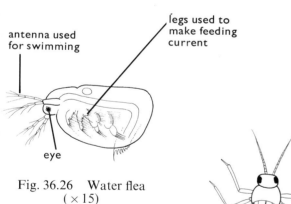

antenna used for swimming

legs used to make feeding current

eye

Fig. 36.26   Water flea
(× 15)

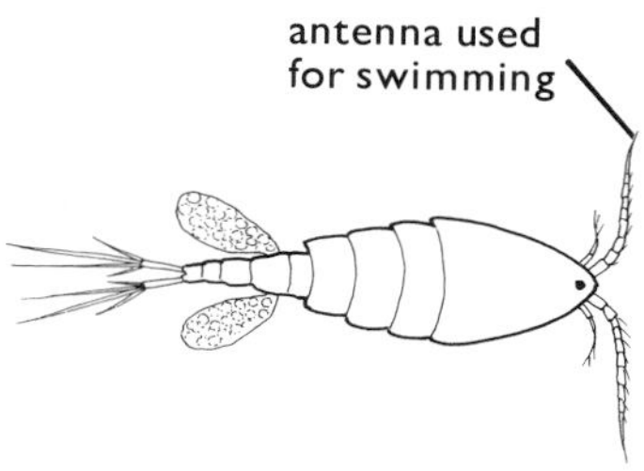

antenna used for swimming

Fig. 36.27   *Cyclops*
(× 15)

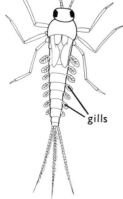

gills

Fig. 36.28   Mayfly larva
(× 1·5)

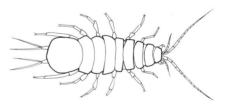

Fig. 36.30   Water louse
(× 1·5)

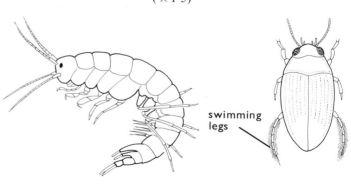

swimming legs

Fig. 36.31   Fresh-water shrimp
(× 2)

Fig. 36.32   Water beetle
(× 1)

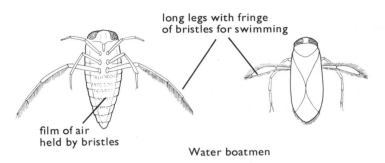

long legs with fringe
of bristles for swimming

film of air
held by bristles

Water boatmen

Fig. 36.33   *Notonecta*   Fig. 36.34   *Corixa*
      ($\times 1$)   ($\times 1$)

Adaptations of aquatic animals

(*a*) **Adaptations for movement.** Rapid movement through a dense medium like water requires a streamlined shape. This is seen in most fish and in some mayfly larvae. The latter fold their legs and gills flat against their bodies and swim with rapid wriggling movements. Water beetles and water boatmen are fairly streamlined but their legs are also adapted for propulsion through water. The last pair of legs is particularly long, slightly flattened and fringed with bristles. The long legs row the insect through the water, the bristles offering maximum resistance during the driving stroke and very little in the recovery stroke.

Some of the aquatic animals have adaptations to make them buoyant. Thus they do not sink to the bottom when they stop swimming. Fish have a swim bladder (p. 159); the transparent phantom midge larva (*Chaoborus*, Fig. 36.35) which floats, almost invisible, near the surface to capture its prey has two pairs of air sacs. The abundant bristles on the antennae of the water flea offer a lot of water resistance and so help it to swim, but they also slow down its rate of sinking.

In swiftly moving streams and rivers, some animals may have adaptations which prevent them being swept away in the current. *Gammarus* and some mayfly larvae are flattened and so offer little resistance to the water flow. Leeches (Fig. 36.36) have suckers which attach firmly to their host animal but also prevent them being carried off in water currents.

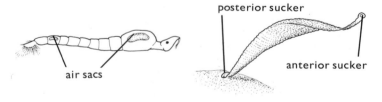

air sacs

posterior sucker

anterior sucker

Fig. 36.35   Phantom midge larva   Fig. 36.36   Leech
          ($\times 3$)   ($\times 0.5$)

(*b*) **Adaptations for breathing.** There are two options open to fresh-water animals; either they extract the dissolved air from the water or they go to the surface and breathe air directly from the atmosphere. Those which use the dissolved oxygen usually have some form of gills which present a large surface to the water. They also have some method of changing the water in contact with the gills. The breathing method of fish is described on p. 160. The gills of the mayfly larvae have branches of the tracheal system (p. 147) running into them. A rhythmic flicking movement of the gills keeps fresh supplies of water moving past them. The caddis larva has gills and forces a stream of water over them by undulations of the body inside the tube.

Tubifex worms (Fig. 36.37) live in the mud at the bottom of ponds where the oxygen concentration is usually low. They build tubes in the mud and their bodies project from them and wave about, so renewing the supply of water in contact with them. The lower the oxygen concentration, the more of their body protrudes from the tube. Their blood contains haemoglobin which helps to absorb what little oxygen there is. Some species of the midge *Chironomus* have larvae (Fig. 36.38) which, unlike most insects, have haemoglobin. These, too, live in tubes in poorly oxygenated mud.

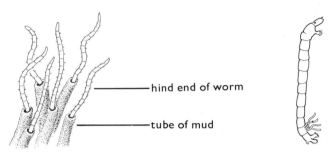

hind end of worm

tube of mud

Fig. 36.37   *Tubifex* worms ($\times 1$). The   Fig. 36.38
less oxygen there is in the water, the   *Chironomus*
more the worm protrudes from its tube   larva ($\times 3$)

Mosquito larvae and pupae hang by a tube ("siphon") from the surface film (p. 153). This siphon allows a gaseous exchange to take place between the air in the tracheal system and the atmosphere. Water beetles carry a store of air under their wing cases and rise to the surface from time to time to replenish the supply. Water boatmen carry a film of air trapped in bristles covering the surface of their bodies. Pond snails have a simple "lung" under their shells. They fill the lung with air at the water surface at intervals.

Inter-relationships

Ponds and lakes may be self-sufficient ecosystems with no new material being brought into them. The oxygen produced by the photosynthesis of green plants in daylight replaces the oxygen used up by the plants and animals. The carbon dioxide produced by plant and animal respiration is used by plants during their daytime photosynthesis.

The dead remains of plants and animals fall to the bottom of the lake or river and decay as a result of bacterial action; the nitrates and phosphates so released into the water are used by the plants for their growth (p. 51).

The plants and animals of fresh water form a complex food web (p. 53). For example, protozoa eat single-celled plants; water fleas eat protozoa; fish and *Hydra* eat water fleas; big fish eat the smaller fish; and herons may eat some of the big fish (Fig. 36.39).

Although suggestions have been made in the text about the food of the pond animals, there is a great deal still to be found out about what they eat. In many cases, it depends on the species. One species of water beetle may eat plants while another species may be carnivorous. It is not always easy to find out exactly what some of the small animals are eating. It is not clear, for example, whether pond snails eat the leaves of water plants or just scrape off the algae which are growing on the leaves. Some authors claim that water boatmen are carnivorous and pursue their prey but others say they only suck up plant and animal debris. Only by careful observation and by examining the gut contents is it possible to decide what is the main food source of an animal.

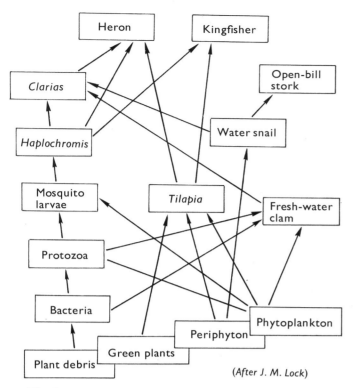

Fig. 36.39   Part of a food web in Lake Nungua
(Many more organisms and arrows could be added)

(After J. M. Lock)

KEY FOR SOME FRESHWATER INVERTEBRATES

1 { Body flattened; not more than about 2 cm long; gliding movement................FLATWORM
{ Body not flattened ....(2)

2 { Body with a shell..............................MOLLUSC (e.g. snail)
{ Body with no shell ....(3)

3 { Body narrow cylindrical and segmented ....(4)
{ Body not narrow and cylindrical............(5)

4 { Obvious head; appendages or mouth parts on front segments ....Insect larva (e.g. Chironomus)
{ No obvious head; no appendages or mouth parts ....ANNELID (e.g. Tubifex)

5 { Head appendages used for locomotion ......Water fleas or Cyclops
{ Other appendages used for locomotion..... (6)

6 { Three pairs of legs ....INSECT (e.g. water boatman)
{ More than three pairs of legs ....CRUSTACEAN (e.g. Gammarus)

USE OF AN IDENTIFICATION KEY

In many, but not all, ecological studies, it is necessary to identify the plants and animals in a community. For example, it would be perfectly possible to compare the distribution of two kinds of snail without being able to name them, provided you could reliably recognise them. On the other hand, if you wanted to compare your work with that of other biologists, you would need to know the names of the organisms in order to relate your results to theirs.

There are several ways of identifying an organism. One is to ask someone with experience in the subject; another way is to compare the organism with photographs or line drawings in a book. A third way is to use a *key*, often in conjunction with drawings.

The key given above offers a method of identifying some of the invertebrates in a fresh water community. To use the key, you must start at 1 and select the alternative which best describes your specimen. This may lead at once to an identification, at least at the level of the phylum (p. 207) or it may refer you to the next number in the key and another pair of alternatives. For example, at step 1, if your specimen has a flattened body and moves with a gliding motion, it is probably a flatworm. If it has neither of these features, you must go to step 2 and decide whether or not it has a shell.

Once you know whether your organism is a flatworm, mollusc, insect, etc. you can refer to another key dealing specifically with the phylum. The key will eventually lead you to the class, order, family and species of the organism.

Keys such as this are often described as "artificial" because they do not employ the important features used to classify organisms into kingdoms, phyla, classes, etc. The key on p. 207 asks questions which are based on the fundamental differences between kingdoms, but the key on this page makes use of superficial features which do not necessarily have any bearing on the principles by which the organism is classified.

For example, a fundamental characteristic of Insects and Crustacea is the possession of jointed limbs. But it is difficult to see the legs of a cyclops or a water flea, let along decide whether they are jointed or not. So, one has to use a superficial criterion, i.e. the use of the antennae for swimming. This would not be a sound basis for classification but is an easily recognisable feature for identification.

QUESTIONS

1. What is the habitat of the larva of the housefly (p. 154)? What else makes up the larva's environment?

2. How would you try to find out the population of *Tridax* plants in (a) a square metre of waste ground and (b) 50 metres of roadside verge?

3. (a) What are the physical features of a soil ecosystem (p. 78)? (b) How might the plant and animal communities of the soil influence these physical features?

4. If you wanted to study the ecology of a population of grasshoppers in an area of grassland, what would you try to find out about (a) the grasshoppers and (b) the grassland?

5. All sampling methods have their disadvantages. Why do you think that the following methods cannot give a wholly accurate measure of the population of animals and plants in a pond community: (a) pulling out pond weed with a grapnel (p. 211) and (b) collecting pond animals with a sweep net?

6. What kind of information can be discovered by using (a) a quadrat frame and (b) a line transect?

7. What do you think are (a) the advantages and (b) the disadvantages of fresh water as an environmental medium? (*See also* p. 65.)

8. Why should an excess of sewage or mineral salts in a fresh-water environment lead to the suffocation of fish? (*See also* pp. 56 and 74.)

9. In what ways, do you think, are (a) fish, (b) mosquito larvae adapted to life in water?

10. The leaves of submerged plants do not have stomata. Use your knowledge of plant physiology to say why you would expect this. (*See* pp. 20 and 68.)

11. A fish is said to be adapted to movement in water by having a smooth outline offering little water resistance. A water flea is said to be adapted to movement in water by having long bristles on its antennae which offer a lot of resistance to the water. Try to explain this apparent contradiction.

37 | Organisms Which Cause Disease

AMONG the viruses, bacteria, fungi, protozoa, flatworms and roundworms, there are species which, if they get into the body of man, may cause disease. These species may be classed as parasites but in some cases the parasite seems to be so well adapted to its host, or the host has become so tolerant of the parasite, that there are no obvious harmful effects. Some of the parasites which do cause harm will now be considered.

VIRUSES

These are very small structures, from 0·02 to 0·3 μm in diameter (1 μm = one thousandth of a millimetre; bacteria are 0·5–8 μm long). Viruses can be seen only by using an electron microscope with a magnification of about $\times 30{,}000$.

A virus particle consists of a protein coat with a core of DNA (deoxyribonucleic acid) or RNA (ribonucleic acid), as shown in Fig. 37.1. (DNA is the substance in the chromosomes of a cell's nucleus which determines what kinds of enzymes and structural proteins the cells will produce. RNA is in the cytoplasm of a cell and controls the chemical build-up of these proteins.)

One type of virus (called a *bacteriophage*) attacks bacteria, as shown in Fig. 37.2 and Plate 65. The DNA of the virus takes control of the bacterial cell, makes it produce virus proteins instead of bacterial proteins and destroys the bacterial cell in the process.

Viruses of polio and influenza, for example, attack human cells in a similar way (except that the whole virus goes into the cell) and cause disease symptoms.

When a virus is not invading a cell, it does not grow or reproduce. It does not feed, respire or excrete. For these reasons it is difficult to decide whether a virus is a living organism as judged by the characteristics described on p. 9. The only living characteristic it shows is the ability to reproduce and it can only do this inside a living cell by using the materials supplied by the cell. Perhaps viruses are best regarded as representing a borderline between the living and non-living state.

Human viruses

Polio, influenza, measles, mumps, chicken pox, trachoma and the common cold are all caused by viruses.

Poliomyelitis. The poliovirus is widespread in human populations where it usually invades the cells lining the nose, throat and intestine, causing only a sore throat, slight fever, headache and vomiting. More often an infection passes without being noticed. In a small minority of cases, however, the virus invades the ventral part of the grey matter in the spinal cord (*see* p. 141) and damages the motor neurones, causing weakness and sometimes paralysis of the muscles supplied by these neurones. If the muscles of the ribs and diaphragm are paralysed, the patient's breathing has to be maintained artificially until the muscles recover.

The viruses are present in the faeces of infected persons and the disease is spread by contamination of water, food, utensils, etc., with house-flies possibly helping to distribute the virus. In communities where sewage disposal is not very advanced or standards of hygiene are low, nearly everyone in the population catches the disease and recovers from it at some time. As a result, most people have an acquired immunity. When standards of hygiene and sewage disposal improve, few people catch the disease and so there is little immunity in the population. When the disease does occur in such populations, it takes the form of an epidemic.

Polio can be controlled by vaccination. A harmless form of the virus is given by mouth. It may cause mild symptoms but it

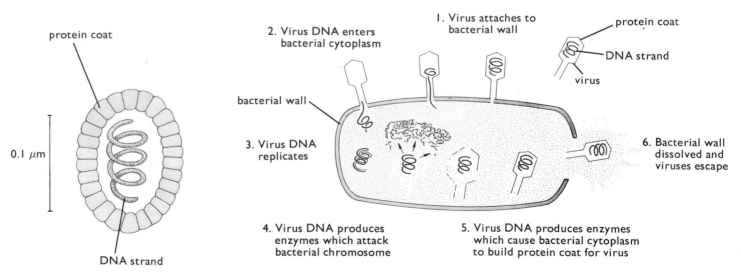

Fig. 37.1   Structure of a virus

Fig. 37.2   How a virus infects a bacterium
(Many more viruses would be involved than are shown here)

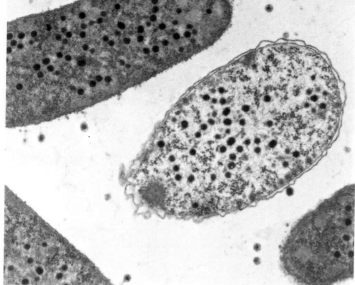

(M. Meader, M. Wurtz and F. Traub)

Plate 65. VIRUSES ATTACKING BACTERIA (× 25,000)
The photograph shows all or part of four bacteria, each containing many viruses which show up as dark blobs

confers long lasting immunity. Although the disease may be eliminated from a population by vaccination and improved sanitation, the immunization programme must be kept up. If it stops, the next generation will have no immunity to polio and will be very susceptible to the disease.

BACTERIA

Unlike viruses, the majority of bacteria are harmless or beneficial to man. Some, for example, play an important part in decay and the recycling of minerals as described on pp. 54 and 71. Some live harmlessly in the human intestine where they help in digestion of plant fibres and even produce vitamin K which the body needs. However, there are a few bacteria which cause diseases.

Bacterial diseases of man

Some of the bacteria which cause human diseases are described on p. 70 and the methods by which they are transmitted are described on p. 71.

Cholera. If the bacteria *Vibrio cholerae* are ingested, they multiply in the small intestine and invade its epithelial cells. When the bacteria die, they release toxins (p. 94), which irritate the intestinal lining and lead to the secretion of large amounts of water and salts. This causes acute diarrhoea, and the loss of body fluid and salt leads to dehydration and kidney failure. Antibiotics like tetracycline will kill the vibrios but it is more important to restore the salt and water balance of the body by drinking a solution made by dissolving one teaspoon of sugar and a pinch of salt in a cupful of water after each bout of diarrhoea.

A vaccine made from the killed bacteria will give immunity for 3–6 months. Since infection can occur only by ingesting bacteria derived from the faeces of an infected person (*see* p. 72), the long-term methods of control are to dispose of human sewage safely, ensure that drinking water is free from bacteria and prevent food from being contaminated, as described on pp. 72–4.

Tuberculosis. It is estimated that there are 2–3 million new cases of tuberculosis each year and 1–2 million deaths from the disease.

Pulmonary tuberculosis is caused by *Mycobacterium tuberculosis*, which is inhaled in droplets spread from the coughing of an infected person. *Bovine tuberculosis* is caused by *Mycobacterium bovis*, which is present in the untreated milk of infected cows.

When the tuberculosis bacteria get into the lungs they set up a local inflammation and produce an abscess. This usually heals up and leaves a small patch of scar tissue which shows up on X-ray photographs. Chest X-rays of large numbers of people show that many have had a tuberculous lung infection and recovered from it, often without noticing any symptoms.

In conditions where people are under-nourished, suffering from malaria or other illnesses, or living in crowded, poorly ventilated houses, their antibody defence mechanisms may not keep pace with the invasion and growth of the bacteria, so that large areas of the lungs are destroyed and the bacteria may reach other tissues by way of the lymphatic system. Symptoms of this level of infection are fever, persistent coughing, sometimes with blood being coughed up, loss of weight and general weakness.

The disease can be cured by the drugs *streptomycin, para-amino salicylic acid* and *isoniazid* or combinations of these to stop the bacteria developing resistance to any one of them. A good diet and rest are also needed for a successful recovery. Avoidance of over-crowding, provision of good ventilation and better nutrition help to reduce the incidence of the disease. Heat treatment (*pasteurization*) of milk destroys any *Mycobacterium bovis* present. The BCG vaccine is a harmless form of *Mycobacterium* and gives immunity for 3–5 years. (BCG stands for bacillus Calmette-Guérin, the names of the two French scientists who first prepared the vaccine.)

Venereal (sexually transmitted) diseases. *Gonorrhoea* is caused by a bacterium called *Neisseria gonorrhoeae* or, more usually, *gonococcus*. The causative organism of *syphilis* is *Treponema pallidum*, a spirochaete bacterium. Both bacteria cause diseases of the sexual organs and, since neither can survive for long outside the body, they can be transmitted usually only by sexual intercourse.

Gonococcus multiplies in the epithelium of the male's urethra or the female's cervix and may give rise to pain and a discharge of pus, though in females these symptoms may not appear and the infection is not noticed. The bacteria can damage and block the urethra and, in both sexes, may cause sterility. During birth, a baby's eye may become infected as it passes through the cervix and vagina.

Gonorrhoea can be cured with antibiotics but the bacteria have produced resistant strains. There is no period of immunity after recovery and, since an infected woman may have no symptoms, she may re-infect her partner after he is cured.

The symptoms of syphilis are very variable, but unlike gonorrhoea they may affect any part of the body. At first a hard swelling and ulcer may develop on the sexual organs but this usually heals in a week or two. By this time, however, the bacteria have invaded the body and may cause a skin rash and swollen lymph nodes. If the disease is not treated with antibodies and cured by this stage, the spirochaetes form permanent pockets of infection in the body, causing inflammation, persistent ulcers and obstruction of the arteries. If the bacteria invade the heart or brain they will cause death. In pregnant women, the *Treponema* bacteria can get across the placenta and infect the foetus.

Since the bacteria of syphilis and gonorrhoea are transmitted only by sexual intercourse, the diseases are easily avoided by simply not having sexual intercourse with an infected person. However, the signs of the diseases are often not noticeable and it may not be possible to recognize an infected person with certainty.

FUNGI

Fungi are described in Chapter 15, p. 75. There are not many examples of fungi which cause disease in man, but there are many serious fungal diseases of crop plants, such as the potato blight described on p. 76. Two fairly common fungus diseases in man are tinea and thrush.

Fungus diseases of man

Tinea ("ringworm") and *thrush* (candidiasis) are mild infections of the skin or epithelium. Thrush is an infection of the epithelium of the mouth or vagina by a yeast-like fungus called *Candida*. Although the fungus is normally present on these surfaces, and in the intestine, it is suppressed by the bacteria also present. Intensive antibiotic treatment for a bacterial infection may, by eliminating all bacterial competition, leave the way open for rapid growth of the fungus, but the infection is not usually serious.

Tinea is caused by one or more fungi such as *Microsporum* or *Trichophyton*. The fungi attack only the cornified layer of the skin and give rise to slightly discoloured patches which usually itch intensely. If the scalp is affected, the condition is called "ringworm" and patches of hair may fall out. An infection in the groin is sometimes called "dhobie itch" and between the toes is called "athlete's foot".

Salicyclic acid, aluminium acetate and fungicidal ointments are used to treat infected areas. Although tinea is usually a trivial complaint, it can lead to more serious skin infection if not treated.

Tinea is very infectious and is usually spread by contact or by fragments of skin adhering to towels or clothing.

PROTOZOA

There are a number of protozoa which cause diseases in animals and man.

Entamoeba histolytica is one of a number of species of small amoebae which live in the alimentary canal of man (Fig. 37.3). These are usually harmless protozoa, feeding on bacteria and particles in the intestine. In certain conditions, *Entamoeba* invades the wall of the intestine or rectum causing ulceration and bleeding, with pain, vomiting and diarrhoea, symptoms of amoebic dysentery. The faeces of infected people contain the resistant cysts of *Entamoeba* and so conditions of poor sanitation and hygiene favour the spread of the disease.

Trypanosomes are flagellate protozoans which live in the blood stream (Fig. 37.4). There are several different types of trypanosome and they cause diseases such as *sleeping sickness*, *leishmaniasis* and *Chaga's disease* and, in cattle, *nagana*. The sleeping sickness and nagana parasites are transmitted by the

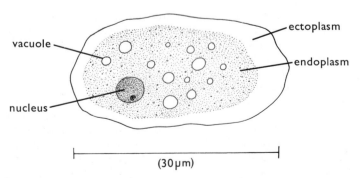

Fig. 37.3 *Entamoeba histolytica*

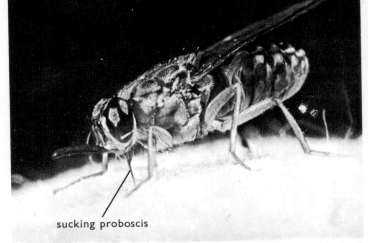

(W. Petana, Dermal Leishmaniasis Research Unit, British Honduras)

Plate 66. TSETSE FLY SUCKING BLOOD FROM HUMAN SKIN (×5)

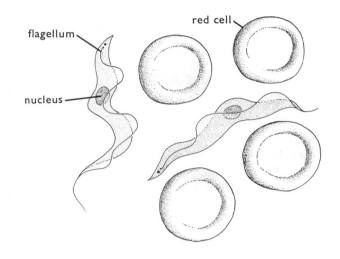

Fig. 37.4 Trypanosomes in the blood

bite of the tsetse fly. The insect has tubular mouth parts, like the mosquito, and pierces the skin to suck blood from a capillary (Plate 66). If it bites an infected person, it sucks up the trypanosomes with the blood. The trypanosomes multiply in the body of the tsetse fly and invade the salivary glands. When the fly bites a healthy person, it injects saliva, which contains the trypanosomes.

The prevalence of tsetse flies in some areas makes it impossible to raise cattle because of the high incidence of nagana. According to your point of view, this is either a bad thing because it prevents the spread of agriculture, or a good thing because it preserves the environment and wildlife against the encroachment of farming. Since wild animals are tolerant of trypanosome infections and because they exploit the vegetation without destroying it, there is something to be said for harvesting the wild game (game-cropping) rather than trying to eradicate the tsetse fly in order to introduce cattle.

Malaria. *Plasmodium* is another protozoan which lives in the blood stream of man but, unlike the trypanosomes, the malarial parasites enter the red cells and feed on their cytoplasm.

The *Plasmodium* divides repeatedly inside the red cell which eventually bursts, liberating dozens of new parasites into the circulation. Each of these can invade another red cell and undergo the same cycle (Fig. 37.5). When thousands of red cells all burst simultaneously, releasing the parasites and their

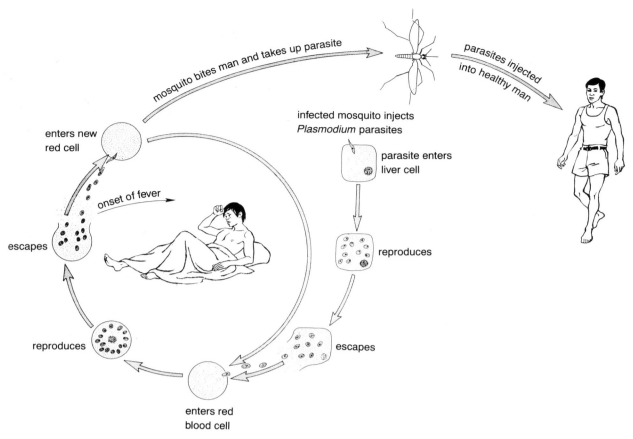

Fig. 37.5   Transmission of malarial parasite

accumulated waste products, the host suffers from a fever. This cycle of feeding, division and release is repeated regularly, so the fever occurs every 48 or 72 hours, according to which of the four species of *Plasmodium* has become established.

The parasites are transmitted from person to person by female mosquitoes of the genus *Anopheles*, which pierce the skin with their sharp, tubular mouth parts and feed on the blood which they suck from the superficial skin capillaries (*see* p. 151). If the blood so taken contains the malarial parasites, these undergo a complicated series of changes within the mosquito, including extensive reproduction, and eventually accumulate in large numbers in the salivary glands. If this mosquito now bites a healthy person, saliva containing hundreds of parasites is injected into his blood stream and he may develop malaria (Fig. 37.5).

It is estimated that 300–500 million people each year catch malaria. In about four years or less, depending on the species of the parasite, *Plasmodium* dies out naturally. However, nearly 3 million people each year die from the disease.

Some forms of malaria can be treated with drugs such as *quinine, choroquine* or *proguanil* but the malarial parasites in many parts of the world have developed resistance to these drugs. Combinations of *chloroquine* and *proguanil* are still effective in South America and parts of Africa, but in the Far East, the drugs are largely ineffective. A relatively new drug, *mefloquine* ('Lariam') is effective against most strains of *Plasmodium* but in about 20 percent of cases it has unpleasant side-effects, sometimes severe in a small number of people.

A herbal drug, *artemesinin*, extracted from the 'wormwood' shrub (*Artemesia annua*) is proving valuable, and resistance is not yet a problem.

Currently there are attempts to develop a vaccine but so far these have not been successful.

If anti-malarial drugs are taken before entering a malarial country, they act as prophylactics, killing off any parasites which get into the blood from an infected mosquito. Unfortunately these drugs suffer from the disadvantages described above, namely that in many cases the parasite has become resistant to them.

If mosquitoes could be prevented from biting humans, the disease would die out. An attempt to eradicate malaria was made in the 1950s by spraying insecticides such as DDT and BHC on the walls of dwellings. The eradication programme failed largely because mosquitoes became resistant to the insecticides.

Other strategies involve draining swamps or turning sluggish rivers into swifter streams. Mosquitoes lay their eggs in static water and the larvae hatch and grow there, so these measures reduce the population of mosquitoes. Water which collects in pots, tin cans, discarded tyres or open tanks is a breeding ground for mosquitoes.

One of the most effective ways of preventing infection with *Plasmodium* is to sleep under mosquito nets impregnated with an insecticide such as *permethrin*. Studies involving thousands of children in Ghana, Kenya and The Gambia have found that deaths from malaria can be reduced by two thirds by adopting this practice.

FLATWORMS

Free-living flatworms occur in freshwater. Liver flukes and tapeworms are fairly large parasitic forms and the blood flukes, *Schistosoma*, are microscopic.

Schistosoma (bilharzia). There are three species of bilharzia worms or blood flukes, called *Schistosoma*, which parasitize man. They are flatworms, 1–2 cm long, which live in the veins of either the bladder, the large intestine or the small intestine. The male worm is broader than the female and during fertilization the pairs are found together, the female partially enclosed in the rolled body of the male (Fig. 37.6).

The illness, *bilharziasis* or *schistosomiasis*, caused by these parasites seems largely due to the damage and inflammation caused by the escape of the eggs from the infected organ to the outside world. The eggs are laid in the veins where the worms are living, and work their way, with the aid of a sharp spine

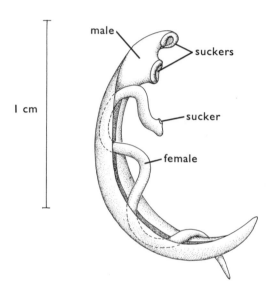

male
suckers
I cm
sucker
female

Fig. 37.6   *Schistosoma* (blood fluke causing bilharziasis): pairing

(Plate 67) and digestive enzymes, through the wall of the bladder or intestine, so causing inflammation, pain and bleeding. The eggs, when they leave the host's body, hatch to small, active larvae which, if they reach a pond or stream, enter the body of a pond snail. In the snail, they undergo phases of development and multiplication. The products of this reproduction, *cercaria* larvae (Plate 68), eventually leave the body of the snail and swim in the water. When a person bathes or paddles in this water, the film of moisture adhering to his body may contain many larvae and these can burrow through the skin to reach a capillary (Fig. 37.7). The bilharzia parasites can also enter the circulatory system if the water is drunk.

The larvae are carried round in the circulation as they develop and in about three months come to rest as adult worms (flukes) in the small veins of the bladder or intestine.

In 1947, it was estimated that 39 million people in the world were affected by the bladder fluke and 75 million by the intestinal forms. In some regions, 100 per cent of the adult population shows some degree of infection.

Some major irrigation schemes have provided systems of sluggish canals and channels in which the snails can live and multiply. As a result, schistosomiasis has greatly increased in these areas.

The drug, niridazole, kills one species of *Schistosoma* but may produce unpleasant side effects. Praziquantel seems to be effective against all three species and has few side effects. Cures, in the absence of control measures to prevent reinfection, may be inadvisable since the presence of a few worms may confer some degree of immunity. The first infection occurs probably at about six years of age and gives rise to severe symptoms which fade as immunity develops. Elimination of the flukes by drugs may destroy this immunity and produce severe symptoms if reinfection occurs. Eradication of the carrier snails could prevent the spread of the disease and this is being achieved by use of *molluscicides* such as Frescon or Bayluscide which kill the water snails without harming fish or other aquatic life (Plate 69).

Ecological study of the distribution of the snails and their peak breeding times enables the molluscicide to be applied at the most effective time and place.

The obvious method of control is to prevent human faeces and urine from reaching water likely to be used for washing,

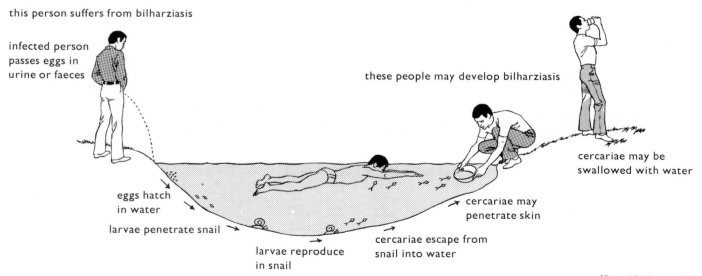

this person suffers from bilharziasis

infected person passes eggs in urine or faeces

these people may develop bilharziasis

cercariae may be swallowed with water

eggs hatch in water

larvae penetrate snail

larvae reproduce in snail

cercariae escape from snail into water

cercariae may penetrate skin

Fig. 37.7   Transmission of bilharziasis

(From Mackean and Jones, Introduction to Human and Social Biology, John Murray)

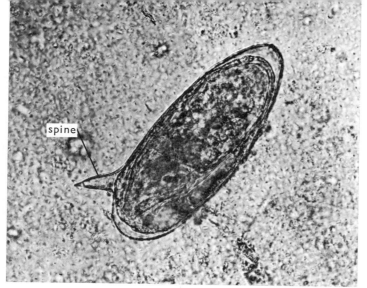

Plate 67. EGG OF *SCHISTOSOMA* (×400)

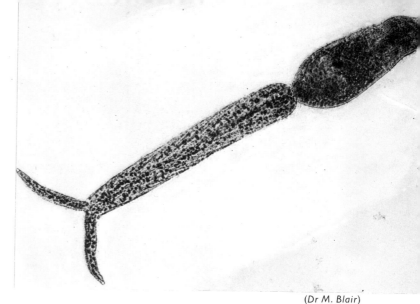

Plate 68. CERCARIA LARVAE OF *SCHISTOSOMA* (×250)

Plate 69. MOLLUSCICIDE APPLICATION

The molluscicide Frescon is allowed to drip into this irrigation channel where it will kill the snails which carry the *Schistosoma* larvae

bathing or drinking. In the two African species, man is the only principal, final host so that if human faeces and urine were kept away from water, the snails could not be infected. Short-term measures can be taken to prevent infection, for example by adding chlorine to the water used for drinking and washing.

Tapeworms. There are several different species of tapeworm which may live in the small intestine of man, attached by hooks or suckers to its lining (Fig. 37.8*b* and Plate 70). They absorb nutriment from the partly digested food and may grow to over 10 m in length. The tapeworm's ribbon-like body (Plate 72) consists of identical segments which are continuously budded off from behind the "head" or *scolex* (Fig. 37.8). At the hind end, the segments containing fertilized eggs (Plate 71) break off, are passed out in the faeces and many retain their powers of infection for up to one year. If the eggs reach human food or drink and are eaten by another person, they will not normally develop into tapeworms. If, however, the eggs are eaten by a pig or cow, as they are quite likely to be if the faeces are left on the surface of the ground, or by a fish, if the faeces reach a stream or lake, the embryos are released from the egg shells and burrow

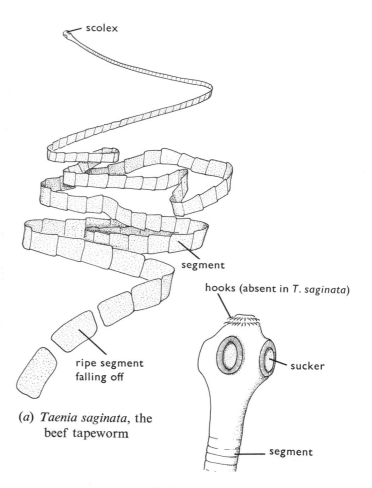

(*a*) *Taenia saginata*, the beef tapeworm

(*b*) Scolex of *Taenia solium*, the pork tapeworm

Fig. 37.8 Tapeworms

through the intestinal walls of the animal. From here, the embryos are carried in the blood stream to the muscles where they lodge and develop, in about 3 months, into a stage called bladder worms. In this stage, the tapeworm's head is enclosed in a small fluid-filled bladder. If the uncooked or under-cooked meat from an infected cow, pig or fish is eaten by a human, the

Plate 70.   HEAD OF *TAENIA SOLIUM*
(× 15)

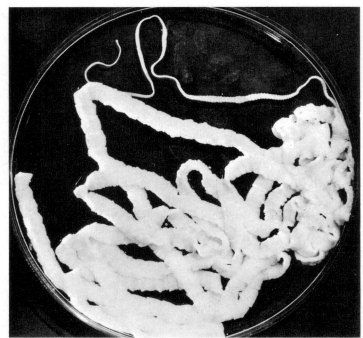

Plate 72.   *TAENIA SAGINATA* EXPELLED INTACT AFTER MEPACRINE TREATMENT

bladder worms will be released in the intestine and develop into a tapeworm (Fig. 37.9).

The three species of tapeworm which can develop in man as a result of eating the infected meat of the cow, pig or fish, are quite distinct from each other, and their eggs will normally develop only in the appropriate animal. There are several species of tapeworm other than those mentioned here, with, for example, dogs and sheep as intermediate or alternative hosts. These parasites can cause serious illness.

Although many millions of people are thought to be infected, e.g. 39 millions with the beef tapeworm, the presence of tapeworms in the intestine does not lead to severe symptoms and many people are unaware of their presence until segments appear in the faeces. Nevertheless, the tapeworms should be removed as far as possible to prevent the possible complication of *cysticercosis*, where tapeworm eggs reach the stomach either by self-infection or by regurgitation from the intestine. The eggs enter the circulatory system and develop into bladder worms as if they had reached their secondary host. Since the bladders often form in the brain, the results are very serious.

Man is an intermediate host to a tapeworm whose final host is the dog. This tapeworm, *Echinococcus*, lives in the dog's alimentary canal and its eggs pass out with the faeces. The eggs can reach man in a variety of ways, e.g. through handling a dog and not washing the hands afterwards, allowing a dog to lick one's face and mouth or to feed from a plate which is also used for human food.

The eggs when swallowed develop into bladders or cysts similar to those described above. Since these *hydatid* cysts, as they are called, can form in, for example, the liver, lungs, kidney or brain, the results may be very serious.

Cattle, pigs and sheep are also intermediate hosts, and the dog becomes infected by eating meat containing the cysts.

Control and cure. A study of the methods of transmission of beef and pork tapeworms indicates clearly how to avoid them. If the faeces of all infected persons are disposed of in such a way

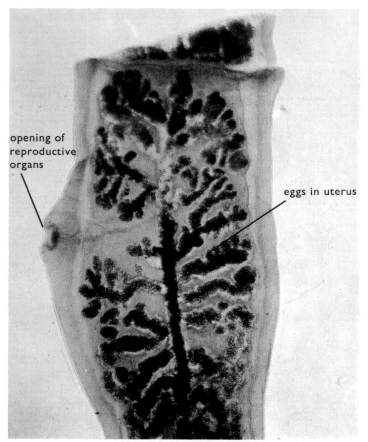

Plate 71.   *TAENIA*: RIPE SEGMENT CONTAINING EGGS
(× 35)

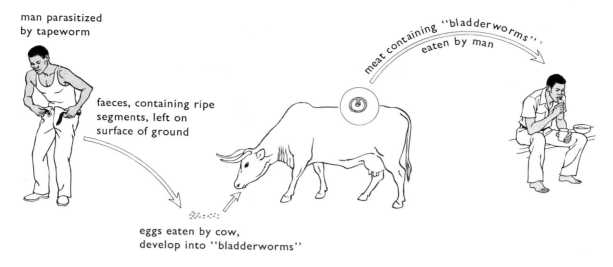

man parasitized
by tapeworm

faeces, containing ripe
segments, left on
surface of ground

meat containing "bladderworms",
eaten by man

eggs eaten by cow,
develop into "bladderworms"

Fig. 37.9   Transmission of the beef tapeworm *Taenia saginata*

that domestic animals and fish cannot eat the eggs, the eggs will die and all meat will be safe. Since it is not always possible to be certain whether or not a person is infected, efficient disposal of faeces should apply to all people.

Cooking is known to destroy the bladder worms in infected meat, so if uncooked or partially cooked meat is avoided, infection from meat is most unlikely. In many countries, meat is inspected before being allowed to enter the shops and markets. Any sign of the bladder worm stages in the meat will lead to its being declared unfit for human consumption.

Drugs such as mepacrine have a purging effect but often remove only the body of the tapeworm, leaving the scolex still lodged in the intestinal lining. This scolex can continue to grow a new tape at the rate of seven or eight segments per day. The drug hydroxychlorobenzamide is very effective, causing complete disintegration of the tapeworm. During treatment, however, the faeces will contain many eggs and are highly infective. They must be passed straight into disinfectant.

Echinococcus is controlled (i) by not allowing dogs to eat uncooked meat from infected carcasses of sheep, etc., (ii) by treating the dogs with drugs to remove the worms from their intestines, and (iii) by taking hygienic precautions when playing with or handling dogs.

NEMATODES

Nematode worms are cylindrical, smooth and tapered at each end (Plate 73). They move about by an undulating, writhing action. There are many species, their sizes varying from microscopic to 30 cm in length. Most of them are *saprozoic*, that is, they feed on decaying organic material and are very widely distributed, e.g. in the soil, but there are also many parasitic species in both plants and animals, including man. Unlike the parasitic flatworms, there is no secondary host in their life cycles.

Intestinal nematodes

Intestinal worms of the genus *Ascaris* are very common in man. They absorb nutriment from the contents of the alimentary canal but rarely seem to cause much trouble unless they wander from the intestine into other organs. Infection takes place as a result of swallowing the eggs which are so resistant that even modern sewage treatment may not destroy them.

Hookworms (*Ancylostoma*) are much smaller intestinal nematodes which attach themselves to and feed on the lining of the small intestine. As they rasp off pieces of the intestinal lining with their hook-like teeth, they damage the blood vessels and cause bleeding into the intestine. As a result, the host becomes anaemic and lethargic.

The eggs of the hookworm leave the intestine in the faeces of an infected person. If these faeces are left on the ground, the eggs hatch into larvae which burrow into the soil. From here they may get washed by rainfall into drinking water and so enter the alimentary canal of healthy people, or they may penetrate human skin directly from the soil or from water used for washing or bathing.

(*Wellcome Museum of Medical Science*)
Plate 73.   *ASCARIS:* MALE AND FEMALE
(the male is smaller)

Hygienic disposal of faeces, purification of drinking water and the wearing of shoes or sandals would do much to eliminate this disease. A drug, bephenium, will kill most of the hookworms in the intestine but total elimination is difficult.

Filaria worms

The filariae are very small nematode worms (threadworms), transmitted to humans by biting flies or mosquitoes. They cause diseases such as *elephantiasis* and *onchocerciasis*.

Onchocerciasis (river blindness). The filarial worms (*Onchocerca volvulus*) are injected into the body when a female blood-sucking fly of the *Simulium* family (blackfly) takes a blood meal from a human. The parasites do not remain in the blood stream but burrow in the deeper layers of the skin. The female worms may grow to 70 cm in length though only a fraction of a millimetre in width. They form small lumps in the skin where they may survive for 15 years, producing offspring called *microfilariae*. The microfilariae burrow about in the skin, producing intense itching. Some of them may enter the lymphatic system and after several years, some reach the eyes and damage its tissues causing blindness (river blindness).

It is estimated that 100,000 people in West Africa have been blinded by onchocerciasis and probably 20 million people are infected.

The disease occurs only in populations that are constantly exposed to the bites of infected blackflies. A short period of exposure to the biting flies is not thought to cause lasting damage.

The larvae of the various species of *Simulium* fly develop only in well-oxygenated water and so the most severely affected human populations are those that settle in the vicinity of fast streams, cascades and the sluices of irrigation schemes and dams.

The drugs *diethylcarbamazine* and *suramin* will kill the parasites in the body but they have unpleasant side-effects, and the only effective method of control is to destroy the *Simulium* larvae in their breeding places. Ecological studies of the blackfly reveal the size of the fly population, the places favoured for breeding and their life span. Although these features vary according to the species of *Simulium*, understanding them enables a scientific strategy of spraying to be carried out.

An onchocerciasis control programme sponsored jointly by four international organizations, including the World Health Organization and the World Bank, has mounted a campaign of spraying the breeding grounds with organo-phosphorus insecticides, using aircraft to reach the otherwise inaccessible stream heads, waterfalls, etc. (Plate 74). By spraying at weekly intervals, the reproductive cycle of the blackflies is severely disrupted. Analysis of the water shows that the insecticide does not harm the fish and plant life.

By 1978 the number of flies in the sprayed areas had been drastically reduced and the number of human carriers had decreased by 75 per cent. However, by 1981 some species of *Simulium* had become resistant to the insecticides and a new method of control is being tried. This is based on the bacterium, *Bacillus thuringiensis*, which attacks and kills the *Simulium* larvae. The bacteria are harmless to other species, can be produced locally and relatively cheaply, and the larvae are less likely to become resistant to it.

(*WHO photo*)

Plate 74.   ATTACKING THE VECTOR OF RIVER BLINDNESS

The aircraft is dropping insecticide into the river to kill the larvae of the blackfly. The adult blackflies carry the filaria worms which cause onchocerciasis

QUESTIONS

1. Why is it difficult to decide whether viruses are living organisms?
2. How does the reproduction of a virus differ from the reproduction of a single-celled organism like *Amoeba* (p. 174)?
3. Which human diseases are most likely to be spread by inefficient sanitation? (*See also* Chapter 14.)
4. Which human diseases are likely to be transmitted by (*a*) contact with an infected person and (*b*) droplet infection? (*See also* p. 71.)
5. What are the disadvantages of using insecticides to control the vectors of human diseases?
6. Why is it unlikely that syphilis and gonorrhoea will be transmitted in any way other than by sexual intercourse with an infected person?
7. Name three examples of vectors of human diseases. Say what diseases the vectors may transmit.
8. Describe ways of controlling the population of malarial mosquitoes without the use of insecticides.
9. Explain why (*a*) eliminating polio by immunization, and (*b*) curing schistosomiasis by drugs, may be undesirable in some communities unless other measures are taken at the same time. What are these other measures?
10. What two human diseases may be spread by irrigation schemes?

38 | Personal Health

HEALTH is not merely the absence of disease. It is physical and mental well-being, including freedom from hunger and anxiety. We rarely appreciate the value of feeling well until we experience a period of ill-health.

Infectious diseases. The illnesses described in the previous chapter are all caused by parasitic organisms. In some cases the chances of catching the diseases can be reduced by taking sensible precautions such as the hygienic preparation of food, (p. 72), boiling of suspect drinking water, immunization and avoidance of contact with infected persons.

With diseases such as malaria, sleeping sickness and river blindness, the individual has only limited means of avoidance, and control of the disease depends on large scale measures applied in whole communities.

Deficiency diseases. Some illnesses are the result of deficiencies in the diet, e.g. insufficient protein, vitamins or minerals (pp. 82–5). This may be the result of ignorance (e.g. the strange belief that feeding eggs to children will turn them into thieves), but very often it results from poverty and poor distribution of resources. For example, a few milligrams of vitamin A distributed each day to vulnerable individuals, could prevent thousands of cases of blindness due to xerophthalmia (p. 84).

Self-inflicted diseases. There are many illnesses which are self-inflicted. This is particularly true in the more affluent western countries. These diseases are heart attack, bronchitis, lung cancer and the sexually transmitted diseases. They are associated with cigarette smoking, over-eating, insufficient exercise and promiscuous sexual activity, all of which can be remedied by changes in behaviour.

CORONARY HEART DISEASE

This is one of the commonest causes of death in countries with a high standard of living. It is caused by the formation of fatty deposits, called *atheroma*, in the lining of the arteries (Fig. 38.1). The arterial lining also grows thicker. These two changes may cause a blockage of the coronary arteries which supply the heart muscle (Fig. 19.7 p. 98). When these vessels become blocked, the heart muscle does not get enough oxygen or glucose and without these, the heart cannot pump properly and it may stop altogether. This is usually what is meant by a "heart attack". Some people are more "at risk" than others because they genetically inherit a tendency towards certain diseases, including heart disease. However, evidence collected scientifically over many years, from a large number of people, shows clearly that whether people are genetically "high risk" or "low risk" they can greatly reduce their chances of early death from coronary heart disease by

(a) taking regular exercise,
(b) keeping their body weight at a reasonable level and
(c) not smoking.

These precautions give protection not only against heart attacks but against many other crippling illnesses such as bronchitis.

Taking exercise

In 1973, a group of 16,882 men between the ages of 40 and 64 and with "office jobs" took part in a study on the possible effects of exercise on heart disease. They kept records of their leisure activities that involved exercise. In the following years, it was found that those men who suffered heart attacks had taken less exercise than those who were still free from heart disease. Light exercise such as housework or walking appeared to be of little benefit. The kind of exercise needed was vigorous activity such as running, playing football or tennis and had to be kept up for at least 30 minutes at a time.

It is not known why exercise helps to reduce heart attacks. The improved blood circulation resulting from exercise could stop the fatty substances from settling down in the lining of the arteries, or the arteries might grow wider and produce more branches.

There is evidence to suggest that vigorous exercise taken during the years of adolescence has a long-term effect on the efficiency of the heart. Steady work or exercise for periods of about an hour, which raises the heart rate to about 140 beats per minute, helps to develop a heart with large ventricles. Vigorous exercise or heavy work, which gets the pulse rate up to about 180 per minute, causes the heart muscle to thicken up and its blood supply improves.

Exercise increases the flow of blood through the muscles and so helps to remove waste products. Contraction of the body muscles during exercise squeezes the veins and lymphatics (p. 100) and so helps to return blood and lymph to the heart. The deep breathing resulting from exercise is probably good for the lungs. The improved appetite resulting from exercise probably helps digestion. Exercise also helps to keep your body weight down, but the best way to do this is to avoid over-eating.

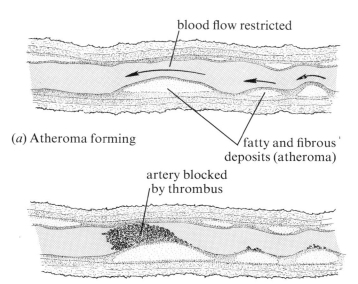

blood flow restricted

(*a*) Atheroma forming

fatty and fibrous deposits (atheroma)

artery blocked by thrombus

(*b*) Thrombus (blood clot) forming

Fig. 38.1   Atheroma and thrombus formation

Controlling body weight

In many tropical countries, the problem is not eating too much but not getting enough to eat. However, in large towns where western life-styles are often adopted, people may be tempted to spend their money on the wrong kinds of food. Some of the most harmful features of western diets are (i) the use of refined sugar, (ii) excessive use of animal fats and dairy products such as butter and eggs, (though this is controversial), (iii) too little vegetable fibre and (iv) too much of everything.

Too much sugar. The white sugar from the sugar bowl is called refined sugar. Some kinds of "brown" sugar consist only of white sugar with a little molasses added to darken it. Sugar comes from sugar-cane or sugar-beet. It is made by the plants along with a large number of other substances. If we ate sugar-cane or sugar-beet, we would probably not do ourselves much harm. It is the purified (refined) sugar which damages our health.

There is plenty of evidence to show that sugar in the mouth is an important cause of tooth decay but refined sugar also affects us in many other ways. It is a very concentrated source of energy. You can absorb a lot of sugar from biscuits, ice-cream, sweets, soft drinks, tinned fruits and sweet tea without ever feeling "full up", so you tend to take in more sugar than your body needs. A high intake of refined sugar, therefore, causes people to become overweight, and this in turn leads to other forms of illness as described below.

There is a connection between sugar intake and heart disease. In the last 200 years, the average sugar consumption in Britain has increased from 2 kg per person to 55 kg per person each year. Fig. 38.2 shows the sugar consumption in different countries and the death rate from heart attacks. This does not prove that sugar *causes* heart disease, but it makes us suspect that excessive intake of sugar does contribute to heart attacks. Similar charts could show a connection between heart disease and the sale of television sets, but it is not suggested that watching television is the cause of heart attacks. Eating a lot of sugar, driving cars and watching television are characteristics of a wealthy society. The members of a wealthy society tend to eat too much (especially sugar and fat) and take too little exercise (car-driving and television-watching). It is probably a combination of these, together with smoking, which increases the likelihood of heart disease.

Too much fat. The fatty layer which forms in the lining of arteries and leads to coronary heart disease contains fats and a substance called cholesterol. The more fat and cholesterol you have in your blood, the more likely you are to suffer a coronary heart attack. Many doctors and scientists think that if you eat too much fat, you raise the level of fats and cholesterol in the blood and so put yourself at risk. There is still a good deal of argument about this. Some scientists think that eating a large amount of fat does not necessarily increase the cholesterol level in the blood. Until more is known, it seems to be a good idea to keep a low level of fats in your diet.

The culprits appear to be animal fats; that is, butter, cream, some kinds of cheese, egg yolk and the fat present in meat. These fats are digested to give what are called *saturated* fatty acids (because of the structure of their molecules). Many of the fats and oils from plants, such as the oil from sunflower seeds, contain *unsaturated* fatty acids. These are thought to be less likely to cause fatty deposits in the arteries. For this reason, it seems to be better to fry food in vegetable oil and to use margarine from certain vegetable oils rather than butter. Oil from sunflower seeds, soya beans and maize has a high proportion of unsaturated fatty acids. Palm and coconut oils

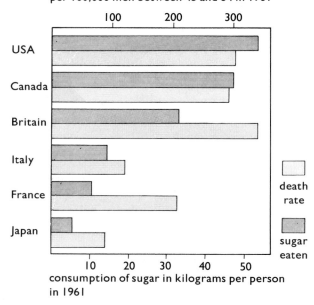

number of deaths from coronary heart disease per 100,000 men between 45 and 54 in 1961

Fig. 38.2 Sugar consumption and heart disease. Generally speaking, the greater the sugar consumption the higher the death rate from coronary heart disease, but this relationship does not prove that sugar *causes* heart disease. (From J. K. Brierley, *Biology and the Social Crisis*, Heinemann, 1967, and *The Sunday Times*, 1964.)

are more like animal fats, having a high level of saturated fatty acids.

Not enough fibre. Traditional tropical diets are not usually lacking in fibre (see p. 84), because they contain a high proportion of vegetable matter such as rice, maize, beans, cassava, yams and fruits. However, as people become more wealthy, they may buy more "westernized" food with its high sugar and low fibre content. White bread, for example, has had much of the "indigestible" fibre removed from it. Vegetables and fruit contain a large amount of cellulose cell walls which constitute the dietary fibre or roughage. Although we may not be able to digest the cell walls ourselves, there are bacteria in our intestines which can do so and we get the benefit from the digested products. Apart from fibre being a source of food, there is evidence to show that it has other highly beneficial effects. It prevents constipation and probably other disorders and diseases of the intestine, including cancer. Eating a diet with a lot of fibre makes you feel "full up" and so stops you from over-eating. A 100-gram portion of boiled potato provides only 340 kilojoules (kJ) (p. 82). (A potato about the size of an egg weighs 50–70 g.) You could feel quite full after eating 300 g of potatoes but would take in only about 1,000 kJ. A 100-g portion of milk chocolate will give you about 2,500 kJ but it is not filling. So a high fibre diet helps to keep your weight down without leaving you feeling hungry all the time.

It is not suggested that fibre in the diet will ward off heart attacks, but it will help to avoid becoming overweight. Overweight people are more susceptible to heart attacks as well as to other illnesses.

Too much of everything. If you eat more food than your body requires for its energy needs or for building tissues, you are likely to store the surplus as fat and so become overweight (Fig. 38.3). An overweight person is much more likely to suffer from high blood pressure, coronary heart disease and diabetes than a

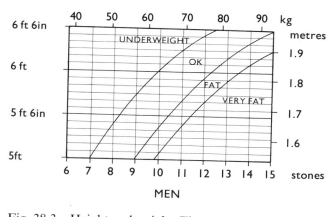

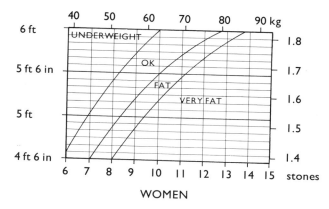

Fig. 38.3 Height and weight. These tables are intended for adults who have reached their full height. They would find their height on the left-hand scale and look along the line till they reached their weight on the bottom scale. (By permission of The Health Education Council, London.)

person whose weight is about right. Being fat also makes you less willing to take exercise because you have to carry the extra weight around.

Whether you put on weight or not depends to some extent on genetics. You may inherit the tendency to get fat. Some people seem able to "burn off" their excess food as heat and never get fat, no matter how much they eat. You can't change your genetics but you can avoid putting on too much weight by controlling your diet. This does not necessarily mean eating less but simply eating differently. Avoid sugar and all processed food with a high sugar level, such as sweets, cakes and biscuits, and include more vegetables, fruit and bread in your diet. Your teeth, waistline, intestines and health in general will benefit from such a change in diet.

SMOKING AND ILL-HEALTH

About 300 chemical compounds have been found in tobacco smoke. Of these, nicotine seems to have most effect on the nervous system. It stimulates some types of synapse (p. 138), increases blood pressure and heart rate by the production of

adrenaline (p. 144), causes vasodilation (p. 110) in the muscles and vaso-constriction in the skin. It is not clear how these changes produce the pleasure derived from smoking. Some regular smokers would claim that smoking calms their "nerves"; others claim that smoking stimulates them.

The short-term effects of smoking cause the bronchioles (p. 102) to constrict and the cilia lining the air passages (p. 14) to stop beating. The smoke also makes the lining produce more mucus. The long-term effects may take many years to develop but they are severe, disabling and often lethal.

Emphysema

Emphysema is a breakdown of the alveoli (p. 102). The action of one or more of the substances in tobacco smoke weakens the walls of the alveoli. The irritant substances in the smoke cause a "smokers' cough' and the coughing bursts some of the weakened alveoli. In time, the absorbing surface of the lungs is greatly reduced (Fig. 38.4). Then the smoker cannot oxygenate his blood properly and the least exertion makes him breathless and exhausted.

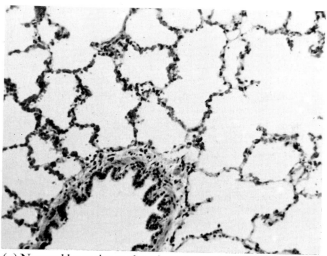

(a) Normal lung tissue showing a bronchiole and about 25 alveoli ($\times 200$).

Fig. 38.4 Emphysema

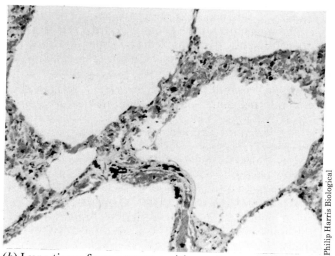

(b) Lung tissue from a person with emphysema. This is the same magnification as (a). The alveoli have broken down leaving only about five air sacs which provide a much reduced absorbing surface.

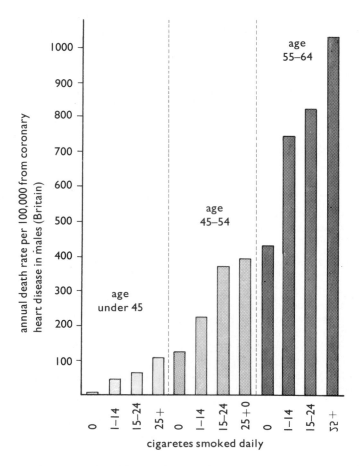

Fig. 38.5 Smoking and heart disease. Obviously, as you get older you are more likely to die from a heart attack, but notice that in any age group the more you smoke, the higher your chances of dying from heart disease. (From *Smoking or Health: a report of the Royal College of Physicians*, Pitman Medical Publishing Co. Ltd.)

Chronic bronchitis

The smoke stops the cilia in the air passages from beating and so the irritant substances in the smoke and the excess mucus collect in the bronchi. This leads to the inflammation known as *bronchitis*. Over 95 percent of people suffering from bronchitis are smokers and they have a 20 times greater chance of dying from bronchitis than non-smokers.

Heart disease

Coronary heart disease is the leading cause of death in most developed countries. It results from a blockage of the coronary arteries by fatty deposits. This reduces the supply of oxygenated blood to the heart muscle and sooner or later leads to heart failure (*see* p. 229). High blood pressure, diets with too much animal fat, and lack of exercise are also thought to be causes of heart attack, but about a quarter of all deaths due to coronary heart disease are caused by smoking (Fig. 38.5).

The nicotine and carbon monoxide from the cigarette smoke increase the tendency for the blood to clot and so block the coronary arteries, already partly blocked by fatty deposits. The carbon monoxide increases the rate at which the fatty material is deposited in the arteries.

Lung cancer

Although all forms of air pollution are likely to increase the chances of lung cancer, many scientific studies show, beyond all reasonable doubt, that the vast increase in lung cancer (4,000 percent in the last century) is almost entirely due to cigarette-smoking (Fig. 38.6 and Plate 78, p. 236).

There are at least 17 substances in tobacco smoke known to cause cancer in experimental animals, and it is now thought that 90 percent of lung cancer is caused by smoking. The table below shows the relationship between smoking and the risk of developing lung cancer.

Number of cigarettes per day	Increased risk of lung cancer
1–14	× 8
15–24	× 13
25+	× 25

Other risks

About 95 percent of patients with disease of the leg arteries are cigarette-smokers and this condition is the most frequent cause of leg amputations.

Strokes due to arterial disease in the brain are more frequent in smokers.

Cancer of the bladder, ulcers in the stomach and duodenum, tooth decay, gum disease and tuberculosis all occur more frequently in smokers.

Babies born to women who smoke during pregnancy are smaller than average, probably as a result of reduced oxygen supply caused by the carbon monoxide in the blood. In smokers, there is twice the frequency of miscarriages, a 50 percent higher still-birth rate and a 26 percent higher death rate of babies.

In 1976 two famous doctors predicted that one in every three smokers will die as a result of their smoking habits. Those who do not die at an early age will probably be seriously disabled by one of the conditions described above.

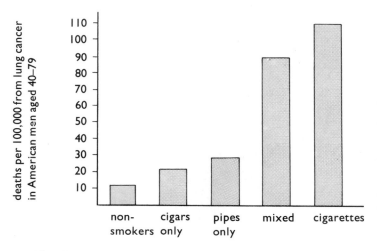

Fig. 38.6 Smoking and lung cancer. Cigar and pipe smokers are probably at less risk because they often do not inhale. But notice that their death rate from lung cancer is still twice that of non-smokers. (From *Smoking and Health Now: a report of the Royal College of Physicians*, Pitman Medical Publishing Co. Ltd.)

Reducing the risks

By giving up smoking, a person who smokes up to 20 cigarettes a day will, after 10 years, be at no greater risk than a non-smoker of the same age. The pipe- or cigar-smoker, provided he does not inhale, is at less risk than a cigarette-smoker but still at greater risk than a non-smoker.

The risk of lung cancer may be reduced by changing to low-tar cigarettes. However, smokers often compensate for the milder taste of the low-tar brands by taking deeper and more frequent puffs and leaving shorter stubs. Changing to low-tar brands does not reduce the likelihood of heart and arterial diseases.

Now that western countries are, at last, beginning to reduce their consumption of tobacco, the tobacco companies are seeking to maintain their sales by intensive advertising and promotion campaigns in the developing countries.

SEXUALLY TRANSMITTED DISEASES

Sexually transmitted diseases, (sometimes called venereal diseases) are caught by having sexual intercourse with an infected person. Very rarely, they can be passed on by touching the reproductive organs or by kissing. The germs which cause the diseases can live only in warm moist conditions and so they do not survive long outside the body. For this reason, they can only be caught by direct sexual contact. It is not easy to avoid catching colds or influenza because the germs may be floating about in the air. It is quite possible to avoid catching venereal diseases by simply not having sexual intercourse with an infected person.

Since the symptoms of the disease are often not obvious, it is difficult to recognize an infected person. So the disease must be avoided by not having sexual intercourse with a person who *might* have the disease. Such persons are (a) prostitutes, who have sexual intercourse for money, (b) other people who are thought to have had sexual relationships with many others ("slept around"), and (c) casual acquaintances whose general background and past sexual activities are not known.

Venereal diseases are on the increase and more people from the younger age groups are becoming infected. If untreated, the diseases can have very serious effects and can affect unborn children. There are two important venereal diseases, *gonorrhoea* and *syphilis*. They are described on p. 221.

QUESTIONS

1. What is the function of the coronary arteries?
2. What three things can you do to protect yourself against coronary heart disease?
3. For exercise to be of long-term benefit, it needs to be vigorous enough to make you out of breath and raise your heart beat to 120 or more per minute. What regular exercise do you take which does these things?
4. What are the effects of exercise on (a) the circulatory system, (b) the lungs?
5. (a) If you feel hungry between meals, why is it better to eat some fruit rather than a bar of chocolate?
(b) If you are going to do a long-distance walk, why is it better to take chocolate bars than fruit?
6. 100 g of boiled potato will give you 340 kJ, but 100 g of fried potatoes give you 990 kJ. Why do you think there is such a big difference?
7. Why should a "high fibre" diet help to stop you putting on weight?
8. What are (a) the immediate effects and (b) the long-term effects of tobacco smoke on the trachea, bronchi and lungs?
9. Why does a regular smoker get out of breath sooner than a non-smoker of similar age and build?
10. If you smoke 20 cigarettes a day, by how much are your chances of getting lung cancer increased?
11. Apart from lung cancer, what other diseases are caused by smoking?
12. Why is it often difficult to recognize the symptoms of venereal disease?
13. How can a baby become infected with venereal disease?
14. (a) How can venereal disease be cured?
(b) What are the difficulties in bringing about a cure?

39 | World Health, Population and Pollution

SOME diseases occur throughout the world, others are restricted to more or less precise geographical areas. The mosquitoes which carry the malarial parasite (p. 222) cannot breed above 3000 metres and consequently mountainous areas are free from malaria. Similarly, the tsetse fly occurs only in Africa and thus the disease of sleeping sickness caused by trypanosomes (p. 222), carried by the flies, is restricted to Africa. Even if tsetse flies were introduced to a northern European country they could not survive and breed.

Diseases with a world-wide distribution are often those transmitted by contamination (e.g. cholera) or by a vector with a wide distribution such as the rat flea which carries bubonic plague. The movement of infected individuals between countries makes possible the introduction of a disease to a country from which it is normally absent.

From about AD 1400 different countries have set up *quarantine regulations* to try and prevent the entry of certain serious diseases to their countries. Such regulations aim to keep immigrants in isolation long enough for any signs of cholera, plague or yellow fever to appear. It is unlikely, in the past, that these measures were very successful because the methods of transmission of disease were not understood. For example, rats infected with plague could still escape from ships on to land and carriers of cholera often show no signs of illness though their faeces are heavily contaminated with the cholera vibrio.

In 1851 the first of a series of International Sanitary Conferences was held in France to try and achieve co-operation between nations in preventing the spread of such devastating diseases. Although a great deal of progress was being made as a result of new discoveries in individual countries (e.g. the transmission of cholera in drinking water, the role of the mosquito in carrying yellow fever, and the benefits of vaccination against smallpox) there was little co-operation and exchange of information on a world scale. In 1909, an International Public Health Office was established in France to collect and pass on information about infectious diseases and their prevention. After the first world war, the League of Nations established a Health Organization to try and control and prevent disease on an international scale and brought into being expert committees which drew on the knowledge and experience of experts from all countries to report on matters such as nutrition, malaria, housing, health centres and other aspects of international public health.

The World Health Organization (WHO)

In 1948, after the Second World War, the World Health Organization was set up with its headquarters in Geneva and regional offices in Alexandria, Brazzaville, Copenhagen, Manila, New Delhi and Washington. There are now 135 member states and an annual budget of about 100 million dollars provided by the member countries in proportion to their ability to pay, e.g. the USA provides about one third of the total. The objective of WHO is "the attainment by all peoples of the highest level of health . . . without distinction of race, religion, political belief or social condition". Health is defined as "a state of complete physical, mental and social well-being and not merely the absence of disease or infirmity".

There are many ways in which the WHO strives to achieve its objectives but basically they consist of seeking and disseminating information that will assist nations to improve the state of their public health. Thus knowledge resulting from progress in one country is made available to all nations. This information may be obtained (*a*) by calling a conference of experts to obtain an up-to-date consensus on some topic, e.g. the African Conference on bilharziasis held in Brazzaville in 1956, or (*b*) by promoting and co-ordinating research, such as that on the best methods of preventing goitre conducted in 1949, and the research into prevention and treatment of leprosy conducted in 1973. The information is disseminated by publications like the technical reports of the expert committees, e.g. the first report of the Expert Committee on trypanosomiasis in 1962. Alternatively teams of experts may be sent from one country to another to advise on health matters or the setting up of medical schools or health centres. Information about outbreaks of disease is provided by a daily bulletin of epidemic news broadcast on eight wavelengths for seaports, airports, ships and health authorities so that measures can be taken quickly to localize epidemics and prevent their spreading.

Practical aid to individual countries is often undertaken in collaboration with other organizations such as the Food and Agriculture Organization (FAO) or the United Nations Childrens Fund (UNICEF). In the Malaria Eradication Campaign, WHO provides the expertise and UNICEF (and other organizations) provide insecticides, spraying equipment and transport. One example of successful practical assistance was the elimination of typhus from Afghanistan in 1953 by a massive campaign to destroy the body lice which transmit the disease. About 345,000 persons, 20,000 homes, 2 million items of clothing, 1300 horse-drawn tongas and 29 public baths were dusted with DDT. In 1979 WHO completed a ten-year programme to eradicate smallpox throughout the world. In the countries where smallpox normally occurred, teams were trained to seek out cases of the disease, isolate infected persons and vaccinate all contacts. Russia, the USA and other countries provided aid in the form of vaccine and vaccine-testing services. As a result of this campaign, it looks as if smallpox has been eliminated from the world. In 1955 WHO launched a campaign to eradicate malaria, and the disease has been eliminated from 36 countries and reduced in many others, though it now seems unlikely that total eradication can be achieved.

Despite the undoubted success of WHO's many undertakings, the control of infectious diseases demands constant vigilance from health authorities in all countries and the improvement and maintenance of national public health standards. A disease like cholera, for example, cannot be eliminated until all people have access to uncontaminated drinking water.

(UNICEF)

Plate 75.   MOTHERS LEARN TO PREPARE NUTRITIOUS
FOOD
at a welfare centre supported by UNICEF

(WHO)

Plate 76.   SMOKE DISCHARGE FROM FACTORIES
Although the smoke is discharged above the nearby buildings,
the atmosphere as a whole is polluted

Other organizations. UNICEF, the United Nations Childrens' Fund, is part of the United Nations Organization but its policies are determined independently by representatives from 30 nations. Seventy-five per cent of its budget is provided by voluntary contributions from 138 different countries and the rest from independent fund-raising activities. Its objective is to help the children in greatest need in all parts of the world by providing assistance to the governments of the countries concerned. Every incentive is given to countries to solve their problems themselves; for example, a government requesting UNICEF aid for a particular project is expected to meet 75 per cent of the cost.

Nearly half of UNICEF's budget helps towards the provision of improved community health care, pure water supplies and the training of local teams in preventative medicine so that problems can be tackled locally even when doctors are not available. Grants are made for training doctors, nurses and health workers, setting up health centres, providing vaccines and drugs and improving sanitation and water supplies.

A quarter of UNICEF'S aid is used to improve educational facilities by training teachers and equipping schools. For example, UNICEF helped Ethiopia with paper and printing units to produce over three million new textbooks. Another important area of aid is in the fight against malnutrition. Here the objective is to improve diets based on locally produced foods rather than to rely on imported food. This is done by programmes of education and training (Plate 75) for the benefits that these will bring in the future.

The Red Cross began in 1863 when four citizens of Geneva set up the International Committee for the Relief of the Wounded. The Objective was to persuade the combatants in a war to recognize the wounded and those looking after them as neutral and so keep them immune from attack. The Committee chose the red cross as their emblem and made it the same for all armies so that all ambulances, hospitals and medical personnel were protected. The International Committee also instituted the Geneva Convention which, in its present form, has been signed by 133 governments and sets out conditions for the humane treatment of the wounded, prisoners of war and the civilians of occupied countries.

Today, 116 countries have set up their own National Red Cross Societies which are responsible for emergency medical and social care in their own territory. They send medical teams to assist the army medical corps in times of armed conflict, provide food, clothing and shelter for refugees, set up hospitals and nursing schools and offer training in first aid. The activities of the National Societies are linked by the League of Red Cross Societies so that information is exchanged and relief efforts for the victims of natural disasters such as earthquakes and floods are efficiently co-ordinated and the drugs, vaccines, food and medical supplies provided by the National Societies reach the areas in greatest need.

There is also an International Committee of the Red Cross with a permanent staff of Swiss nationals whose responsibility is towards prisoners of war, political prisoners and internees. Their staff are admitted to prisons and camps and allowed to check that the treatment and living conditions of the prisoners conforms to certain humane standards. The International Committee also collects and distributes information about prisoners so that relatives and dependants are kept informed of their whereabouts and condition.

Nutritional needs which arise during an emergency are met by diet supplements such as the corn-soya-milk mixture which was provided in 1974 when eight African countries were affected by drought. Similarly, high dose vitamin capsules were supplied to the children of Bangladesh in the same year. Such special assistance is offered to children of countries affected by war, earthquake, floods and other disasters.

Population

The term *population* refers to the number of plants or animals of a given species present in an ecosystem. In a stable ecosystem the numbers of a species remain more or less constant despite the fact that the seeds or offspring initially greatly outnumber their parents. The factors which control the level of a population are difficult to determine with certainty. The availability of plant food may limit the growth of a population of herbivores and the numbers of carnivores may also help to keep the herbivore population within certain limits. In addition to competing for food among animal communities, competition for mates and nesting sites and the susceptibility to disease will help to limit populations.

In the case of man, early hunting communities were probably limited by their ability to obtain food and withstand harsh conditions. The development of agriculture reduced the limiting effect of food and the world population increased, to be limited until recent times by the high death rate of infants and the devastation of diseases such as malaria and cholera. The development of modern medicine has greatly reduced infant mortality in some parts of the world and brought most infectious diseases under control almost universally. The result is that more people are surviving to maturity and reproducing.

population in millions

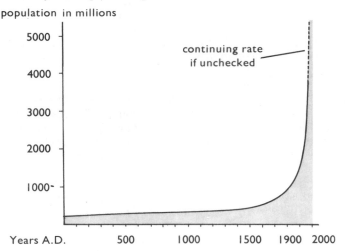

Fig. 39.1   World population growth in the last 2000 years

In Europe the recent population growth has been taking place over 50 years or more. The death rate in Britain fell from 20 to 14 per thousand between 1870 and 1920. In Sri Lanka, on the other hand, an intensive campaign against diseases spread by flies and mosquitoes reduced the death rate from 22 to 14 per thousand in the five years from 1946 to 1951. If the birth rate declined as rapidly as the death rate, the population would soon achieve stability. To some extent this has been happening in the industrialized countries where contraceptive methods are widely used to limit family sizes. In countries where the fight against infectious diseases has been most successful, however, the birth rate is already high, e.g. Africa's is about 40 per thousand compared with Europe's 20–25 per thousand. Unless there is a marked decline in the birth rate, the population in these countries will continue to increase at unprecedented rates, e.g. South America's population doubles every 26 years.

The World population, as a whole, is doubling every 35 years (Fig. 39.1) and threatens to outstrip the supply of food and to deplete the non-renewable supplies of energy and raw materials, quite apart from the tendency to make the biosphere uninhabitable by the destruction and pollution of the natural environment. In some parts of Asia, famines are already a frequent occurrence and in the industrialized countries with their factories, cars and machinery, every increase in their population results in disproportionate demands on the World's energy and mineral resources and adds disproportionately to the amount of pollutants in the biosphere.

Pollution

One of the consequences of the rapidly increasing numbers of man is the damage he does to the environment in obtaining his food and disposing of the waste-products of his body and his industries. The environmental damage caused by intensive agriculture has been described on p. 79, the pollution of natural waters by treated sewage effluent is discussed on p. 56 and the long-term pollution effects of certain insecticides are dealt with on p. 58. The pollution resulting from industrial development is no less significant and affects the atmosphere, rivers, lakes, oceans and the organisms which inhabit them.

When waste materials are discharged effectively into the sea or into the air they are diluted so much that they do not constitute a health hazard. They also undergo chemical changes which convert them from poisonous to harmless compounds. The problems of pollution arise when a large volume of toxic matter is released into a restricted environment such as a lake or river or the harmful compounds decompose only very slowly (e.g. DDT or radioactive waste) with the result that they can be accumulated in the bodies of living organisms over a long period and eventually reach harmful concentrations.

Air pollution. When coal is burned, it produces carbon dioxide and water which are harmless but it also produces smoke and sulphur dioxide. Oil, when burned, forms little or no smoke but does produce sulphur dioxide. Smoke obscures sunlight in industrial cities and the carbon particles of which it largely consists form a nucleus for the condensation of water leading in certain conditions to dense fogs. When the smoke particles settle out from the air they make streets and buildings dirty and have harmful effects on plant life. The direct effect on man is not known to be harmful even though exposure to smoke over a long period may blacken the lining of his lungs. Nevertheless, during dense fogs in London in 1952 there were 4000 more deaths than usual from respiratory diseases and the smoke and sulphur dioxide contents of the fog were almost certainly contributory factors. Since the Clean Air Act of 1956 prohibited the discharge of smoke in certain areas, including London, there have been no more disastrous fogs and the number of hours of sunlight in the city have increased (December sunshine has increased by 70 per cent).

The products of combustion from factories are usually released from tall chimneys (Plate 76) so that the smoke and sulphur dioxide are diluted by being distributed over a wide area. Usually the sulphur dioxide combines with ammonia so that in less than two days it has formed the harmless compound ammonium sulphate which is washed into the soil with rain water. If sulphur dioxide itself reaches plant life, however, it causes visible damage and reduces crop yields even at

Plate 77.   "SMOG" IN AN AMERICAN CITY

(WHO)

Plate 78.   LUNG CANCER
The cancerous growth almost fills this human lung. Cigarette smoking is not the only cause of lung cancer but is one of the most important   (Crown Copyright)

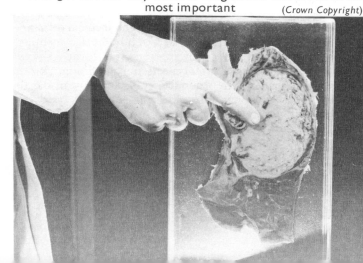

concentrations as low as 0·1 part per million (ppm). The industries of Britain alone discharge six million tonnes of sulphur dioxide per year into the atmosphere and though there is no decisive evidence that sulphur dioxide in concentrations of 1 ppm has harmful effects on man it seems wiser to remove as much sulphur dioxide as possible from industrial waste gases and extract the sulphur from it.

Aluminium smelters and brick works, in addition to sulphur dioxide release into the atmosphere fluorides which are poisonous to plants and animals. These waste gases have killed trees and poisoned cattle in the vicinity of such industries.

The exhaust gases of motor cars add to the pollution of the atmosphere. They contain carbon monoxide, lead and oxides of nitrogen. Carbon monoxide is a poisonous gas which combines with the haemoglobin in the blood and reduces its oxygen-carrying capacity. In dense traffic, levels of carbon monoxide in the air have reached 200 ppm for short periods. Short-term exposures to this level have not been proved to cause damage but it is thought that prolonged exposures can have adverse effects on the arteries.

Lead tetraethyl is a compound added to petrol to improve the performance of the car's engine. On busy roads, the lead expelled in the exhaust gases has been known to contaminate roadside vegetation to a level of 500 ppm, making it quite poisonous to eat. The direct effect on man is less certain but since lead is not easily excreted from the body it seems foolish to add to our intake from any source if it can be avoided.

In certain climatic conditions, the oxides of nitrogen in car exhaust gases are acted on by sunlight to form peroxacyl nitrates which are harmful at concentrations even as low as ten parts per hundred million causing visible damage to crops and discomfort to animals. In California and parts of Japan and Europe, these chemicals give rise to a hazy fog (Plate 77) ("smog"), cause eye irritation and damage trees and crops over a wide area. It is possible, at a price, to reduce the amount of lead in petrol and to control the output of car exhaust gases.

Perhaps the most intensive form of personal and public air pollution is brought about by smoking. The smoker takes into his lungs carbon monoxide and particles of tar and carbon greatly in excess of anything likely to be inhaled from even a grossly polluted atmosphere (Plate 78). The carbon monoxide level of a smoker's blood is higher than that induced by traffic in cities and the association between smoking and diseases of the respiratory organs and the arteries is well established (p. 231).

Water pollution. The oceans are so vast that if the toxic chemicals produced by industry and agriculture were completely dispersed in them, the levels of contamination would be infinitesimal. However, uniform dispersal is not a practical proposition and many areas of coastal water, enclosed seas, estuaries, rivers and lakes have become seriously polluted. The Mediterranean and Baltic are enclosed seas whose level of pollution and oxygen deficit have reached serious proportions.

One of the most widespread forms of water pollution is the oxygen deficiency brought about by eutrophication as a result of excessive phosphates and nitrates reaching lakes and rivers from treated sewage, detergents, agricultural fertilizers and effluent from animal rearing units. The causes and effects of eutrophication are discussed more fully on p. 56. Apart from their effect on oxygen supplies, the level of nitrates in some drinking waters has reached toxic proportions at least for babies. More toxic still are the mercury compounds which reach the sea from industries such as wood pulp manufacture. In Minamata Bay, South West Japan, in 1953 there appeared the first signs of an unidentified disease which by 1971 affected 121 people of whom 45 died. The disease turned out to be a form of mercury poisoning. A factory on the shore was discharging waste mercury compounds into the bay and although the levels in the sea were too low to be detected, the compounds were being taken up by algae and concentrated by organisms such as shellfish, crustacea, eels and other fish to dangerously high levels. The inhabitants of the bay depended for their food on such marine life and many of them were ingesting levels of mercury which, over the years, produced acute poisoning, mental disorder, paralysis and death. Mercury compounds occur naturally in sea water and are concentrated by fish but not to such toxic levels. Inland waters, enclosed seas and estuaries are particularly at risk from discharges of toxic waste; seals and porpoises in the Baltic have up to 55 ppm DDT in their body fat. There is evidence to suggest that DDT is now very widely distributed in the oceans of the world as well as in the air and rain water, though at very low levels at present.

Radioactive waste. Intense radiation either from X-rays or the radioactive emission from chemicals causes severe burns and death. Repeated low-level doses of radiation cause cancer and mutations (p. 184) and it seems likely that even very low levels can have cumulative effects. Our bodies absorb radiation from a variety of natural sources and it seems desirable to avoid adding to this natural dose as far as possible.

Testing atomic bombs in the atmosphere releases radioactive elements such as strontium-90. The radioactive "fallout" from an atomic explosion covers very wide areas of the Earth's surface and increasing levels of strontium-90 have reached agricultural land and eventually been incorporated into vegetation and animal products such as milk. Strontium is chemically similar to calcium and so is deposited in bone tissue where, in its radioactive form, it may interfere with red cell production by the bone marrow (p. 93), leading to a form of cancer called leukaemia. Russia, USA and Britain stopped the atmospheric testing of atomic bombs in 1963 but France and China continue to do this.

As world supplies of oil and coal run out, industrial countries have turned increasingly to the use of atomic power to provide their electricity. Unfortunately, the waste products of nuclear power stations include radioactive elements like plutonium-239 which takes 24,000 years to lose half its original radioactivity: such dangerous radioactive wastes need to be stored in ever increasing amounts for perhaps half a million years before they can be safely released into the environment. The possibility of accidents in nuclear power stations or the leakage of stored radioactive waste is a constant threat to the environment, and alternative methods of obtaining energy, e.g. from sunlight, tidal power, or wave action, are urgently needed.

Terrestrial pollution. The effect of soot, sulphur dioxide and fluorides on vegetation has been discussed on p. 236. Other chemicals used to control weeds, destroy parasitic fungi or insects on crops may be harmful either because they are very poisonous to the people who have to apply them (e.g. some organo-phosphorus compounds) or because they kill not only the harmful organisms but harmless and beneficial ones as well. DDT, an organochlorine insecticide, though relatively harmless to man is very poisonous to fish and, by being concentrated in food chains, reaches harmful proportions in the bodies of predatory animals (see p. 58).

There are no easy answers to the problems of pollution. We cannot do without nitrogenous fertilizers to increase the yield of crops, or chemicals like DDT to destroy the insects which would eat them, but we have to make a choice between our wish to reproduce freely, to keep improving our standards of living (in the materialistic sense) and the eventual environmental destruction that seems to be a consequence of these two activities.

Carbon dioxide and global warming

The Earth's surface receives and absorbs radiant heat from the sun. It re-radiates some of this heat back into space. The sun's radiation is mainly in the form of short wavelength energy and penetrates our atmosphere easily. The energy radiated back from the Earth is in the form of long wavelengths (infrared or IR), much of which is absorbed by the atmosphere. The atmosphere acts like the glass in a greenhouse. It lets in light and heat from the sun, but reduces the amount of heat which escapes (Fig. 39.2).

If it were not for this 'greenhouse effect' of the atmosphere, the Earth's surface would probably be at −18°C. The 'greenhouse effect', therefore, is entirely natural and desirable.

Not all the atmospheric gases are equally effective at absorbing IR radiation. Oxygen and nitrogen, for example, absorb little or none.

The gases which absorb most IR radiation, in order of maximum absorption, are water vapour, carbon dioxide, methane and atmospheric pollutants such as oxides of nitrogen and CFCs (p. 239). Apart from water vapour, these gases are in very low concentrations in the atmosphere, but some of them are strong absorbers of IR radiation. It is assumed that if the concentration of any of these gases were to increase, the greenhouse effect would be enhanced and the Earth would get warmer.

In recent years, attention has focused principally on carbon dioxide. If you look back at the 'carbon cycle' on p. 56, you will see that the natural processes of photosynthesis, respiration and decay would be expected to keep the carbon dioxide concentration at a steady level. However, since the Industrial Revolution, we have been burning the 'fossil fuels' derived from coal and petroleum and releasing extra carbon dioxide into the atmosphere. As a result, the concentration of carbon dioxide has increased from 0.29 to 0.35 per cent since 1860. It is likely to go on increasing as we burn more and more fossil fuel. Could this result in an increase in the Earth's temperature, i.e. global warming?

The answer is that we do not know for certain. There are many computer models of the possible effects but they depend on the very complex and uncertain interaction of many variables.

Changes in climate might increase cloud cover and this might reduce the heat reaching the Earth from the sun. Oceanic plankton absorb a great deal of carbon dioxide. Will their rate of absorption increase or will a warmer ocean absorb less of the gas? An increase in carbon dioxide should, theoretically, result in increased rates of photosynthesis, bringing the system back into balance.

None of these possibilities is known for certain. The worst scenario is that the climate and rainfall distribution will change and disrupt the present pattern of world agriculture; the oceans will warm up and expand and the polar ice-caps will melt causing a rise in sea level; extremes of weather may produce droughts and food shortages.

In fact, it is not possible to produce figures which prove that the global temperature is rising. An average of temperature records from around the world suggests that, since 1860, there has been a rise of 0.5–0.7°C, most of it in the last 10 years, but this is too short a period to draw any conclusion about long-term trends (Fig. 39.3). There is evidence that there have been far more extreme fluctuations in the distant

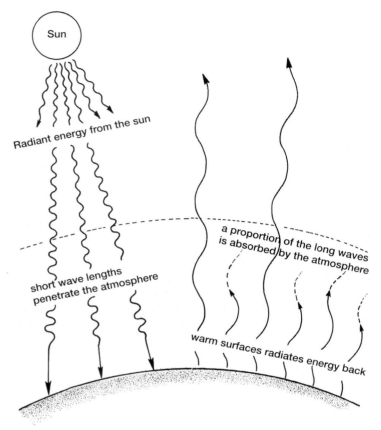

Fig. 39.2   The greenhouse effect and its contribution to global warming.

past. If the warming trend continues, however, it could produce a rise in sea level of between 0.2 and 1.5 metres in the next 50–100 years.

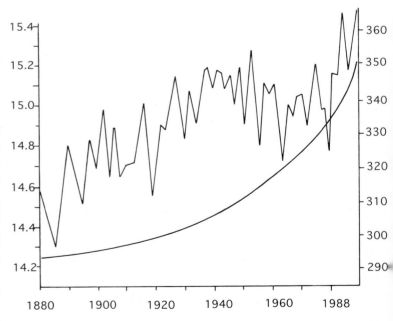

Fig. 39.3   Annual average global temperatures since 1880. Although there appears to be a rising trend in the last 100 years, the fluctuations make interpretation difficult, e.g. the temperature in 1980 was little different from that in 1885.

Despite the uncertainties, most scientists think that there is a threat of global warming.

At the Kyoto (Japan) Conference in 1997, 33 countries agreed to cut their emissions of carbon dioxide by an average of 5.2 per cent (from 1990 levels) by the year 2010. Different countries agreed to different levels, e.g. Japan 6%, USA 7% and Europe 8%. Generally it is felt that the richer nations, who have so far been responsible for the greatest proportion of emissions, should make greater cuts than the poorer countries, who might even be allowed to increase their emissions.

This agreement is a step in the right direction but the cuts, even if implemented, are far too small to make much difference to global climate change. We really need to be aiming for an average 60% cut in the next 30 years.

As can be imagined, reducing carbon dioxide emissions from transport and industry can be costly and, since global warming is a probability rather than a certainty, industry puts pressure on governments to resist changes which will cost them money. The best strategy would be to adopt the **'Precautionary principle'** which says that if global warming is taking place, and if we do nothing about it now, it may be too late to avoid serious and irreversible changes. Moreover, there are other advantages in cutting carbon dioxide emissions such as saving energy, conserving stocks of fossil fuel and reducing emissions of other pollutants.

Chlorofluorocarbons (CFCs) and the ozone layer

Chlorofluorocarbons (CFCs) are gases which readily liquefy when compressed. This makes them useful as refrigerants, propellants in aerosol cans and for making the gas bubbles in plastic foams. CFCs are very stable and accumulate in the atmosphere where they react with ozone (O_3).

Ozone is present throughout the atmosphere but reaches a peak at about 25 km above the Earth's surface, where it forms what is called the 'ozone layer'. This layer filters out much of the ultraviolet radiation in sunlight.

The chlorine from the CFCs reacts with ozone and reduces its concentration in the ozone layer. As a result, more ultraviolet (UV) radiation reaches the Earth's surface. Higher levels of UV radiation can lead to an increase in skin cancer. A survey in Australia showed a threefold increase in certain forms of skin cancer between 1992 and 1995. Increased UV radiation can also affect crops, damage marine plankton and even distort weather patterns.

The reactions between chlorine and ozone are complex. There are natural processes which restore ozone, but these do not keep pace with the rate of destruction.

CFCs are not the only ozone-depleting compounds. Others include methyl chloride, (used for destroying pests in soil), and halons, (for use in fire extinguishers).

The greatest destruction of ozone takes place over the North and South Poles. This is a result of the very low temperatures and other climatic conditions. The thinning of the ozone layer over the Arctic and Antarctic regions has led to the formation of 'ozone holes'. Their formation is seasonal but, nevertheless, the ozone holes get deeper and more extensive year after year. Between 1969 and 1993 there was a 14 per cent reduction in the ozone layer over North America and Europe in the winter. Figure 39.4 shows the decrease in ozone levels in the Antarctic over a 40-year period.

Protecting the ozone layer

The appearance of 'ozone holes' in the Arctic and Antarctic, and the thinning of the ozone layer elsewhere has spurred

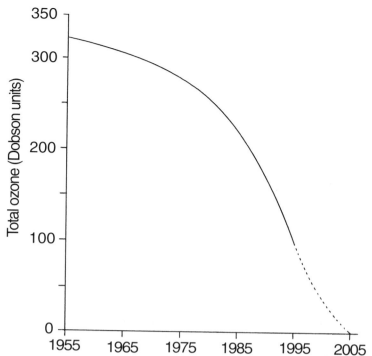

Fig. 39.4　Spring levels of ozone in the Antarctic. At current rates, the ozone layer might disappear by 2005.

countries to get together and agree to reduce production and use of CFCs and other ozone-damaging chemicals.

1987 saw the first Montreal Protocol which set targets for the reduction and phasing out of these chemicals. In 1990, nearly 100 countries agreed to the next stage of the treaty, which committed them to reduce production of CFCs by 85 per cent in 1994 and phase them out completely by 1996. In 1995, 150 governments were party to the ozone treaty.

The use of CFCs is now banned in the industrialised countries but world production still stood at 360,000 tonnes in 1995 because developing countries are still permitted to produce and import CFCs until at least 2010. The CFCs are largely used for refrigeration and air conditioning equipment.

Third World countries, quite reasonably, point out that 90 per cent of CFCs in the atmosphere come from the richer countries and these should agree to meet the cost of replacing them with less harmful chemicals. So far, the industrialised countries are not providing sufficient funds to meet even the 2010 deadline.

Less harmful replacements include hydrochlorofluorocarbons (HCFCs) which still contain chlorine but cause only one third of the damage of CFCs, and hydrofluorocarbons (HFCs) which contain no chlorine and do not react with ozone. The ozone treaty includes a programme for phasing out HCFCs but unless funds are provided for the production of alternatives, the targets are unlikely to be met.

QUESTIONS

1. In what ways might improved education lead to a reduction in transmissible diseases?
2. *(a)* What natural factors might put limits on the rate of growth of the human population?
　(b) What artificial methods can be employed to limit the growth of the human population?
3. List the processes which contribute to *(a)* atmospheric pollution, *(b)* water pollution. Name the pollutants in each case.
4. Why might an increase in atmospheric carbon dioxide lead to global warming?
5. What are CFCs and where do they come from? What effect do CFCs have on the ozone layer and why is this effect harmful?

Examination questions

The following questions are selected from the long answer section of the O level Biology papers set between 1976 and 1983 by the following boards: Cambridge Overseas (C), East African Examinations Council (E), London Overseas (L), and the Kenya National Examinations Council (K).

Biological principles

1. Write a brief essay on the importance of respiration in plants and animals. [C]

2. (a) Give a balanced equation which summarises the process of tissue respiration.
(b) What are the differences between aerobic and anerobic respiration?
(c) Describe an experiment which demonstrates that germinating seeds give off heat.
(d) How does a *named* protozoan obtain its oxygen supply? [L]

3. (a) Distinguish carefully between aerobic and anerobic respiration.
(b) Describe an experiment to show that respiring plants release carbon dioxide.
(c) How does gaseous exchange take place in: (i) mammals and (ii) fishes? [L]

4. (a) What are the characteristics of enzymes and what is their importance to living organisms?
(b) Describe an experiment which demonstrates that the efficiency of a named enzyme is affected by increase of temperature.
(c) Name two factors, other than temperature, which could affect enzyme efficiency.
(d) Describe the digestion of fat in a mammal. [L]

5. (a) What are enzymes?
(b) Describe an experiment that you could perform to show the effect of temperature on the activity of a named enzyme. Include in your answer a description of the results you would expect to obtain and a suitable control. [C]

6. (a) Define the following terms: (i) excretion, (ii) secretion, (iii) osmoregulation.
(b) Indicate briefly how excretion of carbon dioxide occurs in (i) *Amoeba*, (ii) a fish, (iii) a mammal. [C]

7. If you were given dry bean seeds for the purpose of studying growth, how would you use them to find:
(i) the region of growth in a shoot,
(ii) changes in dry mass as growth takes place. In this latter case, indicate by means of a graph the type of result you would expect. [E]

8. (a) What is the biological meaning of the term *sensitivity* (irritability)?
(b) Give an example of sensitivity in:
(i) a named invertebrate, e.g. an earthworm,
(ii) the root of a flowering plant.
(c) How do plants respond to the external stimulus of light?
(d) How may the smell of appetising food cause a person's mouth to water? [C]

9. All embryos, whether they develop internally or externally to their parent, or in a seed, have similar food requirements. They need the raw materials of growth, energy sources and certain elements and vitamins. Describe how different types of embryos obtain the food they need. [C]

10. You are provided with the following materials and apparatus: potato, starch powder, distilled water, sugar, tap water, a piece of muslin cloth, a scalpel blade and a beaker.
(a) Out of this list select the most appropriate ones for carrying out an experiment on osmosis. For each of the ones not selected give a reason why it is not appropriate.
(b) Draw two labelled diagrams:
(i) to illustrate how you would set up the selected apparatus and materials,
(ii) to illustrate the expected results.
(c) Of what biological importance is osmosis and diffusion? [K]

Plant structure and life cycles

11. Give an illustrated account of the shape and internal structure of the leaf of a flowering plant and explain how the leaf is suited to photosynthesis. [L]

12. Describe the process of sexual reproduction in a named, insect-pollinated, flowering plant. In your answer refer to pollination, fertilization, seed and fruit formation and dispersal. [L]

13. (a) What do you understand by cross pollination?
(b) Describe pollination, fertilization and fruit formation in a named insect-pollinated flower. [E]

14. (a) With reference to a named example, explain how insect pollination may occur.
(b) With reference to a named example, explain how seed dispersal may be brought about when the seeds or fruits of a flowering plant become attached to the outside of an animal's body. [C]

15. (a) State the conditions necessary for germination of the seeds of a plant.
(b) Show, by means of three labelled diagrams, the stages in the germination of a named seed, as far as the production of the first foliage leaf. [C]

Plant physiology

16. (a) Describe, with the help of diagrams and giving full experimental details, how you would demonstrate that a green potted plant requires carbon dioxide in order to photosynthesize.
(b) State briefly how you would demonstrate that, in certain circumstances, the same plant can give off carbon dioxide from respiration. [C]

17. How would you demonstrate that a green plant produces (a) starch and (b) oxygen, during photosynthesis? (Suitable controls should be given.) [C]

18. (a) What is chlorophyll?
(b) Why is chlorophyll important in the process of photosynthesis?
(c) How does a mould (such as *Mucor* or *Rhizopus*), which lacks chlorophyll, obtain its food? [C]

19. (a) State the functions of iron, phosphorus and potassium in the healthy growth of a green plant.
(b) With the aid of a diagram, describe how you would show the necessity of magnesium in plant growth. Indicate the results you would expect after three months. [E]

20. (a) Describe an experiment that would enable you to measure the uptake of water by a leafy shoot. Include in your account a labelled diagram of the apparatus you would use.
(b) State three environmental factors that are known to influence the rate of water loss from a plant and briefly explain how these factors affect water loss. [C]

21. Describe how a flowering plant absorbs, transports and loses water. [L]

22. (a) What is osmosis?
(b) Describe an experiment to illustrate osmosis.
(c) How does a root hair cell absorb (i) water and (ii) mineral ions?
(d) Why is osmoregulation necessary in freshwater protozoa but not in marine protozoa? [L]

23. With the aid of large labelled diagrams explain: (a) osmosis in root hairs, (b) phototropism in young shoots of plants, (c) the opening and closing of stomata in the leaves of a dicotyledonous plant. [K]

24. (a) (i) Different regions of a plant grow at different rates. Describe how you would use the stem of a named potted seedling to test the truth of this statement.
(ii) What processes do cells undergo to bring about growth and development of a plant? *(Part question)* [K]

Soil, agriculture, natural cycles

25. (a) Describe briefly the components of a fertile soil and the part that each plays in the life of a plant.
(b) Give reasons why (i) poor drainage and (ii) excessive drainage hinder the growth of plants. [C]

26. (a) Describe with full practical details how you would analyse a sample of soil in order to demonstrate
(i) the presence of different sizes of particle,
(ii) the amount of air in the soil sample,
(iii) the amount of water in the sample.
(b) What are the beneficial effects of adding lime to soil? [C]

27. (a) How would you demonstrate the presence of bacteria (or other microscopic organisms) in a sample of fresh soil?
(b) State briefly the ways in which bacteria are involved in making nitrogen available in the soil for green plants. [C]

28. (a) Describe the following methods of soil conservation. Terracing, afforestation, mulching and strip cropping.
(b) How can the fertility of an overcultivated piece of land be renewed?

Ecology and interdependence

30. (a) Give an explanation of the process of photosynthesis.
(b) Describe how the following organisms are dependent on this process: (i) a mould, (ii) a caterpillar, (iii) a bird of prey. [C]

31. Describe what is meant by the following: (a) food chain, (b) food web, (c) carbon cycle. [C]

32. (a) Name the major living components of ecosystems.
(b) By means of a diagram illustrate the flow of energy through an ecosystem.
(c) Write a chemical equation for the process by which energy enters any ecosystem.
(d) Name and describe the effects on the environment of each of (i) three air pollutants, (ii) three water pollutants. [L]

33. Explain by reference to specific examples how man's activities have affected the lives of other organisms in the environment. [L]

34. (a) For an ecological study you have carried out, explain how you made use of any two of the following: (i) line transect, (ii) capture–recapture, (iii) quadrat. (Part question) [E]

35. The Government of Kenya is very much concerned about the destruction of our environment and the need to conserve it.
(a) In what ways is the environment being destroyed?
(b) Suggest possible ways of conserving it. [K]

Vertebrate physiology

36. (a) Explain how a solid starchy food is broken down from the time it is taken into the mouth to the time it is absorbed in the intestine.
(b) What happens to the absorbed food when it reaches the liver? [K]

37. (a) Describe the route taken by a molecule of glucose from the time of absorption until it reaches a muscle cell in the leg of man.
(b) (i) Suggest and explain the adverse effects of having a reduced number of white and red cells in the body.
(ii) Suggest ways in which the number of blood cells would be increased. [K]

38. (a) Give an account of the functions of the mammalian placenta.
(b) Compare and contrast the composition of blood supplied to the liver with that which leaves the liver. [E]

39. Describe the breathing mechanism in a named mammal. [K]

40. (a) Explain the term excretion.
(b) Describe how carbon dioxide is removed from the blood in the lungs.
(c) Explain the role of the kidney in the purification of blood. [K]

41. (a) How does the skin of mammals help them to maintain a constant body temperature in cold conditions?
(b) Outline the advantages to a mammal of having a constant body temperature. [C]

42. (a) Describe the nutrition, respiration and excretion of a mammalian embryo (diagrams are not required).
(b) What advantages are there for a mammalian embryo developing in the uterus as compared with a bird embryo developing in the egg? [C]

43. Explain how muscles contribute to movements of the limbs and gut and to accommodation and iris movements within the eye of a mammal. [L]

44. Draw and label a generalized diagram of a vertebra in either anterior (front) or posterior (rear) view.
Explain the function of the vertebra in relation to (a) support, (b) the central nervous system and spinal nerves, (c) muscles and movement. [C]

45. (a) Draw a labelled diagram to show the structure of a molar tooth of a named mammal.
(b) Describe the dentition of a named mammal and distinguish between juvenile and adult sets of teeth. [C]

46. (a) Draw a diagram of the mammalian ear and label the ear drum, ossicles, oval window, cochlea and semi-circular canal.
(b) Explain how sound waves reach the auditory nerve.
(c) Explain how the eye adapts itself to seeing distant objects. [K]

47. (a) An eye may be defective because the focal length of its lens is too short (i.e. the lens is "too powerful"). Explain the condition caused by this defect and, with the aid of a simple diagram, show how it may be corrected.
(b) How, and in what conditions, is the pupil of the eye made smaller? [C]

48. When a person's hand accidentally touches a hot object it is quickly withdrawn. With the aid of large labelled diagrams explain what causes this response. [K]

49. (a) With the aid of a large labelled diagram, illustrate a simple reflex arc.
(b) Giving examples differentiate between voluntary (deliberate or reasoned) action and conditioned action.
(c) A person sees a snake and runs away immediately. Explain how the nervous system and the adrenal glands work together to bring about the action. [K]

50. With reference to insulin, adrenalin and thyroxin, describe how mammalian hormones control blood sugar level, rate of metabolic activity and growth. [C]

Cell division, genetics, evolution

51. With the aid of labelled diagrams, give a simple account of
(a) the process of division in Amoeba,
(b) the process of mitosis (nuclear division) followed by cell division in a cell of a plant root tip. [C]

52. (a) (i) What is fertilization?
(ii) How is sex in man determined during fertilization?
(b) Explain the role of variation and natural selection in the continued existence of a species.
(c) Pure lines of red flowered and white flowered plants were crossed to give F_1 generations whose flowers were all pink. The F_1 were selfed. Work out the F_2 generation and indicate their phenotypic ratio (use R to represent red and W to represent white). [K]

53. What is the difference in the result of cell division by mitosis and meiosis? What is the significance of the two processes in the life of man?
In wild rabbits fat beneath the skin is white. Certain domestic breeds have yellow fat. When a pure strain of wild rabbit is crossed with a pure strain of domestic rabbit, F_1 individuals all have white fat. If F_1 males are mated with F_1 females to produce an F_2 generation, white and yellow fat individuals are found in a proportion of 3 white and 1 yellow, show in a diagrammatic form how this ratio is arrived at. [E]

54. (a) Explain the term "mutation" and what causes it.
(b) State the similarities and differences between mitosis and meiosis.
(c) What are the advantages and disadvantages of sexual and asexual reproduction in agriculture? [K]

Diseases, their cause and transmission

55. Write an account of disease in Man with particular reference to causative agents, their transmission and control. [C]

56. For each of the following, describe the causative agent of the disease, the way it is transmitted and measures that can be taken to control the disease: (a) a disease caused by a bacterium, (b) a disease caused by a protozoan, (c) a disease of plants caused by a fungus. [C]

57. (a) Name one disease caused by a virus and one disease caused by a bacterium. For each of these diseases describe
(i) how it is passed from one person to another,
(ii) a symptom or an effect of the disease,
(iii) how it may be controlled, so that its spread is limited.
(b) Indicate briefly the body's reaction to (i) bacteria and (ii) viruses. [C]

58. Select one of the diseases listed below and (a) name and describe the organism that causes the disease, (b) state how it is transmitted from one host to another, (c) describe the methods used to combat the disease.
Diseases: amoebic dysentery; malaria; sleeping sickness (select one). [C]

59. (a) Distinguish between saprophytic and parasitic modes of nutrition.
(b) Give the name of one disease caused by a protozoan. Name the protozoan and indicate how this disease is transmitted.
(c) What methods can be used to control the spread of the disease named in (b)? [C]

60. List the general characteristics of parasites. Explain how (a) the structure and (b) the life cycle of a tapeworm suit it to its parasitic mode of life. How do tapeworms affect the health of man? [L]

Insects

61. (a) Describe the life history of a housefly.
(b) Describe an experiment that would show that houseflies carry bacteria. [K]

62. Why may the adult stage of each of the following be regarded as pests? (a) Housefly, (b) Mosquito or gnat or aphid or other named insect pest. [C]

63. Describe the structure, life-history and economic importance of a named non-social insect. [L]

Fungi

64. (a) Explain how damp bread goes mouldy and then becomes almost liquid in consistency.
(b) Write a short account of the transmission and control of a disease caused by a fungus.
(c) Distinguish between the two types of organism dealt with in sections (a) and (b) with respect to their mode of nutrition. [C]

65. (a) What are the advantages of (i) asexual reproduction, (ii) sexual reproduction?
(b) Describe, with the help of diagrams, the process of asexual reproduction in a mould such as Mucor or Rhizopus. [C]

66. (a) What is a parasite and how does it differ from a saprophyte?
(b) Name a plant disease caused by a fungus and indicate how it is transmitted from plant to plant. How does Man attempt to control this disease? [C]

Further examination questions

The following questions have been selected from Paper 2 of the Cambridge Overseas O level examinations between 1993 and 1995 and are reproduced here with permission from The University of Cambridge Local Examinations Syndicate whose copyright they are. Do not write on this page. Where necessary copy drawings, tables or sentences.

1. Fig. 1 shows the structure of a flower.

Fig. 1

(a) Describe how the process of pollination is most likely to be carried out in this flower. Your answer should include identification of structures **A**, **B** and **C**.
(b) (i) What are the advantages to an organism of asexual reproduction?
    (ii) What are the commercial advantages of asexual reproduction?

2. Fig. 2 shows a section through a green leaf.

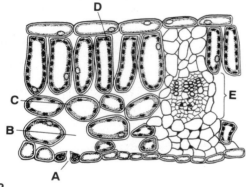

Fig. 2

(a) With reference to the parts **A** to **E**, explain how a leaf is involved in the manufacture of carbohydrates.
(b) Explain how these carbohydrates are distributed to the rest of the plant.

3. (a) List the differences between (i) *monocotyledonous* and *dicotyledonous* plants, (ii) *bacteria* and *fungi*.
(b) In what ways are bacteria and fungi important for the healthy growth and development of green plants?

4. Describe the part played by microorganisms in (a) the production of any **two** of the following: bread, alcohol, cheese, yoghurt, (b) the nitrogen cycle, and (c) the carbon cycle.

5. (a) Distinguish clearly between *complete dominance* and *codominance*.
(b) Explain how a man with blood group A and a woman with blood group B can have a child with blood group O.
(c) The presence of hairs on the stems of a certain species of plant is controlled by a single pair of alleles. When a pure-breeding plant with a hairy stem is crossed with a pure-breeding plant with a smooth stem, all the offspring have hairy stems. Use a genetic diagram to show a cross which would produce offspring with hairy stems and smooth stems in a ratio of 1:1 and explain the symbols you use.

6. (a) Explain, with examples where possible,
    (i) how mutations are brought about, and
    (ii) how they may lead to a change in phenotype.
(b) Explain how mutation and natural selection may lead to evolution.

7. (a) Define the terms *tissue*, *organ* and *organ system*, naming **one** example of each.
(b) Explain how a sudden bright light brings about a response in tissues in the iris.

8. (a) What is meant by the term *homeostasis*?
Fig. 3 shows the body temperature of a person before, during and after taking a cold bath. (The temperature of the bath water was 22°C.)

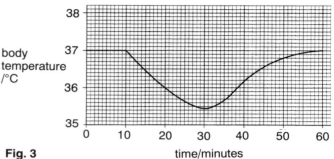

Fig. 3

(b) For how long was the person in the bath?
(c) Explain why the person's body temperature fell.
(d) Explain the roles played by the following in helping to return body temperature to normal:
    (i) the liver; (ii) blood vessels in the skin; (iii) muscles of the body.

9. (a) State **two** main functions of the ileum.
(b) How do villi improve the efficiency of the ileum?
Fig. 4 shows a villus, in longitudinal section, from the ileum of a mammal.

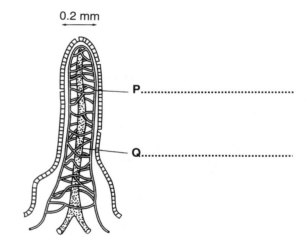

Fig. 4

(c) (i) On the diagram, label **P** and **Q**.
    (ii) What are the functions of **P** and **Q**?
    (iii) Explain how **P** is adapted to carry out its particular functions.

10. (a) What is meant by a *double (dual) circulation*?
(b) How do the two parts of a double circulation differ from one another?
(c) Describe how the circulatory system (i) helps to stop bacteria entering a cut in the skin, and (ii) deals with bacteria which may have entered the cut.

11. (a) Describe the events which occur from the moment a person accidentally touches a very hot object to the moment the hand is lifted clear.
(b) Explain how the action of deliberately raising the arm differs from the sequence of events described in (a).

12. (a) What is a reflex action?
(b) Nerves and hormones are both used to control processes within the body. Using examples, show how nervous control and hormonal control (i) resemble, and (ii) differ from one another.

13. (a) State the ways in which the human body is naturally protected against the entry of harmful bacteria.
(b) (i) What measures could a person take to reduce the risk of bacterial infection and the development of bacterial disease?
    (ii) Describe the processes occurring in the body after the bacteria have gained entry.
(c) Why is a tissue graft from a near relative more likely to be successful than one from an unrelated donor?

Glossary of Scientific Terms

These are some words often used in scientific books but not explained in the text.

acid a sharp-tasting chemical, often a liquid. Some acids can dissolve metals and turn them into soluble salts. Nitric acid acts on copper and turns it into copper nitrate, which dissolves to form a blue-coloured solution. Acids of plants and animals (animo acids, fatty acids) are weaker and don't dissolve metals. Amino acids and fatty acids are organic acids. Hydrochloric, sulphuric and nitric acids are called mineral acids or inorganic acids

agar a clear jelly extracted from one kind of seaweed. On its own it will not support the growth of bacteria or fungi, but will do so if food substances (e.g. potato juice or peptides) are dissolved in it. Agar with different kinds of food dissolved in it is used to grow different kinds of micro-organism

alcohol usually a liquid. There are many kinds of alcohol but the commonest is ethanol (or ethyl alcohol) which occurs in wines, spirits, beer, etc. It is produced by fermentation of sugar. Ethanol vaporizes quickly and easily catches fire

alkali the opposite of an acid. An alkali can neutralize an acid and so remove its acid properties. Sodium hydroxide is an alkali. It neutralizes hydrochloric acid to form a salt, sodium chloride

$$Na[OH + H]Cl \longrightarrow NaCl + H_2O$$
$$\text{salt} \quad \text{water}$$

amino acids organic acids whose molecules contain nitrogen in an amino (—NH_2) group.

is a simple amino acid called glycine. Proteins are made up of long chains of amino acids joined together. When proteins are digested, the amino acids are set free

atom the smallest possible particle of an element. Even a microscopic piece of iron would be made up of millions of iron atoms. When we write formulae, the letters represent atoms. So H_2O for water means an atom of oxygen joined to two atoms of hydrogen

capillary attraction the tendency of water to fill small spaces is called capillary attraction. If a narrow bore tube is placed in water, the water will rise up it for several centimetres. In a similar way, water will creep into the spaces between the fibres in a piece of blotting paper or between the particles in soil

carbon a black, solid non-metal which occurs as charcoal or soot, for example. Its atoms are able to combine together to make ring or chain molecules (see "glucose"). These molecules make up most of the chemicals of living organisms (see "organic"). One of the simplest compounds of carbon is carbon dioxide (CO_2)

carbon dioxide a gas which forms 0·03 per cent (by volume) of the air. It is produced when carbon-containing substances burn ($C + O_2 \rightarrow CO_2$). It is also produced by the respiration of plants and animals. It is taken up by green plants to make food during photosynthesis

catalyst a substance which makes a chemical reaction go faster but does not get used up in the reaction. Platinum is a catalyst which speeds up the rate at which nitrogen and hydrogen combine to form ammonia, but does not get used up. Enzymes are catalysts for chemical reactions inside living cells

caustic a caustic substance can damage the skin and clothing and therefore should be handled with great care

cellulose a chemical which makes up plant cell walls. It occurs in paper because this is made from wood, and in the clear plastic material called Cellophane. The cellulose molecule is made up of about a thousand glucose molecules joined end to end to form a long chain:

compound two or more elements joined together form a compound. Carbon dioxide, CO_2, is a compound of carbon and oxygen. Potassium nitrate, KNO_3, is a compound of potassium, nitrogen and oxygen

cubic centimetre (cm^3) this is a unit of volume. A tea-cup holds about 200 cm^3 liquid. One thousand cubic centimetres are called a cubic decimetre (dm^3) but this volume is also called a litre. Some measuring instruments are marked in millilitres (ml). A millilitre is a thousandth of a litre and therefore the same volume as a cubic centimetre. So 1 cm^3 = 1 ml

dissolve a substance which mixes with a liquid and seems to "disappear" in the liquid is said to dissolve. Sugar dissolves in water to make a solution

element an element is a substance which cannot be broken down into anything else. Sulphur is a non-metallic element. Iron is a metallic element. Oxygen and nitrogen are gaseous elements. Water (H_2O) is not an element because it can be broken down into hydrogen and oxygen

energy this can be heat, movement, light, electricity, etc. Anything which can be harnessed to do some kind of work is energy. Food consists of substances containing chemical energy. When food is turned into carbon dioxide and water by respiration, energy is released to do work such as making muscles contract

expand if a metal rod is heated strongly it gets longer. It is said to have expanded. If air is heated, it will expand and take up more space. If air, or any gas, is heated in a closed container which will not allow the gas to expand, the gas pressure will rise instead

fatty acids organic acids containing carbon, hydrogen and oxygen only.

is butanoic acid. The group makes it acid. Fats are made up of various kinds of fatty acid combined with glycerol

filtrate the clear solution which passes through a filter; e.g. if a mixture of copper(II) sulphate solution and sand is filtered, the blue copper(II) sulphate solution which passes through the filter paper is called the filtrate

formula a way of showing the chemical composition of a substance. Letters are chosen to represent elements, and numbers show how many atoms of each element are present. The letter for carbon is C and for oxygen is O. A molecule of carbon dioxide is one atom of carbon joined to two atoms of oxygen and the formula is CO_2. There are more elements than letters in the alphabet, so some of the elements have two letters, e.g. Mg for magnesium. Other elements have letters standing for the latin name, e.g. sodium is Na (=natrium)

glucose one kind of sugar. Its formula is $C_6H_{12}O_6$ and the atoms are arranged something like this:

It is often represented by

glycerol an organic compound containing carbon, hydrogen and oxygen. Its formula is

Each —OH group can combine with a fatty acid and so make a fat

gram (g) a unit of weight in the metric system.
1000 grams is a kilogram (kg).
One thousandth of a gram is a milligram (mg).

humidity the amount of water vapour in the atmosphere. The warm, moist air of tropical forests makes them very humid.

hydrogen a gas which burns very readily. It is present in only tiny amounts in the air but forms part of many compounds such as water (H_2O), and organic compounds like carbohydrates (e.g. $C_6H_{12}O_6$ glucose), fats and proteins

inorganic substances like iron, salt, oxygen and carbon dioxide are inorganic. They do not have to come from a living organism. Salt is in the sea, iron is part of a mineral in the ground, oxygen is in the air. Inorganic substances can be made by industrial processes or extracted from minerals

insoluble an insoluble substance is one which will not dissolve. Sugar is soluble in water but insoluble in petrol

243

joule just as a centimetre is a unit of length, a joule is a unit of heat or energy. It is the amount of heat that would raise the temperature of 4.2 grams of water one degree Celsius. The energy value of food can be measured in joules or in calories (1 calorie = 4.2 joules)

latent heat (evaporation) the heat which has to be supplied to water to turn it into water vapour. It takes 420 joules to raise 1 gram of water from 0 °C to 100 °C but it takes another 2300 joules to evaporate it

lime water a weak solution of lime (calcium hydroxide) in water. When carbon dioxide bubbles through this solution, it reacts with the calcium hydroxide to form calcium carbonate (chalk) which is insoluble and forms a cloudy suspension. This makes lime water a good test for carbon dioxide.

$$Ca(OH)_2 + CO_2 \rightarrow CaCO_3 + H_2O$$

maltose a sugar which has the same formula as sucrose $C_{12}H_{22}O_{11}$. It is formed when starch is broken down by enzyme action

molecule the smallest amount of a substance which you can have. For example, the water molecule is H_2O, that is, two atoms of hydrogen joined to one atom of oxygen. A drop of water consists of countless millions of molecules of H_2O moving about in all directions and with a lot of space between them

organic this usually refers to a substance produced by a living organism. Organic chemicals are things like carbohydrates, protein and fat. They have very large molecules and are often insoluble in water. Inorganic chemicals are usually simple substances like sodium chloride (salt) or carbon dioxide (CO_2).

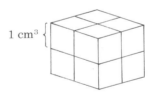

molecule of a fatty acid
C_4H_9COOH (organic)

molecule of carbon dioxide
CO_2 (inorganic)

oxygen a gas which makes up about 20 per cent (by volume) of the air. It combines with other substances and oxidizes them, sometimes producing heat and light energy. In plants and animals it combines with food to release energy

peptide a peptide is smaller than a protein. A dipeptide is made from two amino acids joined together. A polypeptide consists of many amino acids but is still not large enough to be called a protein. When proteins are digested they are first broken down to peptides

permeable allows liquids or gases to pass through. A cotton shirt is permeable to rain but a PVC mackintosh is impermeable. Plant cell walls are permeable to water and dissolved substances

pH this is a measure of how acid or how alkaline a substance is. A pH of 7 is neutral. A pH in the range 8–11 is alkaline, while those in the 6–2 range are acid; pH 6 is slightly acid, and pH 2 is very acid

pigment a chemical which has a colour. Haemoglobin in blood is a red pigment; chlorophyll in leaves is a green pigment. A black pigment called melanin gives a dark colour to human skin, hair and eyes

pipette a glass tube designed to deliver controlled amounts of liquid. A bulb pipette has a plastic squeezer on one end so that it can deliver a drop at a time. A graduated pipette has marks on the side to show how much liquid has run out

proteins organic chemicals with large molecules containing carbon, hydrogen, oxygen and nitrogen (and usually sulphur). Proteins are made up of long chains of amino acids, often a hundred or more. The long chain is twisted and folded in a way which gives the protein a special shape. Enzymes and the structures in cells are made mostly of protein

reaction (chemical) a change which takes place when certain chemicals meet or are acted on by heat or light. The change results in the production of new substances. When paper burns, a reaction is taking place between the paper and the oxygen in the air

refraction a change in the direction of light rays when they pass from air to water or from air to glass. The light rays are "bent" as they pass from one substance to another

salt a compound formed from an acid and a metal. Salts have double-barrelled names like sodium chloride (NaCl), and potassium nitrate (KNO_3). The first name is usually a metal and the second name is the acid. Potassium (K) is a metal, and the nitrate (NO_3) comes from nitric acid (HNO_3)

sodium hydrogencarbonate at one time this was called sodium bicarbonate. It is a salt which is used to make carbon dioxide in experiments. Its formula is $NaHCO_3$. It may also be called sodium hydrogentrioxocarbonate(IV)

sodium hydroxide (NaOH) an alkali with caustic properties, i.e. its solution will dissolve flesh, wood and fabrics

soluble a soluble substance is one which will dissolve in liquid. Sugar is soluble in water

solution when something like sugar or salt dissolves in water it forms a solution. The molecules of the solid become evenly spread through the liquid

volume the amount of space something takes up, or the amount of space inside it. A milk bottle has an internal volume of one pint. Your lungs have a volume of about 5 litres; they can hold up to 5 litres of air. This cube has a volume of 8 cubic centimetres (8 cm^3)

$1\ cm^3$

Glossary of biological terms

The explanations of terms given in this glossary are not meant to be formal definitions, but reminders, and are restricted to the context in which these terms are used in the book. The numbers in brackets are page references.

abdomen (106) the part of the body below the diaphragm which contains stomach, intestines, kidneys, liver, etc; in insects it refers to the third region of the body which has no limbs or appendages

accommodation (132) changing the shape and hence the focal length of the eye lens to focus on near or distant objects

adipose tissue (91) fatty tissue in mammals

adrenal gland (144) one of the endocrine glands, situated above the kidneys; it produces the hormone adrenaline

aerobic respiration (45) the chemical process which uses oxygen to release energy from food

albinism (196) absence of colour in skin, hair, and eyes; an inherited condition

algae (6) simple green plants, single celled or many celled but not organized into root, stem, and leaves

alimentary canal (85) the tube running through an animal from mouth to anus; digestion and absorption of food takes place inside it

alleles (192) genes controlling the same characteristic (e.g. hair colour) but producing different effects (e.g. black or red), and occupying corresponding positions on homologous chromosomes

amino acids (82) chemicals produced by the digestion of proteins or assembled to make proteins

amnion (115) a fluid-filled bag or sac surrounding an embryo

amphibia (6) frogs, toads, newts, etc; they can move and breathe equally well on land or in water

ampulla (135) a bulge in each of the semicircular canals; contains sensory organs

amylase (85) a starch-digesting enzyme

anaerobic respiration (47) the chemical process which releases energy from food but does not need oxygen to do so

anaphase (178) a late stage in mitosis or meiosis when the chromosomes or chromatids are separating

androecium (28) the male part of a flower; the stamens

anther (29) the upper part of a stamen; contains the pollen

antibodies (94) chemicals made in the blood which combat bacteria or their poisons

antigen (94) a foreign organism or chemical in the blood which stimulates the system to make antibodies against it

antitoxin (72) an antibody which neutralizes bacterial poisons

aorta (95) the main artery from the heart to the body

aqueous humour (130) the fluid in the front part of the eye

arteriole (97) a branch of an artery

arthropod (146) an animal with an outer cuticle and jointed legs (e.g. crabs, lobsters, insects)

asexual reproduction (23) production of new individuals by a single organism (e.g. budding) without involving gametes

atrium (98) the upper chamber of the heart receiving blood from the veins

auxin (42) a plant hormone which may affect rates of growth in roots and shoots

axon (138) part of a nerve cell; the fibre carrying impulses away from the cell body

back-cross (192) mating an organism with the same genetic type as its grandparents; one method of investigating the genetic make-up of an organism

bile (84) a green fluid made in the liver and delivered to the small intestine where it assists digestion of fats

bivalent (186) a pair of homologous chromosomes, closely associated at prophase of meiosis

bract (30) a leaf borne on a flower stalk

bronchiole (102) a branch of a bronchus

bronchus (102) either one of the two air-pipes branching from the windpipe and going to the lungs

caecum (86) a blindly ending sac at the junction of the small and large intestine

calyx (28) the ring of sepals on the outside of a flower

cambium (17) a layer of cells inside a plant stem; by their division the cambial cells increase the thickness of the stem

capillary (97) the smallest type of blood vessel in the circulatory system; its walls are only one cell thick

carpals (120) the wrist bones

carpel (28) a component of the female part of the flower which contains the potential seeds

central nervous system (139) the brain and spinal cord

centriole (177) a small body in an animal cell which divides first at cell division

centromere (178) that part of a chromosome which becomes attached to the spindle at mitosis or meiosis

centrum (122) the solid, cylindrical part of a vertebra

cerebellum (142) part of the brain; an outgrowth of the roof of the hind-brain

cerebral cortex (142) a layer of grey matter on the outside of the cerebral hemispheres; many connections between nerve cells are possible here

cervix (112) the narrow passage connecting the top of the vagina with the uterus (womb)

chemoreceptor (149) a sense organ which responds to chemicals; produces sensations of smell or taste

chiasma (186) region of close contact between homologous chromosomes at meiosis; when first formed, a chiasma indicates where exchange of chromatid portions is taking place

chlorophyll (19) a green chemical present in all green parts of plants; can trap sunlight and use its energy for promoting chemical changes

chloroplast (19) a cytoplasmic body in a plant cell; it contains the chlorophyll

choroid (130) a layer of cells and blood vessels in the eye, between the retina and sclerotic

chromatid (178) when a chromosome replicates, it produces two identical chromatids which are separated at cell division, one going to each new cell

chromosome (180) a long, rod-like structure in a nucleus; it appears at cell division and is thought to carry the genes

cilia (14) hair-like cytoplasmic projections from a cell; they can flick and so produce movement

ciliary body (130) part of the eye between the lens and the choroid which contains the ciliary muscle

ciliary muscle (130) the muscle in the eye which alters the shape and focal length of the lens during accommodation

clavicle (119) the "collar-bone"; it joins the shoulder to the breast-bone

cleavage (163) cell division in a fertilized egg

clinostat (41) an apparatus which rotates plants to make the effects of light and gravity equal on all sides

coccus (70) a bacterium, spherical in shape

cochlea (134) a coiled tube in the inner ear; contains sensory nerve endings which respond to sound vibrations

codominance (195) where both alleles are equally expressed in the phenotype, i.e. neither of two contrasting allelomorphic genes is dominant

coleoptile (39) the protective casing outside the shoot of a cereal seedling

collecting tubule (107) the final part of the kidney tubule where the water content of the blood is adjusted

colon (86) the first part of the large intestine; water is absorbed here

compensation point (49) the time when photosynthesis is as rapid as respiration; carbohydrates are produced as fast as they are used

cone (131) a light-sensitive cell in the retina of the eye; it is colour sensitive

conjugation (173) one form of sexual reproduction in which individual cells join and exchange gametes

conjunctiva (130) the transparent skin over the front part of the eyeball

consanguinity (198) intermarriage of close relations having a relatively high proportion of genes in common

consumer (53) an organism assigned a position in a food chain because it feeds on other organisms or their products

contraception (118) prevention of fertilization by "artificial" means

co-ordination (137) the linking together of systems to make them work effectively together

cornea (84) the transparent part of the sclerotic in the front of the eyeball

cornified layer (109) the outer layer of the skin consisting of dead cells

corolla (28) a ring of petals on a flower

corpus luteum (114) the structure formed from the follicle of an ovary in a mammal after an ovum has been released; it produces the hormone progesterone

cortisone (144) the hormone produced from the outer layer (cortex) of the adrenal gland

cotyledon (37) a specialized leaf, often swollen with food reserves, making up part of the embryo in a seed

covert (166) one of the feathers of a bird contributing to the general covering of the body

Cowper's gland (113) part of the male mammalian reproductive system; it adds a secretion to the sperms at ejaculation

crista (135) the sensory part of an ampulla in the semicircular canal

crossing over (186) occurs when chromatids at meiosis exchange portions with their homologous partners

crustacea (6) a group of animals with an external cuticle and jointed legs (e.g. crabs and lobsters)

cupula (135) a structure in the ampulla of a semicircular canal which is deflected during rotatory movements

cuticle of a leaf (19) a thin, non-cellular layer outside the epidermis

cuticle of an insect (146) the hard casing covering the body and limbs

cytoplasm (11) the semi-fluid matter, other than nucleus, in a cell; it contains enzymes and other substances which maintain life in the cell

deamination (92) removal of the nitrogenous part of an amino acid prior to converting it to glycogen

dendrite (138) one of many fibres in a nerve cell conducting impulses towards the cell body

dendron (138) a single, long fibre of a nerve cell conducting impulses to the cell body

denitrifying bacteria (54) bacteria in the soil which convert compounds of nitrogen into gaseous nitrogen

dentine (125) the layer of bone-like tissue beneath the enamel of a tooth

deoxyribonucleic acid (DNA) (184) the chemical in the chromosomes which controls activities in the cell; it is thought to constitute the genes

dermis (109) the deepest layer of the skin

detoxication (92) the rendering harmless by the liver of poisonous chemicals in the blood

diabetes (144) the disease resulting from an inability to control the level of sugar in the blood due to inadequate production of insulin by the pancreas

dialysis tubing (65) cellophane tubing with selectively permeable properties used for dialysis and experiments on osmosis

diaphragm (86) the sheet of muscular tissue separating the thorax and abdomen

diatoms (53) single-celled green plants constituting a large part of the phytoplankton

dicotyledon (6) a plant having two cotyledons in its seed

diffusion (60) movement of molecules of a gas or dissolved solute from a region of high concentration to one of low concentration

diploid (181) the number of chromosomes in the body cells of most animals and plants; there are two of each type of chromosome

discontinuous variation (197) relatively large differences between members of the same species, without intermediates (e.g. black or white mice)

dominant (192) the gene, of a pair of alleles, which is expressed in the phenotype

dormancy (40) a "resting" stage in which no growth or movement is observable from outside

dorsal root (140) the spinal nerve bringing sensory impulses into the spinal cord

Drosophila (181) the small fruit fly used for breeding experiments

duodenum (88) the first part of the small intestine, opening from the stomach

dwarfism (185) normal size head and trunk but very short limbs (one type); an inherited condition

ecdysis (146) moulting or shedding the cuticle in insects, usually accompanied by rapid increase in size

echinoderms (6) a group of invertebrate animals such as starfish

ectoplasm (174) the outer layer of clear cytoplasm in a single-celled animal such as Amoeba

egestion (86) the passing out of undigested food residues and other matter from a food vacuole or the intestine

embryo (116) the stage during which an organism develops from a fertilized egg to an independently functioning individual

enamel (125) the outer layer of a tooth

endocrine gland (144) a gland which produces chemicals called "hormones", which are released directly into the blood circulation

endolymph (134) the fluid in the semicircular canals and the cochlea of the ear

endoplasm (174) the inner, granular, fluid cytoplasm of a single-celled animal such as Amoeba

endoskeleton (119) a skeleton inside the organism (e.g. that of man and other vertebrates)

endosperm (38) a food store inside a seed

endothelium (96) the layer of cells lining the inside of blood vessels

enzyme (85) a chemical made in the protoplasm of cells which speeds up the rate of certain chemical reactions

epicotyl (37) that part of the shoot of a seedling between the cotyledons and the stem; its elongation brings the cotyledons above the soil

epidermis: human (109) the outer layer of the skin

    plant (15) the layer of cells on the outside of a structure such as a stem or leaf

epididymis (113) a long coiled tube between the testis and the sperm duct; sperms are stored here

epigeal (38) the type of germination in which the cotyledons are brought above the ground

epiglottis (86) a flap of cartilage behind the tongue, which helps direct food away from the windpipe and into the gullet

epithelium (89) a layer of cells in an animal, lining the inside of certain organs

erosion (79) loss of topsoil due to action of wind or rain

erythrocyte (93) a red cell in the blood

etiolation (42) the effect of growing a shoot in the absence of light

eugenics (197) the application of genetics to eliminate or reduce hereditary diseases and improve human qualities

Euglena (176) a single-celled green plant

Eustachian tube (87) the tube running from the middle ear to the throat

eutrophication (56) over-production of microscopic plants in lakes and rivers due to excess of mineral salts reaching them

evolution (201) the production of new species of organisms from existing organisms by a series of small changes over a long period

excretion (106) the getting rid of the waste products of chemical reactions in the cells of the body

exoskeleton (146) a skeleton outside the body of an organism (e.g. the cuticle of an insect)

F_1 generation (192) the offspring from the mating of two individuals

F_2 generation (192) the offspring resulting from mating two individuals of the F_1 generation with each other

faeces (89) the undigested material plus bacteria, etc., left in the colon after food has been digested and absorbed

fatty acid (88) one of the chemicals produced when a fat is digested

femur (119) the upper bone of the hind limb

fermentation (47) the breakdown of food material by yeast or bacteria to produce energy plus carbon dioxide and in some cases, alcohol

fertilization (33) the combining of the nuclei of male and female reproductive cells (gametes) to form a zygote

fibrin (94) the protein fibres which form a network across a wound and cause a blood clot to form

fibrinogen (91) the protein in the blood plasma which, when blood vessels are damaged, turns into fibrin and forms a blood clot

fibula (119) the smaller of the two bones in the lower leg

field capacity (78) the maximum amount of water which the soil can hold against gravity

filament (28) the stalk of a stamen in a flower

flagellate (174) a single-celled organism propelled by means of a flagellum

flagellum (176) a long filament of cytoplasm which projects from a flagellate and whose lashing movements propel it through the water

foetus (115) the later stages of an animal's embryo when all the organs are present

follicle (*see* Graafian follicle or hair follicle)

fossil (201) the remains of a plant or animal preserved in sedimentary rock

fovea (131) the small area in the retina of the eye having the greatest concentration of sensory cells, hence giving it the most accurate vision

fruit (33) the fertilized ovary of a flower

fungi (75) organisms whose bodies are made of hyphae rather than cells and they feed as saprophytes or parasites

gall bladder (86) a small sac in or near the liver which stores bile

gamete (33) a reproductive cell such as a sperm or ovum

ganglion (139) a group of cell bodies and sometimes synapses, at one point in a nerve

gene (183) a "particle" in the nucleus which determines the presence or absence of certain characteristics in organisms

genetics (177) the study of the way in which characters are inherited

genotype (192) the genetic constitution of an individual, i.e. all the different genes present, whether expressed or not

geotropism (41) a change in the direction of growth of a root or shoot as a result of the direction in which gravity is acting

germination (38) the development of the embryo in a seed into an independent plant

gestation (116) the period of time between fertilization and birth

glomerulus (107) a coiled "knot" of capillaries in the cortex of the kidney; blood serum is filtered out

glycogen (90) an insoluble carbohydrate similar to starch but stored in the liver and muscles of mammals

Graafian follicle (114) the region in a mammal's ovary which contains a maturing egg

granular layer (109) the living inner layer of cells in the epidermis of the skin

grey matter (142) areas of brain and spinal cord occupied principally by the cell bodies of nerve cells

guard cells (19) the cells in the epidermis of a leaf or stem, on either side of the stoma which control its aperture

guttation (64) the exudation of drops of water from leaves in certain conditions

gynaecium (30) the female part of a flower, consisting of carpels

haemocoel (147) the space in an insect between the body wall and internal organs; it is filled with blood

haemoglobin (93) the red, iron-containing pigment in the red blood cells; it can combine with oxygen

haemophilia (190) an inherited disease in which the time needed for blood to clot is greatly increased

haploid (186) containing a single set of chromosomes in which each chromosome is represented only once; usually applies to the nucleus of gametes

hepatic portal vein (89) the vessels carrying the blood from all parts of the alimentary canal to the liver

heterozygous (192) carrying a pair of contrasted genes for any one character; will not breed true for this character

hibernation (111) prolonged phase of inactivity during adverse winter conditions with, in mammals, a corresponding fall in body temperature

holophytic (59) a type of nutrition involving the building up of food from simple substances; a characteristic of plants

holozoic (59) taking in complex substances for food and breaking them down to simpler substances by digestion; characteristic of animals

homeostasis (108) the regulation of the composition, within narrow limits, of the body fluids and internal conditions

homoiothermic (110) body temperature, on average above that of the surroundings and maintained at a constant level

homologous chromosomes (181) corresponding chromosomes of same shape and size derived from each parental gamete

homozygous (192) possessing a pair of identical genes controlling a given character; will breed true for this character

hormones (144) chemicals produced by endocrine glands and released into the circulatory system; they control the rate of various bodily activities

humerus (119) the upper bone of the fore-limb

humus (78) the finely divided organic matter incorporated into soil crumbs

hydrotropism (42) change in direction of growth in roots supposedly as a result of a one-sided stimulus of water

hyphae (75) the microscopic living threads which make up the structure of a fungus

hypocotyl (37) that part of a seedling between the cotyledon and radicle; its elongation brings the cotyledons above the soil

hypopharynx (151) a component of insects' mouth parts

hypothalamus (108) the region of the brain just above the pituitary gland and which controls the activities of this gland

ileum (86) the major part of the small intestine

imago (154) a fully formed adult insect

incisor tooth (120) one of the teeth in the front of the jaw

incus (134) the second of the chain of small bones in the middle ear

indoleacetic acid (IAA) (42) a plant growth hormone

inflorescence (28) a group of flowers on the same stalk

ingestion (86) the taking in of food

inoculation (95) injection with a harmless form of a disease so that the system will make antibodies

insulin (144) the hormone produced by the pancreas; controls sugar metabolism

integument (33) the outer coat of a developing seed

intercostal muscles (104) the muscles between the ribs which play a part in the breathing movements

internode (15) the length of stem between two adjacent leaves

karyogram (182) a chart showing the shapes and numbers of the chromosomes in a cell of an individual

labium (151) a component of an insect's mouth parts

labrum (151) a component of an insect's mouth parts

lachrymal duct (130) the tube running from the eye to the nasal cavity

lacteal (89) the tube in the centre of a villus into which pass the products of fat digestion in the intestine

lactic acid (47) an intermediate product of the breakdown of glucose during respiration

lactose (90) a sugar present in milk

lamina (18) the flat part of a leaf

larva (153) the stage in the life cycle of certain insects which hatches from the egg

larynx (86) the upper part of the windpipe which communicates with the pharynx

latent heat (111) the heat energy needed to evaporate a liquid

lateral line (158) a sense organ on each side of a fish which responds to vibrations in the water

leguminous plants (55) plants of the pea family; their roots contain nitrogen-fixing bacteria

lenticel (15) a gap in the bark of a twig through which exchange of oxygen and carbon dioxide can occur

leucocyte (93) a white blood cell

ligaments (120) the tough, fibrous strands holding bones in place at a joint

linkage (188) the occurrence of genes on the same chromosome so that they tend to stay together during inheritance

lipase (85) an enzyme which digests fats

loam (79) a type of soil containing both sand and clay with adequate humus

lymph (100) a fluid in the body, derived from blood plasma and returned to the circulation via the lymphatic system

lymphatic (98) a vessel which returns lymph from the tissues to the circulatory system

lymphocyte (100) a type of white cell which makes antibodies

malleus (134) the first of the chain of small bones in the middle ear

Malpighian layer (109) the deepest layer of epidermal cells in the skin; these cells reproduce and replace the cells above them

maltose (87) a sugar produced by the digestion of starch (e.g. in germinating seeds)

mandibles: bird (151) extensions of the skull and lower jaw to form the beak
  insect (147) the first pair of mouth parts on the head

maxillae (151) form the second pair of insects' mouth parts

meiosis (186) the form of nuclear division which takes place when cells divide to produce gametes and the chromosome number is halved

Meissner's corpuscle (128) a sensory nerve ending in the skin which responds to touch

melanin (184) a black pigment in the hair and skin of animals

menstruation (118) the breakdown of the lining of the uterus which occurs when an egg has not been fertilized

mesophyll (18) the palisade and spongy layers of cells in a leaf

metabolism (48) all the chemical changes going on in the cells of an organism

metacarpals (120) the bones of the hand

metamorphosis (154) the series of changes by which a larval form of an animal becomes an adult

metaphase (178) a stage in mitosis or meiosis when the chromosomes are arranged on the equator of the spindle

metatarsals (119) the bones of the foot

micropyle (33) a small hole in an ovule or seed of a plant

midrib (18) the main vein and supporting tissue running down the middle of a leaf

mitosis (177) the events in a nucleus at cell division

molar tooth (125) a tooth at the back of the jaw

monocotyledon (6) a plant having only one cotyledon in its seed

monoculture (58) the agricultural practice of growing large numbers of a single species of plant together

monoploid (188) see haploid

mosaic image (149) the kind of "picture" likely to be produced by an insect's compound eye

motor fibre or **neurone** (138) a nerve fibre or cell which carries impulses from the central nervous system and causes some action at the other end (e.g. muscle contraction or enzyme secretion)

mucus (88) a sticky fluid produced by animals to lubricate and protect delicate surfaces

multifactorial inheritance (192) where many genes are involved in controlling a characteristic

multipolar neurone (138) a nerve cell in the central nervous system with many fibres making synapses with adjacent neurones

mutation (184) a spontaneous change in a gene or chromoseome which usually produces an observable effect in the organism concerned

mycelium (75) the mass of hyphae which make up a fungus

natural selection (204) a theory which tries to explain how evolution could have occurred

neural spine (122) the bony projection from the dorsal surface of a vertebra

neurone (138) a nerve cell

nictitating membrane (161) a third, transparent eyelid in birds

nitrifying bacteria (54) bacteria whose activities increase the amount of nitrate in the soil.

nodules (54) swellings on the roots of leguminous plants which contain nitrogen-fixing bacteria

nucleic acid (184) a chemical present in nuclei which is thought to control the activities of the cell and the pattern of inheritance

nucleolus (177) a small structure within a nucleus

nucleoplasm (11) the protoplasm of the nucleus

nucleus (11) the structure in a cell which determines the shape and controls the activities of a cell

nymph (154) an immature stage in the life cycle of certain insects

ocellus (149) a simple eye of an insect

oesophagus (86) the gullet, a tube conveying food from the mouth to the stomach

oestradiol, oestrogen, oestrone (144) female sex hormones

ommatidium (149) one of the many light receptors in an insect's compound eye

omnivorous (59) having a diet equally composed of animal and plant material

oogenesis (186) the series of cell divisions in the ovary which give rise to egg cells

operculum (158) the bony plate covering the gills on each side of a fish's head

orbit (120) the cavity in the skull which houses the eye

organ (13) a group of tissues working together to do a particular job

osmoregulation (65) the control of the quantity of water entering and leaving the cells of an organism

osmosis (61) the movement of water from a weaker to a stronger solution

ossicles (134) a chain of three tiny bones in the middle ear, which transmit vibrations from the ear drum to the middle ear

otoliths (135) chalky granules in the utriculus which helps it respond to changes in posture

oviduct (112) the tube which conveys eggs from the ovary to the uterus or to the outside world

ovipositor (147) an appendage on the last abdominal segment of an insect which helps it to place its eggs below the surface

ovulation (114) the release of mature eggs from the ovary, ready to be fertilized

ovule (28) the part of the ovary of a flower which contains the female gamete and will become the seed

ovum (114) the unfertilized egg of an animal

Pacinian corpuscle (128) a sensory receptor in the skin which responds to pressure

palisade cells (19) the layer of cells on the upper surface of a leaf just below the epidermis

pancreas (88) a gland beneath the stomach which secretes digestive enzymes into the small intestine

Paramecium (175) a single-celled, ciliated animal

parasite (59) an animal or plant which derives its food from another organism without necessarily killing it

patella (119) the bone of the knee-cap

pepsin (87) a protein-digesting enzyme produced in the stomach

peptide (87) a chemical consisting of a chain of amino acids and resulting from the partial digestion of a protein

perennial (23) a plant which survives successive winters or dry seasons

pericarp (28) the outer coat of the ovary of a flower; it becomes the fruit wall

perilymph (134) the fluid in the inner ear

periosteum (121) the fibrous tissue covering bones

peristalsis (86) the muscular contractions which move food down the gullet and along the alimentary canal

petiole (17) a flower stalk

phagocyte (93) a white cell which can ingest foreign particles

phalanges (120) the bones of the fingers or toes

pharynx (86) the area at the back of the mouth cavity leading into the nasal cavity, gullet, and windpipe

phenotype (192) the observable characteristics of an organism

photosynthesis (48) the production of food by green plants from carbon dioxide, water, and salts using light as a source of energy to drive the chemical reactions involved

phototropism (41) a change in the direction of growth of a shoot in response to one-sided illumination

phylum (6) a major group of animals or plants

phytoplankton (57) microscopic green plants living in the surface waters of the sea, lakes, etc.

pituitary body (144) an outgrowth from the floor of the brain which acts as an endocrine gland producing many hormones

placenta, mammal (116) the organ in the uterus which enables food, oxygen, and waste products to pass between the embryo and its mother

plankton (53) the microscopic plants and animals living in the surface layers of natural waters

plasma (93) the liquid component of the blood

plasmolysis (62) partial collapse of a cell as a result of withdrawal of water by osmosis

platelets (93) small bodies in the blood which play a part in clot formation

pleural fluid (104) the fluid secreted by the pleural membrane into the pleural cavity

pleural membrane (104) the membrane lining the outside of the lungs and the inside of the thorax

plumule (37) the leafy part of the embryonic shoot in a seed

poikilothermic (158) body temperature almost the same as the surroundings and varying with the latter

polar body (186) a functionless female gamete produced when an egg mother cell undergoes meiosis

polymorphism (206) a variation which is always present between individuals in a population

potometer (68) an apparatus for measuring water uptake in a shoot

primary feathers (166) the large flight feathers on a bird's wing inserted in the skin over the "hand" bones

proboscis (152) projecting, sucking mouth parts in an insect

producer (53) organisms, mainly plants, assigned a position in a food chain because they make their own food

progesterone (115) the female sex hormone produced by the corpus luteum in the ovary after ovulation

prophase (177) the earliest stage in mitosis or meiosis; the chromosomes appear and shorten

proprioceptor (129) an internal sense organ responding to changes usually in muscles

prostate gland (113) an accessory male sex organ in mammals; adds a secretion to the sperms at ejaculation

protein (82) the class of foodstuffs which provide the raw material for making the cytoplasm of cells

proteinase (85) an enzyme which breaks down proteins

protista (176) a collective name for single-celled animals and plants

protoplasm (11) the living material in cells; cytoplasm and nucleoplasm

protozoa (174) single-celled animals such as Amoeba

pseudopodium (176) a temporary protrusion of cytoplasm extended by an Amoeba during locomotion

pseudotracheae (152) the channels in the proboscis of a housefly or blowfly which carry saliva and digested food

puberty (114) the stage when men and women become capable of sexual reproduction

pulmonary artery and vein (95) the blood vessels from the heart carrying blood to or from the lungs

pupa (146) the inactive stage in the life cycle of certain insects when the organs of the adult are being formed

pyloric sphincter (86) a ring of muscle which controls the exit of the stomach

radicle (37) the embryo root in a seed

radius (119) one of the bones of the lower fore-limb

receptacle (28) the expanded end of a flower stalk bearing the parts of the flower, petals, etc.

recessive (192) gene which, in the presence of its contrasting allele, is not expressed

recombination (188) a combination of genes in the offspring which was not present in either of the parents

rectum (86) the last part of the large intestine

reduction division (186) *see* meiosis

reflex (139) an automatic response to a stimulus which is not under conscious control

reflex arc (140) the nervous pathway conducting the impulses which result in a reflex action

renal artery or vein (95) the vessels from aorta or vena cava conducting blood to or from the kidneys

rennin (87) a digestive enzyme in the stomach which coagulates the protein in milk

replication (179) making a new gene or chromosome exactly like the original

retina (131) the layer of light-sensitive cells inside the back of the eye

rhabdom (148) a microscopic transparent rod in the centre of one of the components (ommatidia) of an insect's compound eye

rhizome (23) a horizontal, underground stem swollen with stored food and capable of producing new independent plants from its buds

rickets (84) soft, easily distorted bones in children lacking vitamin D

roan (195) a coat colour in cattle resulting from incomplete dominance of two genes for colour

rod (131) a light-sensitive cell in the retina of the eye; it responds to weak light but not to colour differences

roughage (84) the indigestible portion of food; usually cellulose from plants

sacculus (134) a sense organ of the inner ear which may respond to changes of posture

sacrum (120) the part of the spinal column to which the pelvic girdle is joined

saprophytic (59) a form of nutrition in which dead organic matter is digested externally and the products absorbed (e.g. in fungi)

scapula (120) the shoulder blade

scion (27) a bud or shoot which is grafted into another plant's stem

sclera (130) the tough tissue on the outside of the eyeball

scrotum (112) the sac of skin which encloses the testes outside the body cavity

scurvy (83) skin and blood vessels susceptible to damage and infection due to lack of vitamin C

sebaceous gland (109) a gland which secretes an oily substance on to the skin at the top of a hair follicle

secretin (144) a hormone produced by the lining of the duodenum when the acid contents of the stomach reach it; it stimulates the pancreas to produce enzymes

segment (147) a division of the body into sections visible in certain invertebrates such as worms and insects

segregation (192) the separation of allelomorphic genes into different gametes at meiosis

semicircular canals (134) sensory organs consisting of fluid-filled tubes in the inner ear which respond to rotatory movements

semi-lunar valves (98) pocket-like valves in the main arteries leaving the heart which prevent return of blood to the ventricles

semi-permeable membrane (61) a membrane which permits water to pass through it more readily than dissolved substances

sepal (28) a leaf-like structure on the outside of a flower

serum (93) blood plasma from which fibrinogen has been removed

sieve plate (14) the perforated cross-wall which allows communication between two sieve tube cells

sieve tube (17) a row of cells which transport food in the vein of a plant

silt (78) very fine mineral particles, smaller than sand grains, in the soil

special senses (129) the eyes, ears, nose, and tongue which are specialized for detecting certain types of stimulus

specialization (13) the development of a structure or process to do one particular job

species (6) a group of animals or plants possessing a great many features in common and capable of breeding with each other

sphincter (87) a circle of muscle in a tube or duct; its contraction reduces the diameter of the tube or closes it altogether

spikelet (30) a group of flowers in the inflorescence of a grass

spindle (178) a structure in a cell which appears at mitosis or meiosis and plays a part in separating the chromosomes or chromatids

spiracle (146) an opening in an insect's cuticle which admits air to the tracheal system

Spirillum (70) a family of bacteria with a spiral shape

Spirogyra (172) a filamentous green alga occurring in fresh water

spleen (93) an organ in the abdomen, near the stomach; it makes white cells, destroys worn-out red cells, and removes foreign particles from the blood

spongy layer (18) the lower layer of cells in the mesophyll of a leaf blade

sporangium (75) a small capsule containing reproductive spores produced by fungi and other types of plant

spores (72) a reproductive cell of a fungus and certain other types of plant which can grow to produce a new individual

stamens (28) the male reproductive organs in a flower; each stamen consists of a stalk (filament) and an anther

stapes (134) the last of the chain of bones in the middle ear; fits into the oval window

Staphylococcus (70) a family of bacteria with spherical shape whose cell division produces clumps rather than chains.

sterilization: bacterial (74) the destruction of bacteria by heat, chemicals, or radiation

genetic (198) rendering a person incapable of breeding

sternum (104) the breast-bone; it joins the front end of the ribs

stigma (28) the part of the carpel in a flower which receives the pollen

stoma (17) the opening in the epidermis of a leaf or stem through which oxygen, carbon dioxide, and water can pass

Streptococcus (70) a family of spherical bacteria whose cell division produces chains of individuals

style (28) the part of the carpel of a flower between the ovary and the stigma

sucrose (49) a sugar produced mainly from sugar-cane or sugar-beet

suspensory ligament (130) the fibres running from the edge of the lens in the eye to the ciliary body

synapse (138) the junction between one nerve cell and the next across which the nerve impulse has to pass

synovial membrane (120) the lining of the capsule of a moveable joint in the skeleton; it secretes the synovial fluid which lubricates the joint

system (13) a series of organs working together to a certain purpose (e.g. the circulatory system)

tarsals (119) the bones of the ankle

telophase (178) the final stage of mitosis or meiosis when the chromosomes become less visible and the nuclear membrane re-forms

temporalis muscle (123) a muscle from the lower jaw to the skull which closes the jaws during chewing

tendon (99) the bundle of tough fibres attaching a muscle to a bone

terminal bud (15) the bud at the end of a shoot or branch

testa (37) the outer coat of a seed

testis (112) the male reproductive organ of an animal; it produces sperms

testosterone (144) a male sex hormone produced by the testis

thoracic duct (100) a large lymphatic duct emptying the lymph from most of the body into the circulatory system near the heart

thorax: man (102) the upper part of the trunk above the diaphragm which contains the heart and lungs

insect (146) the three middle segments of the body carrying limbs and wings

thyroid (144) an endocrine gland in the neck; it produces the hormone thyroxine

thyroxine (144) the hormone produced by the thyroid gland; it controls rates of metabolism

tibia (119) the larger of the two bones in the lower hind limb

tissue (13) a group of cells similar in structure and function (e.g. muscle)

tissue respiration (45) the chemical breakdown of food in cells to provide energy for living activities

toxin (71) a poison produced by bacteria

trachea: man (86) the windpipe; it conducts air from the mouth and nose to the bronchi and lungs

insect (146) a component in the system of tubes which carries air from the spiracles to all parts of the body

tracheole (146) a branch of a tracheal tube in an insect

translocation (66) the transport in plants of food and other dissolved substances

transpiration (67) the evaporation of water from the shoot, particularly the leaves, of a flowering plant

tropisms (41) a change in the direction of growth of a root or shoot in response to the direction of an external stimulus

trypsin (88) a protein-digesting enzyme secreted by the pancreas into the small intestine

tuber (23) a food store producing a swelling in a root or stem

turgid (62) the condition in a plant cell when the vacuole is pressing outwards strongly on the cell wall

ulna (120) one of the two bones in the lower forearm; it runs from elbow to wrist

umbilical cord (116) the cord containing blood vessels which conduct embryonic blood to and from the placenta

urea (91) a nitrogen-containing chemical formed in the liver from excess amino acids; it is an excretory product

ureter (106) the tube conducting urine from the kidney to the bladder

urethra (106) the tube conducting urine from the bladder to the outside world

urine (108) a mixture of water, salts, urea, etc. removed from the blood by the kidneys

uterus (112) the part of the female reproductive system in which the embryo develops

utriculus (134) a sensory organ in the inner ear; it responds to changes in posture

vaccine (95) a preparation of dead, inactive, or harmless bacteria or viruses which, when introduced to the body, causes it to produce antibodies

vacuole (8) the fluid-filled cavity in the centre of a plant cell or the droplets of fluid in the cytoplasm of animal cells

vascular bundle (16) groups of vessels, sieve tubes, and strengthening fibres which conduct water and food through a plant

vector (153) an animal which transmits a disease-causing organism from one plant or animal to another

vena cava (95) the large vein returning blood from the body to the right atrium of the heart

ventilation (45) a method of exchanging the air or water in contact with a respiratory organ

ventral root (140) a nerve carrying motor fibres from the spinal cord to the body

ventricles (98) the lower, more muscular chambers of the heart which pump blood into the arteries

venule (97) a blood vessel emptying into a vein

vertebra (122) one of the bones of the spinal column

vertebral column (122) the "backbone" or spine

vertebrate (6) an animal possessing a vertebral column

vessel (17) a water-conducting tube of a plant made up of dead cells joined end to end

villus (89) one of thousands of finger-like protrusions from the internal surface of the small intestine

virus (220) a sub-microscopic particle living in cells of plants and animals and causing disease

vitamin (83) complex chemicals which must be present in the diet for normal health but have no energy value

vitreous humour (130) the jelly-like fluid in the main part of the eye

voluntary muscles (122) muscles under conscious control (in man)

white cells (93) cells in the blood, lacking haemoglobin but possessing a nucleus and, in some cases, powers of independent movement

white matter (142) the area of the brain and spinal cord consisting of nerve fibres as distinct from cell bodies

wilting (62) excessive loss of water from a plant leading eventually to a collapse of the leaves and stem

X chromosome (188) the chromosome which, in the absence of a Y chromosome determines that certain animals will be female

xerophthalmia (84) a disorder of the skin affecting the conjunctiva of the eye resulting from a deficiency of vitamin A

xylem (17) the tissue in the vascular bundle of a plant, composed of vessels and supporting cells

Y chromosome (188) the chromosome whose presence determines that certain animals will be males

zooplankton (53) microscopic animals living in the surface waters of oceans, lakes, rivers, etc.

zygospores (172) the zygote produced by sexual reproduction of some algae and fungi which can resist adverse conditions

zygote (33) the cell produced when a male and female gamete fuse; it can grow into a new individual

zymase (77) a starch-digesting enzyme produced by yeast

Reagents

Benedict's solution (1 litre)

Dissolve 173 g sodium citrate crystals and 100 g sodium carbonate crystals in 800 cm^3 warm distilled water. Dissolve separately 17·3 g copper sulphate crystals in 200 cm^3 cold distilled water. Add the copper sulphate solution to the first solution with constant stirring.

Note. (1) Benedict's solution is preferable to Fehling's solution as it is less caustic and does not deteriorate on keeping.

(2) The red deposit of cuprous oxide that coats the inside of test-tubes used for the sugar tests can be removed with dilute hydrochloric acid.

Iodine solution (1 litre)

Dissolve 10 g iodine and 10 g potassium iodide in 1 litre distilled water by grinding the two solids in a mortar while adding successive portions of the water. The solution should be further diluted for class use, e.g. 5 cm^3 in 100 cm^3 water.

Hydrogencarbonate indicator

Dissolve 0·2 g thymol blue and 0·1 g cresol red powders in 20 cm^3 ethanol. Dissolve 0·84 g "Analar" sodium hydrogencarbonate in 900 cm^3 distilled water. Add the alcoholic solution to the hydrogencarbonate solution and make the volume up to 1 litre with distilled water.

Shortly before use, dilute the appropriate amount of this solution 10 times, i.e. add 9 times its own volume of distilled water.

To bring the solution into equilibrium with atmospheric air, bubble air from outside the laboratory through the diluted indicator using a filter pump or aquarium pump. After about 10 minutes, the dye should be red.

Acknowledgements

I am indebted to all the people who have provided photographic material, allowed me to reproduce or adapt drawings, and to quote or use data from their experiments. They are acknowledged individually with the captions to the relevant illustrations.

I am grateful to the Cambridge, London and East African examining boards, and the Kenya National Examinations Council for permission to reproduce some of their examination questions.

I am particularly grateful to Mr W. G. Goldstraw, Mr S. W. Hurry, Dr R. G. Pearson, Dr C. H. Rice, and Dr C. O. Carter for carefully reading the manuscript of *Introduction to Biology* as a whole or in part, and for their corrections and valuable suggestions· to Mr A. E. Ellis, Miss H. G. Q. Rowett and Mr K. Thomas for their constructive criticisms of the first edition; to Mr A. E. Pound for his helpful comments on the second edition and to Mr E. Holden for suggestions for the fourth edition; and to Mr Denys Baker for his advice in the early stages of making the drawings.

In revising the Tropical Edition I have received valuable help from Mr R. Scholes, Miss M. E. Ashton, Mrs A. Walkinshaw, Dr F. J. Bealing and Mr D. Sharpe with particular regard to East African, Malaysian and Caribbean organisms. Although much of the content specific to West Africa has been changed in order to make the book more widely acceptable, the help and advice given by Mrs J. Mitchelmore, Mr J. B. Hall and Mr T. A. G. Wells in preparing the first tropical edition has undoubtedly influenced the new edition.

In revising the New Tropical Edition, the comments and advice of D. W. Khatete and H. A. Muthui have been particularly useful.

I am glad also of this opportunity to thank the many teachers in Nigeria and Kenya who gave up their time to discuss the book with me and suggest changes and improvements.

D.G.M.

Index